FUTURE COAL PROSPECTS: Country and Regional Assessments

World Coal Study

Robert P. Greene and J. Michael Gallagher
Editors

Carroll L. Wilson
Project Director, Massachusetts Institute of Technology

Ballinger Publishing Company • Cambridge, Massachusetts
A subsidiary of Harper & Row, Publishers, Inc.

This material is based on research supported in part by the U.S. Department of
Energy under contract No. EX-76-A-01-2295 with MIT. Any opinions, findings,
conclusions or recommendations contained herein are those of the authors and
do not necessarily reflect the views of the U.S. Department of Energy.

PRINTED AT THE NIMROD PRESS, BOSTON

Library of Congress Cataloging in Publication Data

World Coal Study.

    Future coal prospects.

    "The second and final WOCOL report."

    "Companion report, Coal—bridge to the future."

    1. Coal.   I. Greene, Robert P.   II. Gallagher, J. Michael.

    III. Wilson, Carroll L.   IV. Title.

TP325.W82   1980a   333.8'22   80-17319

ISBN 0-88410-098-7

TABLE OF CONTENTS

FOREWORD

The World Coal Study (WOCOL) has been an international project involving over 80 people from 16 major coal-using and coal-producing countries.

WOCOL came into being as a result of my belief that there was an urgent need to examine the role that coal might play in meeting world energy needs during the next 20 years. Such a choice is being forced upon us. Oil from OPEC countries can no longer be relied upon to provide expanding supplies of energy, even with rapidly rising prices. Neither can nuclear energy be planned on for rapid expansion worldwide until present uncertainties about it are resolved. Yet the world's energy needs will continue to grow, even with vigorous energy conservation programs and with optimistic rates of expansion in the use of solar energy.

Coal already supplies 25 percent of the world's energy, its reserves are vast, and it is relatively inexpensive. But no major attempt has previously been made to examine the needs for coal on a global scale, to match requirements of users with potential capacities of producers, to look at the markets coal might fill, or to examine the obstacles to a rapid expansion in coal use and how they might be overcome.

This experiment in international collaboration in WOCOL follows directly from the Workshop on Alternative Energy Strategies (WAES), which I directed. In WAES we concluded, in our report published in early 1977,[1] that the world might find its oil supplies being constrained by limitations on exports from OPEC countries at some time during the 1980s. This report was generally regarded at the time as being too pessimistic. In fact, it proved to be optimistic—it is now clear that we are already in that position in 1980.

WAES assembled a group of people who could engage in free-ranging discussion and who worked hard together and reached agreement on a plausible range of global energy futures. These people came from key positions in governments and private and public organizations in the world's major energy-using countries, as well as from some of the largest OPEC countries. They came however as individuals, each free to represent his own views rather than those of the organization with which he was affiliated.

We learned a great deal in WAES, not just about energy, but about how to work together as an international group. These lessons have been applied in WOCOL. I was responsible for the selection of the individuals taking part. I sought a mix of nationalities, a balance of public and private sector viewpoints, a common concern with energy policy, a knowledge of the coal or energy industry, and the ability to work effectively in a group effort. The total was no greater than the number of people who could, in dialogue around a table, function as a working group. The language of the Study was English.

Members of WOCOL came from 16 countries that use 75 percent of the world's energy. They produce and use about 60 percent of the world's coal. Although not able to take a full part in the Study, Observers from the People's Republic of China attended WOCOL meetings and furnished a report for their country.

---

[1] *ENERGY: Global Prospects 1985-2000* (New York: McGraw-Hill, 1977).

The senior members of WOCOL, called Participants, gave policy direction to the Study and reviewed its work as it proceeded. It is their consensus on the Study conclusions that represents the principal summary of WOCOL. Moreover, Participants chose Associates from within their organization who devoted much of their time to WOCOL under the direction of the Participant and collaborated with other Associates both in their own country and elsewhere. Each Participant arranged for the financing of all work done at a national level and for the time, travel, and other expenses of himself and his Associate.

Formal liaison was established with the U.S. Department of Energy and with the Electric Power Research Institute (EPRI), which both provided Study members who served in the role of Associates without Participants. Costs of the headquarters, located at the Massachusetts Institute of Technology, Cambridge, Massachusetts, were sponsored by foundations, companies, and the U.S. Department of Energy. A small, capable, and extremely dedicated staff at M.I.T. coordinated this global project within some very tight deadlines.

WOCOL Participants developed together an agreed purpose, plan, and schedule for the Study. Cases were developed to project a range of future coal production, use, and trade. Like WAES these projections build on detailed country studies conducted by WOCOL teams as well as on special studies for regions not represented in the Study. Unlike WAES the projections were based on existing national energy studies rather than on a specific global macroeconomic framework developed for the Study.

Our analysis goes to the year 2000. Over the next 5 years the use of different fuels is heavily constrained by decisions made in the past and by the fact that new energy facilities being planned now cannot be brought to completion in less than 5 to 10 years. The substantial shift to coal will therefore begin in the mid to late 1980s based on decisions being made in the early 1980s. Major effects of this expansion will be felt in the 1985-2000 period. The twenty years from now to the turn of the century are thus critical. The full effects of the switch to coal will, however, not be seen until the early decades of the next century. At that time the need for coal will still be great although renewable energy systems should be coming into use on a significant scale.

The major summary of the WOCOL findings is in a companion report, *COAL —Bridge to the Future* (Cambridge, Massachusetts: Ballinger, 1980). The WAES study left the world with a well-defined world energy problem. WOCOL presents a solution to that problem—*COAL—Bridge to the Future*. This is an optimistic message about energy—a rarity these days. But this optimism is justified only if many decisions are taken very soon because of the long lead times required. Our most precious resource is time which must be used as wisely as energy.

This book is the second and final WOCOL report and contains the full texts of the reports prepared by the teams from each country in WOCOL as well as the specially commissioned studies of other regions.

In the immediately following pages are the names and affiliations of those who took part in WOCOL; our conclusions; a description of how the Study actually proceeded; and acknowledgments of the support that made it possible.

CARROLL WILSON

STUDY PARTICIPANTS, ASSOCIATES, AND STAFF

PROJECT DIRECTOR

Carroll L. Wilson

PARTICIPANTS

Australia

Dr. Donald D. Brown
Deputy General Manager and
   Director
CSR Limited

Dr. Robert A. Durie
Chief Scientist
R.W. Miller Co. Pty. Ltd.

Mr. Kenneth G. Wybrow
Member, Joint Coal Board

Canada

The Hon. Jack Austin Q.C.
The Senate

Mr. Garnet T. Page
President
The Coal Association of Canada

Dr. Charles H. Smith
Senior Assistant Deputy Minister
Department of Energy, Mines &
   Resources

China, Peoples Republic of

Mr. Liu Huanmin[1]
Director, China Coal Society
Advisor, China Coal Industry
   Technical Installation Corporation

Denmark

Mr. Poul Sachmann
Executive Vice President
ELSAM

Finland

Mr. Kaarlo K. Kirvelä
Vice President and Director
   of the Energy Sector
Ekono Oy

France

Dr. Thierry de Montbrial
Director, Institut Français
   des Relations Internationales
Professor, L'Ecole Polytechnique

M. Jean-Claude Sore
Deputy Managing Director
Charbonnages de France

M. Albert Viala
Vice President
A.T.I.C.

Germany, Federal Republic of

Dr. rer. oec. Harald B. Giesel
Member of the Board
Gesamtverband des deutschen
Steinkohlenbergbaus

Dr. H-D. Schilling
Head, Department of Coal Utilization
Bergbau-Forschung GmbH

Professor Hans K. Schneider
Director
Institute of Energy Economics
University of Koeln

India

Shri S.K. Bose
Joint Secretary
Ministry of Energy

Indonesia

Mr. S. Sigit
Secretary General
Department of Mines & Energy

Italy

Dr. Marcello Colitti
General Manager
ENI

Professor Umberto Colombo
Chairman, Comitato Nazionale per
   l'Energia Nucleare (CNEN)

Japan

Mr. Toyoaki Ikuta
President
Institute of Energy Economics

---

1 Observer

vii

Mr. Hidezo Inaba
Vice Chairman
Committee for Energy Policy
   Promotion

Dr. Saburo Okita[2]
Chairman
Japan Economic Research Center

Mr. Setsuo Takagaki
Director of Research Affairs
Institute of Energy Economics

Netherlands

Dr. A.A.T. van Rhijn
Deputy Director-General for Energy
Ministry of Economic Affairs

Netherlands/UK

Mr. Frank Pecchioli
Managing Director
Shell Coal International Ltd.

Poland

Mr. Eugeniusz Ciszak
Deputy Managing Director,
Director Tech.
Chief Mining Studies & Design Office
(Ministry of Mining)

Sweden

Mr. Arne S. Lundberg
The Royal Swedish Academy of
   Engineering Sciences

United Kingdom

Mr. Robert Belgrave
Director, BP Trading Ltd.
Policy Adviser to Board of Directors,
   British Petroleum Co.

Sir Derek Ezra
Chairman
National Coal Board

Professor Sir William Hawthorne
Chairman, Advisory Council on
   Energy Conservation (1974-1979)
Master, Churchill College

Sir Ronald McIntosh
Executive Director
S.G. Warburg & Co. Ltd.
Former Director General of National
   Economic Development Office

United States

Mr. Thornton F. Bradshaw
President
Atlantic Richfield Co.

Mr. Gordon R. Corey
Vice Chairman
Commonwealth Edison Co.

Mr. W. Kenneth Davis
Vice President
Bechtel Power Corp.

Mr. Pierre Gousseland
Chairman and Chief Executive Officer
AMAX Inc.

Prof. Robert C. Seamans, Jr.
Dean, School of Engineering
Massachusetts Institute of Technology
Former Administrator, Energy
   Research & Development Admin.
   (ERDA)

Mr. Russell E. Train
President, World Wildlife Fund–U.S.
Former Administrator, Environmental
   Protection Agency (EPA)

**International Institute of
Applied Systems Analysis**

Prof. Wolf Häfele
Deputy Director
Program Leader, Energy Systems

ASSOCIATES

Australia

Mr. Keith Laverick[3]
Market Development Manager–Coal
The Broken Hill Proprietary
   Company Limited

Mr. David B. Tolmie
Principal Project Officer
New Business & Development Group
Minerals & Chemicals Division
CSR Limited

Canada

Ms. Barbara Ettles[4]
Manager of Information Services
The Coal Association of Canada

---

2 Until appointed Foreign Minister November
1979

3 Associate without Participant

4 Until September 1979

ASSOCIATES, AND STAFF

Dr. John H. Walsh
Senior Advisor, Energy Technology
Dept. of Energy, Mines & Resources

China, Peoples Republic of[5]
Mr. Wang Quingyi
Engineer
China Coal Society

Mr. Li Weitung
Professor, Deputy Dean of the
China Mining Institute

Ms. Sung Yafan
Engineer
China Coal Society
China Coal Industry Technical
Installation Corporation

Mr. Li Zhongmin
Engineer
China Coal Society

Denmark
Mr. Hartmut Schulz
Manager Coal Purchase
ELSAM–Fuels Division

Finland
Dr. Seppo Hannus
Senior Science Officer
Ministry of Trade and Industry
Energy Department

Mr. Juha Kekkonen
Senior Advisor
Ministry of Trade and Industry
Energy Department

France
M. Daniel Cretin
A.T.I.C.

M. Marc Ippolito
Head of EEC and International
Relations Department
Charbonnages de France

Germany, Federal Republic of
Dr. Dieter Schmitt
Head, Institute of Energy Economics
University of Koeln

Mr. Detlef Wiegand
Chief Economist
Dept. of Coal Utilization
Bergbau-Forschung GmbH

5 Observers

Italy
Dr. Oliviero Bernardini
Planning and Development/
Technology Assessment
Montedison

Dr. Eugenio Nardelli
Division for Planning & Development
ENI

Japan
Mr. Seiko Ichikawa
General Manager of First Overseas
Coal Dept.
Mitsui and Co. Ltd.

Mr. Tohru Kimura
Chief Economist
Institute of Energy Economics

Mr. Akira Kinoshita
Senior Economist
Dept. of General Planning
Electric Power Development
Company

Mr. Seiji Kobayashi
Manager, Thermal Coal Section
C. Itoh & Co. Ltd.

Mr. Takao Sato
Manager, Research Division
Committee for Energy Policy
Promotion

Netherlands
Mr. Rik Bosma
Manager of Coal Studies
Energy Study Center
Netherlands Energy Research
Fnd/ECN

Mr. Robert van der Wart
Program Coordinator, Non-Nuclear
Energy Systems
Netherlands Energy Research
Fnd/ECN

Netherlands/UK
Mr. Brian K. Elms
Planning Manager
Shell Coal International Ltd.

Sweden
Mr. Kurt Lekås
Project Manager, Coal 90
Luossavaara-Kiirunavaara AB

ix

Mr. Håkan Neuman
Economist, Corporation Development
Luossavaara-Kiirunavaara AB

United Kingdom

Mr. Peter R. Horrobin
Executive Director
S.G. Warburg Co. Ltd.

Dr. William Q. Limond
Policy Analyst, Policy Review Unit
British Petroleum Co. Ltd.

Mr. Kenneth N. McKinlay
Manager, Planning & Economics
BP Coal Department

Mr. Richard Ormerod
Department of Central Planning
National Coal Board

Mr. Michael Parker
Director of Central Planning
National Coal Board

United States

Dr. Arnold B. Baker
Senior Consultant
Policy Analysis & Forecasting
Atlantic Richfield Co.

Mr. Michael Gaffen[3]
Director, International Coal Analysis
U.S. Department of Energy

Dr. Irving Leibson
Vice President
Bechtel Inc.

Mr. Robert L. Major
Manager, Business Research
AMAX Coal Company

Mr. René H. Malès[3]
Director, Energy Analysis &
   Environment Division
Electric Power Research Institute

Mr. Joseph P. McCluskey
Director, Environmental Affairs
Commonwealth Edison Co.

Mr. F. Taylor Ostrander
Assistant to the Chairman
AMAX Inc.

Dr. John Stanley-Miller[3]
Director, Energy Modeling &
   Analysis Division
U.S. Department of Energy

Dr. David Sternlight
Chief Economist
Atlantic Richfield Co.

STAFF

MIT Program Staff

Mr. Robert P. Greene
Deputy Director

Dr. J. Michael Gallagher
Technical Director

Mr. Gerald Foley
Consultant

Mr. Ralph Chang
Research Assistant

MIT Support Staff

Ms. Roberta Ferland
Secretary

Ms. Susan Leland
Administrative Assistant

Ms. Lynette McLaughlin
Office Assistant

Ms. Kathleen Romano
Financial Manager

Ms. Susan Williamson
Administrative Secretary

European Support Staff

Ms. Karin Berntsen, Luxembourg

Ms. Elaine Goldberg, Spain

Ms. Dalia Jackbo, Norway

---

3 Associate without Participant

CONCLUSIONS

The Conclusions of the World Coal Study were discussed in detail by Participants at the final WOCOL meeting.

It is their consensus on these conclusions—the text included here is as agreed at that meeting—that represents the principal summary of WOCOL. The companion volume *COAL—Bridge to the Future* describes the WOCOL findings in detail and presents the supporting analysis.

CONCLUSIONS

It is now widely agreed that the availability of oil in international trade is likely to diminish over the next two decades. Vigorous conservation, the development and rapid implementation of programs for nuclear power, natural gas, unconventional sources of oil and gas, solar energy, other renewable sources, and new technologies will not be sufficient to meet the growing energy needs of the world. A massive effort to expand facilities for the production, transport, and use of coal is urgently required to provide for even moderate economic growth in the world between now and the year 2000. Without such increases in coal the outlook is bleak.

Our major conclusions after eighteen months of study are as follows.

1. Coal is capable of supplying a high proportion of future energy needs. It now supplies more than 25% of the world's energy. Economically recoverable reserves are very large—many times those of oil and gas —and capable of meeting increasing demands well into the future.

2. Coal will have to supply between one-half and two-thirds of the additional energy needed by the world during the next 20 years, even under the moderate energy growth assumptions of this Study. To achieve this goal, world coal production will have to increase 2.5 to 3 times, and the world trade in steam coal will have to grow 10 to 15 times above 1979 levels.

3. Many individual decisions must be made along the chain from coal producer to consumer to ensure that the required amounts are available when needed. Delays at any point affect the entire chain. This emphasizes the need for prompt and related actions by consumers, producers, governments, and other public authorities.

4. Coal can be mined, moved, and used in most areas in ways that conform to high standards of health, safety, and environmental protection by the application of available technology and without unacceptable increases in cost. The present knowledge of possible carbon dioxide effects on climate does not justify delaying the expansion of coal use.

5. Coal is already competitive in many locations for the generation of electricity and in many industrial and other uses. It will extend further into these and other markets as oil prices rise.

6. The technology for mining, moving, and using coal is well established and steadily improving. Technological advances in combustion, gasification, and liquefaction will greatly widen the scope for the environmentally acceptable use of coal in the 1990s and beyond.

7. The amount of capital required to expand the production, transport, and user facilities to triple the use of coal is within the capacity of domestic and international capital markets, though difficulties in financing large coal projects in some developing countries may require special solutions.

The final conclusions of this Study are cautiously optimistic. Coal can provide the principal part of the additional energy needs of the next two decades. In filling this role it will act both as a bridge to the energy systems of the future and as a foundation for the continued part that coal will play in the next century. But the public and private enterprises concerned must act cooperatively and promptly, if this is to be achieved. Governments can help in particular, by providing the confidence and stability required for investment decisions, by eliminating delays in licensing and planning permissions, by establishing clear and stable environmental standards, and by facilitating the growth of free and competitive international trade. A recognition of the urgent need for coal and determined actions to make it available in time will ensure that the world will continue to obtain the energy it requires for its economic growth and development.

ACKNOWLEDGMENTS

Sponsors and Institutions

Many organizations and institutions have provided direct financial support and other services for WOCOL. The Study gratefully acknowledges the following sponsors for their generous support of the secretariat and related activities:

AMAX
Atlantic Richfield Company
Bechtel National Inc.
Cummins Engine Foundation
Alfried Krupp von Bohlen und
  Halbach Foundation

Massachusetts Institute of Technology
The Andrew W. Mellon Foundation
The Rockefeller Foundation
U.S. Department of Energy

The Study also gratefully acknowledges the many institutions in each country that have contributed financial or professional support for the Study or for the WOCOL country reports including:

Australia
The Broken Hill Propriety Company
  Limited
CSR Limited
Joint Coal Board
R.W. Miller Co. Pty. Ltd.
Commonwealth Government
  Department of National Develop-
    ment and Energy
  Department of Trade and Resources
  National Energy Advisory
    Committee
New South Wales Government
  Coal Export Strategy Study Task
    Force
  Department of Mineral Resources
    and Development
  Electricity Commission of N.S.W.
  Energy Authority of N.S.W.
  Hunter Valley Research Foundation
  Maritime Services Board
  Planning and Environment
    Commission
  Public Transport Commission of
    N.S.W.
  State Pollution Control Commission
New South Wales Combined Colliery
  Proprietors' Association
Queensland Government:
  Co-ordinator General's Department

State Electricity Commission of
    Queensland
  Department of Mines
  Queensland Colliery Proprietor's
    Association
Victorian Government:
  State Electricity Commission of
    Victoria
  Victorian Brown Coal Council

Canada
Department of Energy, Mines &
    Resources
The Coal Association of Canada

China, People's Republic of
China Coal Society

Denmark
ELSAM
Odense Steel Shipyard Ltd.

Finland
Ekono Oy
Ministry of Trade and Industry

France
Association Technique d'Importation
    Charbonnière (ATIC)
Charbonnages de France

Institut Français des Relations
  Internationales (IFRI)

Germany, Federal Republic of
Bergbau-Forschung GmbH
Gesamtverband des deutschen
  Steinkohlenbergbaus
Institute of Energy Economics/
  University of Koeln

India
Central Mine Planning Design
  Institute/Ranchi Planning
  Commission

Indonesia
Department of Mines & Energy

Italy
Comitato Nazionale per l'Energia
  Nucleare (CNEN)
Ente Nazionale Idrocarburi (ENI)
Montedison

Japan
Committee for Energy Policy
  Promotion
C. Itoh and Co. LTD
Electric Power Development Company
Federation of Electric Power
  Companies
Institute of Energy Economics
Japan Economic Research Center
Mitsui and Co. LTD

Netherlands
Energie Studie Centrum ECN
Havenbedrijf der Gemeente Rotterdam
Havenbedrijven van Amsterdam,
  Delfzijl, Dordrecht en Terneuzen
Hoogovens IJmuiden B.V.

N.V. tot Keuring van
  Elektrotechnische Materialen
Ministerie van Economische Zaken
Nederlandse Energie Ontwikkelings
  Maatschappij B.V.
N.V. Nederlandse Gasunie
Shell Coal International Limited
Shell Nederland Verkoopmaatschappij
  B.V.
SHV Nederland N.V.
Stichting Energieonderzoek Centrum
  Nederland
Frans Swarttouw B.V.

Netherlands/U.K.
Shell Coal International Ltd.

Poland
Ministry of Mining/Warsaw

Sweden
Luossavaara-Kiirunavaara AB
The Swedish State Power Board
Sydkraft AB

United Kingdom
British Petroleum Company
National Coal Board
University of Cambridge:
  Engineering Department
S. G. Warburg & Co. Ltd.

United States
AMAX Inc.
Atlantic Richfield Co.
Bechtel Incorporated, and
  Bechtel Power Corporation
Commonwealth Edison Co.
Electric Power Research Institute
Massachusetts Institute of Technology
U.S. Department of Energy
World Wildlife Fund–U.S.

THE WORLD COAL STUDY

THE WOCOL APPROACH

The Participants adopted a purpose, plan and schedule for the World Coal Study at their first meeting held at Aspen, Colorado, in October 1978. It was agreed that:

"The World Coal Study is designed to be an action-oriented assessment of future prospects for coal. . . . Its objective is to examine the future needs for coal in the total energy system and to assess the prospects for expanding world coal production, utilization, and trade to meet these needs. . . . It will rely as much as possible on available and appropriate analysis performed by others. It will apply its own resources in areas where other satisfactory work is not available and it will undertake its own evaluation of possible coal development strategies. Environmental issues will be given special attention because of their importance in the expansion of the production and use of coal."

The Study has proceeded in accordance with these guidelines.

WOCOL MEETINGS

There were five week-long meetings of Study members from October 1978 through January 1980—three in Europe and two in the United States. Participants attended these meetings for the first two and one-half days to review the progress of the work and to provide guidelines for the next phase of the Study. Associates met for the remainder of the week to formulate a work program which was then carried out by country teams, the coordinating secretariat at M.I.T., and groups of Associates with particular interest in and knowledge of a subject.

Each country team also met several times during the course of the Study to develop and review the country reports prepared for WOCOL.

UNITS

Throughout this report we use *mtce* or *million metric tons of coal equivalent* as our standard measure of energy. On an energy basis, 76 mtce/year is equivalent to 1 million barrels per day (mbd) of oil.

A *ton of coal equivalent* (tce) as used in this report is a metric ton (2,205 pounds) of coal with a specific heating value (7,000 kcal/kg or 12,600 Btu/lb). Because coals vary significantly in heat content, more than 1 metric ton of coal is often required to produce the energy content of 1 tce. For example, 1 tce is equivalent to 1.4 metric tons of subbituminous western United States coal (assuming 9,000 Btu/lb). A *ton* of coal refers to a metric ton unless otherwise stated. In some country reports, the term *tonne* is also used to refer to a metric ton.

UNCERTAINTIES

The fragility and uncertainty of the world's energy system has become increasingly clear during the 18 months of this Study. The world price of oil increased from $13/barrel to $30/barrel during this time. The developments in Iran and

Afghanistan and the Three Mile Island nuclear accident have all had their impacts, the full effects of which remain to be seen. They provide examples of what may lie ahead.

There could also be pleasant surprises. Technological breakthroughs in a variety of areas, such as more economical or more efficient processes for obtaining oil from shale, tar sands, or heavy oils; or an increase in the average recovery rate of conventional oil; or in-situ coal gasification; or the extraction of gas from tight formations; or the rapid development and deployment of low-cost solar energy technologies could all make more energy available in some countries than a prudent estimate of energy prospects would now consider likely.

The WOCOL country studies are based on the facts available. The members of the Study have built into projections for their countries expected changes in government policy, particularly those relating to a more rapid increase in energy efficiency (conservation). But the analysis cannot include the effects of surprises. Surprises are just that—unpredictable events.

STUDY REPORTS

This Report—*FUTURE COAL PROSPECTS: Country and Regional Assessments*—contains the full text of the comprehensive country studies by WOCOL teams in the 16 countries participating in the World Coal Study as well as assessments for other regions of the world. It is the result of our individual work in each country and our deliberations together, which included 5 week-long meetings during the 18 months of the project. It is accompanied by a second volume, *COAL—Bridge to the Future*, which is the Final Report of the Study and represents the collective effort and findings of the Study members.

THIS REPORT

Most of the substance of this Report was completed on January 18, 1980. Data collection by WOCOL members began in October 1978 and was largely complete by October 1979.

The Conclusions were discussed in detail by Participants at the final WOCOL meeting and the text included here is as agreed at that meeting.

Each country team prepared its own report, and, as a result, there is considerable variety in the prose. Editing has not aimed at eliminating this, but has concentrated on clarity of the terminology, units, and the data contained within each report.

Participants and Associates have taken part in WOCOL as individuals and the country reports therefore do not necessarily represent the views of the public or private organizations with which WOCOL members are associated. No single member had the time or the expertise to judge every topic covered; moreover, on some topics individuals held different views. The reports in such cases have sought the consensus of the majority and it is accepted that each member does not necessarily subscribe to all the statements in the reports. Nevertheless, all WOCOL members agree on the general analysis and the main findings of the study and the role coal must play in meeting the energy needs in their countries.

Part I of this Report, "WOCOL Countries," contains the comprehensive country studies prepared by the teams from each of the 16 WOCOL countries. These reports describe for each country the present role of coal in the national energy system, the approach used in the national WOCOL analysis, and projections of coal consumption, production, imports and exports to the year 2000. They also consider transportation and port infrastructures, capital requirements, environmental issues, and obstacles and constraints associated with the projected coal expansion.

WOCOL members from each country took responsibility for preparing the country chapters. Individual responsibilities within the various countries are described in the chapters.

Each of the 16 country chapters in Part I was reviewed by the Associates and 'Participants from that country at various stages of drafting. Robert P. Greene, J. Michael Gallagher, and Susan Williamson at the M.I.T. WOCOL Secretariat provided final editorial assistance.

Part II of this Report, "Non-WOCOL Countries and Regions," contains the assessments of coal prospects for other regions of the world, which are based on special studies prepared by several WOCOL members, as described at the beginning of Part II.

Robert P. Greene and J. Michael Gallagher managed this Report and the project secretariat assisted by Susan Leland, Susan Williamson, and Kathleen Romano. Coordinating such a project of 80 people from 16 countries, bringing it to an agreed conclusion in 18 months, and producing a 2-volume report against very tight deadlines has taken exceptional talents, energy, and teamwork. At M.I.T. they have been aided by Ralph Chang, Roberta Ferland and Lynette McLaughlin; at our meetings in Europe, by Karin Berntsen, Elaine Goldberg, and Dalia Jackbo.

On behalf of the members of the World Coal Study I wish to express our great appreciation to all who have helped to make this report possible.

C.L.W.

PART I

WOCOL COUNTRIES

CHAPTER 1

AUSTRALIA

SUMMARY

For Australia the most important conclusions arising from the World Coal Study are:

(a) Coal will be the major source of the world's incremental energy needs between 1980 and 2000.

(b) Many countries do not have indigenous reserves of economically recoverable coal and must increase their reliance on imported coal. The World Coal Study projections indicate that world coal trade will grow from the present figure of 200 mtce to 370-470 mtce in 1990 and to 560-980 mtce in the year 2000, and even higher quantities if oil supplies are further restricted or nuclear power investment is further delayed.

(c) As one of the countries with large coal resources at reasonable depth, of satisfactory quality, and within reasonable distance of deep-water port sites, Australia will be called on to supply increasing quantities of coal—particularly steam coal—to the world coal trade. The importing country Participants in the World Coal Study forecast that the demand for Australian coal exports may rise from the present 38 mtce to about 200 mtce by the year 2000.

This Australian national report for the World Coal Study examines aspects of the Australian coal industry relevant to the question whether Australia will be able to supply the forecast export demand as well as meet its own growing coal needs.

It is the view of the Australian participants in this WOCOL national report that the Australian coal industry will be able to increase its coal exports to between 160 mtce and 200 mtce by the year 2000—given that key decisions by consumers and producers are made sufficiently early, and given a background of encouragement by governments, statutory bodies, unions and the community.

FOREWORD

This report on the Australian coal scene has been prepared for the World Coal Study (WOCOL). The structure, content and length of the report have been influenced by the guidelines for the WOCOL national reports.

The report has been written by the Australian World Coal Study group which consists of:

Dr. D.D. Brown	Deputy General Manager, CSR Limited
Dr. R.A. Durie	Chief Scientist, R.W. Miller & Co. Pty. Ltd.
Mr. M.K. Laverick	Market Development Manager—Coal, The Broken Hill Proprietary Company Limited
Miss J.C. Miller	Chief Statistician, Joint Coal Board
Mr. D.B. Tolmie	Principal Project Officer, Minerals & Chemicals Division, CSR Limited
Mr. K.G. Wybrow	Member, Joint Coal Board

Considerable assistance has been provided by Commonwealth and State Government Departments, various Statutory Authorities and by members of the Australian coal industry in assembling the data required, in providing critical and constructive comment on the projections made, and in discussion of the constraints to be faced in enlarging coal production, use, and exports. This assistance is gratefully acknowledged.

Although many have contributed directly and indirectly to the preparation of the report, responsibility for the contained projections and opinions rests with the Australian Participants in the World Coal Study.

Dr. D.D. Brown
Dr. R.A. Durie   Participants, January 1980
Mr. K.G. Wybrow

GENERAL BACKGROUND TO THE AUSTRALIAN COAL INDUSTRY

Coal has been important to the development of Australia from the early 19th century as a major source of energy within the country and as a significant export commodity. With the establishment in the 1950's of an oil refining industry in Australia the availability of cheap fuel oil temporarily slowed the coal industry's growth. Reorganisation and mechanisation, however, resulted in high productivity and competitive coal prices and laid the foundation for major coal industry growth in the 1960's and 1970's.

Australia has large resources of coal and also significant resources of oil, natural gas, shale oil and uranium. In energy units, coal accounts for over 97% of the total fossil fuel resources identified in 1978 as economic, demonstrated and recoverable (Ref. 1). Oil and natural gas each account for about 1½%. Shale oil is not included in these percentages. Notwithstanding coal's predominance in Australia's fossil fuel resources its share of the total primary energy* use is only 37%

* Primary energy includes energy in its original form of supply e.g., as coal, crude oil or natural gas. It includes energy lost in production of such secondary forms as electricity, oil from coal conversion, coke, refined petroleum products. Hydroelectricity is included on a coal-equivalent basis, using 13.04 MJ/kWh, for consistency with the earlier Workshop on Alternative Energy Strategies (WAES) (Ref. 3) and other WOCOL national reports.

4

(Ref. 2). Approximately 45% of the total primary energy use is supplied by liquid fuels, with about 60% of the latter going to the transport sector.

Australia currently obtains about 70% of its oil supplies from local sources but will not maintain this degree of self-sufficiency unless new oilfields are discovered. Import parity pricing for oil was not adopted until the latter half of 1978 and its effect on the pattern of oil consumption has not yet been assessed.

With the current and projected oil supply difficulties there is a trend to replace oil used in the nontransport sector by coal (or natural gas) wherever possible and in the transport sector by rail electrification. For the longer term, studies are under way to supplement transport fuel supplies with liquids from oil shale and coal, and alcohols from natural gas, biomass and coal. These possibilities are anticipated in the projections made in the accompanying tables.

Australia's large coal resources are concentrated in the Eastern States. In New South Wales and Queensland the coals are primarily black and have a wide range of rank and other properties. Volatile matter yields range from high to low and although ash values of the raw coal tend to be high, the sulphur content is almost universally low. Victoria has very large resources of brown coal which currently are used predominantly for power generation. New uses are under investigation.

The coal resources in other States, accessible by current technology, are relatively small, in most cases comprising isolated deposits of sub-bituminous coal or lignite. The major use for these coals in South Australia and Western Australia is in State-owned power stations.

Electricity generation is strongly oriented toward the use of coal, as shown in Table 1-1.

Table 1-1. (Ref. 4). Power Stations Energy Source (1977)

Source	mtce*	%
Coal	25.0	74
Oil	1.0	3
Gas	1.6	5
Hydro	6.1	18
Total	33.7	100

* Million tons coal equivalent, in terms of a standard coal of calorific value 12600 BTU/lb., (7,000kcal/kg, 29.308 MJ/kg)
 1 mtce = 27.7×10^{12} BTU = 29.308×10^{15} J

The growth in exports of bituminous coal from both New South Wales and Queensland over the last 20 years has been rapid. Total exports have risen from less than 1 million tons in 1958 to 12.5 million tons in 1968 and to 38.7 million tons in 1978, the latter figure representing about half of the saleable production of black coal. Much of the growth in exports has been metallurgical coal (87% of coal exports in 1978) (Ref. 5), but steam coal has been exported whenever a satisfactory market existed. Japan has been the main customer but markets are developing elsewhere in the Western Pacific area and European markets are expanding despite the significant transport cost.

Large sections of the Australian coal industry have become completely dependent on the export market, many mines and associated infrastructures having been specifically developed on the basis of export contracts.

Over the last few years, the Australian coal industry has been faced with problems arising from weak demand for metallurgical coal by the world steel industry and by uncertainties and delays in determining the demand for steam coal. As a result, there is at present spare capacity for production of metallurgical coal in some existing mines and a number of new mining projects have been deferred pending the emergence of an adequate market.

Government, private companies and mining unions are keenly interested in further major expansion of the coal export trade. Factors which are seen by these groups as important to the successful development of the trade are a substantial degree of security in the level of demand, and prices which give an adequate financial return to the investor. Other essentials are secure and satisfying employment for the people working in the industry, good working conditions, and adequate safeguarding of the environment, including rehabilitation of worked-out areas.

The Australian coal industry is currently regarded as efficient, but improvements are possible. For example, recovery factors at underground mines need to be improved. A better integration of mine development and infrastructure, particularly in the transport system, needs to be developed in some areas.

Employment in the Australian coal industry has been increasing steadily (up 49% over the past 10 years) (Ref. 5) and no major difficulty is expected in finding personnel for continued expansion. There may be shortages, however, in certain skill categories, particularly in underground mining, if adequate training programmes are not established.

There is widespread acceptance that Australian ownership and control of coal mining projects is desirable, but foreign participation up to 50% is also generally accepted. Foreign participation greater than 50% usually requires demonstration that market access will be facilitated and that there is insufficient Australian participation available.

The Australian coal industry has demonstrated its ability to increase production and to build up a substantial export trade. Given the assurance of increased export markets and adequate returns on investment, the industry and the various authorities involved appear ready to initiate new projects to provide for a continued high rate of growth. This growth might well involve doubling exports in each of the next two decades.

There are two major aspects of rapid expansion of the Australian coal industry, however, which are of concern:

(a) The national and local benefits from rapid expansion of Australia's export coal trade need to be sufficiently recognised by the community so that there will be adequate public acceptance of the social and environmental impacts involved.

(b) Because the Australian coal industry is so dependent on exports it would suffer disproportionately if downturn in consumer country economies caused the deferment or cancellation of contracted purchases.

THE AUSTRALIAN WOCOL ANALYSIS

The national scenario parameters assumed for Australia are summarised in Table 1-2.

The projections of the Department of National Development have been modified for use as a basis for the WOCOL analysis of Australian energy demand (Refs.

6

Table 1-2. National Scenario Parameters—Australia

PARAMETER	1977	1985 Low Coal Case (1)	1985 High Coal Case (2)	1990 Low Coal Case	1990 High Coal Case	2000 Low Coal Case	2000 High Coal Case	1977-2000 Cpd. Annual Growth %/yr. Low Coal Case	1977-2000 Cpd. Annual Growth %/yr. High Coal Case
World Oil Price[1,2] (1979 U.S. Dollars/ barrel)	20	20	35	20	40	25	50	1.0	4.1
Economic Growth (GNP, 1978 $US $\times$ 10^9) (6)	95.6	126	126	149	149	210	210	3.5	3.5
Population (Millions) (7)	14.2	15.4	15.4	16.3	16.3	18.0	18.0	1.0	1.0
Economic Growth (GNP per capita, $US000's (1978))	6.75	8.17	8.17	9.13	9.13	11.67	11.67	2.4	2.4
Total Primary Energy (3) Consumed (mtce)	102.3	144	141	180	174	259	260	4.1	4.1
Primary Energy Consumed per capita (tce)	7.20	9.35	9.15	11.04	10.65	14.41	14.47	3.1	3.1
Total Oil Imports				(8)		(8)			
a) (million barrels/day)	0.19	0.28	0.19	0.44	0.07	0.84	0.08	6.6	−3.5
b) (mtce)	14.3	21.0	14.2	32.9	5.0	62.7	6.3		
Production of Electricity									
a) 1 Oil used (mtce)	1.0	1.1	1.1	1.0	1.0	0.9	0.9	−0.5	−0.5
2 Gas used (mtce)	1.6	3.4	3.4	3.3	3.3	3.0	3.0	2.7	2.7
3 Hydro used (mtce) (4)	6.1	7.0	7.0	7.4	7.4	8.1	8.1	1.2	1.2
4 Coal used (mtce)	25.0	42.9	42.9	64.2	64.2	107	107	6.5	6.5
b) Primary energy used (mtce)	33.7	54.4	54.4	75.9	75.9	119	119	5.7	5.7
c) Total installed electric capacity (GWe)	20.8	34	34	46	46	72	72	5.5	5.5
d) Nuclear capacity (GWe)	—	—	—	—	—	—	—	—	—
e) Coal-fired capacity (GWe)	13.4	25	25	37	37	62	62	6.9	6.9
f) Coal capacity with sulphur scrubbers (GWe) (5)	—	—	—	—	—	—	—	—	—

(1) WOCOL Low Coal Case assumes a low price path for oil.
(2) WOCOL High Coal Case assumes a high price path for oil.
(3) Primary Energy is defined on second page of this report.
(4) Hydro electricity is corrected to a coal equivalent basis, using 13.04 MJ/kWh.
(5) Australian steam coals are low in sulphur; no scrubbers are in use or envisaged.
(6) Assumes $A = $US 1.10 throughout the period.
(7) Bureau of Census and Statistics.
(8) See p. 15 for explanation of lower imports in these years.

2, 6). These extend only to 1987 and were prepared before the Australian Government adopted (in August 1978) a policy of import parity pricing for indigenous oil and before the further large increases in world oil prices in 1979. It is too early to assess the effect of these changes on Australian economic growth (as measured by GDP) or Australia's long-term energy demand.

We have taken the Department of National Development projection of a 4% p.a.* GDP growth rate until 1985, and then assumed a 3.5% p.a. growth rate for 1985-1995 and a 2.7% p.a. growth rate for 1995-2000. This results in a GDP

* Per annum.

growth rate of 3.5% p.a. for the period 1977-2000. As suggested by the WOCOL Project Secretariat, we have not assumed any significant difference in economic growth between the WOCOL Low Coal and High Coal Cases.

In Australia's WOCOL Low Coal Case, no growth in the real price of oil is assumed until 1990, when it increases from US $20/barrel to US $25 (1979 dollars) by 2000. The real oil price is already over US $20, so this case could be regarded as a minimum oil price path. The WOCOL High Coal Case assumes that the real oil price rises from US $20 in 1979 to US $35 by 1985, and US $50 by 2000 (all in 1979 dollars). At these price levels it is assumed that alternative sources of oil are brought into use in Australia (viz. oil from shale and alcohols from natural gas and biomass (1990), coal conversion (1995)).

While GDP growth has been projected to slow after 1985, it is expected that the pricing and security of supply of Australia's coal-based electricity will become increasingly attractive to energy-intensive industries and will boost electricity demand. In the WOCOL Low Coal Case, growth in total primary energy demand was therefore assumed to be 4% p.a. for the period 1977-2000 (as for GDP growth projections to 1985), further incremented for aluminum smelter electricity demand in the 1980's, resulting in a compound growth rate of 4.1% p.a. for the period 1977-2000.

In estimating total primary energy demand for the Australian WOCOL High Coal Case, we have assumed that by the year 2000, compared with the WOCOL Low Coal Case, there is:

(a) a reduction in consumption of "conventional crude oil"* (both indigenous and imported) due to higher oil prices,
(b) an increase in "synthetic liquid fuels"* consumption partially offsetting (a),
(c) an increase in coal consumption to provide for coal to oil conversion, including energy lost during conversion.

These adjustments in the WOCOL High Coal Case roughly compensate each other in the year 2000, resulting in a total primary energy demand growth rate of 4.1% p.a. for the period 1977-2000, which is similar to that in the WOCOL Low Coal Case.

The Department of National Development's projection for natural gas consumption has been adjusted by assuming that startup of North West Shelf production is delayed from 1983 to 1985. After 1985, an initial growth rate of 8% p.a. for domestic consumption of natural gas is assumed, of which 4% is due to GDP growth and 4% is due to substitution of oil by gas because of availability and convenience. The projected growth rate for natural gas demand is progressively reduced, with diminishing GDP growth rate and diminishing availability of substitution, to 4% p.a. by 2000. The growth assumption for natural gas is the same for WOCOL Low Coal and High Coal Cases.

Domestic supplies of crude oil are based on projections of the expected level of production from presently producing and presently known oil fields plus, in the WOCOL Low Coal Case, a small addition for oil from new discoveries. In the

---

* The term "conventional crude oil" is used here to denote oil whose origin is natural underground accumulations to distinguish it from "synthetic liquid fuels" produced from all other sources, such as oil from coal and alcohols from natural gas and biomass. Shale oil is here included as a "synthetic liquid fuel."

WOCOL High Coal Case it has been assumed that exploration will be moderately successful, leading to some additional production, and that the high oil price will make development of smaller fields economic. The assumptions used are consistent with somewhat similar projections made by others (Ref. 7).

Only in the WOCOL High Coal Case is it considered that the development of unconventional sources of oil will be economically feasible. We have assumed that oil will be produced from shale by 1990 and from coal by 1995.

COAL CONSUMPTION

Projections for Australia's energy consumption to 2000 are shown in Tables 1-3 to 1-7, with particular reference to coal. Some of these projections are illustrated in Figure 1-1.

**Figure 1-1.   Energy Consumption Projections for Australia
WOCOL High Case**

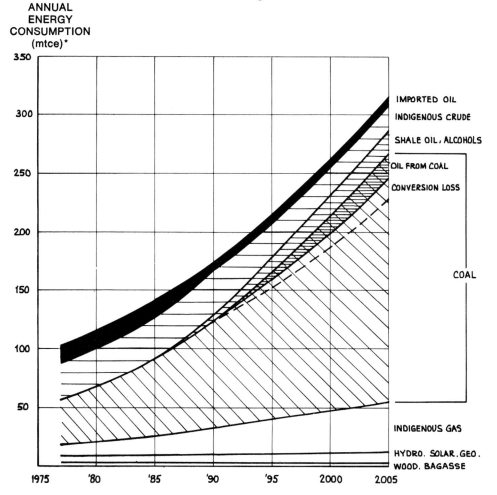

ANNUAL
ENERGY
CONSUMPTION
(mtce)*

Table 1-3. Coal Use in Final Demand Sectors—Australia[1]
(mtce)

	1977	1980 Low Coal Case[5]	1980 High Coal Case[6]	1985 Low Coal Case	1985 High Coal Case	1990 Low Coal Case	1990 High Coal Case	1995 Low Coal Case	1995 High Coal Case	2000 Low Coal Case	2000 High Coal Case	2005 Low Coal Case	2005 High Coal Case	1977-2000 Cpd. Annual Percentage Growth %/yr. Low Coal Case	1977-2000 Cpd. Annual Percentage Growth %/yr. High Coal Case
Coal Use by Sector (mtce)															
Electric[2]	25.0	29.3	29.3	42.9	42.9	64.2	64.2	83.4	83.4	107.3	107.3	138.0	138.0	6.5	6.5
Industrial Steam[3]	4.4	7.1	7.1	11.1	11.1	13.5	13.5	15.0	15.0	16.1	16.1	17.3	17.3	5.8	5.8
Metallurgical	8.3	9.6	9.6	10.3	10.3	12.2	12.2	14.5	14.5	16.8	16.8	19.5	19.5	3.1	3.1
Synthetic Fuels[4]	—	—	—	—	—	—	—	—	12.5	—	24.9	—	37.4	n.a.	n.a.
Residential/Commercial	0.3	0.3	0.3	0.3	0.3	0.3	0.3	0.3	0.3	0.3	0.3	0.3	0.3	—	—
Total Coal Consumed (mtce)	38.0	46.3	46.3	64.6	64.6	90.2	90.2	113.2	125.7	140.5	165.4	175.1	212.5	5.9	6.6
Total Primary Energy Consumed (mtce)	102.3	117	117	144	141	180	174	217	214	259	260	310	315	4.1	4.1
Coal Penetration by Sector															
% of Ttl. Primary Energy	37	40	40	45	46	50	52	52	59	54	64	56	67	1.7	2.4
% of Electric	74	75	75	79	79	85	85	88	88	90	90	92	92	0.9	0.9
% of Industrial Steam	20	25	25	30	30	35	35	40	40	45	45	50	50	3.6	3.6

[1] Refer to Table 1-2 for major assumptions.

[2] Coal (mtce)   1977   2000
Black   17.3   74.7
Brown   7.7   32.6
Total   25.0   107.3

[3] Industrial Steam includes coal used directly in industry and other miscellaneous uses.

[4] Assumes 60% conversion efficiency.

[5] WOCOL Low Coal Case.

[6] WOCOL High Coal Case.

Table 1-4. Source of Energy for Electricity Generation—Australia[1]
(mtce Fuel Input)

Energy Source (mtce)	1977	1980 Low[2] Coal Case	1980 Case High[3] Coal	1985 Low Coal Case	1985 High Coal Case	1990 Low Coal Case	1990 High Coal Case	1995 Low Coal Case	1995 High Coal Case	2000 Low Coal Case	2000 High Coal Case	2005 Low Coal Case	2005 High Coal Case	1977–2000 Cpd. Annual Percentage Growth %/yr. Low Coal Case	1977–2000 Cpd. Annual Percentage Growth %/yr. High Coal Case
Nuclear	—	—	—	—	—	—	—	—	—	—	—	—	—	—	—
Hydro	6.1	6.4	6.4	7.0	7.0	7.4	7.4	7.?	7.7	8.1	8.1	8.1	8.1	1.2	1.2
Gas Turbines/Combined Cycle	(0.2)			included with oil and gas steam											
Geothermal/Solar/Other	—	—	—	—	—	—	—	—	—	—	—	—	—	—	—
Fossil Steam															
—Oil	1.0	0.9	0.9	1.1	1.1	1.0	1.0	1.0	1.0	0.9	0.9	0.9	0.9	-0.5	-0.5
—Gas	1.6	2.4	2.4	3.4	3.4	3.3	3.3	3.1	3.1	3.0	3.0	2.8	2.8	2.7	2.7
—Coal	25.0	29.3	29.3	42.9	42.9	64.2	64.2	82.4	83.4	107	107	138	138	6.5	6.5
Total Energy Input for Electricity	33.7	39.0	39.0	54.4	54.4	75.9	75.9	9?	95.2	119.0	119.0	149.8	149.8	5.7	5.7
Coal Penetration (%)	74	75	75	79	79	85	85	88	88	90	90	92	92	0.9	0.9

[1] See Table 1-2 for major assumptions.
[2] WOCOL Low Coal Case.
[3] WOCOL High Coal Case.

Coal consumption within Australia has been steadily expanding and accelerated growth is forecast during the next 20 years (compound annual increase 1977-2000 of 5.9% p.a. for WOCOL Low Coal and 6.6% p.a. for WOCOL High Coal Cases), representing an increasing proportion of the total primary energy use.

Particularly high growth (6.5% p.a.) is forecast in the use of coal for power generation, an area which is already strongly based on coal. Strong growth (5.8% p.a.) is forecast also in the industrial steam market from the existing relatively small base, as the substitution of coal for oil becomes increasingly attractive.

In the WOCOL High Coal Case, two coal conversion plants are projected to be operating by 2000, requiring a total of 25 mtce per year of coal to produce about 24% of Australia's liquid fuel demand (Table 1-6). In respect of other consumers only modest growth rates for coal usage have been projected.

For coal consumption in the Australian steel industry, WOCOL projections assume a compound growth of 3.1% p.a. (slightly less than the assumed growth in GDP) (Table 1-3). This rate of growth does not make provision for any large-scale growth in the export of pig iron or crude steel, a development which receives consideration from time to time. In this regard it is relevant to note that several years ago plans for the establishment of a new "jumbo" export steel plant were deferred.

In the steel industry, replacement of the fuel oil injected into the blast furnaces by coal or coal-derived fuels can be expected. To the extent that this replacement occurs and is not offset by other economies, there will be a small increase in coal used per ton of steel.

Plans have been announced for the establishment in Australia of several new aluminum smelters using coal-based electricity and these have been included in our forecasts for power generation. Other plants which use significant quantities of electricity may also be attracted to Australia.

The projections therefore provide for total electricity generation to increase at an annual growth rate of 5.7% in the period 1977 to 2000. Over the same period, coal penetration of power generation is expected to increase from 74% to 90% with a coal usage growth rate of 6.5% p.a. The States with large coal resources are currently engaged in strong programmes of expansion in coalfield power stations. Other States are also taking steps to increase their use of coal and to decrease their use of oil. In Queensland, where large blocks of high volatile coal are available to the electricity supply industry, consideration is being given to stripping volatiles for liquid fuels production and generating electricity from combustion of the residues.

Table 1-5. Total State Authority Electricity Generation Capacity— Australia
Gigawatts Electrical (GWe)

Installed Capacity (GWe)	June 1977	1980 Low[2] Coal Case	1980 High[3] Coal Case	1985 Low Coal Case	1985 High Coal Case	1990 Low Coal Case	1990 High Coal Case	1995 Low Coal Case	1995 High Coal Case	2000 Low Coal Case	2000 High Coal Case	2005 Low Coal Case	2005 High Coal Case	1977-2000 Cpd. Annual Percentage Growth %/yr. Low Coal Case	1977-2000 Cpd. Annual Percentage Growth %/yr. High Coal Case
Nuclear	—	—	—	—	—	—	—	—	—	—	—	—	—	—	—
Hydro	5.7	6.0	6.0	6.6	6.6	7.0	7.0	7.4	7.4	7.7	7.7	7.7	7.7	1.4	1.4
Gas Turbines/Combined Cycle	0.7	0.8	0.8	1.1	1.1	1.0	1.0	1.0	1.0	1.0	1.0	1.0	1.0	1.6	1.6
Geothermal/Solar/Other	—	—	—	—	—	—	—	—	—	—	—	—	—	—	—
Fossil Steam															
—Oil } —Gas }	1.0	1.2	1.2	1.4	1.4	1.5	1.5	1.4	1.4	1.3	1.3	1.3	1.3	1.1	1.1
—Coal	13.4	15.7	15.7	24.9	24.9	36.5	36.5	48.2	48.2	62	62	80	80	6.9	6.9
Total Electricity	20.8	23.7	23.7	34	34	46	46	58	58	72	72	90	90	5.5	5.5
Coal Penetration (%)	64.4	66	66	73	73	79	79	83	83	86	86	89	89	1.3	1.3

[1] See Table 1-2 for major assumptions:
[2] WOCOL Low Coal Case.
[3] WOCOL High Coal Case.

Table 1-6. Total Energy Consumption—Australia (mtce)

Energy Source (mtce)	1977	1980 Low³ Coal Case	1980 High⁴ Coal Case	1985 Low Coal Case	1985 High Coal Case	1990 Low Coal Case	1990 High Coal Case	1995 Low Coal Case	1995 High Coal Case	2000 Low Coal Case	2000 High Coal Case	2005 Low Coal Case	2005 High Coal Case	1977-2000 Cpd. Annual Percentage Growth %/yr. Low Coal Case	1977-2000 Cpd. Annual Percentage Growth %/yr. High Coal Case
Domestic Oil															
—Indigenous Crude	31.3	32.8	32.8	32.1	36.0	23.3	41.1	15.8	31.1	9.0	22.9	7.4	22.2	-5.3	-1.3
—Shale Oil, Alcohols, etc.	—	—	—	—	—	—	3.7	—	11.2	—	18.7	—	18.7	—	n.a.
—Oil from Coal¹	—	—	—	—	—	—	—	—	7.5	—	14.9	—	22.4	—	n.a.
Imported Oil	14.3	16.1	15.5	21.0	14.2	32.9	5.0	48.0	5.5	62.7	6.3	72.7	7.0	6.6	-3.5
Total Oil	45.6	48.9	48.3	53.1	50.2	56.2	49.8	63.8	55.3	71.7	62.8	80.1	70.3	1.8	1.2
Indigenous Gas	9.4	12.3	12.3	16.0	16.0	22.9	22.9	29.2	29.2	35.4	35.4	43.3	43.3	6.0	6.0
Imported Gas	—	—	—	—	—	—	—	—	—	—	—	—	—	—	—
Hydro/Geo/Solar	6.1	6.4	6.4	7.0	7.0	7.4	7.4	7.7	7.7	8.1	8.1	8.1	8.1	1.2	1.2
Nuclear	—	—	—	—	—	—	—	—	—	—	—	—	—	—	—
Wood & Bagasse	3.2	3.2	3.2	3.2	3.2	3.3	3.3	3.3	3.3	3.4	3.4	3.6	3.6	0.3	0.3
Coal (excl. Exports)	38.0	46.3	46.3	64.6	64.6	90.2	90.2	113.2	125.7	140.5	165.4	175.1	212.5	5.9	6.6
Total Energy Use²	102.3	117	117	144	141	180	174	217	214	259	260	310	315	4.1	4.1
Coal Penetration (%)	37	40	40	45	46	50	52	52	59	54	64	56	67	1.7	2.4
Black Coal (mtce)	29.2	36.3	36.3	51.1	51.1	69.1	69.1	86.6	99.1	106.8	119.2	132.0	156.9	5.8	6.3
Brown Coal (mtce)	8.8	10.0	10.0	13.5	13.5	21.1	21.1	26.6	26.6	33.7	46.2	43.1	55.6	6.0	7.5

¹ The energy content of the oil produced from coal, together with the conversion losses, is already included under Coal.
² Totals are rounded.
³ WOCOL Low Coal Case.
⁴ WOCOL High Coal Case.

Much of the oil shown for power generation (Table 1-4) is supplementary fuel in coal-fired plants.

Hydroelectricity generation growth is constrained by water resource availability, and the Department of National Development projection has been extended from 1985 to 2000 at a growth rate of only 1% p.a. Likewise the use of solar energy for power generation is not seen as being significant in the period of this study.

No allowance has been made for any nuclear power plants, but in Western Australia, which is less well-endowed with coal resources, nuclear power generation is regarded as a long-term option. Also under study in Western Australia is the use of natural gas for power generation, for industrial steam raising, and for combined cycle generation of power and steam-using gas turbines. Two 200 MW units in Western Australia have recently been converted from oil to coal firing.

The use of brown coal for power generation is expected to rise from 7.7 mtce in 1977 to 32.6 mtce in the year 2000, while the use of black coal for power generation is expected to increase from 17.3 mtce to 74.7 mtce (Table 1-3).

In June 1978, less than 8% of the installed capacity in the Australian State electricity authorities' power stations was oil-fired (Table 1-5). About half of this was less than 8 years old. Conversion of some of this capacity to coal-firing is proceeding. Planned new generating capacity announced includes 12,515 MW coal-fired and only 50 MW oil-fired (the latter in the Northern Territory and the Pilbara region of Western Australia) (Ref. 4).

The industrial steam and power market (i.e., the market other than that supplied by the State electricity authorities) currently uses significant tonnages of oil and higher prices for oil should provide opportunities for coal to recover some of the market share lost during the 1950's and 1960's. Where it is available at competitive prices, however, natural gas is preferred by users as an industrial fuel. A strong growth rate of (5.8% p.a.) is projected for coal in this market (Table 1-3).

The Australian WOCOL High Coal Case assumes a crude oil price progression high enough to encourage some supplementation of liquid fuels by shale oil and alcohols by 1990, and by the product of two coal conversion plants (one based on brown coal and one on black coal) by 2000. Coal conversion on this scale would require a combined input of 25 mtce per annum. By the year 2005 a third plant, based on black coal, is included in this schedule (Table 1-6 and Figure 1-2).

The net result in this scenario (the WOCOL High Coal Case) suggests that Australia could be largely self-sufficient in respect of liquid fuels at the end of the century. For this case, imports in the year 2000 are estimated at 0.08 million barrels per day. This scenario, however, requires early decisions to enable production of liquid fuels from these alternative sources (oil shale, alcohols and coal) by the dates indicated. To the extent that such production is not achieved, additional oil imports will be required and the production of coal for liquefaction will be reduced.

In the WOCOL Low Coal Case, the crude oil price progression assumed is insufficient to encourage production of "synthetic liquid fuels" or to discourage a greater demand for oil products. Furthermore, as described in the section on the WOCOL Analysis, a less intensive exploration programme and a less favourable discovery rate are projected in this case, resulting in less production of indigenous crude oil. Accordingly, Australia's projected dependence on imported oil in the

Figure 1-2. Oil Supply Projections Australia
WOCOL High Case

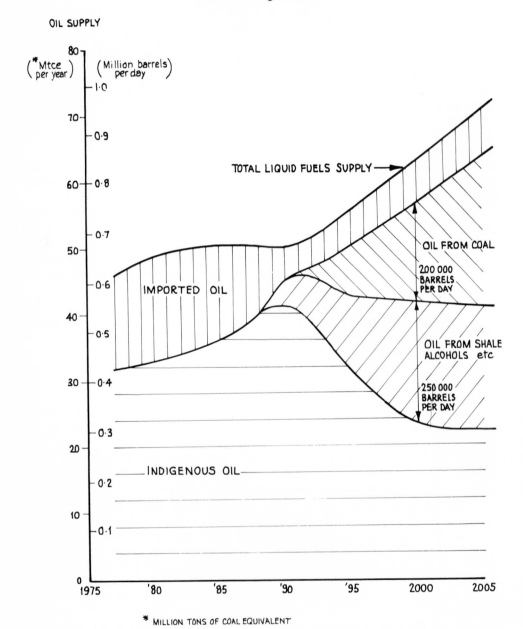

OIL SUPPLY

WOCOL Low Coal Case increases from about 30% now to about 87% by the year 2000 (Table 1-6 and Figure 1-3).

Natural gas usage is expected to increase strongly in those States with access to supplies, giving an overall average growth rate of 6.0% p.a., i.e., comparable to the rates forecast for coal (Table 1-6). It is assumed that the North West Shelf (off Western Australia) will be producing gas by 1985 and that additional supplies will be available from other fields to satisfy growing demands in the other states.

It is likely that due to development of new technologies such as solvent refined coal (SRC), briquetting and formed coke, both brown coals and a wider range of black coals will find increasing use as a metallurgical coal substitute. The produc-

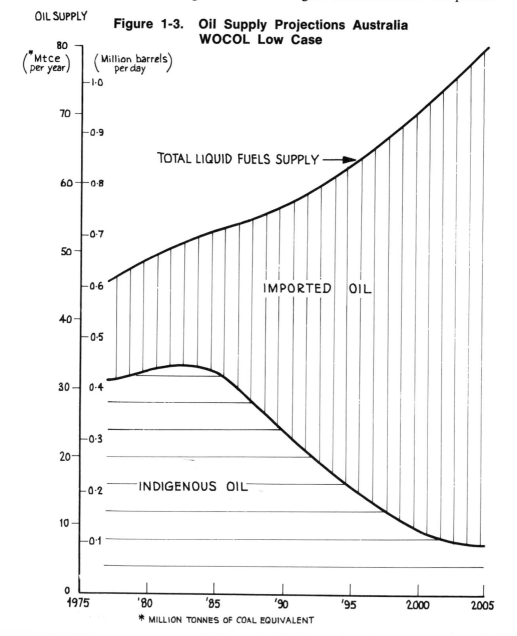

Figure 1-3. Oil Supply Projections Australia WOCOL Low Case

OIL SUPPLY

* MILLION TONNES OF COAL EQUIVALENT

tion of SRC will allow conversion of brown coal into an exportable product and on a large scale. (Some char is exported already.) While no specific allowance has been made for SRC in Australian export projections, it is unlikely to have a significant effect on the projections for black coal exports. It will possibly replace some metallurgical coal in consumer country import projections. It is possible also that production of coke, char and coal-based specialty carbons for export will develop during the next twenty years, but again such production will not change significantly the quantity of black coal exports projected.

In summary, growth in coal consumption within Australia from 38 mtce in 1977 to 141 mtce in the year 2000 is indicated in the WOCOL Low Coal Case and to 166 mtce in the WOCOL High Coal Case. The corresponding growth rates are 5.9% p.a. and 6.6% p.a. (Table 1-3).

Coal penetration of Australian total primary energy consumption is projected to rise from a current level of about 37% to 54% in the WOCOL Low Coal Case and to 64% in the WOCOL High Coal Case in the year 2000 (Table 1-3).

Additional details of the use of coal in final demand sectors and of the sources of energy for the generation of electricity are set out in Tables 1-3 to 1-7.

Table 1-7.   Coal Consumption—Australia

Parameter	1977	1985 Low[2] Coal Case	1985 High[3] Coal Case	1990 Low Coal Case	1990 High Coal Case	2000 Low Coal Case	2000 High Coal Case	1977-2000 Cpd. Annual Growth %/yr. Low Coal Case	1977-2000 Cpd. Annual Growth %/yr. High Coal Case
Coal Penetration in Major Markets									
(a) Total Coal Use									
(i) mtce	38.0	64.6	64.6	90.2	90.2	140.5	165.4	5.9	6.6
(ii) as % of primary energy use	37	45	46	50	52	54	54	1.7	2.4
(b) Coal Use in Electricity Generation									
(i) mtce input	25.0	42.9	42.9	64.2	64.2	107.3	107.3	6.5	6.5
(ii) as % of primary energy input to electricity	74	79	79	85	85	90	90	0.9	0.9
(c) Coal Use for Industrial Steam									
(i) mtce	4.4	11.1	11.1	13.5	13.5	16.1	16.1	5.8	5.8
(ii) as % of industrial steam	20	30	30	35	35	45	45	3.6	3.6
(d) Coal Use for Synthetic Fuel—mtce	—	—	—	—	—	—	24.9	—	—
Distribution by Use Sector %									
(i) Metallurgical	22	16	16	14	14	12	10	—	—
(ii) Electricity	66	67	67	71	71	77	65	—	—
(iii) Industrial Steam[1]	12	17	17	15	15	11	10	—	—
(iv) Residential/Commercial	0	0	0	0	0	0	0	—	—
(v) Synthetic Fuels	—	—	—	—	—	—	15	—	—
Total Coal Use	100	100	100	100	100	100	100	—	—

[1] Industrial Steam includes coal used directly in industry and other miscellaneous uses.
[2] WOCOL Low Coal Case.
[3] WOCOL High Coal Case.

COAL RESOURCES

Table 1-8 summarises the latest information available to us on Australia's black coal resources.

The largest and economically most significant deposits of black coal in Australia are concentrated in the Bowen Basin of Eastern Queensland and the Sydney Basin in New South Wales. The Galilee Basin in Queensland also contains a large resource and the Surat and Clarence-Moreton Basins are of significance (Figure 1-4).

Of Australia's proved black coal reserves, much is bituminous but there are large unexplored sub-bituminous coal resources and some anthracite.

The data in Table 1-8 is given in two reliability categories, one comprising the better known part of the resources, "proved reserves", and the other the lesser known part, "additional resources". "Proved reserves" include those reserves sometimes called "measured" and, for the purpose of this report, also include those reserves sometimes called "indicated". "Additional resources" include those resources sometimes called "inferred". "In Place" in both cases refers to reserves or resource in the ground. Only part of these are "Recoverable" by mining. Further losses occur in washing or other treatment necessary to produce "Marketable" coal.

For a deposit of black coal to be classified as a "proved reserve", points of observation (e.g., drill holes) are generally required at distances apart not greater than 2 km. "Additional resources", at best, are based on sparse drilling, but more generally on extrapolation over large distances, analogy with better known adjacent areas and upon geological inference.

For coal to be included in either reliability category it must comply with certain specifications for ash content, seam thickness, etc.

Figure 1-4.   Coal Resources—Australia

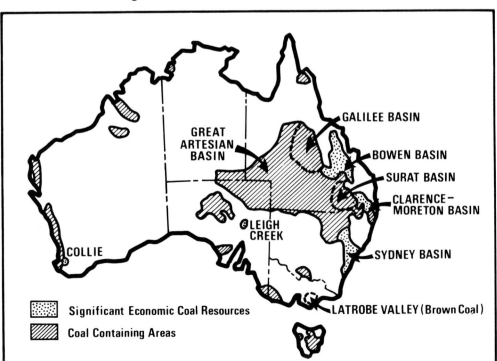

Table 1-8. Australian Resources of Black Coal (Million Tonnes)

	Proved Reserves in Place		Proved Recoverable[1] Reserves		Additional Resources in Place	
	Bituminous	Sub-bituminous	Bituminous	Sub-bituminous	Bituminous	Sub-bituminous
New South Wales						
Northern	17,602	—	8,854	—	398,153	—
West & Central	1,390	—	941	—	75,061	—
Southern	3,251	500	1,877	450	6,822	10,000
Total	22,243[2]	500[3]	11,672	450[3]	480,036[4,5]	10,000[5]
Queensland						
Northern	10,884	—	6,394	—	} 22,640	90,260
Central	10,849	245	5,883	169		
Southern	2,768	—	2,204	—		
Total	24,501[6]	245	14,481	169	22,640	90,260[7]
Western Australia	—	204	—	161	—	2,087
South Australia	—	720	—	720	—	2,300
Tasmania	139	—	69	—	200	—
Australia	46,883	1,669	26,222	1,500	502,876	104,647

Note: [1] "Proved Recoverable Reserves" are the estimated quantities of "Proved Reserves in Place" that can be physically mined at an acceptable cost. Both refer to raw coal.
[2] Within maximum depth of 1000 metres. Minimum seam thickness for underground mines is usually taken as 1.5 metres, and for surface mines 0.3 metres if linear overburden to coal ratio $\leq$ 10:1 and maximum mining depth $<$ 200 metres. Surface mining criteria are based on currently available mining techniques.
[3] Oaklands area.
[4] Includes some coal unlikely to be economically mineable in the foreseeable future viz. 130,000 million below 1000 metres.
[5] Recovery of about 230,000 million tonnes from the New South Wales 480,083 million tonnes of "Additional Resources in Place" may be possible, based on current mining experience. This figure would be reduced, however, to the extent that mining may be restricted or prohibited in any areas, such as those covered by National Parks.
[6] Within maximum depth of 900 metres; minimum seam thickness for underground mines is 1.5 metres; surface mines maximum mining depth for reserves estimation in Queensland is 60 metres. This is a conservative criterion as surface mining is now being extended to depths greater than 60 metres.
[7] Galilee Basin and Callide Basin.

Sources: N.S.W.—Ref. 8
Queensland—Ref. 9 for Proved Reserves. The estimate of Additional Resources was supplied by the Queensland Department of Mines to the Australian Minerals and Energy Council in 1977 as "hypothetical reserves." Data for other States were supplied by the relevant State Authorities during 1979.

Some of these specifications, which vary from State to State, are indicated in the footnotes to Tables 1-8, 1-9 and 1-10. In Australia, a depth of 1,000 metres is generally taken as the current limit for bituminous coal to be regarded as economically extractable (Ref. 1).

Proved Reserves in Place of black coal total 46,883 million tonnes bituminous and 1669 million tonnes sub-bituminous. The Proved Recoverable Reserves total

Table 1-9. Proved Black Coal Reserves of Surface Mining Potential—Australia[1]
(million tonnes)

	Proved Reserves in Place	Proved Recoverable Reserves	Proved Marketable Reserves[2]	Notes on marketable coal[3]
New South Wales				
Northern	2,699	2,353	1,610	777HV coking, 833HV steam
West & Central	303	268	146	HV steam
Southern	500	450	450	sub-bituminous
Total	3,502	3,071	2,206	
Queensland				
Northern	2,381	2,143	1,662	1063 coking, 599 steam
Central	1,262	1,136	892	293 coking, 599 steam
Southern	2,050	1,845	1,500	mainly steam
Total	5,693	5,124	4,054	
Western Australia	186	152	152	Sub-bituminous
South Australia	720	720	720	Sub-bituminous
Australia	10,101	9,067	7,132	

Notes: [1] See notes to Table 1-8.
[2] Marketable reserves are estimates of the quantities of coal which, under certain assumptions as to future market requirements, may be available for sale from the recoverable reserves after treatment (e.g., washing).
[3] HV = high volatile; LV = low volatile.

Table 1-10. Proved Black Coal Reserves—Underground—Australia[1]
(million tonnes)

	Proved Reserves in Place	Proved Recoverable Reserves	Proved Marketable Reserves[2]	Notes on marketable coal[3]
New South Wales				
Northern	14,903	6,501	4,339	3237HV coking, 1102HV steam
West & Central	1,087	673	581	533HV steam, 48HV coking
Southern	3,251	1,877	1,423	1339 coking mostly LV
Total	19,241	9,051	6,343	
Queensland				
Northern	8,503	4,251	3,125	2521 coking, 604 steam
Central	9,832	4,916	4,136	1633 coking, 2503 steam
Southern	718	359	292	mainly steam
Total	19,053	9,526	7,553	
Western Australia	18	9	9	Sub-bituminous
Tasmania	139	69	53	Sub-bituminous
Australia	38,451	18,655	13,958	

Notes: [1] See notes to Table 1-8.
[2] See note (2) to Table 1-9.
[3] HV = high volatile; LV = low volatile.

26,222 million tonnes bituminous and 1,500 million tonnes sub-bituminous. Additional Resources in Place are very large, e.g., about 500,000 million tonnes in New South Wales, according to a recent assessment (Ref. 8). It is expected that part of these "Resources" will gradually be upgraded to "Reserves" as growing demand warrants close drilling.

Detailed exploration of Australia's coal resources is proceeding, but at present, much of the total resources cannot be given precise quality classifications. Furthermore, exploration in many areas has been confined to relatively shallow depths and in most States, seams of less than 1.5 metres have been excluded from the calculations (Ref. 9).

Major brown coal deposits are located in Victoria where the Latrobe Valley contains proved recoverable reserves of some 35,000 million tons (within the limits of maximum mining depth 200 metres and minimum seam thickness 15 metres) (Ref. 10). This includes some 6000 million tons under township planning scheme areas, etc. Additional probable recoverable resources are of the order of 88,000 million tons. The average moisture content is 62% and the lower heating value, as received, ranges from 6.0 to 12.5 MJ/kg (2,580 to 5,370 BTU/lb.).

COAL PRODUCTION

During the 10 years to June 1978 Australian production of black coal increased by 125% for raw coal (8.4% p.a.) and by 105% for saleable coal (7.4% p.a.) (Ref. 5).

For the WOCOL Low Coal Case it is assumed that from 1977 to 2000 production of black coal can be increased at the average rate of 6.2% p.a. (Table 1-11). Over the same period brown coal production is assumed to increase at the average rate of 6.0% p.a., in line with domestic consumption. Much of this brown coal will come from a large surface mine now being developed at Loy Yang, in southeastern Victoria.

In the WOCOL High Coal Case, it is assumed that additional production of both black and brown coal will take place after 1990, to provide coal for liquefaction plants. These developments are not expected to reduce the availability of coal for export in the period to 2000.

The above assumptions result in black and brown coal production figures as shown in Table 1-11.

A review of current projects suggests that a rate of growth of black coal production somewhat higher than 6.2% p.a. might be achievable in the period to 1990, should demand be sufficiently strong. Subsequent growth might then be at a slower rate but the incremental tonnage increases would be larger than in the earlier period. Factors suggesting a higher growth rate to 1990 include the present surplus capacity in some mines and the present accumulation of deferred mine developments. Factors suggesting a slower growth after 1990 are the possible need for an increasing proportion of output to be won from underground mines and the need to replace existing mines which will become exhausted during the 1990's.

It may be assumed that black coal production for major local consumers (viz., the steel industry, the electricity authorities and some cement producers) will expand as required with little effect on coal available for export, since a large proportion of this coal is supplied from captive mines. In certain cases these mines can

AUSTRALIA

Table 1-11. Saleable Coal Production Projections
(mtce)

	1977	1985		1990		2000		1977-2000 Cpd Annual Growth % /yr.	
		Low[1] Coal Case	High[2] Coal Case	Low Coal Case	High Coal Case	Low Coal Case	High Coal Case	Low Coal Case	High Coal Case
Metallurgical									
Black	42.6	71	71	80	80	102	102	3.9	3.9
Brown	—	—	—	—	—	—	—	—	—
Total	42.6	71	71	80	80	102	102	3.9	3.9
Steam									
Black	24.3	59	59	94	94	165	178	8.7	9.0
Brown	8.8	13	13	21	21	34	46	6.1	7.5
Total	33.1	72	72	115	115	199	224	8.1	8.7
Total									
Black	66.9	130	130	174	174	267	280	6.2	6.4
Brown	8.8	13	13	21	21	34	46	6.0	7.5
Total	75.7	143	143	195	195	301	326	6.2	6.6

[1] WOCOL Low Coal Case
[2] WOCOL High Coal Case

produce both metallurgical and steam coals and there has been a recent trend for traditional domestic consumer/producers to enter the export market.

Production expansion to supply coal for export will depend in the first place on the availability of suitable markets at satisfactory prices. Assuming that such markets will be available, some other possible growth constraints need to be considered. These are discussed in other sections but include the supply of capital for mines and infrastructure, the availability of engineering resources and manpower, environmental issues, community and trade union support, the policies of the relevant statutory authorities and the policies of governments (both Commonwealth and State).

Labour productivity at both underground and surface black coal mines has increased in recent years. In the ten years to 1977/78, the output per manshift worked (OMS) increased at underground mines by 13% to 10.1 tons; at surface mines the increase was 31% to 30.2 tons (Ref. 5). These OMS figures are calculated on a raw coal basis, and include all persons working in or about the mine. It is expected that levels of productivity higher than the 1977/78 rates will be achieved in the new mines now being planned.

Employment in the industry has risen by 49% to 24,424 during the 10 years to June 1979 (Ref. 5). The industry works a 35-hour week, wages are relatively high, and, in general, no difficulty has been experienced in recruiting labour. From time to time some shortages have occurred in respect of some classifications where special qualifications are needed, e.g., undermanagers, deputies, etc. The numbers involved are relatively small. Currently, special attention is being paid to programmes which will train new entrants to the industry. Given sufficient lead times

23

the supply of manpower, both skilled and unskilled, should not be a restraint on the rate of expansion of production.

During the 1970's Australia became a centre for the manufacture of many types of machinery and equipment used by the coal industry. This should facilitate further expansion of the industry. There are, however, major items of equipment such as draglines which require long lead times between ordering and commissioning. Also, for the mine production facilities to be effective, the major components of infrastructure (e.g., rail and port facilities) need to be in place as early as possible (see the section on Coal Transportation).

Several practical considerations in expanding of coal production in Australia are:

(a) While large deposits exist which can be developed as single-product mines, in some Australian coal fields, particularly in the Upper Hunter Valley, metallurgical and steam coal sometimes must be mined at the same time. If the best use is to be made of these resources it is desirable that a suitable balance be achieved in the growth in markets for both types of coal.

(b) Coal for export is usually washed to reduce ash content and to ensure uniform quality. The coal quality specified by the consumer will significantly influence the amount of saleable coal (in tce) available from a given production of raw coal, since the yield of washed coal usually varies inversely with the ash specification. Where only metallurgical coal is produced it is not uncommon to have washery rejects amounting to 40% of the raw coal.

(c) Both underground and surface mining are currently important methods of mining coal in Australia. Maximum extraction of coal resources will require that full use be made of the advantages of both methods. Where coal deposits have surface mining potential, the use of surface mining will ensure a raw coal recovery of over 90 per cent and allow extraction of some thin seams otherwise unmineable. The application of surface mining in such circumstances and to greater depths than in the past is widely accepted.

As indicated by the data in Tables 1-9 and 1-10, however, by far the greater proportion of Australia's black coal reserves can only be won by underground methods. Some mining districts have no open-cut potential. The underground coal mining industry in Australia is generally efficient and soundly based and research to improve underground mining techniques and recovery rates is being undertaken.

To meet the projected rapid growth in demand for coal, concurrent development of both underground and surface mines will be needed, and full advantage should be taken of existing mining operations and their associated support industries.

COAL SUPPLY/DEMAND INTEGRATION

Based on the preceding assessment of Australian consumption and production of coal, the quantities available for export are projected to increase from 37.7 mtce in 1977 to 78 mtce in 1985, 105 mtce in 1990 and to at least 160 mtce by the year

2000. Metallurgical coal exports included in the figures are forecast to grow at 4.0% p.a. Export demand for steam coal is expected to grow from 3.4 mtce in 1977 to at least 75 mtce by the year 2000, an average growth rate of 14.4% p.a. (compare Ref. 11). The case and data supporting the export demand figures for Australian coal are to be found in the main WOCOL report and are not developed again in this Australian national report.

The projections of coal production and consumption for Australia are summarized in Table 1-12, together with the export potential (which is illustrated in Figure 1-5). Total Australian coal production (black & brown) is projected to increase from 75.7 mtce in 1977 to 301 mtce in the WOCOL Low Coal Case and to 326 mtce in the WOCOL High Coal Case by the year 2000. In both cases about half of the production will be required to meet domestic demand.

Higher levels of production than those projected for 1990 and 2000 in Table 1-12 could be achieved only if a major and sustained programme of development was commenced immediately. Given a reduction in project lead times of, say, two years, the export levels projected in the year 2000 might possibly be increased by 25% (from 160 mtce to 200 mtce).

In our view, however, this would require a high degree of cooperation by all concerned, viz., buyers, sellers, communities, unions and governments, and also a recognition of the national and international importance of increasing coal exports.

Table 1-12. Coal Export Projections—Australia

	1977	1985		1990		2000		1977-2000 Cpd Annual Growth % /yr.	
		Low[3] Coal Case	High[4] Coal Case	Low Coal Case	High Coal Case	Low Coal Case	High Coal Case	Low Coal Case	High Coal Case
COAL PRODUCTION (mtce)									
Metallurgical	42.6	71	71	80	80	102	102	3.9	3.9
Steam	33.1	72	72	115	115	199	224	8.1	8.7
Total coal[1]	75.7	143	143	195	195	301	326	6.2	6.6
COAL CONSUMPTION (mtce)									
Metallurgical	8.3	10	10	12	12	17	17	3.2	3.2
Steam	29.7	55	55	78	78	124	149	6.4	7.3
Total[2]	38.0	65	65	90	90	141	166	5.9	6.6
COAL EXPORTS (mtce)									
Metallurgical	34.3	61	61	68	68	85	85	4.0	4.0
Steam	3.4	17	17	37	37	75	75	14.4	14.4
Total	37.7	78	78	105	105	160	160	6.5	6.5
(mt Actual)									
Metallurgical	32.4	61	61	68	68	85	85	4.3	4.3
Steam	3.8	19	19	42	42	85	85	14.5	14.5
Total	36.2	80	80	110	110	170	170	7.0	7.0

[1] For black & brown coal projections refer to Table 1-11
[2] For black & brown coal projections refer to Table 1-6
[3] WOCOL Low Coal Case
[4] WOCOL High Coal Case

Figure 1-5. Australia—Coal Exports

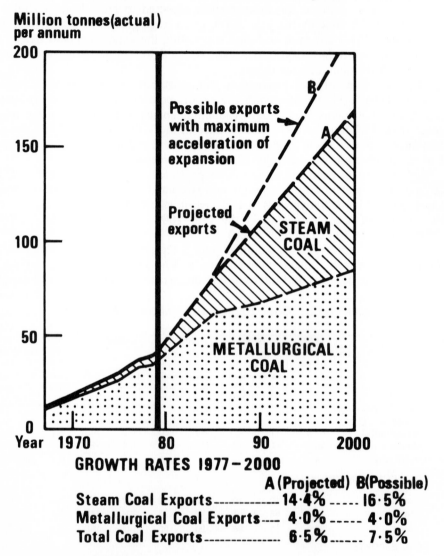

GROWTH RATES 1977-2000

	A (Projected)	B(Possible)
Steam Coal Exports	14·4%	16·5%
Metallurgical Coal Exports	4·0%	4·0%
Total Coal Exports	6·5%	7·5%

COAL TRANSPORTATION

Export coal producing areas, present and potential, together with rail distances to port, are listed in Table 1-13. Coal from some mines must first be hauled significant distances by road to the rail system.

The Bowen Basin production is currently exported through Hay Point and Gladstone (with a little through Bowen). The Sydney Basin production is exported through Newcastle, Port Kembla, and Sydney (see Table 1-14).

The geographical distribution of exportable coal resources and the constraints of rail corridors to the ports determine that most of the growth in coal exports will be through Hay Point, Gladstone, Newcastle and Port Kembla (see Figures 1-6 and 1-7).

Table 1-13. Rail Distances to Port from Actual & Potential Coal-Producing Areas

(Some distances are approximate)

HAY POINT (QLD)

Mine Area	Rail Distance (km)
Blair Athol	305
Capella	350
Collinsville	86[1]
Daunia	180
German Creek	274
Goonyella	195
Hail Creek	155
Harrow Creek	200
Nebo	225
Newlands	230
Norwich Park	267
Oaky Creek	280
Peak Downs	192
Saraji	216

NEWCASTLE (NSW)

Mine Area	Rail Distance (km)
Boggabri	355
Breeza	274
Cessnock area	56
Gunnedah	320
Maitland area (E. Greta)	33
Muswellbrook area	129
Newcastle area (Hexham)	16
Ravensworth area	99
Singleton area	79
Ulan	275[2]
Warkworth area	87
(Mt. Thorley)	
(Lemington)	

GLADSTONE (QLD)

Mine Area	Rail Distance (km)
Blackwater	330
Callide	150
Cook	320
Curragh	320
Gregory	380
Kianga/Moura	200
Leichhardt	320
South Blackwater	350
Theodore	232
Yarrabee	280

SYDNEY (NSW)

Mine Area	Rail Distance (km)
Bargo	104
Bird's Rock	156
Burragorang Valley (Glenlee)[3]	63
Clarence	144
Lithgow area	158
Tahmoor (Glenlee)[3]	63
Wolgan	180

PORT KEMBLA (NSW)

Mine Area	Rail Distance (km)
Bargo	193
Bird's Rock	235
Burragorang Valley (Glenlee)	142
Clarence	223
Coal Cliff	28
Lithgow area	237
South Bulli	10
Tahmoor (Glenlee)[3]	142
Ulan (Road & Rail)	447
Wolgan	259

Notes:
[1] To port of Bowen.
[2] Based on proposed new line.
[3] Excludes road haul to Glenlee.

Figure 1-6. Rail Transport Network, Queensland

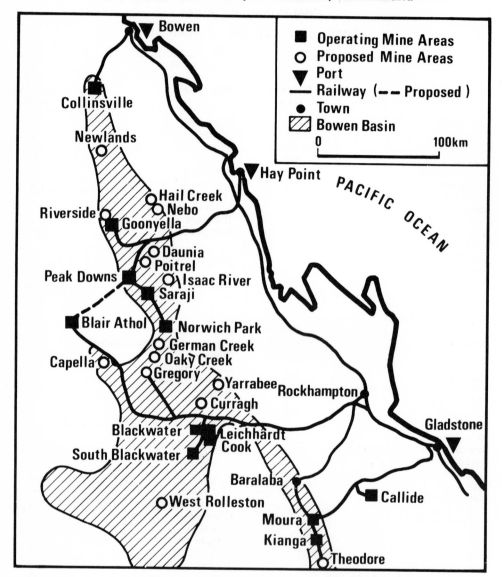

Legend:
- ■ Operating Mine Areas
- ○ Proposed Mine Areas
- ▼ Port
- — Railway (— — Proposed)
- ● Town
- ▨ Bowen Basin

0   100km

PACIFIC OCEAN

Bowen
Collinsville
Newlands
Hay Point
Hail Creek
Nebo
Riverside
Goonyella
Daunia
Poitrel
Peak Downs
Isaac River
Saraji
Blair Athol
Norwich Park
German Creek
Capella
Oaky Creek
Gregory
Yarrabee
Rockhampton
Curragh
Gladstone
Blackwater
Leichhardt
Cook
South Blackwater
Baralaba
Callide
West Rolleston
Moura
Kianga
Theodore

Figure 1-7. Rail Transport Network, N.S.W.

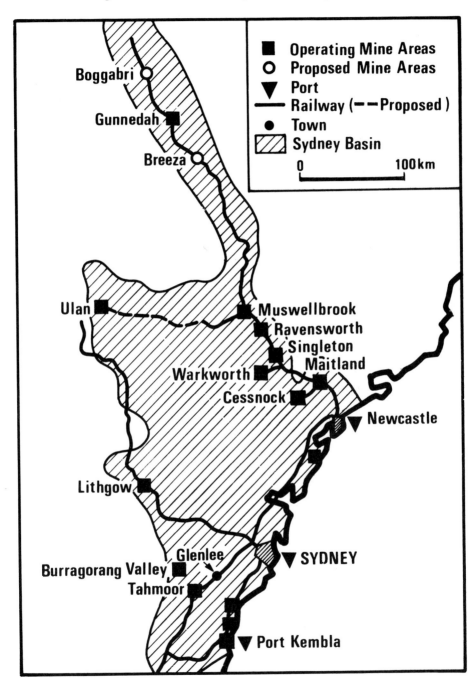

The ports (and proposed ports) are listed in Table 1-14, together with notes on draft and loading capacities, and the throughput rates which might be achieved by the year 2000 (Ref. 12). This possible growth is illustrated in Figure 1-8. Current throughputs of export coal are also listed in Table 1-14.

At Hay Point, with coordinated development of a multi-user port facility, a total throughput of 60 mtpy* would be possible.

The Clinton port facility being established currently at Gladstone should allow total port throughputs of over 20 mtpy to be achieved by Stage 1, and over 30 mtpy by Stage 2.

At Newcastle, with expansion of the present coal loaders and construction of a new loader on Kooragang Island, a throughput of 60 mtpy is technically feasible, with room for a further 40 mtpy deepwater inshore port in the Newcastle area.

Port Kembla coal-handling capacity is currently being expanded to 14 mtpy, with conceptual plans in hand for a total throughput of over 30 mtpy when the demand develops.

In each of these ports an expansion of the rail systems would be required to achieve the potential throughputs, although at current rates of export there is spare track capacity, particularly at Newcastle.

Most export coal in Australia is carried to port in diesel electric unit trains although in NSW some road transport is still necessary. Implementation of plans to extend the electrification of the railway system should result in a transport cost saving and reduced consumption of liquid fuels.

Train loading and unloading rates of 3,000-4,000 tph are already available in common-user and single-user facilities, some of which are privately owned.

Coal mined for domestic power generation is usually carried by conveyor to coalfield power stations (as in NSW and Victoria) although some such coal is carried on the rail system, particularly in Queensland, South Australia and Western Australia. Only in Queensland does this domestic power coal traffic compete for available rail capacity with export coal traffic.

Coal mined for domestic metallurgical cokemaking is transported by road and rail; coal for Whyalla steelworks in South Australia is loaded into ships at Gladstone, Newcastle and Port Kembla.

To date, pipelines have not been used in Australia to transport coal, but they may be suitable for some locations in the future. One major producer/consumer/exporter is constructing a demonstration pipeline in the Newcastle area.

Infrastructure investment requirements are generally greater in Queensland than in NSW because of the location of Queensland coal resources in relatively undeveloped regions.

In NSW the main rail system is State owned and already serves most regions where steam coal production growth is likely to occur. Some NSW ship-loading facilities are owned by private enterprise and some by the Maritime Services Board. The Board operates most of the ship-loading facilities, but some of the coal receival and stockpiling facilities are operated by private enterprise.

In Queensland the coal exporter provides the funds for rail system expansion, which is then constructed and operated by the State as a part of the State rail system. The exporter pays freight to the State and his capital investment is refunded over an agreed-upon period of time, depending on the railing of scheduled tonnages.

---

* mtpy = million tons per year.

Figure 1-8. Australia, Projected Coal Exports
Required Port Capacities

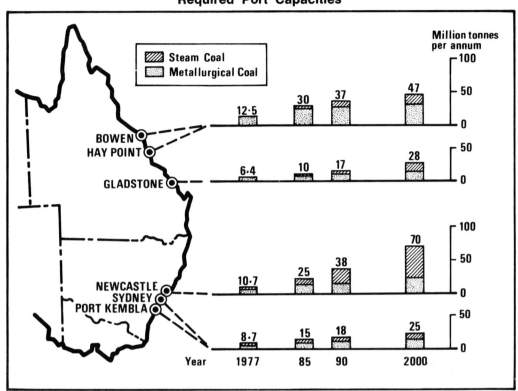

Queensland coal ports are generally managed by local harbour authorities, with some coal-handling and loading facilities being privately owned and operated. The State controls port development and coordinates multiuser investment and access. Both Queensland and New South Wales Governments have plans for further port dredging to accommodate larger ships.

In both States the State Governments coordinate investment in coal transportation infrastructure. Exporters and Governments need to liaise closely so that the firming of coal sales contracts, the commitments to provide adequate coal transportation infrastructure and the determination of rates and charges can be coordinated to mutual advantage.

Without large ships the world coal exports forecast by WOCOL in the year 2000 may not be possible, because of congestion of the ports and sea lanes. Rationalisation of on-shore coal handling by reduction in the number of varieties of coal in international trade will be required to minimise rail and port costs, maximise throughput, and facilitate the loading of large ships.

In summary, the capacities of current port-handling facilities are 35 mtpy in Queensland and 26 mtpy in New South Wales. Developments already in hand will increase port capacities in the early 1980's to 40 mtpy in Queensland and 40 mtpy in New South Wales. To service the export tonnages projected for the year 2000 would require a further capacity increase of 35 mtpy in Queensland and 55 mtpy in New South Wales.

31

Table 1-14. Required Port Capacities for Projected Australian Coal Exports
(WOCOL Low Coal Case and WOCOL High Coal Case)
(mtpy saleable coal)

PORT	1978/79 (actual)			1985			1990			2000			NOTES
	Steam	Met.	Total	Steam	Met.	Total	Steam	Met.	Total	Steam	Met.	Total	
Bowen	—	—	—										(2)
Hay Point/Dalrymple Bay	—	12.5	12.5	3	27	30	9	28	37	15	32	47	(3)
New Queensland Port	—	—	—										(4)
Gladstone	0.2	6.2	6.4	1	9	10	6	11	17	14	14	28	(5)
Brisbane	—	—	—	—	—	—	—	—	—	—	—	—	(6)
Newcastle	1.8	8.9	10.7	10	15	25	21	17	38	47	23	70	(7) (8) (9)
New Port in Newcastle Area	—	—	—	—	—	—	—	—	—	—	—	—	(10)
Sydney (Port Jackson)	1.2	1.5	2.7	2	2	4	2	2	4	2	2	4	(11) (12)
Sydney (Botany Bay)	—	—	—	—	—	—	—	—	—	—	—	—	(13)
Port Kembla	1.8	4.2	6.0	3	8	11	4	10	14	7	14	21	(14) (15) (16)
Total (mt)	5.0	33.3	38.3	19	61	80	42	68	110	85	85	170	
Total (mtce)				17	61	78	37	68	105	75	85	160	

Refer to accompanying notes.

Notes to Table 1-14

(1) Forecasts in the table and the following notes are based on the best information currently available on port planning, on geographical distribution of steam and metallurgical coal reserves relative to railways and ports as well as minimum times required to plan and construct facilities. Actual provision of facilities would be dependent also on satisfactory economic returns to investors and compliance with Government requirements (including environmental impact).

(2) BOWEN

Draft is only 7 metres (m).

In 1978 20,000 t steam coal was exported although export capacity of 0.7 mtpy exists.

A new port at Abbot Point is under consideration, capable of accommodating vessels of 60,000-100,000 dwt.

(3) HAY POINT

Drafts (at low water)
No. 1 Berth loading basin 16.8 m
No. 2 Berth loading basin 17.0 m
Channel 13.4 m

Tidal range
Mean high water springs 5.5 m
Mean high water neaps 4.1 m
Mean low water springs 0.6 m

Loader capacities
No. 1 Berth 4,000 tph } 20 mtpy
No. 2 Berth 6,000 tph }

Maximum vessel size
By taking advantage of the high tidal range, vessels of 160,000 dwt can be loaded to over 150,000 dwt.

(4) NEW QUEENSLAND PORT

An additional coal stockpiling and offshore loader is planned for Hay Point/Dalrymple Bay, with an initial capacity of approximately 10 mtpy.

Hay Point/Dalrymple Bay port may eventually reach a capacity limit. A new railway from the central Bowen Basin to a new port could be considered.

An offshore loader may be required to reach sufficient draft for 150,000 dwt vessels, as at Hay Point.

(5) GLADSTONE

Drafts (at low water)
Auckland Point berth 11.28 m
Barney Point berth 12.19 m
Clinton loading basin 12.2 m
Main port channel 10.36 m

Tidal range
Mean high water springs 3.8 m
Mean high water neaps 3.0 m

Loader capacities
Auckland Point 1600 tph }
Barney Point 2000 tph } 20 mtpy
Clinton (Stage I) 4000 tph }

Maximum vessel size

At present approximately 60,000 dwt. Clinton berth is designed for possible future deepening to 16.5 m at low water to load vessels of up to 120,000 dwt. This would also require a considerable amount of dredging in the main port channel. Vessels up to 120,000 dwt can be part-loaded at present.

(6) BRISBANE

Export of metallurgical coal substitutes (e.g., solvent refined coal), together with some co-product steam coal, may occur by the year 2000.

Brisbane could be included as a possible port development for this purpose.

Some export of steam coal from the West Moreton field (west of Brisbane) may also be possible.

(7) NEWCASTLE

Drafts (at low water)
Carrington Basin berths   11.6 m
Carrington Basin approach 11.0 m
(may be deepened to 13.1 m)
Port Waratah berths   12.0 m
(to be deepened to 16.5 m)
Steelworks channel   11.0 m
(being deepened to 15.2 m)
Entrance channel   11.0 m
(being deepened to 15.2 m)
Maximum departure draft of vessels is based on a 1.25 m tide and 10% underkeel clearance.

Vessel length limits
Carrington Basin 250 m
(navigational limitation)
Port Waratah   250 m
(increasing to 290 m after present dredging)

Vessel beam limits
Carrington Basin 32.3 m
(navigational limitation)
Port Waratah   40 m
(increasing to 43 m after present dredging)

Maximum vessel size
At completion of current dredging in 1981 the maximum sizes of fully laden vessels will be:
Carrington Basin 60,000 dwt
Port Waratah   100,000 dwt

Loader capacities
Carrington Basin 2000 tph
Port Waratah   4000 tph

Total port throughput, based on berth occupancies of 64-70%, is expected to be:
At present   15 mtpy
After dredging (1981)   20 mtpy
After Port Waratah upgrading
                                              25 mtpy

(8) NEWCASTLE

Kooragang Island is the likely site of the next coal loader in Newcastle. It will have access to channels of 15.2 m depth, and relatively large land area served by rail from the coalfields. The initial stages of a 35 mtpy coal loading facility could be in operation in the 1985-1990 period is required.

(9) NEWCASTLE

Further deepening of the entrance and steelworks channels from 15.2 m to 17.2 m would allow 170,000 dwt vessels to be fully loaded at both the Port Waratah and Kooragang Island loaders.

(10) NEW PORT IN NEWCASTLE AREA

To achieve in the long term the possible high levels of steam coal exports from coalfields with transport links to Newcastle, it will be necessary to develop a major new bulk port in the Newcastle area. Several conceptual schemes are being considered; if needed, a new port could be established in the 1990's under an accelerated programme.

(11) SYDNEY

Balmain (Port Jackson) draft : 11.6 m (at low water). This coal loader is currently being upgraded from 2.8 mtpy to 4.5 mtpy and will be able to fully load vessels of up to 55,000 dwt.

(12) SYDNEY

A small coal loader at Balls Head, with a capacity of 1 mtpy, accommodates export shipments of up to 25,000 dwt. After planned dredging shipments of 35,000 dwt will be possible.

(13) BOTANY BAY

The construction of a coal loader on Botany Bay was rejected by the NSW Government in 1977 on environmental grounds.

(14) PORT KEMBLA—EXISTING LOADER
Drafts (at low water)
Existing loader berth   11.6 m
Eastern Basin (main area) 13.1 m
Navigation channels   15.25 m
Vessels can be loaded to a departure draft of 12.5 m.

Vessel length limit 267 m

Vessel beam limit   40 m

Loader capacity 2500 tph (7.2 mtpy)

Maximum vessel size
Vessels up to 60,000 dwt can be fully loaded; partial lifts up to 81,000 dwt have been achieved in larger vessels.

(15) PORT KEMBLA—NEW LOADER
Drafts (at low water)
Berth   16.25 m
Eastern Basin (eastern side) 15.25 m
Navigation channels   15.25 m
It will be possible for vessels to be loaded to a departure draft of 15.0 m.

Vessel length limit 290 m

Vessel beam limit   45 m

Loader capacity (Stage 1)
5000 tph (14 mtpy) operation is planned for 1982.

Maximum vessel size
Vessels up to 110,000 dwt may be fully loaded;
Vessels up to 170,000 dwt may be partially loaded.

For loader throughputs over 14 mtpy additional storage facilities would be needed.

An additional wharf and shiploader, similar in capacity and design to that in Stage 1 of the current expansion, would lift the throughput of the two new berths to over 20 mtpy.

(16) PORT KEMBLA
Dredging of navigation channels between the port entrance and the new coal berths in the eastern basin to a depth of 17.2 m and the berths to a depth of 18.75 m would permit vessels to be fully loaded at the berths to a draft of 16.76 m (170,000 dwt approximately).

ENVIRONMENTAL, HEALTH & SAFETY CONSIDERATIONS

The need to minimize the environmental impact of the production, preparation, transport, storage and utilization of the coal is accepted in Australia as being a necessary part of such activities, as is the need to protect the health and safety of employees and the community at large.

CURRENT ENVIRONMENTAL STANDARDS IN BLACK COAL PRODUCTION

When planning a new coal mining operation, attention must be directed to potential air, water and noise pollution and social impact and the need for progressive rehabilitation during and subsequent to mining. The costs involved are regarded as an integral part of the overall costs of coal production.

There are special risks associated with underground mining operations. Such risks include pneumoconiosis, toxic and explosive gas emissions, gaseous and dust explosions and roof falls. The magnitude and likelihood of such hazards vary widely from coal seam to coal seam. In the Australian coal industry there are strict legislative requirements which seek to protect the health and ensure the safety of all personnel. One result of such measures has been the virtual elimination of pneumoconiosis from the industry. The provision of adequate safety precautions during the mining of coal is accepted as essential and the cost of such precautions is generally more than offset by the increased well-being of the workforce.

Any feasibility study into the establishment of a new surface or underground mine requires the preparation of an environmental impact statement (EIS). The EIS must also cover the washing and transport of the coal. It needs to be prepared hand in hand with the development of mining plans since environmental considerations can significantly influence the latter. The EIS must be accepted by the responsible authorities before a mining lease is granted.

In New South Wales there is a State Pollution Control Commission (SPCC) administering four Acts dealing with environmental pollution control—The Clean Air Act, 1961/72; The Clean Waters Act, 1970/76; the State Pollution Control Commission Act, 1970/72; and the Noise Control Act, 1975. This environmental control legislation places emphasis on prevention. The responsible authority may attach conditions for controlling pollution to any approval.

The New South Wales Government is setting up a Department of Environment and Planning, which is intended to coordinate development approval procedures including Environmental Impact Statements and land-use proposals (see Table 1-19). The SPCC will continue to administer the legislation dealing with noise, clean air, clean water and pollution.

In Queensland coordination of development planning and environmental matters is the responsibility of the Coordinator-General's Department. The Department of Local Government is responsible for the day to day administration of the three principal pollution control Acts, *viz.,* the Clean Air Act 1963/78, the Clean Waters Act 1971/79 and the Noise Abatement Act 1978. Other relevant Acts also apply. Depending on the particular impact of a project the approval of a number of Statutory Authorities may be required (see Table 1-20).

The Environment Protection (Impact of Proposals) Act 1974 is a Commonwealth Act designed to ensure that environmental matters are taken into account in Commonwealth Government decision making, specifically where export approvals or Commonwealth funds are involved.

Restoration of areas disturbed by surface mining operations has been required at Australian open cuts for many years. It is an accepted practice.

CURRENT ENVIRONMENTAL STANDARDS IN COAL USE

To date, considerations of convenience and competitiveness rather than environmental constraints have determined the extent to which coal has been used to meet the energy demand within Australia. Along the eastern seaboard, coal has generally been competitive as a fuel for electricity generation.

In pulverised fuel technology, which is used exclusively in modern coal-fired power stations, over 85% of the ash produced leaves the furnace in suspension with the hot combustion gases (fly ash). The capital and operating costs associated with the provision of electrostatic precipitators or other devices to collect this fly ash are regarded as an integral and essential component of the overall cost of the plant.

In New South Wales the Clean Air Act Regulations require particulate emissions to be limited to 0.25 g/m^3 of stack gas for new plant (this compares with 0.456 g/m^3 in Queensland for new and existing plant and 0.456 g/m^3 for existing plant in New South Wales). No sulphur dioxide emission limits are specified and the sulphur levels of coals in use for power generation and for other purposes are sufficiently low to be of no major concern. The current emission limit for nitrogen oxides in New South Wales is 2.5 g/m^3 (see Table 1-16).

It is necessary to obtain the approval of the SPCC before any combustion equipment may be installed. Discharge of liquids to waterways requires approval in respect of both impurities and temperature.

In Queensland it is necessary, prior to proceeding with any development to consult with the Air Pollution Council, the Noise Abatement Authority and the Water Quality Council to determine if licences are required.

In Victoria, licences for discharge must be obtained from the Environment Protection Authority. A draft policy for the air environment in Victoria, currently being formulated, proposes very stringent air quality and emission standards.

Table 1-15. Australian Regulatory Practices for Emission of Particulate Matter

State	Allowable Emission Concentration	Remarks
Queensland	0.456 grams per normal cubic metre of dry gas	
Victoria	0.5 grams per normal cubic metre of dry gas	The Environmental Protection Authority in Victoria enforces a requirement for dust fallout rates to be less than 130 mg/m² day (new source plus pre-existing level).
New South Wales	0.25 grams per normal cubic metre of dry gas adjusted to 12% CO_2 for new plant. 0.40 grams/cu. metre for old plant.	
Western Australia	No specific limit. "Best Practicable Means" required	Scientific Advisory Committee of the Public Health Department employ 0.456 grams/cu. metre as an emission limit.
South Australia	0.450 grams/cubic metre	

Table 1-16. Australian Regulatory Practices for Stack Gases

State	Sulphur Oxides		Oxides of Nitrogen	
	Allowable Emission Concentration	Allowable Ground Level Concentration	Allowable Emission Concentration	Allowable Ground Level Concentration
New South Wales	None stated.	Level not stated in the regulations. State Health Authority has a preferred maximum three-minute ground level concentration of 16 pphm SO_2 for single stacks and 35 pphm* for a multiple source.	2.5 g/m³ as NO_2	Not stated.
Queensland	None stated.	Preferred maximum three-minute ground level concentration of 35 pphm SO_2 for areas of low existing background levels.	2.5 g/m³ as NO_2	Not stated, since, with present fuels, design for SO_x requirements gives satisfactory NO_x level.
South Australia	None stated.	Level not stated in the regulations. State Health Authority Requirements not available.	2.5 g/m³	Not stated.
Victoria	None stated.	Level not stated in the regulations but the Environment Protection Authority stipulates maximum three-minute level of 16.7 pphm $SO_2 + NO_x$.	None	See comment for Sulphur Oxides.
Western Australia	None stated.	Level not stated in the regulations but State Health Authority stipulates maximum three-minute level of 20 pphm SO_2 for total installed capacity.	Not stated.	Not stated.
		Recent trend has been to classify industrial complexes as "E" districts and to set a maximum level of 10 pphm SO_2 (24-hour mean) for whole area. The operation of proposed stacks must not cause the existing SO_2 level to increase beyond 10 pphm SO_2. This results in more stringent measures than dictated by the three-minute level of 20 pphm.		

* Part per hundred million.

POSSIBLE FUTURE ENVIRONMENTAL, HEALTH & SAFETY STANDARDS

Environmental, health and safety standards are kept under continual review by the responsible authorities. An important element in this context is the assessment for Australian conditions of changes in standards overseas. There is a need at all times for a cautious, rational approach to ensure that any changes to local standards are relevant to Australian conditions and based on valid and proven evidence.

INDICATIVE COST ESTIMATES FOR CONTROL MEASURES

In respect of rehabilitation costs subsequent to mining, the industry contributes about $A0.022 per raw ton of coal won underground in New South Wales to cover the cost of all mine subsidence damage. The present requirements in New South Wales and Queensland for the rehabilitation of lands surface mined using draglines is estimated to cost approximately $8,000 per hectare, which corresponds in a typical situation to about $0.30 per ton of saleable coal. Other cost estimates associated with the production and transport of coal appear in Table 1-17.

Table 1-17. Australian—Indicative Cost Estimates for Specific Environmental Measures in Coal Mining and Transportation

(Approximate $/Tonnes of Saleable Coal 1978 Aust. $)

COAL MINING		
	Surface	Underground
1. Rehabilitation of surface mined areas	$0.20-$0.80	
2. Prevention of mine subsidence		$0.02 See note 1
3. Provision for reclamation of abandoned mines on completion of working	(included in reclamation of active mines)	$0.05-$0.10
4. Dust control	See note 2	See note 2
5. Mine drainage, control of water quality	$0.05-$0.20	$0.02-$0.20
6. Occupational health and safety requirement		See note 3
7. Prevention of run-off from storage and water from coal cleaning	included in item 5.	

COAL TRANSPORTATION				
	By Road	By Rail	Slurry Pipeline	Harbours
1. Dust control, prevention of spills, control of run-off	$0.25	unknown	—	$0.35
2. Treatment of slurry water	As yet, there are no coal slurry pipelines in Australia, although interest is developing (see p. 30).			

Note 1. Most underground mining in Australia is Bord and Pillar and where necessary subsidence is controlled by leaving appropriate pillars.

Note 2. In NSW and Queensland there are specific statutory limitations on levels of dust in or about coal mines.

Note 3. Occupational Health and Safety Requirements are considered to be a necessary part of the mining function and mining could not proceed without these expenses. It is irrelevant and impractical to attempt to estimate the savings that might be made if unsafe practices were adopted or occupational health factors disregarded unless the degree of relaxation of safety requirements is completely specified.

Australian requirements in respect of mine safety and occupational health are not regarded as unnecessary or unrealistic by the coal mining industry.

On the utilization side, the cost of particulate control by electrostatic precipitation approximates to $A0.8/ton coal burnt, oxides of nitrogen control (through modified combustion techniques) $A0.02/ton, and ash disposal $A0.25/ton (see Table 1-18).

Table 1-18. Australia—Indicative Cost Estimates for Environmental Measures in Coal Utilization

Environmental Measure	Cost $A/t coal	Comments
1. Control of Waste Heat Emissions	0.42	Cooling towers are only employed where they provide the best technical solution for the purpose of power-station waste heat rejection.
2. Particulate Control a) ESP b) Scrubber c) Baghouse (conventional)	0.8 — 0.8	
3. Control of SO_x a) Lime/limestone FGD b) Dry FGD		Requirements for control of SO_x are met by constructing the flue gas stacks to sufficient height to provide adequate dispersion under all atmospheric and operational conditions. Australian coals are typically very low in sulphur and flue gas desulfurization is therefore not required.
4. Ash Disposal a) Conventional b) As a hazardous material	0.25 —	Some ash is sold and the remainder disposed of as fill in suitably constructed storages. Power-station ash is not considered to be a hazardous material.
5. Control of NO_x a) Combustion techniques (where possible) b) Dry ash transport	0.02	Refer Table 1-15.

EVALUATION OF KEY ENVIRONMENTAL ISSUES

Environmental, health and safety issues are not expected to prevent future expansion of the production of coal in Australia, although they could cause significant delays. Special care will be required in some areas, however, in respect of the possible additive effects of numerous major new projects. Also, special challenges exist in the planning of future coal exports, particularly in respect of the volume of traffic in and out of major ports, and the environmental impact where road haulage and the maintenance of large stockpiles are involved. Special environmental issues may need to be examined as the coal liquefaction industry is developed.

An important aspect of the environmental issues is the lead time taken by the relevant authorities to assess and process environmental impact statements. Under present procedures the time required in obtaining environmental approval is disproportionately high compared with that required for other aspects of a project. Where assessment procedures are coordinated and streamlined, significant reductions in this lead time are possible.

Other environmental issues which are receiving attention in New South Wales are the possible sterilization of coal deposits by uncoordinated surface developments, the safety of mining under stored waters, and the question of mining in catchment areas and under national parks. Much of the undeveloped steam coal is, however, unlikely to be affected by these constraints.

Table 1-19. Obtaining Environmental Approval—New South Wales

In New South Wales a number of authorities, separately, must give environmental or other approval for development projects. Those which could be involved in an export coal project include:

> Planning & Environment Commission* (including
> > State Pollution Control Commission
> > Heritage Commission
> > National Parks & Wildlife Service)
> Department of Mineral Resources & Development
> Department of Public Works & Ports (including
> > Maritime Services Board
> > Metropolitan Water Sewerage & Drainage Board)
> Energy Authority of NSW
> Joint Coal Board
> Public Transport Commission of NSW
> Department of Local Government
> Shire Councils
> Electricity Commission of NSW
> Forestry Commission
> Pastures Protection Board
> Soil Conservation Service
> Treasury
> Water Resources Commission
> Commonwealth Department of Environment

*A new Department of Environment & Planning is being established which will be responsible for both land use and Environmental Impact Statements. The SPCC will continue to administer the legislation dealing with noise, clean air, clean water and pollution.

Table 1-20. Obtaining Environmental Approval—Queensland

In Queensland procedures have been established whereby all State Agencies must take environmental considerations into account in decision making. Coordination of environmental matters and of development planning is the responsibility of the Coordinator-General's Department which will advise which authorities should be consulted for a particular development project.

The Departments and Statutory Authorities which could be involved in an export coal project include:

> Coordinator-General's Department
> Mines Department
> Queensland Coal Board
> Railway Department
> Department of Harbours & Marine
> Department of Lands, Forestry & Water Resources
> Department of Local Government
> Department of Works & Housing
> Treasury Department
> State Electricity Commission of Queensland
> Commercial & Industrial Development Department
> Shire Councils
> Harbour Boards
> National Parks & Wildlife Service
> Commonwealth Department of Environment

CONSTRAINTS TO EXPANDED COAL PRODUCTION AND USE, AND IMPLEMENTING ACTIONS REQUIRED

A special feature of the Australian coal situation is that about half of the coal production is for export and the projected growth rates will maintain this relativity.

The most important action required to initiate a sustained growth in production for export rests with the coal-importing countries and requires them at an early stage to enter into firm, long-term sales contracts satisfactory to both buyer and seller. Steam coal prices up to 1979 have not provided any incentive for accelerating the development of mines and associated infrastructure solely to supply steam coal. There is a risk that the necessary price increases may not happen in time for the demand to be met.

POSSIBLE CONSTRAINTS TO COAL PRODUCTION

Coal resources are not a constraint but their geographical location, quality and mode of occurrence will influence development. Large quantities of coal exist at relatively shallow depths. The existence of both steam coal and metallurgical coal in some mines necessitates careful balancing of overall resource recovery and market requirements. It would not be good resource management, for example, to sell metallurgical coal as steam coal.

In the face of the heavy expenditure involved in the development of a new mine, the coal industry is reluctant to proceed with increasing production capacity before markets are assured. At the same time, Governments will not encourage new mine developments to proceed without evidence that these will be serving new markets. An important feature of the Australian scene is that there are regulatory bodies (e.g., the Joint Coal Board) charged, among other things, with the responsibility of ensuring that the establishment of new mines does not bring instability to the industry. There is a strong awareness in the industry that because many Australian mines are entirely dependent on exports they are particularly vulnerable to economic downturn in consumer countries.

Where new areas are to be developed, there is the need to obtain firm tenure through the issue of a mining lease. The procedures involved in acquiring a lease require the interaction of numerous Government bodies and can involve long lead times. Part of this lead time is often due to the time required for the participants in a particular project joint venture to reach agreements involving the ownership, the financing and the conduct of the venture. There is a need for Government to keep under continual review the procedures involved in considering mining lease applications and the associated environmental impact statements.

The lead times required to bring a mine into production can vary widely depending on the location and the adequacy of existing infrastructure. In some areas, particularly in New South Wales, the coal occurs adjacent to population centres, where much of the necessary infrastructure may already exist. In Queensland, by comparison, most of the coal resources are remote and mine development must be accompanied by extensive infrastructure development.

The capital requirements for an increase in Australia's saleable coal production from 76 million tons per annum in 1977 to 326 million tons p.a. in the year 2000, an increase of 250 million tons, are formidable. Table 1-21 analyses the approximate capital required.

Table 1-21. Capital Requirements and Projected Expansion of Coal Production—Australia

Expansion in Coal Facilities for	Increase in Production between 1977 and the year 2000 (WOCOL High Coal Case) mtce per annum	Approximate capital[1] cost per 1 million tons of annual capacity $A millions (1978 $)	Total capital Requirements 1980 to 2000 $A millions (1978 $)
Domestic Consumption —Electricity Authorities	82.3		
—Steel Industry	8.5		
—Industrial Sector	11.7		
—Coal for synthetic fuels	24.9		
Total Domestic	127.4	40[2]	5,096[2]
Export	122.3	80	9,784
Total	250		14,880

Notes: [1] The low capital cost per million tons of annual capacity estimated in this table for coal used for domestic consumption is because the major user, *viz.* power generation, is generally sited on the coalfields and does not require the construction of ports nor in most cases railroads and other large infrastructure items.

[2] The cost of power plants and coal conversion plants is not included in this figure, only the cost of the mines to produce the coal for such plants.

From this table it can be seen that an annual expenditure for the next 20 years of about A$750 million p.a. (in 1978 dollars) would be required for the coal production facilities envisaged in the Australian WOCOL High Coal Case scenario. This represents approximately 1% of the present Australian GDP or about 6% of present Australian private gross fixed investment.

The raising of this capital at the same time as other major projects in Australia are seeking capital for development, would need to draw on sources external to Australia. This would be so at least until the large cash flow generated by the export sales started to provide a growing source of Australian funds.

The amounts are so large as to have significant effects on the Australian economy in respect of inflation, monetary policy, exchange rates, foreign investment policy and capital inflows, employment, etc.

However, while these effects need further analysis, we do not consider that they would seriously reduce the growth rates projected.

In addition to the capital question, the ability of local and overseas engineering industries to supply plant and equipment at the rate projected might also become a limiting factor, notwithstanding the extensive facilities now available in Australia to construct most of the equipment required.

POSSIBLE CONSTRAINTS IN THE ELECTRIC POWER INDUSTRY

Future increases in the demand for electricity will be met predominantly with coal-fired thermal power stations located adjacent to the mines and using low-sul-

41

phur coals. Although there will be some environmental and other requirements to be met, these should not inhibit the use of coal for this purpose. Such requirements will affect the ultimate cost of power generation, but only to a minor degree.

Due to the comparatively low cost of power generation in Australia, a trend is already developing for industries which are heavy users of energy to expand in Australia rather than in energy-importing countries. Several new aluminum smelters are planned. Some State Governments are actively encouraging such secondary processing of energy resources, but this objective is not expected to constrain economically viable coal export projects.

Throughout Australia the generation of electricity for general public use is under the control of the various State Governments. Special Authorities established under Acts of Parliament are charged with the responsibility of anticipating and meeting the requirement for electricity. The Australian Government has recently extended the borrowing facilities available to these Authorities to facilitate assembling some of the capital required for power station and mine development.

In some states the Electricity Commissions are actively interested also in export sales from the coal resources under their control. State governments are endorsing such activity which is seen as a means of accelerating development of their States. This interest is motivated by the desire to:

(i) maximise the use of their coal resources where metallurgical coal as well as steam coal can be produced from a particular coal seam or a number of seams involved with the one mining operation, and

(ii) obtain revenue to help finance expansion in the production and distribution of electricity. (In NSW, revenue from coal sales has been proposed as a means of financing the electrification of sections of the railway network.)

Another opportunity to maximise resource recovery is to strip volatiles from coal for liquid fuel production, leaving the residue for combustion in power stations.

POSSIBLE CONSTRAINTS IN THE IRON AND STEEL INDUSTRY

In the metallurgical sector, demand is primarily dependent on that for iron and steel, and there is no doubt that increased metallurgical coal production will be required.

The range of coals used for metallurgical purposes is being extended, and additional metallurgical coal could be required if export markets for Australian coke are further developed.

As in the electric power industry, most of the coal used in the iron and steel industry is supplied from captive mines. Current expansion of production of both metallurgical and steam coal will meet domestic requirements and provide coal for export.

POSSIBLE CONSTRAINTS IN THE INDUSTRIAL SECTOR

An increased use of coal in the industrial sector will largely be determined by the price of oil and natural gas and uncertainties about continuity of oil supply. Coal could be used for direct combustion in boilers and kilns, for gasification, etc. In the interest of oil conservation, increased use of coal could be encouraged and accelerated by Government incentives such as accelerated depreciation allowance or other taxation concessions. Some action along these lines was taken in the 1979 Commonwealth Budget.

In the industrial steam sector there are a number of potential constraints. These relate to environmental requirements, the cost and inconvenience of handling coal and disposing of the ash, and the capital cost of converting or replacing existing plant. Also, use of coal in locations remote from the coalfields, either for power generation or for other purposes, is hindered by the cost of transport and lack of handling facilities. Other constraints on coal usage growth in the industrial sector are inadequacies in marketing and distribution methods and the need for improved availability of efficient and reasonably priced coal-burning equipment.

As the cost of oil continues to increase in line with world prices and the uncertainties in respect of continuous availability increase, the use of coal will expand, particularly when new or replacement plant is required. At current prices natural gas is competitive with coal for certain uses in the industrial sector in New South Wales.

POSSIBLE CONSTRAINTS TO COAL LIQUEFACTION

The interest in producing liquid transport fuels from coal in Australia is growing, and Governments are currently supporting R & D related to coal liquefaction. The lead times for the planning, design, construction and commissioning of commercial plants are expected to be long.

Major constraints are posed, however, to the early initiation of coal liquefaction projects by uncertainties about the most appropriate technology, the high capital and operating costs, the possibility of discovering further indigenous oil and the economics of extracting oil from shale.

The projected introduction of coal-to-oil conversion by 1995 (WOCOL High Coal Case) anticipates a coal requirement for 25 mtce per annum assuming an overall efficiency of about 60%. Coal consumption for liquefaction would represent 15% of the projected total domestic coal consumption in 2000 (7.6% of the total production) (Table 1-7). There is a growing interest also in coal conversion for metallurgical applications with the product intended for export (e.g., SRC). Production of specific coals for these liquefaction and metallurgical purposes will be on a large scale but is not expected to reduce the availability of other coal for export. If coal is to make a significant contribution to the demand for liquid fuels in the 1990's, decisions to proceed, at least to the pilot plant stage, need to be made soon. This virtually implies that, in the first instance, the initiatives rest largely with Governments on the basis of strategic considerations.

ACTIONS REQUIRED TO ACHIEVE EXPORT PROJECTIONS

The major actions required to increase Australia's coal exports are:

(1) Secure sufficient long-term buyer commitments at prices which justify investment in mines and infrastructure

(2) Accelerate the development of infrastructure, particularly rail and port facilities, to ensure timely and reliable export capability.

(3) Reduce the lead times involved in securing mining leases, environmental impact approval and the many other interactions between developers and government agencies.

The export projections in this WOCOL Australian national report (see Table 1-12) have been based on lead times recently experienced and currently considered realistic.

Given a reduction in project lead times of, say, two years, the export levels projected in the year 2000 might possibly be increased by 25% (from 160 mtce to 200 mtce).

In our view, however, this would require a high degree of cooperation by all concerned, *viz.,* buyers, sellers, communities, unions and governments, and also a recognition of the national and international importance of increasing coal exports.

REFERENCES

(1) National Energy Advisory Committee, Report No. 2, "Australia's Energy Resources: An Assessment", December 1977.

(2) Department of National Development, "Demand for Primary Fuels, Australia, 1976-77 to 1986-87", Canberra, April 1978.

(3) Workshop on Alternative Energy Strategies (WAES), "Energy: Global Prospects 1985-2000", McGraw-Hill, May 1977.

(4) Electricity Supply Association of Australia, "The Electricity Supply Industry in Australia, 1977/78".

(5) Joint Coal Board, "Black Coal in Australia, 1977-1978, A Statistical Year Book", Sydney, June 1979.

(6) Department of National Development, "End-use Analysis of Primary Fuels Demand, Australia, 1973-74 to 1986-87", Canberra, November 1978.

(7) National Energy Advisory Committee, private communication.

(8) Joint Coal Board, "The Black Coal Resources of New South Wales", Sydney, 1979.

(9) Queensland Government Mining Journal, July 1979.

(10) World Energy Conference, Australian National Committee, private communication.

(11) International Energy Agency, "Steam Coal—Prospects to 2000", Paris, 1978.

(12) Coal Export Strategy Study, report of a New South Wales Government Task Force, March 1979.

Summary Worksheet

I. Coal Use, Production, and Trade	1977	1985		1990		2000		1977-2000 Avg. annual growth—%/yr.	
		A	B	A	B	A	B	A	B
Coal use in major markets (mtce)									
Metallurgical	8.3	10.3	10.3	12.2	12.2	16.8	16.8	3.1	3.1
Electric	25.0	42.9	42.9	64.2	64.2	107.3	107.3	6.5	6.5
Industry	4.4	11.1	11.1	13.5	13.5	16.1	16.1	5.8	5.8
Synthetic Fuels	–	–	–	–	–	–	24.9	–	–
Residential/Commercial	0.3	0.3	0.3	0.3	0.3	0.3	0.3	0	0
Total coal use	38.0	64.6	64.6	90.2	90.2	140.5	165.4	5.9	6.6
Distribution of coal use by market sector (%)									
Metallurgical	22	16	16	14	14	12	10	—	—
Electric	66	67	67	71	71	77	65	—	—
Industry	12	17	17	15	15	11	10	—	—
Synthetic Fuels	–	–	–	–	–	–	15	—	—
Residential/Commercial	0	0	0	0	0	0	0	—	—
Total coal use	100%	100%	100%	100%	100%	100%	100%	—	—
Coal consumption/imports (mtce) Consumption									
Metallurgical	8.3	10	10	12	12	17	17	3.2	3.2
Steam	29.7	55	55	78	78	124	149	6.4	7.3
Total coal consumption	38.0	65	65	90	90	141	166	5.9	6.6
Imports									
Metallurgical									
Steam									
Total coal imports									
Coal production/exports (mtce) Production									
Metallurgical	42.6	71	71	80	80	102	102	3.9	3.9
Steam	33.1	72	72	115	115	199	224	8.1	8.7
Total coal production	75.7	143	143	195	195	301	326	6.2	6.6
Exports									
Metallurgical	34.3	61	61	68	68	85	85	4.0	4.0
Steam	3.4	17	17	37	37	75	75	14.4	14.4
Total coal export	37.7	78	78	105	105	160	160	6.5	6.5

Summary Worksheet

II. Coal's Role in Total Energy System	1977	1985		1990		2000		1977-2000 Avg. annual growth–%/yr.	
		A	B	A	B	A	B	A	B
Total Primary Energy Use (mtce)									
Oil, Domestic[1]	31.3	32.1	36.0	23.3	44.8	9.0	41.6	-5.3	1.2
Oil, Imported	14.3	21.0	14.2	32.9	5.0	62.7	6.3	6.6	-3.5
Gas, Domestic	9.4	16.0	16.0	22.9	22.9	35.4	35.4	6.0	6.0
Gas, Imported	--	--	--	--	--	--	--	--	--
Nuclear	--	--	--	--	--	--	--	--	--
Hydro, Solar, Other	9.3	10.2	10.2	10.7	10.7	11.5	11.5	0.9	0.9
Coal, Domestic	38.0	64.6	64.6	90.2	90.2	140.5	165.4	5.9	6.6
Coal, Imported	--	--	--	--	--	--	--	--	--
Total energy use	102.3	144	141	180	174	259	260	4.1	4.1
Coal penetration (%)	37	45	46	50	52	54	64	—	—
Total primary energy (mtce) input to electricity									
Oil and Gas	2.6	4.5	4.5	4.3	4.3	3.9	3.9	1.8	1.8
Hydro, Solar, Other	6.1	7.0	7.0	7.4	7.4	8.1	8.1	1.2	1.2
Nuclear	--	--	--	--	--	--	--	--	--
Coal	25.0	43.9	42.9	64.2	64.2	107	107	6.5	6.5
Total energy input	33.7	54.4	54.4	75.9	75.9	119	119	5.7	5.7
Coal penetration (%)	74	79	79	85	85	90	90	—	—
Total electric capacity (GWe)									
Oil and Gas	1.7	2.5	2.5	2.5	2.5	2.3	2.3	1.3	1.3
Hydro, Solar, Other	5.7	6.6	6.6	7.0	7.0	7.7	7.7	1.4	1.4
Nuclear	--	--	--	--	--	--	--	--	--
Coal	13.4	24.9	24.9	36.5	36.5	62	62	6.9	6.9
Total capacity	20.8	34	34	46	46	72	72	5.5	5.5
Coal Penetration (%)	64.4	73	73	79	79	86	86	1.3	1.3
Peak load	15	25	25	34	34	54	54	5.7	5.7
Peak reserve margin (%)	28	27	27	26	26	25	25	—	—
Total oil imports (mbd)	0.2	0.3	0.2	0.4	0.1	0.8	0.1	6.6	-3.5
Total oil consumption (mbd)									
Transportation	0.35	0.44	0.41	0.47	0.42	0.62	0.54	2.6	2.0
Residential/Commercial	0.05	0.05	0.05	0.06	0.05	0.07	0.06	1.5	0.9
Industry—Boilers	0.04	0.03	0.03	0.03	0.03	0.03	0.03	-1.3	-2.2
Industry—Other	0.16	0.17	0.16	0.18	0.16	0.23	0.20	1.5	0.9
Electric utilities	0.01	0.02	0.02	0.01	0.01	0.01	0.01	-0.5	-0.5
Total oil consumption	0.61	0.71	0.67	0.75	0.67	0.96	0.84	1.8	1.2
World oil price assumed for national coal analysis (1979 U.S. dollars/barrel)	$20*	20	35	20	40	25	50	1.0	4.1
Economic growth assumed for national coal analysis (GNP, billion 1978 dollars)	95.6	126	126	149	149	210	210	3.5	3.5

(1) Includes oil from shale but excludes oil from coal (which is counted as coal).

46

CHAPTER 2

CANADA

AUTHORS' NOTE

The revised National Chapter for Canada, to appear in final form in the report of the World Coal Study in May 1980 along with those for other participating nations, was prepared for a meeting of the WOCOL Associates February 23-March 3, 1979, and revised following the Participants' and Associates' Meeting, June 24-30, 1979. The chapter was drafted following discussion of the previous Phase I Discussion Paper at a Seminar on the World Coal Study held in Vancouver, April 4, 1979. This seminar was convened by Mr. Garnet T. Page, Participant, with the objective of informing appropriate representatives of the coal industry and provincial and federal governments about WOCOL, and the input regarding Canada that is being developed by the Canadian Participants and Associates. These three sectors were well represented, and ample opportunity was provided for comments and suggestions to the Participants and Associates.

Provincial governments were invited because Canada's coal resources are owned by the provinces in which they are located, and they exercise prime jurisdiction over matters relating to leasing, production and royalties payable on coal.

Subsequently, during November 1979, Mr. Page invited comments about the final draft chapter for Canada from representatives of provincial governments and the coal industry. A considerable number of helpful comments were received and taken into account.

However, the opinions and estimates appearing in this draft national chapter remain those of the authors' alone and do not constitute the official views of either The Coal Association of Canada, its Members; or the federal Department of Energy, Mines and Resources or the Governments of the Provinces. The information contained in this submission can only be interpreted in the light of the framework chosen by a consensus of the individuals participating in this international non-official study, and should not be viewed in isolation from the agreed structure of the study.

PREFACE

The World Coal Study (WOCOL) is an ad hoc, international project involving about seventy-five individuals from sixteen major potential coal importing or exporting countries. Its objective is to examine the future needs for coal in the total energy supply system and to assess opportunities for expanding world coal production, utilization, and trade to meet these needs. This Study includes (a) the identification of likely constraints to increased coal production and use; and (b) development of desirable policies to lessen certain constraints and uncertainties and to reduce the lead times to meet future needs for coal.

The Participants are 37 key industrial, governmental and academic people from sixteen countries who, through their experience in the coal and energy field, provide overall direction to the study. The Associates are provided by the Participants who take part in the work program needed as the basis for the findings and conclusions of the study. Participants and Associates are invited to act in their own personal capacity, not as representatives of their employers or other agencies.

The World Coal Study is organized under the leadership of Professor Carroll L. Wilson of the Massachusetts Institute of Technology (MIT). Canadian participation in the study is as follows:

Participants for Canada:

The Hon. Jack Austin Q.C.   The Senate of Canada, Ottawa

Mr. Garnet T. Page   President, The Coal Association of Canada, Calgary

Dr. C.H. Smith   Senior Assistant Deputy Minister, Department of Energy, Mines and Resources, Ottawa

Associates for Canada:

Ms. Barbara A. Ettles, The Coal Association of Canada, Calgary (to Sept. 30, 1979)

Dr. J.H. Walsh, Department of Energy, Mines and Resources, Ottawa

Secretariat:

The Project Director (Professor Wilson) and his staff are located at the MIT School of Engineering.

Following the inaugural meeting of Participants and Associates October 18-21, 1978, the Phase I Discussion Paper was prepared by the Canadian Associates and approved by the Canadian Participants. This paper, together with similar submissions from Associates in other countries represented in WOCOL, formed the basis of the discussion at the Associates' meeting of February 25-March 3, 1979, and the meeting of Participants and Associates held June 24-30, 1979. Another meeting of Participants and Associates was held September 30-October 6, 1979; and a final meeting was held January 13-19, 1980.

The Canadian Participants acknowledge the advice and assistance given them by the Coal Association of Canada, its member companies, and senior officials of the Canadian Governments interested in coal.

INTRODUCTION

The role of coal in the Canadian economy is complex. Much of the complexity can be explained by three factors: (i) the geography of Canada, (ii) the variety of alternative energy supply options available to Canada, and (iii) the projected requirement for coal for use as an adjunct fuel in the extraction and the processing of the oil sands and heavy oils of Alberta and Saskatchewan.

Most of Canada's coal resources occur in western Canada in the provinces of British Columbia, Alberta and Saskatchewan, and, while local markets are growing, this coal is distant from the established larger coal markets in the industrial region of central Canada. The availability of other important energy resources in the western region—especially natural gas—limits the regional opportunities for coal. In Ontario, on the other hand, the proximity to the Appalachian region of the USA has led to a continuing supply of both thermal and metallurgical grades of coal from that nation. In recent years, there has been an increasing flow of coal from western Canada to Ontario. Limited quantities of metallurgical coal are also shipped to Ontario from Cape Breton in Nova Scotia. This geographical distribution accounts for the unusual pattern of Canadian coal production and utilization as noted below:

- Only 8.8% of Canada's primary energy consumption was supplied from coal in 1978, despite large resources of western coal that can be mined at attractive costs, but which is expensive to transport to major markets in central Canada.
- Canada has been a net importer of coal and its coal trade will remain in approximate balance in both quantity and volume terms until the early 1980's; it continues to be a net exporter of metallurgical coal; it also exports a high percentage of its coal production—45% in 1978.
- Regional patterns of coal consumption vary widely, from 21% of Saskatchewan's primary energy supply being met from coal (the highest proportion in Canada) to essentially a negligible contribution in the case of Quebec. In Alberta, coal presently meets more than 75% of the province's electrical needs, and in accordance with that government's announced policies, coal is expected to supply about 95% in 2006.
- Mines are often established in Canada to supply coal exclusively to export markets on the basis of long-term contractual arrangements.

The Canadian chapter for the World Coal Study relies upon energy supply/demand balances prepared for the Department of Energy, Mines and Resources in 1978-9. In the WOCOL reference High Coal Case it was assumed that the domestic requirement for primary energy would reach 16.4 quads, or 592 million tons of coal equivalent (mtce)* by 2000, an increase from the 1978 level of 8.3 quads, or 299 mtce. In this period the contribution from the electrical system is estimated to increase at a 4.1% annual rate from the present 35% to 47%, while the overall contribution from coal—largely consumed in the electrical sector—is expected to increase from 8.8% to 20%. In the WOCOL reference Low Coal Case, domestic requirements for primary energy are expected to reach 14.1 quads, or 509 mtce in 2000. The contribution from the electrical sector remains about the same as in the High Coal Case (48%) but the proportional contribution expected from coal is reduced to 16%. The High Coal Case was assumed related to a high rate of increase of international oil prices (5% per year real after 1985). This higher price

---

* 1 mtce = million tons of coal equivalent = 27.78×10^{12} BTU = 29.31×10^{12} MJ = 7.00×10^6 kcal (HHV); energy content of coals currently available are: lignite 15.6-18.0 MJ/kg; subbituminous 17.9-21.0 MJ/kg; bituminous (western) 29.0-36.0 MJ/kg; bituminous (Nova Scotia)—24.0-34.0 MJ/kg.

level allowed Canadian coals to become competitive in a number of specific markets, both domestic and abroad. The Low Coal Case assumed generally less use of coal for electricity in the domestic economy, few opportunities to develop new applications and more restricted export markets.

The two estimates were prepared for domestic coal in the following consuming sectors: electrical, industrial and conversion to other forms, but only one estimate was made for metallurgical coal demand. These estimates were prepared in the light of Canadian circumstances, namely: a continuing strong performance by the domestic steel industry notwithstanding some downturns elsewhere; a continuing high growth in electrical consumption in those regions where coal is the dominant fuel for generation; the possibility of special opportunities in Canada for medium-BTU gas production for use in industry, and an estimate of the possible requirement for coal in the extraction and the processing of the oil sands and heavy oils. No provision is made here for the production of synthetic natural gas (SNG) before 2000, but one coal liquefaction plant is assumed justified in the WOCOL High Coal Case by the end of the century. Two cases were also prepared for Canadian coal exports and imports.

The resource base appears adequate for the expansion of the coal production required for both the WOCOL Low Coal and High Coal Cases, and aside from environmental considerations, no specific barrier to increased production has been identified. It is assumed here that these production targets could be met by the industry, provided export market prices give a satisfactory rate of return and that long-term contracts could be negotiated to allow sufficient time for the installation of the necessary facilities and infrastructure. This time requirement is lengthening as public concern over environmental and related issues increases.

One of the major energy supply problems facing Canada arises from the declining availability of the light and medium grades of crude oil from conventional reservoirs in the western Canadian sedimentary basin. While there have been some promising new discoveries recently, there is little long-term prospect of a reversal of this declining trend. Canadian coal has an important role in overcoming this situation affecting the Canadian economy, and in helping meet the energy needs of its trading partner nations.

At the Tokyo Economic Summit of 1979 the Federal government announced its intention to keep net oil imports from exceeding 600,000 bbl/day in 1985. In subsequent policy statements issued in November 1979, its intention to increase domestic oil prices to international levels by the mid-1980's was reaffirmed. Both targets offer opportunities for the Canadian coal industry.

APPROACH TO THE NATIONAL WOCOL ANALYSIS

THE OVERALL FRAMEWORK

Expectations for economic growth in Canada are less than would have been assumed a decade ago. Canada shares with other developed nations a slowing population growth and a generally difficult economic climate caused in part by rising energy prices. These two effects together may lead to still less growth in energy consumption in the future, but there is disagreement whether the lower rate of increase in energy consumption is due to cyclical or structural factors. It is certain, however, that energy consumption per unit of national output has been falling.

It is generally believed that significantly more capital will be needed per unit of energy production; the installation and adoption of energy-saving facilities and procedures will also require additional capital to offset the rise in real energy prices. The large capital requirements of the electrical system, now about 60% of the total investment in the energy system and about 12% of total Canadian private and public investment, is especially noteworthy. (The energy industry share of total investment in 1978 was 20.5%, which amounted to 4.4% of GNP in that year.)

Canada is concerned with a number of special factors that complicate the situation, for example:

- immigration: a high percentage of the population growth is due to net migration. This makes population growth extremely difficult to predict.

- rate of growth of energy-intensive industry: Canada is one of the few developed nations with a wide range of energy supply options available, and it may be that the growth of energy-intensive industries, such as steel, will result as a consequence of comparative advantage.

- rate of development of agricultural potential: the world may require additional food supply from producers, such as Canada, which has a greater supply potential than most other countries. Additional energy consumption would then be required, especially for synthetic fertilizers, chemicals, irrigation facilities, machinery and transportation.

With these uncertainties peculiar to Canada, in the sections that follow, a scenario consistent with minimum acceptable economic performance has been developed.

CASE VARIABLES

1. ECONOMIC GROWTH 1975-2000
   Minimum acceptable economic performance—3.5% per year (GNP)

2. WORLD OIL PRICE (FOR "MARKER" CRUDE (34⁰API))
   FOB PERSIAN GULF 1979 US DOLLARS, PER BARREL

   It is assumed that the average international price of $20* will stay constant in real terms until 1985, after which:

   - in the *high* price scenario it is increased 5% per year in real terms, to reach in 2000 . . . *$42/bbl*

   - in the *low* price scenario it is increased 2.5% per year in real terms, to reach in 2000 . . . *$29/bbl*

3. ENERGY DEMAND GROWTH (TABLE 2-1)
   WOCOL High Coal Case—3.0% (1977-2000)
   WOCOL Low Coal Case—2.4% (1977-2000)

For reasons elaborated in the text, except in Alberta and Saskatchewan, coal does not benefit in a simple way from energy demand growth in Canada, due main-

---

* This price level had already been exceeded by late 1979, except for oil supplied by Saudi Arabia ($18). The "marker crude" price level was set at $26 in early 1980.

51

ly to the continued availability of natural gas through the period to 2000. Instead, special opportunities for coal arising from higher oil price increases are identified on a case-by-case basis which are added to estimates of the requirements for coal for electrical production derived from econometric calculations.

Table 2-1. Total Energy Consumption ≠

*Units = mtce

Source	1977	1980		1985		1990		1995		2000		1977-2000 Average Annual Percentage Growth %/Year	
		Low Coal Case	High Coal Case	Low Coal Case	High Coal Case	Low Coal Case	High Coal Case	Low Coal Case	High Coal Case	Low Coal Case	High Coal Case	Low Coal Case	High Coal Case
Domestic Oil	109	99	92	97	101	95	109	97	118	106	127	—	—
Imported Oil	23	46	46	46	46	46	46	46	46	46	46	—	—
Domestic Gas	56	66	68	67	90	72	92	75	85	82	93	1.6	2.2
Imported Gas◆ (exports)	(36)	—	—	—	—	—	—	—	—	—	—	—	—
Hydro/Geo/Solar	75	79	90	84	82	111	94	129	109	148	117	3.1	2.0
Nuclear	9	11	14	21	36	27	53	35	54	45	88	7.2	10.4
Coal†	25	34	30	44	41	55	72	69	93	82	121	5.3	7.1
Total Energy Use	297	335	340	359	396	406	466	451	505	509	592	2.4	3.0
Coal Penetration (%)	9	10	9	12	10	14	15	15	18	16	20	2.5	3.5

† Excludes coal exports.
* 1 quadrillion BTU = 36.1 million metric tons coal equivalent.
≠ Major Assumptions:
   —net oil imports do not exceed 600,000 bbl/day after 1980.
   ◆—gas exports are licensed to continue to 1994. Volumes authorized for export were increased in December 1979.

4. ELECTRICITY DEMAND GROWTH (TABLES 2-2 AND 2-3)

The Canadian experience has been varied since the 1973 oil price events. Quebec growth in electrical consumption has remained high, increasing about 7% per year, because of an official policy to encourage conversion to electricity, especially for space heating. In Alberta, demand has also remained high (8.8% in 1978) due to rapid industrial growth in the province. Other parts of Canada have reduced their electricity growth from previous levels. It now appears that growth in overall national electrical demand has stabilized at about the 5.5% per year level. Installed electrical capacity in 2000 may range between 148 and 210 GWe as compared to 70 GWe in 1977.

There is some evidence that the demand for electricity is more closely related to the capital investment cycle than are other forms of energy. The last few years in Canada have been characterized by relatively low capital investment; presumably, any recovery may lead to increased demand.

5. NUCLEAR PENETRATION (TABLES 2-2 AND 2-3)

The nuclear penetration into electricity generation is concentrated in Ontario, although there is one reactor in Quebec. Besides continuing expansion in Ontario, reactors are under construction in Quebec and New Brunswick. Construction of additional reactors is under study in other regions of the country.

Ontario has recently experienced a drop in electrical load growth from previously expected levels, although demand has since returned to more normal growth levels. In 1978, 29% of the annual average of electrical supply for the province

Table 2-2. Total Electricity Consumption ≠

Units = GWe capacity

Source	1977	1980 Low Coal Case	1980 High Coal Case	1985 Low Coal Case	1985 High Coal Case	1990 Low Coal Case	1990 High Coal Case	1995 Low Coal Case	1995 High Coal Case	2000 Low Coal Case	2000 High Coal Case	1977-2000 Avg Annual % Growth Low Coal Case	1977-2000 Avg Annual % Growth High Coal Case
Nuclear	5	7.5	7.5	10	15	13	25	19	43	26	67	7.4	11.9
Hydro/Pumped Storage	41	45.5	45.5	55	55	62	62	68	68	73	69	2.6	2.3
Gas Turbines/Combined Cycle	2	2.0	2.0	2	2	3	3	3	3	3	4	—	—
Geothermal/Solar/Other	(.5)	1	1	1	1	1	1	1	1	1	2	—	—
Fossil Steam —Oil Steam	7	7	7	7	7	6	6	4	4	4	4	—	—
—Gas Steam	3	3	3	3	3	3	3	3	3	3	3	—	—
—Coal Steam	12	15	15	20	20	22	30	29	43	38	61	5.2	7.3
Total Electricity	70	81	81	98	103	110	130	127	165	148	210	3.3	4.9
Coal Penetration (%)	17	19	19	20	19	20	23	23	26	26	29	1.9	2.3

≁ Major Assumptions:
—for the WOCOL High Coal Case, electrical capacity in 2000 taken from "Energy Futures for Canadians"—EMR 1979; Intermediate years interpolated; capacity estimates includes provision for net electrical exports.
—for the WOCOL Low Coal Case, data from Department of Energy, Mines and Resources, August 1979.

Table 2-3. Total Electricity Consumption ≠

Units = mtce fuel input

Source	1977	1980 Low Coal Case	1980 High Coal Case	1985 Low Coal Case	1985 High Coal Case	1990 Low Coal Case	1990 High Coal Case	1995 Low Coal Case	1995 High Coal Case	2000 Low Coal Case	2000 High Coal Case	2005 Low Coal Case	2005 High Coal Case	1977-2000 Avg Annual % Growth Low Coal Case	1977-2000 Avg Annual % Growth High Coal Case
Nuclear	9	11	14	21	36	27	53	35	54	45	88			7.2	10.4
Hydro/Pumped Storage*	72	78	81	93	82	109	93	125	109	143	116			3.0	2.1
Gas Turbines/Combined Cycle	1	1	1	1.5	1	1.5	1.5	1.5	1.5	1.5	1.5			—	—
Geothermal/Solar/Other	(0.5)	(0.5)	0.5	0.5	(0.5)	0.5	0.5	0.5	0.5	0.5	0.5			—	—
Fossil Steam —Oil Steam	4	4	4	3	3	2	2	2	1	1	—			—	—
—Gas Steam	4	4	4	4	4	3	3	4	3	4	3			—	—
—Coal Steam	17	25	20	31	28	37	40	43	49	50	65			4.8	6.0
Total Electricity	108	124	125	154	154	180	193	211	218	245	274			3.6	4.1
Coal Penetration (%)	15	20	16	20	18	21	21	20	22	20	24			1.3	2.1

≁ Major Assumptions:
* Hydro-pumped storage values in this table calculated by difference. Discrepancies occur with respect to the Hydro/Geo/Solar values in Table 2.
These differences result probably from the difficulty in accounting for net electrical exports by energy source.

was derived from nuclear sources (36% for June 1978), but uncertainty of demand forecasts has led to a "stretching-out" of the proposed nuclear-plant construction program.

Nevertheless, Canadian-installed nuclear capacity is presently about 6 GWe and present firm commitments will raise this total to 15 GWe in the 1980's. Canadian nuclear capacity could be in the range 26-67 GWe in 2000. The International Energy Agency 1978 study "Steam Coal Prospects to 2000," assumes a range of 36-40 GWe at the end of the century. A nuclear "pause," or moratorium, in Canada and the USA would affect coal requirements in two quite distinct ways: more coal would be required in absolute terms, and less coal might be available from the USA for use in Ontario to supply Canadian markets although net electrical exports to the USA complicate the situation. Canada would also be confronted with a major production and transportation problem if large quantities of coal had to be moved from western to central Canada on relatively short notice.

6. NATURAL GAS (TABLE 2-1)

The continued availability of natural gas from conventional and nonconventional reservoirs at competitive prices in western Canada, and later from the frontier regions, suggests that this fuel will have a preferred position, especially in markets in eastern Canada. There are indications that the national pipeline network will be extended to reach these new market areas. Additional gas supplies may be discovered in eastern offshore areas, particularly off Nova Scotia and the coast of Labrador. It may be assumed that there will be a steady penetration of natural gas into markets now served by oil, and, in some cases, to replace electricity used for space heating and hot-water production. For these reasons, natural gas is assumed to meet about 20% of Canada's primary energy requirements through to 2000.

With gas available, coal will not likely be introduced into new markets, other than for medium- to large-scale industrial applications. However, because of the high investment needed to expand the natural gas system, after 2000, the production of SNG from coal will no doubt be justified as an incremental backup for the system. Before 2000, the production of medium-BTU gas is expected to be economically justified by some large natural gas users, mostly in western Canada, to allow shipment of natural gas into distant markets; i.e., substitution of natural gas by displacement.

SELECTION OF VARIABLES FOR WOCOL HIGH COAL AND LOW COAL CASES

	WOCOL High Coal Case	WOCOL Low Coal Case
Economic Growth (1975-2000)	3.5%	3.5%
World Oil Price in 2000 (US Dollars FOB Persian Gulf)	$42/bbl	$29/bbl
Annual Growth Rate in Electrical Demand (1977-2000)	4.1%	3.6%
Primary Energy Demand Growth Rate (1975-2000)	3.0%	2.4%
Nuclear Capacity (2000)	67 GWe	26 GWe

ANALYTICAL METHODS USED IN THE NATIONAL ANALYSIS

1. COAL CONSUMPTION

Domestic coal consumption estimates have been prepared in two ways:

(a) *Method of energy balances:* An estimate of Canada's total energy requirement in 2000 from econometric analysis was combined with an estimate of the changing position of coal in the national primary energy mix in that year. This approach indicates that domestic coal consumption may grow from 8% of a total primary energy requirement of 8 quads in 1975 to 20% of a total of 16.4 quads, or 121 mtce in 2000 in the High Coal Case, or to 16% of a total of 14.1 quads, or 82 mtce in the Low Coal Case in the same year.

(b) *Method of industrial sector analysis:* Projections of demand from the utility and steel industries were used. Additional estimates were then prepared for new market opportunities, such as coal conversion and the processing of the oil sands and heavy oils of Alberta and Saskatchewan. These new applications were considered as being quite sensitive to changes in the price of oil, because other energy demands would likely be met from natural gas and adjusted accordingly. It must be stated, however, that this class of estimate can only be considered as judgmental.

2. COAL PRODUCTION

The opening of export markets for the metallurgical grades of coal mainly in Japan in the early 1960's marked the beginning of the resurgence of that segment of the industry of Western Canada based upon the mining of the coals of the higher ranks. The industry had previously supplied coal to railroad, home and local industrial markets, and thus was severely affected by the turn away from coal in the post-war period. In essence, an important segment of the Canadian coal industry has been reestablished which depends mainly upon exports. While the demand for metallurgical coal has been maturing in recent years, the Canadian industry expects to at least maintain its share of the market and the well-being of this industry is especially important in regional economic expansion activities. Although only modest quantities of the thermal grades of coal are presently exported from Canada, contracts for additional shipments have been signed recently, and, given favourable conditions, a second export-led expansion of the high-rank coal industry will occur which will have important implications for the development of the regions affected.

It was considered that coal production for both domestic and export markets is essentially demand limited, especially under the conditions pertaining to Western Canada. Given sufficient notice, long-term contracts, and minimum regulatory delays, it appears that mines and their related infrastructure and transportation links could be ready to meet the estimated demands predicted in this and other studies. The resource base appears adequate to support the intended production, except, perhaps, in a few special situations. However, implementation of more stringent regulatory standards, and increased public concern about the environment may cause delays.

An attempt was made to assign plausible deployment schedules, taking into account characteristic mine sizes for the various coal resource regions, and it appeared possible to meet the demand schedule.

The major problem, given Canadian mining and transportation costs, is firm market commitments at prices to justify production.

3. NATIONAL COAL SUPPLY/DEMAND INTEGRATION

Most of the coal consumed in Canada to the year 2000 will be for the generation of electricity. A steadily growing portion of this coal will be used at mine-mouth power plants in western Canada. Because the mining operations are essentially integrated with power stations, it does not seem sensible in the Canadian case to make generalized estimates of electrical demand and then assign a portion of that demand to be supplied by coal—the decision to open the mine is directly linked to the decision to build the dependent power station. A reliable estimate of export potential cannot be made by subtracting domestic demand from possible domestic supply as defined from possible development schedules, especially as it appears that, without new preparation and drying processes, the candidate coals available for export for thermal power-plant purposes are not those upon which local power generation will be based.

For this reason, and also because of the large reserves available, the export potential of Canada will be independent of the needs of the Canadian economy except, of course, in extreme situations such as in the case of a nuclear moratorium.

In other situations, coal for thermal generation may be available as a co-product from mines which produce metallurgical coal. This grade of coal may also be offered in export markets, but the quantities of related coal production for thermal uses will depend upon conditions in the metallurgical market. Without sufficient market opportunities for metallurgical coal, new mines may not be opened at all.

In summary, it appears most logical to make a "free-standing" estimate of export potential for the thermal grades of coal from Canada. Given the available resource base, the essential requirement is a satisfactory rate of return to the mine owner, which calculation must include costs necessary to mitigate environmental impacts. Very high domestic demand for Canadian coals, which could arise in the case of unusual circumstances such as a nuclear moratorium, might lead to a reduction in the quantity of coal which otherwise would be available for export.

4. COAL TRANSPORTATION

Transportation charges form a large part of the delivered cost of coals shipped from the west, either for use in Ontario or export from Canada. The rail costs amount to about $19 per ton for bituminous coal shipped to the Great Lakes port of Thunder Bay (about 2,000 km) and about $12-14 per ton for metallurgical coal moving to Pacific Coast ports (about 1,300 km) from the main coal-producing areas of Western Canada. Despite the most modern-unit train operations, coal transport costs tend to hinder large thermal coal exports under current international price relationships. Even so, Canadian metallurgical coals are cost/quality competitive in the international marketplace. In three respects, however, Canada has advantages:

(a) Deep-water terminals are operating on the West Coast, and suitable sites are available for expansion on both coasts.

(b) In the Atlantic region, the coal is produced at tidewater in Cape Breton.

(c) The Great Lakes transportation system allows the low-cost movement of coal from either Canadian or US sources. While it does not appear likely today that significant amounts of coal from western Canada will move through the lakes to export markets, because of high rail costs from mines to Great Lakes ports, it is possible that coal from USA Appalachian or midcontinent sources could be delivered to east coast Canadian ports for transfer into deep-water vessels. Because of the critical importance of transportation costs to the coal industry, attention is being paid to improved rail and other technologies, including slurry pipelines.

5. ENVIRONMENTAL CONSIDERATIONS

All coal-producing and consuming nations must deal with a variety of environmental problems, and Canada is no exception in this regard. While coal production is now relatively low—about 30 million tons in 1978—the many studies and projections prepared by private research organizations, governments and industry suggest that output could increase to the 125-mtce range by the year 2000. These projections lead to an intensification of expression of concern about the impact of this larger production on the economy, society at large and the environment.

In addition to the well-known problems arising in mining, cleaning and transport, and in utilization sectors, especially for electric power production and coke-making, special aspects must be taken into account in the case of Canada. A few of those factors noted in more detail in the last section of this report are:

- Occurrence of important segments of the resource base in parks and scenic areas of importance to the tourist industry.
- Competing claims for land use such as for agricultural purposes on the "plains" and the forest industry in the "foothills" and "mountains"; although the actual surface disturbed is small (see the section on environmental health and safety considerations).
- Long-unit train hauls with consequent possibility of dust and noise nuisance.
- Limited number of access corridors to export ports and the necessity to provide sufficient area for stockpiles at these ports. These stockpiles lead to dust generation, water contamination and general nuisance unless adequate precautionary measures are taken.
- Sulphur and nitrogen oxides and trace metals, all of which can appear in particulates, are emitted from combustion processes. These pollutants and the acids produced from the oxides can affect water (especially sensitive lakes), vegetation and human health.
- Acidification of lakes and damage to forests has occurred in eastern Canada. Greater pollution resulting from uncontrolled increase in the use of coal could lead to further deterioration of environmental conditions.
- These problems in eastern Canada are directly related to the proximity of industrial activity in the USA. The Department of the Environment is assessing this combined loading and the resulting impact of acidic precipitation on eastern Canada.
- Responsibilities for the management of the environment are divided between the federal government and the province.

Seldom in the past could a single environmental difficulty be specified as limiting the rate at which the coal industry could expand. Now, however, the long-range transport of air pollutants and other new concerns have the potential to delay or even, in extreme circumstances, to limit expansion in this industry. Also, when the entire coal utilization "chain" is considered, together with the many difficulties and regulatory delays that may arise at the various stages, satisfying the environmental requirements may prove among the most important factors in restricting the rapid expansion of the coal industry, both in the production and in the utilization phases.

6. IMPLEMENTING ACTIONS REQUIRED FOR THE TOTAL COAL SYSTEM

The implementing actions identified in the last section of this report require that the following factors should be taken into consideration:

(a) Since coal has little presence in the current Canadian primary energy consumption balance (about 9%), there is no well-informed large national public constituency to support its more widespread use.

(b) Since Canada is a federal state, the responsibilities for the coal policy development are divided between the federal and provincial levels of government.

(c) Provincial and municipal governments are reluctant to allow the establishment of new one-industry towns in previously unsettled areas, without clear assurances of long-term continuance of coal mining operations to provide a lasting economic base.

(d) In the western provinces, coal development is only one of the available energy supply options. This is particularly true in Alberta. Conventional oil and gas, oil sands and heavy oil, and indeed certain renewable resources, such as hydroelectric power, geothermal and biomass (mostly from the forests) energy are also available.

(e) The resource extraction industries in general are perceived as having a relatively high impact on the environment. It appears that the general public remains to be convinced that coal mining operations can be carried out in an environmentally acceptable way.

(f) The concurrent development of various forms of energy supply place competitive demands within a region for capital labor, specialized equipment, etc. This can make the management of a regional economy extremely difficult.

(g) Implementing actions to expand coal production in Canada require relevant action by the transportation industry including construction of new lines, upgrading of existing lines and the provision of new terminals. Rail lines will not be built without long-term contracts. Transportation companies have indicated that they wish to share in "economic rents" arising from sudden energy price rises denied to them when shipments are made under long-term contracts, even when cost escalation clauses are provided.

(h) In some cases, potential coal mining areas fall within parks, wilderness reserves or other recreational regions. There is a reluctance by provincial authorities to allow mining in these regions.

(i) While there is a large mineral industry in Canada with attendant service and supply organizations, the coal industry is not large enough at present to support extensive domestic design and manufacture of the specialized equipment needed for either underground or surface mining operations. Because a rapid expansion of the Canadian coal industry will likely coincide with similar developments in other countries, it is possible that unexpectedly long delays may occur for the acquisition of certain major items, particularly because similar classes of equipment may be needed for expanded oil sands or other mining operations. For the same reasons, the supply of skilled labor may also present problems to the coal industry.

(j) Total environmental accounting procedure may be required to assess the real costs of pollution abatement. This procedure should include any "hidden" costs of environmental damage as it may affect other industrial sectors: e.g., such as possible damage to the forests that could affect the Pulp and Paper Industry.

COAL CONSUMPTION

POTENTIAL COAL MARKETS

Coal is consumed in Canada principally for the generation of electricity and for use in the steel industry. Other uses are currently minor but significant opportunities for additional coal consumption may arise in connection with the development of the oil sands and heavy oils of Alberta and Saskatchewan within the time frame of interest. There are also possibilities for the liquefaction of coal and the production of medium-BTU gas for use in certain industries.

1. MARKETS FOR METALLURGICAL COAL

The main primary steelmaking facilities in Canada are located in the Province of Ontario, where the coking operations have been traditionally supplied with metallurgical coal from the USA Appalachian region. Increasing quantities of metallurgical coal are now arriving from western Canadian sources (approx. 1 mt/yr). Some high-volatile coking coal is also shipped to Ontario mills from the Cape Breton mines in Nova Scotia (approx. ½ mt/yr).

Primary steelmaking facilities are also located in Cape Breton, Nova Scotia, where the locally mined coal is used with blends of low-volatile coal produced either in western Canada and shipped via the Panama Canal or in the USA. Proposals to modernize the present facilities are under consideration, but a plan to build an entirely new steelmaking facility oriented toward supplying semifinished products to export markets is now in abeyance, in view of the present downturn in the steel industry globally.

In the Province of Quebec, primary steelmaking is based upon the direct reduction of iron ore, using natural gas as the reductant. No market for metallurgical coal now exists. Other electric smelting operations exist in Canada, particularly in Quebec, that use coal or coke to produce pig iron from titanium ores, ferroalloys, etc.

Studies related to the possible construction of primary steelmaking facilities in western Canada have been conducted. These projects have been hampered by the lack of a suitable nearby iron ore supply. Given the current availability of natural gas, it is possible that this fuel may be used. It appears, however, that it will be some time before a coking/blast furnace facility could be justified in the region, and it may be that some other coal-using reduction process, selected from the several now being developed around the world, would be attractive at a later date.

No foundry coke is produced currently in Canada, but some nonrecovery oven coke is produced in British Columbia to meet the needs of the nonferrous metals industry in Canada and the USA.

The Canadian steel industry was not as severely affected by the recent general worldwide downturn as was the industry in other countries. Due to various factors, including the domestic availability of ore and fuel and an active market, it appears that the Canadian industry has considerable comparative advantage. It is anticipated, therefore, that there will be a continuing increase in its productive capacity from the 1979 annual level of 18.5 million tons of crude steel to about 35 million tons in 2000. Metallurgical coal consumption in the industry is expected to grow accordingly from about 8 million tons at present to 15 million tons in 2000. Gains in efficiency of energy use will continue, but the Canadian steel industry already ranks high in the world in this respect. There may be some tendency to displace oil, and possibly gas, used by the industry, e.g., by the coal-using blast furnace tuyere injection processes.

The share of the coal supply that will be supplied by Canadian sources remains unclear for various reasons. In this study, it is assumed that up to 10 million tons of metallurgical coal will continue to be supplied annually on favorable terms from the USA to the year 2000, in the WOCOL Low Coal Case. Accordingly, 5 million tons would be supplied from mainly western sources but including some high-volatile coking coal from Nova Scotia. In the WOCOL High Coal Case, however, due to the much higher price for oil, it is assumed that USA exports of metallurgical coal would be relatively less attractive due to either price effects or limitations in physical supply, and metallurgical coal imports in 2000 are taken as 5 million tons, thus leaving 10 million tons to be supplied from Canadian sources.

Canadian metallurgical coal exports, shipped mainly to Japan but increasingly to other Pacific rim countries, some European markets and Latin America, are assumed here to be essentially independent of conditions in the domestic market; price, contract length and infrastructure factors being the main determinants of the rate of development of the industry for export markets. Metallurgical coal exports are projected at 27 million tons in 2000.

2. MARKETS FOR COAL TO GENERATE ELECTRICITY

The Canadian need for coal to generate electricity may be discussed in three main market areas:

(a) In the western region of Canada, electricity generation is now based on hydroelectric sources, plus natural gas, or surface-mined low-rank coals. One power station operates in part on coproducts (middlings) of metallurgical coal production, and another such installation is planned. The decreasing number of undeveloped low-cost hydroelectric sites, the increasing price of natural gas, and the relatively small size of the utility systems which make large nuclear installations difficult to assimilate in the power systems, combine to create a situation where rising electrical demand in the future will be met with thermal-power generation based on low-rank coals. Electrical demand is continuing to increase at a generally high rate in the region, and this rate of growth may well continue through to 2000. This is especially true in Alberta because of the needs of the expanding oil sands/heavy oil industry. Coal already provides over 75% of the electrical energy consumed in Alberta and may provide as much as 95% by 2000.

At the present time, consideration is being given to improved linkages among the utilities serving western Canada. In the near term an improved grid might allow underutilized hydroelectric potential, particularly in Manitoba, to supply part of the growing demand which would otherwise be met through the installation of additional coal-burning facilities. In the longer term, the availability of such a grid might permit coal-derived electricity to reach wider markets. Until now, electricity has been generated in stations typically equipped with 150-375 MWe units with boilers especially designed to handle low-rank coals. Electrostatic precipitators are used to control particulate emissions and the low-sulphur coals of the area often present some difficulty in this respect because of the characteristically high electrical resistivity of the ash particles. Water is cooled in nearby lakes, or especially constructed ponds.

Although no assessment of long-range transport of air pollutants has yet been made in the West, the western and other utilities in Canada have come under some criticism in recent years, especially in regions close to the USA border, for not adopting processes that reduce sulphur emissions. The high water consumption and discharge of contaminated waste water primarily from once-through cooling and ash-handling systems to boundary waters have also aroused controversy. The western utility industry has begun some studies on the possible application of pressurized fluidized-bed combustion and combined-cycle processes to low-rank coals.

(b) In Ontario, electricity is produced at hydroelectrical sites, from nuclear installations using the Canadian-designed heavy water-moderated natural uranium-fueled reactor known as the "CANDU," and from fossil-fuel stations using coal and oil normally for medium-range or peaking operations. Electrical energy is exported to neighboring states in the USA. At the end of 1977, fossil-fueled stations accounted for 12 GWe of the 24 GWe total capacity (or 50%) in the province. The Nanticoke Station on Lake Erie with eight 500-MW units is the largest coal-fired station outside the USSR at present. While the bulk of the coal requirement of 7.6 million tons was supplied in the form of bituminous coal from eastern USA sources, western Canadian sources have started to supply increasing quantities of bituminous coal (perhaps 2.5 million tons in 1979). Low-rank coals will also be used in northwestern Ontario, supplied by mines in western Canada, and a large deposit located at Onakawana in Northern Ontario is being evaluated.

Nuclear capacity in Ontario reached 20% of total capacity at the end of 1977 and as much as 36% of the electrical supply has been generated at nuclear stations over short-term periods. Additions to nuclear-generating capacity are under construction and still more are planned, although construction schedules have been stretched out in response to weakening demand for electricity and increasing public resistance to the proliferation of nuclear-power stations.

The demand for coal for electrical generation in this region is subject to the two factors of electrical load growth and the extent of nuclear penetration into that load growth. It is still uncertain how much of Ontario's coal requirements will be derived from Canadian sources, although the provincial government is preparing a policy in this regard.

For the WOCOL Low Coal Case, it was assumed that the annual imports of bituminous coal from the USA would be 10 million tons by 2000. For the WOCOL High Coal Case, it was assumed that no further demand for coal would arise in the province, which implies that such extra demand would be met from an accelerated or reinstated nuclear option. It was assumed, however, in the High Coal Case, that imports of thermal coal would fall to 5 million tons in 2000 because of the increased internal USA demand due to the higher oil price, which would make Canadian coal more competitive in this market even in the event that the USA coal were to continue to be physically available for export.

No allowance is made here for delays due to nuclear-safety issues. Presumably, any such eventuality would also be occurring simultaneously in the USA. In this case, large quantities of coal from western Canada would be needed to meet both load-growth requirements and replacements of USA coal imports. While such a situation would strain both the capability of the coal industry to supply such quantities of coal and the transportation system required to move it, the coal could be supplied provided the transportation infrastructure was in place.

Additional quantities of coal might also be needed to displace the oil now consumed in some thermal plants. Coal-in-oil mixtures might be employed or retrofitting to burn coal might be necessary.

The Province of Quebec relies heavily upon water power to meet its electrical-energy needs, although there is one nuclear installation and a second is under construction. Some oil-fired steam- and gas-turbine capacity exists (0.6 GWe), part of which could conceivably be converted to coal-in-oil-mixture combustion technology if the necessity arose.

(c) In the Atlantic Provinces, there is still much undeveloped low-cost hydropower in Labrador. However, icebergs present difficulties in laying cables from the mainland across the Strait of Belle Isle to bring this energy to the island of Newfoundland, and a tunnel has been studied for this purpose. One nuclear station is under construction in New Brunswick, while additional coal-fired capacity is under construction in both Nova Scotia and New Brunswick in 150- to 300-MW sizes. As this region depends heavily upon imported oil, alternate methods of electricity generation are being investigated. The major tidal resource in the Bay of Fundy is under study, although the initiation of this project might depend on the export sale of electricity to neighboring states in the USA. Special attention is being paid to the conversion to coal of existing oil-fired capacity in the region. A small coal-in-oil combustion project is presently operating with the unique feature of incorporating a mineral-matter (including pyrite) separation stage using oil itself as the separating medium. Studies of the introduction of atmospheric-pressure fluidized-bed combustion technology are also in progress. Such a development is especially important in this region because the coals locally available are medium-to-high in sulphur content. It is difficult to predict how much coal will be consumed in retrofitted facilities, but thermal-power generation will consume much of the nonmetallurgical coal production of the region by 2000. Total annual coal availability may range from 7 to 10 million tons in 2000.

3. COAL FOR INDUSTRIAL MARKETS

Except for the utility and metallurgical industries, very little coal is consumed in Canada, only 1.7 million tons in 1977. Any prospects for significantly increased use of coal in industry depend upon the development of a distribution infrastructure and the adoption of improved coal-utilization technologies. Studies have identified possible industrial users and it appears that only industries with a large energy requirement would likely find coal a suitable energy source. The successful adoption of fluidized-bed combustion technology may allow environmentally acceptable use by these industries of coals with a higher sulphur content; however, a comprehensive demonstration of this technology (including its environmental impact) is required

One of these industries, the forest group, may have the additional option of producing their steam requirements from wood wastes or even specially harvested wood. In some instances coal might be used with wood.

As in other countries, the cement industry has used coal in the past and may well convert when economic circumstances allow. Studies have indicated that conversion of coal to a medium-BTU gas might allow some process industries, especially in western Canada, to replace natural gas. The natural gas thus "freed" would become available for transport by pipeline to distant markets. In principle, nothing prevents the use of this technology in oil refining, in the steel industry, and in other large-scale industrial operations in central Canada. Most such potential sites can be served by coal delivered by lake freighter, but the relative cost advantage of using coal to produce a medium-BTU gas as compared to natural gas may be less because of the higher costs of transporting coal.

Despite these possible additional uses for coal, the WOCOL Low Coal Case estimate for Canada assumes that only 16 million tons will be used for such purposes by 2000. In the case of the WOCOL High Coal Case estimate, it has been assumed that the higher price of energy would prove sufficient inducement to the larger energy-consuming industries to use more coal internally in their facilities. An additional requirement of 15 million tons of coal (mostly of subbituminous rank) has been estimated, resulting in a total of 31 million tons for this category of use in 2000.

4. COAL FOR CONVERSION TO OTHER FORMS

In estimating the amounts of coal which might be converted to other forms, the complexities in the Canadian energy system become especially evident, which are further complicated by the difficulty in predicting the future economics of the various systems that would be available. The production of large amounts of synthetic natural gas (SNG) is considered unlikely before 2000, since natural gas continues to be available domestically at acceptable prices. Nevertheless, there are indications that the cost of producing SNG from prairie surface-mined coals will be less than the delivered cost of some offshore natural gas resources thought to exist in the Arctic regions. Moreover, the gas pipeline system will expand from now to 2000, and it would appear, therefore, that some production of SNG might be justified after 2000 to ensure full use is made of the distribution network and the major investment it represents. Some "synthetic" natural gas is already produced in Canada from naphtha by-products of petrochemical operations at Sarnia, Ontario; it is noteworthy that there are current applications to export some of this gas from this and other such projected facilities at the higher price it can command in the USA market.

Predicting levels of conventional coal liquefaction in Canada also proves difficult. The lowest cost coals occur in regions having other hydrocarbon resources, especially Alberta with its oil sands and heavy oils. The cost of mining coal and processing it to liquid fuels should not, in principle, be any more expensive in Canada than in other countries contemplating the introduction of these processes. Canada could conceivably have the option of producing oil from both nonconventional resources of petroleum and coal.

However, the major opportunity existing for the conversion of coal to liquids in Canada lies in the use of coal as an adjunct to the recovery and processing of bitumen and heavy oil occurring in the provinces of Alberta and Saskatchewan. If economically and technically successful, the use of coal would, in effect, permit a greater production of oil than through the use of part of the recovered hydrocarbon as process fuel. The simplest application lies in the production of steam for some "in-situ" recovery methods. Coal might also be used to produce hydrogen which would, in turn, supply the needs for this gas. In other cases, liquid-forming substances in the coal could be extracted with solvents derived from the recovered bitumen or heavy oil itself; the coal residuum left after extraction would serve as the necessary fuel. The coal occurs generally from 250 to 350 km from the oil sands or heavy oil plant sites. Should rail transportation costs be too high, water-slurry pipelines or mine-site conversion to a medium-BTU gas to be piped directly to field boiler sites at "in-situ" operations might overcome the problem. The converted gas could also be used to provide a source of hydrogen, or to augment locally available process gases.

Coal will be used for steam raising in a heavy oil "in-situ" recovery facility in the Cold Lake region of Alberta. This facility will be capable of producing about 145,000 bbls/day and will use in excess of one million tons of coal per year.

In the WOCOL study, it has been assumed in the Low Coal Case, that about 9 million tons (6 mtce) of mainly subbituminous coal would be used for this purpose by 2000 in two facilities using 3 mtce each every year. In the WOCOL High Coal Case, it was assumed that five such facilities would be operating in that year and, in addition, that the first "free-standing" coal liquefaction plant would be installed producing 50,000 bbl/day from 6.5 mtce per year. This would lead to a coal consumption, again mostly of subbituminous coal, of about 32 million tons (21.5 mtce) in 2000. Such large consumption would again be subject to environmental study.

64

Coal used for medium-BTU gas production has been classified here as used for "industrial" purposes while that used as an adjunct fuel in oil sands/heavy oils extraction and processing has been classified as used for "synthetic-fuel" production.

5. OTHER APPLICATIONS FOR COAL

Only very limited opportunities appear to exist for other markets for coal, such as for household heating. While it is possible that some centralized district heating systems may be installed in central Canada, possibly involving co-generation of electricity, no allowance has been made in this study for coal combustion in these markets.

PROJECTIONS OF COAL CONSUMPTION FOR WOCOL HIGH COAL AND LOW COAL CASES

See Tables 2-1 and 2-4.

Table 2-4. Coal Use In Final Demand Sectors ≠

*Units = mtce

Sector	1977	1980		1985		1990		1995		2000		1977-2000 Average Annual Percentage Growth %/Year	
		Low Coal Case	High Coal Case	Low Coal Case	High Coal Case	Low Coal Case	High Coal Case	Low Coal Case	High Coal Case	Low Coal Case	High Coal Case	Low Coal Case	High Coal Case
Electric	17	25	21	31	28	37	40	43	50	50	65	4.8	6.0
Industrial Steam*	1.5	2	2	4	4	7	10	10	15	11	20	7.7	10.6
Metallurgical	6.5	7	7	9	9	11	11	13	13	15	15	3.7	3.7
Synthetic Fuels	—	—	—	—	—	—	11	3	15	6	21	(6.5)	(6.7)***
Residential/Commercial	—	—	—	—	—	—	—	—	—	—	—	—	—
Total Coal Use	25	34	30	44	41	55	72	69	93	82	121	5.3	7.1
Total Primary Energy Use	297	335	340	369	396	406	466	451	505	509	592	2.4	3.0
Coal Penetration (%)													
—Total	9	10	9	12	10	14	15	15	18	16	20	2.5	3.5
—Electric**	15	20	16	20	18	21	21	20	22	20	24	1.3	2.0
—Industrial Steam	—	—	—	—	—	—	—	—	—	—	—	—	—

1 million metric tons coal equivalent = .0277 quadrillion BTU.
* 1 quadrillion BTU = 36.1 million metric tons coal equivalent.
≠ Major Assumptions:
  * Includes conversion to medium-BTU gas by industry.
  ** indicative only; balance not possible due mainly to difficulty to allowing for contribution to coal from expected net growing electrical exports reflected in capacity data in Table IV.
  *** calculated from 1990.

IMPLICATIONS FOR REQUIRED OIL IMPORTS

Canada is different from most coal-producing countries in that an expansion of its coal industry might not lead to direct savings of imported oil much over the range of 150,000-200,000 bbl/day since direct substitution of coal for oil imports can occur only in Quebec and the Atlantic Provinces. Additional coal production may serve the export market and importing nations may, in turn, of course, choose to reduce their oil imports, or Canadian coal might displace coal presently imported from the United States of America. Annual coal production in the Atlantic region might be increased from the 2.9 million raw tons of coal produced in 1978 to the 7- to 10-million-ton range in 2000, including a significant fraction of metallurgical quality. Quantities surplus to the cokemaking needs of the region may be supplied to export or to Ontario markets. Coal for thermal uses produced in the

Atlantic region will have a medium- to high-sulphur content and difficulties in utilization may be encountered. It is conceivable that some coal of western Canadian origin might also displace the use of oil in some industrial applications in central Canada. The policy announced in November 1979 by the federal government to increase domestic oil prices to international levels by the mid-1980's will assist the use of coal in such applications.

It seems likely, however, that a major opportunity for coal to displace imported oil will arise through its potential role in reducing natural gas and bitumen use for fuel (and later possibly for hydrogen) in oil sands/heavy oils extraction and processing. Thus the role of coal is an indirect one in this method of increasing Canada's liquid fuel supply. The resource base available in both oil sands and heavy oils alone could allow Canada to become independent of oil imports. It should be noted, however, that aside from steam-raising applications, for hydrogen production and for bitumen and coal coprocessing, suitable processes remain to be demonstrated, and costly commercial-scale plants must be designed and constructed.

COAL PRODUCTION*

RESOURCES

The coal resources of Canada, appraised in 1978, are listed in Figure 2-1, classified by coal type and by province. The resources of immediate interest consist of coal seams that, because of thickness, quality, depth and location, are considered to be of most immediate interest for exploration and development. These resources exclude coal that may be present in the regions north of 60°N latitude (although minor quantities of coal are produced from time to time in the Yukon Territory and elsewhere in the North), and minor occurrences known in Newfoundland and Manitoba.

Based on the 1978 level of production of 30.3 million tons, the resource base appears to be adequate for foreseeable immediate needs. However, given the threefold or more expansion of production expected by 2000, some limitations may become evident, especially for coal of bituminous rank. This ·occurs especially for those bituminous coals extracted in the Mountain or Cordillera region, where the bulk of the resource can only be recovered by underground mining methods, which encounter severe problems due to geological conditions. While promising results are being obtained by hydraulic mining techniques, the fully satisfactory underground mining technique generally applicable to this resource has not yet been developed. Most existing surface or underground mines are located at sites enjoying generally favorable conditions and mining operations are being modified to meet the exigencies of each local situation. This continuing development suggests that new technology would make increasing amounts of coal mineable, thus more than accounting for the depletion of the more favorable sites. Much depends upon real-price increases to facilitate the development and introduction of new technology, and long-term arrangements with customers are vital in this regard.

Resources of high-volatile bituminous coals in the foothills region of Alberta, while sufficient to support rapid expansion of production through to at least 1990, may also become limited generally to underground sources past that date. Mining conditions are, however, somewhat more favorable than in the mountain region.

---

* This section relies heavily upon E.D. Jamieson's "Status Report on Canadian Coal Mining," presented to the Canadian Institute of Mining & Metallurgy, Montreal, April 1979.

Figure 2-1. Canadian Coal Resources (1978)
(million tons)

| Province and Area | Coal Rank[1] | Resources | | | | | |
| | | Immediate Interest | | | Future Interest | | |
		Measured[2]	Indicated[2]	Inferred	Measured	Indicated	Inferred
Nova Scotia[3]							
Sydney	hvb	175	502	719	—	—	—
Other	hvb	48	41	38	3	50	128
Subtotal	hvb	223	543	757	3	50	128
New Brunswick[4]							
Minto	hvb	18	2	—	—	—	—
Other	hvb	14	14	1	—	—	—
Subtotal		32	16	1	—	—	—
Ontario[5]	lig	218	—	—	—	—	—
Saskatchewan[6]							
Estevan	lig	310	497	437	41	519	6,998
Willow Bunch	lig	748	1,044	1,420	68	1,704	10,388
Wood Mountain	lig	278	733	1,114	44	1,447	5,665
Cypress	lig	162	407	465	8	243	461
Subtotal		1,498	2,681	3,436	161	3,913	23,512
Alberta[7]							
Plains	sub	30,000[8]	—[9]	102,000[10]	—	—	198,000[11]
Foothills	hvb	1,300	—	7,700	—	—	—
Mountains	lvb-mvb	8,000	—	19,000	—	—	—
British Columbia[12]							
Southeastern	lvb-mvb	6,286	9,436	36,317	—	—	—
Northeastern	lvb-mvb	996	462	7,719	—	—	—
Other	mainly lig some sub-hvb	1,845	91	7,439	—	—	—
Canada totals	lig	3,561	2,772	10,875	161	3,913	23,512
	sub	30,000	—	102,000	—	—	198,000
	hvb	1,555	559	8,457	3	50	128
	lvb-mvb	15,282	9,898	63,036	—	—	—

Source: Department of Energy, Mines and Resources (1980).

Notes:

[1] lig = lignitic; sub = subbituminous; hvb = high-volatile bituminous; mvb = medium-volatile bituminous; lvb = low-volatile bituminous.

[2] Includes reserves.

[3] Based on federal/provincial drilling program and Devco data.

[4] Based on information provided by New Brunswick Department of Natural Resources.

[5] Based on EMR study.

[6] Based on federal/provincial coal-resource evaluation program.

[7] Estimates for Alberta have not been prepared by EMR. The figures presented in this table are those reported by Alberta Energy Resources Conservation Board, Report 79-31, December 1978. The ERCB's parameters, evaluation methodology and reporting terminology differ from the EMR system and a direct correlation between the two systems is impossible. For this table the following accommodations have been made:

[8] ERCB "established resources" are reported as EMR "measured resources"; it is recognized these figures include some undetermined amounts that EMR would report as "indicated" and/or "inferred."

[9] There is no ERCB category comparable to EMR "indicated"; such coal is included either in EMR "measured" or "inferred."

[10] EMR "inferred"—ERCB "total resource" (330 Gt) less the deep coal resources (198 Gt; see footnote 11) and less the ERCB "established resource" (30 Gt); some might belong in the "indicated" category.

[11] Deep-coal resources between 200 and 600 m deep (Yurko, 1976).

[12] Based on evaluations by EMR, British Columbia Ministry of Mines and Petroleum Resources and British Columbia Hydro and Power Authority.

— Not determined.

The mineable coal resources of the plains are not considered as candidates for export because of transportation costs which are prohibitive for the coals of low-energy content. The resource base appears adequate to support a continuing electrical supply option in the region, and to supply new uses as may arise in the oil-sands and coal-conversion industries. However, the development of a low-cost drying and briquetting process or other such dewatering techniques may allow these coals to be offered in international markets, and within the period to 2000, the resource base appears adequate to serve possible export markets as well. In addition, a substantial resource exists of these coals that can only be extracted by underground mining methods. Because of the continued availability of coals from surface mines at reasonable costs, it is only now that attention is returning to these resources. It is quite conceivable that high-production mining techniques could be developed for these deeper coals, but costs would then be higher than at present. Ultimately, underground gasification techniques may be also of importance.

One very large low-rank coal deposit occurs at Hat Creek in British Columbia, about 330 km from tidewater. At present, this coal is earmarked for electricity production for use within the province, although liquefaction is a possibility. However, other deposits of this magnitude may yet be found and should coals from such sources prove to be available for export, joint studies will be required with potential consumer nations to devise mutually acceptable means for their development and use.

PRODUCTION

1. MOUNTAIN (CORDILLERA) REGION

Most of Canada's resources of bituminous rank coals occur in the provinces of Alberta and British Columbia, extending in a belt up to 50 km wide from the USA border, northwest into the East Kootenay region of southeastern BC, north into Alberta in the Crowsnest Pass area and into northeastern BC. Elevations range from 1,600 to 3,000 meters, and most of the mining is carried out in alpine or subalpine environments, often above the tree line. The alpine environment is very fragile and susceptible to long-term damage. Several major rivers have their headwaters in this region, making watershed management important. Winter conditions are severe. Forestry, tourism, parks, and nature reserves compete for land use and the scenic value and wildlife habitat of the mountain region is a valuable national resource.

Geologically, this is the most interesting coal region in Canada because mountain building occurred after the seams were deposited. The main center of deposition, in which more than 20 mineable seams were deposited is located in southeastern BC. In some instances, seams can be mined by surface methods over long slope distances; in other cases pockets of greatly thickened coal provide rich deposits for open-pit mines. Large resources are also being discovered and evaluated in the Peace River area to the north.

Mining operations vary according to the local geological conditions, and several pits may be in operation on any one property at a given time. The scale of operations possible also varies with individual situations, but it seems appropriate to choose a nominal capacity of 2 million tons per year per operation as characteristic of individual mine sites available over the longer term.

The capital investment required for a surface mine in the mountain region ranges from $80 to $110 (1978) per annual ton of capacity, exclusive of infra-structure development. To compete with other opportunities in the capital markets, it is generally considered that an average return after taxes on capital investment over the life of the mine of about 15% is required, and that a minimum 15-year contract for the output is necessary to justify operations. The sales and direct oper-ating costs of an existing 2-million-ton mine producing metallurgical grade coal might be:

Figure 2-2.

		$C (000's) (1978)
1.	Net Sales	90,000
2.	Direct Operating Costs:	
	(a) Mining incl. labor	21,300
	(b) Other incl. reclamation	1,600
	(c) Labor fringes	3,100
	(d) Preparation	4,000
	(e) Administrative	6,600
	(f) Land & property taxes	3,400
	(g) Depreciation	4,000
	(h) Amortization of preproduction costs	600
		44,600

From: E.D. Jamieson (1979)

The mountain region is currently crossed by four main rail lines, but expensive spurlines are required to reach remote sites. Expansion of current mining oper-ations and development of new mines require provincial government approval; however, the rate of development currently is more limited by demand factors. Any continuing expansion of supply from this region would also require a steady improvement in mining technology to permit the economic recovery of the larger part of the resource that must be mined underground. The hydraulic mining tech-niques that have been introduced in one mine have shown encouraging results.

2. THE FOOTHILLS REGION OF ALBERTA

Coals from this region, which are mainly of high-volatile bituminous B and C rank, but generally not useful for metallurgical applications, are becoming impor-tant for export thermal-coal markets. Some coal from this region is already ex-ported, and shipments have begun to distant thermal-coal markets in Ontario. Mining conditions are not generally as severe as in the mountain region and likely individual mine sites could produce up to 3 million tons per year, resulting in a lower cost per ton. Most of the resources will have to be extracted by underground mining methods eventually. The resource base available is the smallest of all the categories of coal in Canada, but sufficient to justify a major expansion of mining in this region.

3. THE PLAINS REGIONS OF SASKATCHEWAN AND ALBERTA

The four lignite coal deposits in Saskatchewan are located along the USA border and form the northern fringes of the main lignite zone centered in North Dakota. The subbituminous coal seams of Alberta underlie the southern part of that province from the tectonic front of the Rocky Mountains in the west to their outcrops about 250 km farther east, and form an immense arc from the USA border up to about 56°N latitude, passing east of the cities of Calgary and Edmonton.

The topography is basically flat and traversed by widely separated river valleys with steeply cut banks. The elevation varies from 650 meters in Saskatchewan to 1,300 near Calgary. In the south, the land is used mainly for grain and cattle production, while the northern portions of these provinces are characteristically forest-covered with muskeg swamps. The weather ranges from severely cold in winter with little accumulation of snow, to hot in the summer. Summer winds can cause an erosion problem. The coals in these regions are geologically young, and the quality is highly variable. In Saskatchewan, mining limits may be set by quality criteria; the plains coalfields in that province have been extensively drilled, and the measured resources at 1,652 million tons of mostly surface-mineable zones, defined by 0.8 km centers for drilling, have been estimated fairly accurately.

At the present time, planning and feasibility studies are under way for large mines to supply mine-site power plants. For example, a 2,000-MW baseload plant with a 25-year life would require about 8 million tons of coal per year, indicating the need of a recoverable reserve of about 200 million tons in close proximity to the plant. Mining activities extending over a distance up to 30 km are becoming common in the region. Problems encountered are essentially those of planning and operating large-scale enterprises and addressing environmental impacts of air and water quality and land reclamation. Draglines are key pieces of equipment and the present cost of each machine is in the $30 million range. Delivery times of 2 to 3 years from order to operation could be expected at peak development periods.

It should also be noted that recent studies have suggested that underground longwall retreating methods might be used to extract the larger resources, particularly of subbituminous coals at depths beyond the reach of strip mining. Total production costs (1978) are estimated to be about $14 per ton. However, even at these increased coal costs, local power generation would still be attractive.

Expansion of this branch of the coal-mining industry can keep pace with the needs of both the utility industry and other markets for low-rank coals as they develop, provided regulatory approval is granted by the province for the necessary mining operations.

4. THE ATLANTIC REGION

Although a relatively small quantity of high-sulphur bituminous coal is produced by surface-mining methods in the province of New Brunswick, the Cape Breton Island coalfield in Nova Scotia is the most important of the region. This coalfield is located on the north shore of the island, facing the Cabot Strait and the Atlantic Ocean. The coal is generally of high-volatile bituminous "A" rank and exhibits the typical high-fluid properties characteristic of metallurgical coals of this class. The raw coal varies from medium to high in sulphur content. A modern coal-cleaning plant produces a maximum quantity of metallurgical specification coal with a maximum sulphur content of 1.2% and, since the coal has good washing characteristics, the ash content can be reduced to about 3.5%. A thermal coal coproduct is also produced.

Since the resource lies mostly under the sea, drill ships must be used for exploration. In the course of oil and gas exploration, it was discovered that the coal seams are shallower than previously thought. The seaward dip of the seams is now believed to decrease in the northward direction. A total of 13 holes was drilled off the coast of Cape Breton Island in 1977 and 1978, with very encouraging results. Follow-up planning and feasibility studies are under way.

Improved production rates have been achieved recently and plans for modernization of mining methods may result in increased production.

The capital cost for mines in the area is in the $60-$75 (1978) per annual ton range. During the financial year ending March 31, 1978, the following operation results were reported for the Cape Breton mines:

Figure 2-3.

	$C (000's)
1. Income	87,800[1]
2. Direct Operating Costs:	
(a) Labor & fringes	40,400
(b) Repairs	11,000
(c) Supplies & Power	12,200
(d) Coal preparation & stockpiling	12,900
(e) Administration & training	7,200
(f) Strip mining	500
(g) Loan interest and other expenses	5,400
	89,600[2]
Colliery operating loss (1)-(2)	1,800

From: E.D. Jamieson (1979)

The price of the thermal coal delivered to Nova Scotia power plants is indexed to the equivalent domestic Canadian price of oil, which is presently controlled at about $C15.75/barrel (early 1980) to the refinery, depending upon quality characteristics. The return to the mines in Cape Breton depends upon transportation costs to the power plants served, and the value of the coal is now in the range of $35-$45 per ton. Metallurgical grades of coal are priced between $55 and $60 per ton f.o.b. Sydney, Nova Scotia.

PROJECTIONS OF COAL PRODUCTION

See Table 2-5 and Worksheets attached to this report.

INDICATIVE ECONOMICS OF COAL SUPPLY

As noted previously, mining conditions, and thus mining costs, vary considerably in Canada by both region and mining situation. It is not possible, therefore,

Table 2-5. Coal Supply/Demand Integration Summary

Source	1977	1985		1990		1995		2000		1977-2000 Average Annual Percentage Growth % / Year	
		Low Coal Case	High Coal Case	Low Coal Case	High Coal Case	Low Coal Case	High Coal Case	Low Coal Case	High Coal Case	Low Coal Case	High Coal Case
Coal Consumption (mtce)	25	44	41	55	72	69	93	82	121	5.3	7.1
Potential Coal Production (mtce)	23	48	48	59	87	78	123	92	159	6.2	8.8
million metric tons physical	31	57	52	77	101	103	137	117	174	5.9	7.8
Potential Export (mtce)	11	17	17	19	25	25	40	27	47	4.0	6.5
million metric tons physical	12	20	20	25	35	35	50	34	59	4.6	7.2
Required Imports (mtce)	13	13	10	15	10	16	10	17	9	—	—

to report indicative economics of coal supply without taking these factors into account. For this reason a set of figures has been attached in which:

2-4 the historical division of coal production is illustrated between surface and underground mining methods showing the present major dependence upon surface mining methods despite the fact that most of the coal resources lie at depths such that underground mining techniques will have to be used for their recovery;

Figure 2-4. Canadian Raw Coal Production By Surface and Underground Methods 1950-1978

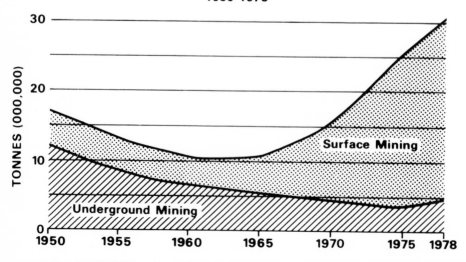

2-5 the raw-coal production is listed by specific mining method, both underground and surface, by regions;

2-6 typical productivity data are provided for the production of saleable coal by mine;

2-7 provides typical productivity data for the production of saleable coal by mining system;

2-8 a typical distribution of mining costs by mine is provided (1977);

2-9 yield is provided of saleable coal from raw coal production by region.

Figure 2-5. Raw Coal Production in Canada
(in 000 tons, by mining methods)

			1974	1975	1976	1977	1978
(a)	*Underground* Longwall	—Maritimes	900	1,500	1,900	2,100	2,600
	Room & Pillar	—Maritimes	200	100	200	300	200
		—Cordillera	1,400	1,400	1,400	1,600	2,200
	Room & Pillar	—Canada	1,600	1,500	1,600	1,900	2,400
	Hydraulic	—Cordillera	700*	900*	700*	600*	700
	Underground	—Canada	3,200	3,900	4,200	4,600	5,700
(b)	*Surface* Dragline	—Maritimes	400	400	400	300	300
		—Plains	8,400	9,400	10,000	11,700	13,200
		—Cordillera	900*	1,500*	900*	1,500*	2,400
		—Canada	9,700	11,300	11,300	13,500	15,900
	Truck & Shovel	—Maritimes	200	200	—	—	—
		—Cordillera	11,000	14,700	11,700	12,200	13,500
		—Canada	11,200	14,900	11,700	12,200	13,500
	Surface	—Canada	20,900	26,200	23,000	25,700	29,400
(c)	Total Surface & Underground	—Canada	24,100	30,100	27,200	30,300	35,100

* Estimated

From: E.D. Jamieson (1979)

Figure 2-6. Typical Productivity Rates by Mine (1978)

		Workforce	Saleable Output (tons)	Productivity Tons/Employee Year
Devco	—Lingan[1]	1,200	1,500,000	1,500
	—No. 26[1]	1,220	700,000	573
	—Overall[2]	2,450	2,500,000	1,020
Luscar	—Bienfait[3]	63	450,000	7,142
	—Boundary[4]	101	1,700,000	16,832
	—Forestburg[4]	54	900,000	16,667
	—Coal Valley[5]	340	2,300,000	6,765
	—Cardinal[6]	694	2,000,000	2,882
	—Overall	1,390	7,350,000	5,288
Byron Creek[7]	(Initial stages)	65	520,000	8,000
Kaiser	—Balmer N.[8]	50[e]	120,000	2,400
	—Balmer S.[9]	302[e]	660,000	2,185
	—Harmer[6]	916	5,400,000	5,895
	—Overall[10]	1,258	6,200,000	4,928
Fording	—Greenhills[5]	N/A	900,000	—
	—Clode/Taylor[6]	N/A	1,900,000	—
	—Overall	1,040	2,800,000	2,692

Notes:
[e] Estimated
[1] Underground longwall.
[2] Devco total includes some room and pillar and surface coal, excludes workforce in preparation plant.
[3] Plains region, dragline strip mining—excludes char plant personnel.
[4] Plains region, dragline strip mining, minesite power plant.
[5] Cordillera region, dragline strip mining plus coal preparation.
[6] Cordillera region, truck and shovel open-pit mining plus coking coal preparation.
[7] Cordillera region, truck and shovel open-pit mining plus thermal coal preparation.
[8] Cordillera region, underground room and pillar mining.
[9] Cordillera region, underground hydraulic mining plus major development.
[10] Kaiser total does not include preparation plant personnel.
From: E.D. Jamieson (1979)

Figure 2-7. Typical Productivity Data

Mining System	Employees/Million Tons Annual Saleable Output
Underground longwall	750
Underground hydraulic (in seam)	240
(with development)	460
Open pit, truck and shovel (multiseam) coking coal	360
Open pit, truck and shovel (large pit)	170
Strip mining, dragline, foothills	150
Strip mining, dragline, plains	60

Note: These figures, particularly for surface mines, will vary greatly dependent upon the size of mine.
From: E.D. Jamieson (1979)

Figure 2-8. Typical Distribution of Mining Cost (1977)

Operations		Labor Incl. Super-vision	Mainte-nance	Supplies	Power	G & A	Other	Total
								%
Devco —No. 26 (UL)		57.9	13.2	10.5	3.9	8.9	5.6	100
—Lingan		41.8	14.1	13.2	2.2	14.6	14.1	100
Luscar —Bienfait	(SD)*	52	10	21	3	7	7	100
—Boundary	(SD)	36	11	39	3	2	9	100
—Forestburg	(SD)	33	9	26	3	13	16	100
—Coal Valley	(SD)	25	12	30	4	5	24	100
—Cardinal	(T/S)	29	17	20	2	4	28	100
Kaiser —Underground Hyd.		56.3	17.1	13.2	5.9	7.5	—	100
—Surface		16.8	48.0	20.1	1.4	13.7	—	100
Fording Coal (T/S)		18	50	27	2	3	—	100

UL—Underground longwall.
SD—Surface dragline.
T/S—Surface truck and shovel.
G&A—General and Administrative.
* Unusual cost distribution.

From: E.D. Jamieson (1979)

Figure 2-9. Yield of Saleable Coal from Raw Coal

Province	Coal Type & Mining Method	1978 Raw-Coal Production (000's tons)	1978 Saleable Production (000's tons)	% Product Yield
Nova Scotia	Bituminous underground	2,553	2,170	85
Saskatchewan	Lignite. All surface mines.	5,068	5,068	100
Alberta	Subbituminous. All surface mines.	8,262	8,262	100
Alberta	Bit. thermal. Foothills Sfce. + U/G	1,427	805	56
Alberta	Bit. Met. Cordillera Sfce. + U/G	5,897	3,527	60
British Columbia	Bit. Met. Cordillera Sfce. + U/G	11,448	8,738	76

From: E.D. Jamieson (1979)

Examination of the historical information provided in Figures 2-4 to 2-9 suggests the following general conclusions:

(a) Surface mining is more productive in terms of output per employee than underground mining, but in the Lingan longwall mine and the Kaiser hydraulic mine, the performance is beginning to approach those of some truck-and-shovel operations.

(b) The overall productivity of the hydraulic mine, because of rock tunneling and major development, has recently fallen from earlier levels. While this is probably a temporary phenomenon, the rates may provide at least an indication of future levels of productivity in extensive mines requiring underground dewatering stations.

(c) Thermal coal production is more productive than coking coal production for similar surface mining systems in the geologically disturbed conditions of the Cordilleran region. More coal is recovered and less sophisticated preparation techniques are required.

(d) Multiseam or multipit truck-and-shovel operations are less productive than large concentrated open-pit operations. The overburden to coal ratio is the all-important criterion.

(e) Dragline strip mining of coal in the Plains region is extremely productive, especially when the consumer is located at the minesite.

(f) No environmental cost analyses were available which would have to be considered in new or expanded operations.

NATIONAL COAL SUPPLY/DEMAND INTEGRATION SUMMARY

See Table 2-5 and Worksheets attached to this report.

COAL TRANSPORTATION

The principal movements of coal within Canada are illustrated in Figure 2-10.

Metallurgical coal for export is produced in the mountain, or Cordilleran region of British Columbia and Alberta. Most of this coal, including some coking coal bound for eastern Canadian markets, is shipped on either of two main rail routes to ports located in Vancouver, British Columbia. The coal is moved in 7,000- to 9,000-ton shipments by modern unit trains which are loaded and unloaded by special high-capacity techniques. The distance from mine to terminal is about 1,300 km through mountainous terrain with difficult winter operating conditions. Improvements are now being made, including grade reductions on one line, and the possibility exists of an interconnection with the British Columbia Railway to provide more secure service at critical periods.

The present level of annual shipments to terminals in the Vancouver, BC area are 12.6 million tons of metallurgical coal and about 0.4 million tons of thermal coal.

Terminal facilities in the Vancouver area are now rapidly approaching their capacity limits, but expansion is now in the planning stages at the deep-water Roberts Bank coal port. The largest shipment from this port to date is 140,000 tons (Figure 2-11).

Rail capacity increases to west coast ports would be possible through the upgrading of another existing transmountain line serving the Port of Prince Rupert, and the construction of a modern coal terminal which is scheduled to be ready by 1985.

Coal moving from western Canada to Ontario markets also moves by unit trains to new coal-loading and storage-terminal facilities located at Thunder Bay, at the west end of Lake Superior. Trains must traverse a distance of some 2,000 km. Low-rank coals produced in Saskatchewan, mainly lignite, are also moved into

Figure 2-10.

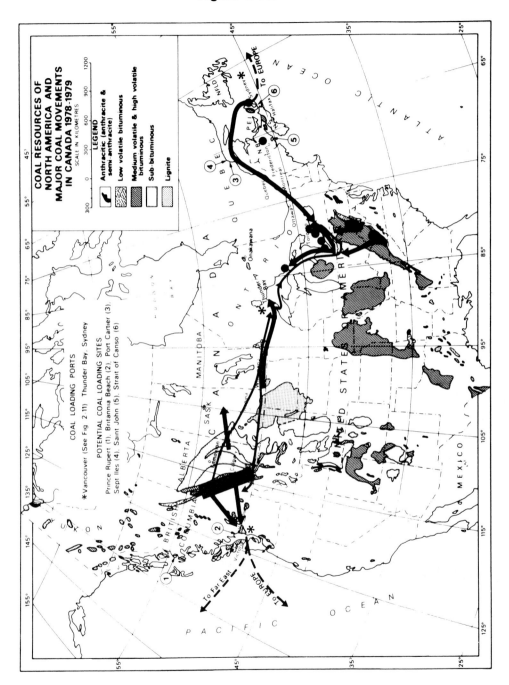

Manitoba and northwestern Ontario for local power generation and some industrial applications, mainly in the forest industry.

Coal from the USA is received in southwestern Ontario through the Great Lakes Waterways system; about 8 million tons of metallurgical coal are shipped annually from USA lake ports such as Toledo. One million tons of metallurgical coal from western Canada and 0.5 million tons from Nova Scotia are also expected to be used in the area in 1979. About 9 million tons of thermal coal of bituminous rank are received from the USA and 2-3 million tons from western Canada are expected in 1979.

The Great Lakes transportation system is unique to North America. With the opening of the St. Lawrence Seaway, special self-unloading vessels have been developed and some lake vessels have been built to strengthened specifications to allow their use in the Gulf of St. Lawrence and, in some instances, in open ocean waters. Loads of up to 55,000 tons are possible from the west to Lake Erie ports, but lock-size restrictions on the Welland Canal linking Lake Erie with Lake Ontario restrict cargoes to a maximum of about 27,000 tons. Maximum vessel size capable of moving through the locks are 222.5 m long and 23.0 m wide with a depth of 7.9 m. The Welland Canal is the bottleneck in the system; currently about 65.7 million tons of cargo move through the locks whose practical capacity at present is set at 67.4 million tons. A number of modifications and improvements are possible without incurring the very large expense of building new locks, and it is believed the capacity could be increased as needed to 90 million tons. It must be noted, however, that not all this additional capacity would be available for increased coal movements; other traffic is growing as well. Tolls through the system currently approximate $1 per ton for passage from Lake Erie to the sea.

The Lake system is closed during the winter months, and the effective shipping season, at present, is limited to 8½ months. Various improvements might allow the season to be extended by another month. Below Montreal, the St. Lawrence River is kept open by icebreakers for year-round shipping, although interruptions sometimes occur during brief periods of particularly cold weather. Efforts are being made to increase the system's capacity by extending operations through most of the year, which would reduce the need to carry inventories of coal over the winter months at loading ports and receivers' facilities.

Deep-water ports are in operation in the lower St. Lawrence River region at Port Cartier and Sept. Iles, built to serve the iron-ore trade. The largest iron-ore shipment to date is 240,000 tons. Coals of either USA or Canadian origin could conceivably be transferred from the smaller Lake vessels to deep-draft vessels at these locations. Sites for deep-water ports also exist in the Strait of Canso and in the Bay of Fundy where large oil tankers now unload. Coal produced in Cape Breton is exported through older facilities located in Sydney Harbour, which also receive metallurgical coals needed for blending purposes, imported from western Canada via the Panama Canal, and from USA Chesapeake Bay ports.

The long distances coal has to be moved from one part of the country to the other, or from mine sites to ports for export, has led to a continuing interest in new transportation technologies. Studies of the possibilities for coal/water and coal/oil slurry pipelines have been made, including investigations of the related problems of "reconstituting" coking coals transported in this manner into a form acceptable in conventional coke ovens. Studies of both physical and fluid-coking techniques for

Fig. 2-11. Vancouver Area Loading Facilities

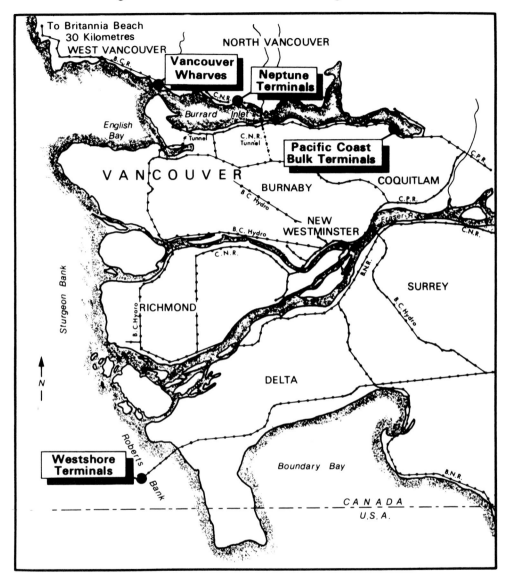

the handling of coal/oil slurries on delivery have also been undertaken. Methods of increasing the energy content of low-rank coals and related briquetting procedures to increase the safety of transport in rail cars have also been examined.

Canada has no ocean-going national flag merchant fleet, the vessels of the lake fleet capable of ocean operations being the only exception. While in principle it may be required for coastal traffic to move in Canadian flag vessels this has not happened in practice, and generally it can be said that without a significant change in present maritime policies, all coal exports from Canada and all movements in the coastal trade will be carried in foreign flag vessels.

ENVIRONMENTAL, HEALTH & SAFETY CONSIDERATIONS

CURRENT PRACTICES

Aside from the coal occurring in the Plains and Foothills regions, much of the nation's coal resources lie in remote areas, and although Canada has been well endowed with large resources of coal, a good part of this coal underlies some of the most beautiful and environmentally sensitive land in the world. Competing uses for this land are the leisure and tourist industries, forest products industry and agriculture.

To conduct exploration programs, access to the area must be provided, involving the construction of roads, the transport of heavy machinery and drilling work. It has already been noted that the largest part of Canada's current coal production is produced by surface-mining methods, necessitating the removal of huge amounts of overburden and temporary disturbance of the landscape with subsequent wind and water erosion problems. Transporting the large amounts of coal which are predicted to move in the future will require careful application of dust and noise abatement techniques, and some further precautionary measures concerning public safety.

1. PRODUCTION

The general public perception of coal mining is negative. Deeply embedded in people's memories are the results of the mining industry's past practices, both in Canada and elsewhere. Restoration of mined-out areas did not take place in past decades, and today the public is very concerned that land be returned, when mining activities cease, to as near as, or better than, original conditions. However, those who are well acquainted with the coal industry find few grounds for objections to present properly managed reclamation programs.

In response to this concern, provincial governments have set standards and the coal-mining companies are required to develop detailed reclamation plans which are submitted to authorities before any mining actually takes place. Reclamation and restoration is now viewed as an integral part of the mining process and not a separate phase. It is not rare, in fact, to see reclamation and mining of acreage being conducted simultaneously. In a country the size of Canada, the area disturbed by coal mining cannot be considered large. In 1976, for example, when a total of 25.5 mt of coal was produced, the area affected was:

- in British Columbia, "mountain" region 182 ha
- in Alberta, "mountain" and "foothills" regions 40 "

    "plains" region 122 "
- in Saskatchewan, "plains" region 130 "

    Canadian total (1976)   474 ha

And while coal production in Canada could increase five- to sixfold by the end of this century, with a resulting increase in the amount of land disturbed, there is no reason to believe that satisfying reclamation criteria would present a severe problem. It should be noted, however, that some constraints may eventually be encountered in the foothills area where the quantities of water needed for mining activities may not be available, especially if severe water-quality disposal standards were to be adopted.

Another facet of coal production is basically a question of land-use policies. Vast resources of coal underlie prime agricultural land, the large grain-producing areas of the prairies. Should a large demand for grain production coincide with a large demand for coal, some conflicts may develop in that area, with resulting possible constraints on coal production unless it is realized that the area of land which would be dedicated to this production is very small.

Canadian reclamation technology is in the development stage, and is complicated by large variations in climate and terrain. Conditions range from those encountered in mountain regions, to heavily forested areas in the foothills, to agricultural land on the prairies. However, even after only a few years of reclamation programs in each of the above areas, there have been encouraging results. Only small quantities of coal are produced by surface methods in the Atlantic Provinces.

The disposal of mine wastes can also present problems. These impacts can include fugitive dust emissions, siltation and leaching from waste piles. The construction of tailing ponds, other waste-water treatment facilities and the reclamation or immobilization of waste piles can control the discharge of most undesirable wastes to the surrounding environment.

Safety issues, especially important in underground mines, present their own challenges. The difficult conditions prevailing in the Cape Breton area of Nova Scotia have resulted in the adoption of new standards of practice and the use of sophisticated mining and monitoring equipment and techniques. The almost unique conditions (thick, steeply pitching seams of friable, sometimes gassy, coals which occur under varying depths of cover) pertaining to the extraction of coal from underground mines in the Cordilleran region suggest that more emphasis will be placed on this subject as it becomes necessary to produce more coal by underground mining. The introduction of hydraulic methods appear to involve safety benefits, and various research programs are under way in other methods and equipment which are directed at improving operational safety.

2. TRANSPORTATION

The major environmental problem in the transportation field has been dust loss from unit-train operations. Various coatings are now sprayed on the surface of the hopper cars which largely control the problem. There is growing opposition, however, to the movement of unit trains through heavily populated areas from the standpoints of both noise pollution and public safety. Increasing unit-train traffic will necessitate the installation of more separated, or protected, level crossings.

Proposals to expand port facilities encounter opposition because of concerns related to dust and noise from train and ship movements, the need for land for terminal facilities and other infrastructure requirements and because shoreline is a limited resource; with resultant delays, public hearings and greater economic costs. Also, expanded coal transportation on the Great Lakes, especially since it will not occur in isolation from an expanded volume of shipping generally, will present challenges to the management of the waterway from both an ecological and capacity point of view.

3. UTILIZATION

Siting problems are becoming a major constraint to the expansion of the coal-based, thermal-power industry. This problem and other constraints result from the environmental impacts on land, air and water.

From an air-pollution viewpoint, the major emissions of concern are particulates, sulphur and nitrogen oxides, trace elements and carbon dioxide. Presently, most Canadian coal-fired power stations are equipped with electrostatic precipitators to reduce the emission of particulates. To meet provincial ambient air requirements for sulphur dioxide, the western low-sulphur bituminous coals are used for blending purposes with the higher sulphur coals of US origin for power generation in southern Ontario. In addition, tall stacks are being employed to disperse air pollutants and therefore reduce their concentrations locally; however, this alternative does not reduce the total quantity of pollutants emitted and thus contributes to the long-range transport of air pollutants. No flue-gas desulfurization devices are currently in use in Canada and the uncontrolled release of sulphur and nitrogen oxides has been identified as an important contributing cause to acidic precipitation. While emissions from thermal-power generation are less than from the nonferrous metals industry in Canada (0.6 as opposed to 2.2 million tons SO_2 per year), this problem must be addressed by industry and government.

Preliminary estimates prepared by the United States/Canada Research Consultation Group on the Long Range Transport of Air Pollutants suggest that Canada imports about four times more sulphur dioxide than it exports to the USA in eastern North America. Studies of environmental damage, especially to lakes, arising from acid rain indicate that the problem has become serious in eastern Canada. Studies of technologies that prevent or control these emissions are in progress by government and industry (e.g., flue-gas desulfurization, fluidized-bed combustion and multistage burners).

A global problem of potentially great significance is that of climatic modification, resulting from increasing concentrations of carbon dioxide in the atmosphere. Current research indicates that a substantial general global warming might result if emissions continue to grow exponentially. In the Canadian north, the warming would be a factor of three or four times that at low latitudes. Such warming could be beneficial or detrimental to Canada. Little is known about the changes in temperature and precipitation which would take place on a regional scale, and their potential impacts. Canada is actively participating in international investigations by operating several baseline carbon-dioxide monitoring stations and by carrying out climatological research.

The amounts of water required for once-through condenser cooling (exceeding 90 percent of total intake) and the mechanical and heat damage to entrained organisms at the intake and heat damage to organisms at the outlet have led to increased interest in off-stream cooling via recirculating towers and ponds and to increasing interest in the utilization of the waste heat produced. In water-short areas the amount of water consumed in cooling may limit the availability of sites and, on water bodies where there is already a high utilization of the available water for cooling, further expansion may be limited to cooling systems which require less water and produce less damage to aquatic organisms. Consequently, there is increasing interest in off-stream cooling via recirculating towers and ponds for new stations.

Cooling towers are in use on one station and are projected for use on a second in the near future. One recirculating cooling pond is operational at the present time and another is planned for a new station in the near future. The majority of existing stations, however, are still once-through cooled.

As a result of increasing concern over the amount of water used and the production of contaminated waste waters from traditional ash collection, transport and disposal methods, dry ash handling is receiving more attention.

Waste disposal is an important problem in those provinces relying extensively on coal to generate electricity. In Alberta alone, currently about one million tons of ash must be handled each year and perhaps 70 to 100 million tons will have to be disposed of cumulatively by the year 2000. Although a number of existing stations still utilize once-through ash lagoons for ash disposal, in western provinces the present practice is to place ash in depleted nearby mines if groundwater conditions permit. However, where the station is remote from the mine, or groundwater conditions are not suitable, methods of lining and preparing the disposal areas to prevent the contamination of groundwaters and adjacent surface waters are used.

There is also a continuing interest in the development of methods to utilize ash economically and to recover products from the ash which have previously been viewed as waste material. At the present time about 5% of the ash produced in Canada is being utilized off-site.

POSSIBLE FUTURE ENVIRONMENTAL, HEALTH & SAFETY STANDARDS

As the environmental, health and safety aspects of increased coal utilization become more apparent, it can be expected that the current standards in Canada will be reviewed and new standards, requiring more stringent controls, implemented.

INDICATIVE COST ESTIMATES

Canadian costs in this field are likely to be similar to those encountered in the USA, except for the case of reclamation in subalpine mountainous regions, where the costs are likely to be strongly site-specific. These costs will have to cover such matters as air and water protection, land reclamation, safety, etc.

KEY ENVIRONMENTAL ISSUES

A summary of key environmental issues is as follows:

- Land-use conflicts: i.e., withdrawal of areas to exploration and development, disturbance of agricultural, forestry and recreational lands;
- Expansion of deep water ports, especially near major population centers;
- Fugitive dust problems from surface mining, coal- and waste-storage piles, and transportation;
- Impacts of increased transportation, especially through populated areas;
- Impacts on ground and water systems arising from coal mining, preparation, coal storage, combustion (cooling and ash transport) and waste-disposal areas;
- Control of sulphur and nitrogen oxide emissions; possible value of recovered sulphur at some locations;
- Climatic change associated with carbon dioxide emissions; and
- Reclamation requirements and standards.

IMPLEMENTING ACTIONS REQUIRED
FOR THE TOTAL COAL SYSTEM

FACILITIES AND RESOURCE REQUIREMENTS

1. COAL MINING AND PREPARATION

Assuming the quantities of coal indicated in the projections used in this study, Canada will be called upon to increase its coal production from the present 30 mtce into the 115-175 mtce range in twenty years. Canada is fortunate in that most of the expansion in coal production foreseen will be produced from surface-mining operations; however, since much of this production will be in the form of the lower rank coals, the physical quantities that have to be handled will increase as the average energy content of the coals fall; lower quality coals will also have to be developed as higher grade resources are depleted. Since much of this coal will be consumed in directly associated thermal plants, the need for new coal-preparation facilities will be restricted mainly to the metallurgical mines and to those mines producing bituminous coal for shipment to distant markets.

"Mountain" region mines are likely to have a characteristic size in the two-million-ton annual range, "foothills" region mines in the three-million-ton range, and "plains" region mines in the six-million-ton range. The undersea mines in Cape Breton will likely be designed to produce two to three million tons per year. In all cases, individual working production units, or "workplaces," are likely to be at the two-million-ton-per-year scale.

Given a total metallurgical coal requirement of 29-33 mtce in 2000, perhaps 10 major new operations with associated coal-preparation plants will be needed.

Given a total production of thermal coal in 2000 comprised of 44 to 101 mtce of low-rank coal and 20 to 25 mtce of bituminous coal, perhaps 20 to 30 major new operations will be needed. Preparation plants will be required only by those that produce bituminous grade and these will be somewhat simpler than those associated with the production of coking coal. The possible upgrading of the low-energy coals into higher energy content forms would require more complex processing facilities.

2. COAL CONVERSION

It is not anticipated that facilities for the conversion of coal to SNG will be required in Canada before 2000. However, medium-BTU gasification plants are expected to be built in connection with oil-refinery operations, methanol and ammonia production, and to supply part of the hydrogen requirements of the oil sands/heavy oils industry. In the two scenarios developed in this study, it has been assumed that 2 and 5 such installations, each consuming respectively about 3 mtce of coal per year, mostly of subbituminous rank, will be operational before 2000.

In the WOCOL Low Coal Case scenario, no allowance has been made for a direct coal-to-liquids plant; in the WOCOL High Coal Case scenario, one such plant has been assumed to be in operation by the year 2000, producing oil at 50,000 bbl/day from 6.5 mtce of mostly subbituminous coal.

Most of the coal for conversion has been assumed to be directly connected with the Canadian oil sands/heavy oils extraction and processing industry. The first applications will be for steam raising, while later, coal will be used in hydrogen production and in extraction processes integrated with bitumen and heavy oils upgrading procedures. By 2000, in the WOCOL Low Coal Case, it has been assumed there will be 2 such operations using coal in this way, each consuming 3 mtce of mostly subbituminous coal, and in the WOCOL High Coal Case, 5.

3. COAL-FIRED ELECTRICITY GENERATION

Through the year 2000 there will be continuing expansion of electrical generation capacity based upon coal. In the shorter term, most of this new capacity will be constructed in the Prairie Provinces, in units ranging from 150 to 375 MWe, built essentially as mine-mouth generating plants and equipped with electrostatic precipitators. In the Atlantic Provinces, some facilities designed to burn oil may be converted to coal-oil combustion processes. It is also possible that some retrofitting may be undertaken in this region, possibly in the form of atmospheric pressure fluidized beds, depending upon the success of the current studies.

In the longer term, it is possible that demonstration plants will be in operation in western Canada by 1990 for the production of electricity from low-rank coals—pressurized fluid-bed combustion or some form of combined-cycle operation involving pregasification of the coal are the prime candidate technologies.

Barring unexpected delays to the planned nuclear-generation program, coal consumption in Ontario for electrical production will be devoted to medium-range and peaking-load requirements.

4. INTERNAL COAL TRANSPORT

By 1985, it is expected that a modern new coal terminal, with efficient unloading facilities for unit-coal trains and capable of loading 150,000 dwt vessels, will be in service near Prince Rupert, British Columbia.

Improvements to the existing rail lines will be required. Port expansion in the Vancouver area to the facility at Roberts Bank will be completed, and the development of a third major terminal area in the lower-Mainland region near Vancouver will be under way if justified by coal traffic. The existing rail lines to Vancouver will have been improved by grade reductions and improved interconnections will make train movements more reliable through the mountains during the particularly difficult winter months. A start will have been made on electrification of the railroads. The first pipelines (coal/water slurry) will have been built to service oil sands plants in Alberta, and possibly the first major long-distance pipeline to the Pacific Coast to carry coking coal will have begun.

The increasing volume of coal shipments to the eastern provinces will be moving over improved rail facilities to an expanded transfer dock at Thunder Bay, Ontario. A somewhat extended shipping season on the Great Lakes will allow increased traffic. Some coal of USA origin will be moving downriver to transfer ports located at existing Gulf of St. Lawrence terminals.

5. SUMMARY FOR TOTAL COAL SYSTEM TO THE YEAR 2000

	WOCOL *Low Coal Case*	*WOCOL* *High Coal Case*
Coal Production		
Required increase in production from 1977	additional 69 mtce	additional 136 mtce
(a) Metallurgical Coal	additional 19 mtce from 9 new mines and associated preparation plants (including 2 in NS)	additional 23 mtce from 10 new mines and associated preparation plants (including 2 in NS)
Thermal coal by-product from mines producing metallurgical coal, but also including sole product thermal coal mines in "mountain" region of BC and Alberta	additional 6.5 mtce, of which 2.0 mtce in "mountains" and 4.5 in NS	additional 7.0 mtce, of which 2.5 mtce in "mountains" and 4.5 in NS
(b) Steam Coal		
—from South Central British Columbia		additional 6.0 mtce from Hat Creek deposit of low-rank coal
—from "foothills" region of Alberta	additional 10 mtce from 3 new mines and associated preparation plants	additional 15 mtce from 5 new mines and associated coal preparation plants
—from the "plains" region of Alberta & Saskatchewan		
subbituminous coal	additional 24.5 mtce from 8 new mines, no preparation facilities	additional 67 mtce from 18 new mines, no preparation facilities
lignite	additional 9 mtce from 3 new mines, no preparation facilities	additional 18 mtce from 6 new mines, no preparation facilities
Coal Transportation	upgrading of line to Prince Rupert	upgrading of line to Prince Rupert
	improve facilities for eastward coal movement	accelerated improvement to facilities for eastward coal movement
	spur line construction northeast BC	spur line construction northeast BC
		interconnection of CP, CN & BCR lines
		oil sands supply pipeline
		start on transmountain slurry pipeline
Coal Ports	expansion at Roberts Bank	expansion at Roberts Bank
	rebuilding of coal loading facilities at Sydney, NS	rebuilding of coal loading facilities at Sydney, NS
	new coal port at Prince Rupert, BC	expansion of coal port at Prince Rupert, BC
		new coal port in lower mainland region of BC
		development of transfer ports on Atlantic

	WOCOL Low Coal Case	WOCOL High Coal Case
Electricity	expansion at the 300-375 MWe size increasing to 500-600 MWe range in west	expansion at the 300-375 MWe size increasing to 500-600 MWe range in west
	introduction of atmospheric and pressurized fluid-bed combustion technology, and combined-cycle technology	introduction of atmospheric and pressurized fluid-bed combustion technology, and combined-cycle technology
	introduction of coal-in-oil combustion technology	introduction of coal-in-oil combustion technology
Industrial Use	expansion of coal use by such energy-intensive consumers as the cement industry	expansion of coal use by such energy–intensive consumers as the cement industry
	use of medium-BTU gasification process by industry— 2 such installations consuming 3 mtce each per year	use of medium-BTU gasification process by industry— 5 such installations consuming 3 mtce each per year
High-BTU Gasification and Liquefaction		
SNG	none	none, but preparations for first plant in progress
Direct Liquefaction	none	1 installation producing 50,000 bbl/day and consuming 6.5 mtce per year
Indirect Liquefaction	2 oil sands/heavy oil plants using 3 mtce each per year	5 oil sands/heavy oil plants using 3 mtce each per year

EVALUATION OF CAPABILITY TO MEET INFRASTRUCTURE REQUIREMENTS

Even though an unprecedented expansion of the Canadian coal industry is called for in this report, the infrastructure requirements can be met if:

- purchases of coal are made over long-term contracts and at prices that will encourage investment in the needed facilities;
- lead times of from 3-4 years are allowed for deliveries from new mines; thus permitting the associated transportation facilities (including new ports and expansions of existing ones) to proceed in phase with mine development;
- efficient regulatory procedures and requirements are promulgated for sufficient periods of time to allow for consistent planning; and
- the public in the coal-producing provinces are convinced that the coal industry is a valuable addition to their industrial base and that coal production is valuable to the economy.

Summary Worksheet

I. Coal Use, Production, and Trade	1977	1985		1990		2000		1977-2000 Avg. annual growth—%/yr.	
		A	B	A	B	A	B	A	B
Coal use in major markets (mtce)									
Metallurgical	7	9	9	11	11	15	15	–	–
Electric	17	31	28	37	40	50	65	4.8	6.0
Industry (includes gasification in industry)	1	4	4	7	10	11	20	11.0	14.6
Synthetic Fuels (includes use in oil sands)	–	–	–	–	11	6	21	–	–
Residential/Commercial	small	–	–	–	–	–	–	–	–
Total coal use	25	44	41	55	72	82	121	5.3	7.1
Distribution of coal use by market sector (%)									
Metallurgical	26	21	21	20	15	18	12	—	—
Electric	67	70	68	67	55	61	54	—	—
Industry	7	9	11	13	15	13	17	—	—
Synthetic Fuels	–	–	–	–	15	8	17	—	—
Residential/Commercial	small	neg.	neg.	neg.	neg.	neg.	neg.	—	—
Total coal use	100%	100%	100%	100%	100%	100%	100%	—	—
Coal consumption/imports (mtce) **Consumption**									
Metallurgical	7	9	9	11	11	15	15	3.4	3.4
Steam	18	35	32	44	61	67	106	5.9	8.0
Total coal consumption	25	44	41	55	72	82	121	5.3	7.1
Imports									
Metallurgical	7	7	5	8	5	9	5	–	–
Steam	6	6	5	7	5	8	4	–	–
Total coal imports	13	13	10	15	10	17	9	–	–
Coal production/exports (mtce) **Production**									
Metallurgical	10	15	17	18	21	29	33	4.7	5.3
Steam	13	33	31	41	66	63	126	7.1	10.4
Total coal production	23	48	48	59	87	92	159	6.2	8.8
Exports									
Metallurgical	10	13	13	15	15	23	23	3.7	3.7
Steam	1	4	4	4	10	4	24	6.2	14.8
Total coal export	11	17	17	19	25	27	47	4.0	6.5

Summary Worksheet

II. Coal's Role in Total Energy System	1977	1985		1990		2000		1977-2000 Avg. annual growth-%/yr.	
		A	B	A	B	A	B	A	B
Total Primary Energy Use (mtce)									
Oil, Domestic	109	97	101	95	109	106	127	--	--
Oil, Imported	23	46	46	46	46	46	46	--	--
Gas, Domestic	56	67	90	72	92	82	93	1.6	2.2
Gas, Imported	(36)	--	--	--	--	--	--	--	--
Nuclear	9	21	36	27	53	45	88	7.2	10.4
Hydro, Solar, Other	75	84	82	111	94	148	117	3.1	2.0
Coal, Domestic	12	31	31	40	62	65	112	7.6	10.2
Coal, Imported	13	13	10	15	10	17	9	--	--
Total energy use	297	359	396	406	466	509	592	2.4	3.0
Coal penetration (%)	9	12	10	14	15	16	20	—	—
Total primary energy (mtce) input to electricity									
Oil and Gas	8	7	7	5	5	5	3	--	--
(1)Hydro, Solar, Other	74	95	83	111	95	145	118	3.0	2.1
Nuclear	9	21	36	27	53	45	88	7.2	10.4
Coal	17	31	28	37	40	50	65	4.8	6.0
Total energy input	108	154	154	180	193	245	274	3.6	4.1
Coal penetration (%)	15	20	18	21	21	20	24	—	—
Total electric capacity (GWe)									
Oil and Gas	10	10	10	9	9	7	7	--	--
Hydro, Solar, Other	43	58	58	66	66	77	75	2.6	2.5
Nuclear	5	10	15	13	25	26	67	7.4	11.9
Coal	12	20	20	22	30	38	61	5.2	7.3
Total capacity	70	98	103	110	130	148	210	3.3	4.9
Coal Penetration (%)	17	20	19	20	23	26	29	1.9	2.3
Peak load	52	74	75	83	96	111	158	3.3	4.9
Peak reserve margin (%)	25	25	25	25	25	25	25	—	—
Total oil imports (mbd)	0.3	0.6	0.6	0.6	0.6	0.6	0.6	--	--
Total oil consumption (mbd)									
Transportation	0.8	0.9	0.9	0.9	1.0	0.9	1.1	--	--
Residential/Commercial	0.3	0.3	0.3	0.3	0.3	0.4	0.4	--	--
Industry—Boilers	0.3	0.3	0.3	0.3	0.4	0.3	0.4	--	--
Industry—Other	0.2	0.3	0.3	0.3	0.3	0.4	0.4	--	--
Electric utilities	0.1	0.1	0.1	--	--	--	--	--	--
Total oil consumption	1.7	1.9	1.9	1.8	2.0	2.0	2.3	--	--
World oil price assumed for national coal analysis (1979 U.S. dollars/barrel)	$20*	20	20	23	26	29	42	2.5% after '85	5.0% after '85
Economic growth assumed for national coal analysis (GNP, billion 1978 dollars)	197	259	259	308	308	434	434	3.5	3.5

(1) Hydro, Solar & Other values calculated by difference. Discrepancies with respect to Total Primary Energy Use are probably due to net electrical exports not otherwise accounted for.

OIL LIMITATION CASE

To calculate the "Oil Limitation" Series for Canada, the following assumptions were made:

- To meet the required reduction in domestic oil consumption, net oil imports were reduced by the calculated amount.
- Because of high relative transportation needs and other applications for oil for industrial and commercial purposes at locations remote from the growing natural-gas pipeline network or otherwise difficult to substitute, it was assumed that the proportion of oil used in the primary energy balance could not fall below the 33-35% range in 1990 and the 28-30% range in 2000. The energy system would call upon the least costly option as this structural limit is reached which, in the Canadian case, is mostly expanded oil production from oil sands/heavy oils resources. The deficit, after reducing demand by the 20% prescribed, was therefore assumed compensated by an accelerated oil sands/heavy oils development, but also with some additional coal liquefaction and oil (or oil substitute) from biomass sources. This extra oil supply is supplied in accordance with the following schedule:

		WOCOL Low Coal Case		WOCOL High Coal Case	
		1990	2000	1990	2000
New supply needed	mtce	—	30	31	35
	bbl/day		(394,000)	(407,000)	(460,000)
Biomass sources	mtce	—	3.8	3.8	3.8
(no coal)	bbl/day		(50,000)	(50,000)	(50,000)
Coal liquefaction	mtce eq.	—	3.8	—	3.8
	bbl/day		(50,000)	—	(50,000)
Coal for liquefaction	mtce	—	6.5	—	6.5
Oil sands/heavy oils	mtce eq.	—	22.4	27.2	27.4
	bbl/day		(290,000)	(357,000)	(362,500)
Extra coal requirement	mtce	—	6.0	7.5	7.5
Total extra coal requirement mtce		—	12.5	7.5	14.0

Note that there is little prospect of meeting the suggested accelerated development schedule in the WOCOL High Coal Case for the oil sands/heavy oils by 1990 when the already ambitious development schedule included in the reference case is considered.

- Economic growth: It is assumed that the oil supply reduction would be accompanied by higher oil prices whose effect would normally be to lower economic growth rates. In the Canadian case, however, it is assumed the accelerated development schedule for the oil sands/heavy oils, coal liquefaction and biomass sources would compensate. Thus, no net economic effect is assumed here.
- The higher oil prices expected would be expected to lead to higher international prices, especially for steam coal. As the prospects for Canadian steam-coal exports depend upon international price rises, some increase in

the exports of steam coal is anticipated here. A reduction in metallurgical- and steam-coal imports has been made, as compared to the reference case for the same reason. The changes from the reference case are shown below:

		WOCOL Low Coal Case		WOCOL High Coal Case	
		1990	2000	1990	2000
		(mtce)			
Exports					
	Steam coal	—	+5	+5	+10
Imports					
	Metallurgical coal	—	−2	−1	−2
	Steam coal	—	−2	−1	−3
	Total	—	−4	−2	−5

Oil Limitation Case

I. Coal Use, Production, and Trade	1977	1985		1990		2000		1977-2000 Avg. annual growth—%/yr.	
		A	B	A	B	A	B	A	B
Coal use in major markets (mtce)									
Metallurgical	7	9	9	11	11	15	15	–	–
Electric	17	31	28	37	40	50	65	4.8	6.0
Industry (includes gasification in industry)	1	4	4	7	10	11	20	11.0	14.6
Synthetic Fuels (includes use in oil sands)	–	–	–	–	19	19	35	–	–
Residential/Commercial	small	–	–	–	–	–	–	–	–
Total coal use	25	44	41	55	80	95	135	6.0	7.6
Distribution of coal use by market sector (%)									
Metallurgical	26	21	21	20	14	16	11	—	—
Electric	67	70	68	67	50	53	48	—	—
Industry	7	9	11	13	13	11	15	—	—
Synthetic Fuels	–	–	–	–	23	20	26	—	—
Residential/Commercial	small	neg.	neg.	neg.	neg.	neg.	neg.	—	—
Total coal use	100%	100%	100%	100%	100%	100%	100%	—	—
Coal consumption/imports (mtce) **Consumption**									
Metallurgical	7	9	9	11	11	15	15	3.4	3.4
Steam	18	35	32	44	69	80	120	7.0	8.6
Total coal consumption	25	44	41	55	80	95	135	6.0	7.6
Imports									
Metallurgical	7	7	5	8	4	7	3	–	–
Steam	6	6	5	7	4	6	1	–	–
Total coal imports	13	13	10	15	8	13	4	–	–
Coal production/exports (mtce) **Production**									
Metallurgical	10	15	17	18	22	31	35	5.0	5.6
Steam	13	33	31	41	80	83	153	8.4	11.8
Total coal production	23	48	48	59	102	114	188	7.2	9.6
Exports									
Metallurgical	10	13	13	15	15	23	23	3.7	3.7
Steam	1	4	4	4	15	9	34	10.1	16.6
Total coal export	11	17	17	19	30	32	57	4.7	7.4

Oil Limitation Case

II. Coal's Role in Total Energy System	1977	1985		1990		2000		1977-2000 Avg. annual growth-%/yr.	
		A	B	A	B	A	B	A	B
Total Primary Energy Use (mtce)									
Oil, Domestic	109	97	101	95	140	137	165	1.0	1.8
Oil, Imported	23	46	46	46	15	15	8	--	--
Gas, Domestic	56	67	90	72	92	82	93	1.6	2.2
Gas, Imported	(36)	--	--	--	--	--	--	--	--
Nuclear	9	21	36	27	53	45	88	7.2	10.4
Hydro, Solar, Other	75	84	82	111	94	148	117	3.1	2.0
Coal, Domestic	12	31	31	40	72	82	131	8.7	10.9
Coal, Imported	13	13	10	15	8	13	4	--	--
Total energy use	297	359	396	406	474	522	606	2.5	3.2
Coal penetration (%)	9	12	10	14	17	18	22	—	—
Total primary energy (mtce) input to electricity									
Oil and Gas	8	7	7	5	5	5	3	--	--
Hydro, Solar, Other	74	95	83	111	95	145	118	3.0	2.1
Nuclear	9	21	36	27	53	45	88	7.2	10.4
Coal	17	31	28	37	40	50	65	4.8	6.0
Total energy input	108	154	154	180	193	245	274	3.6	4.1
Coal penetration (%)	15	20	18	21	21	20	24	—	—
Total electric capacity (GWe)									
Oil and Gas	10	10	10	9	9	7	7	--	--
Hydro, Solar, Other	43	58	58	66	66	77	75	2.6	2.5
Nuclear	5	10	15	13	25	26	67	7.4	11.9
Coal	12	20	20	22	30	38	61	5.2	7.3
Total capacity	70	98	103	110	130	148	210	3.3	4.9
Coal Penetration (%)	17	20	19	20	23	26	29	1.9	2.3
Peak load	52	74	75	83	96	111	158	3.3	4.9
Peak reserve margin (%)	25	25	25	25	25	25	25	—	—
Total oil imports (mbd)	0.3	0.6	0.6	0.6	0.2	0.2	0.1		
Total oil consumption (mbd)									
Transportation	0.8	0.9	0.9	0.9	1.0	0.9	1.1	--	--
Residential/Commercial	0.3	0.3	0.3	0.3	0.3	0.4	0.4	--	--
Industry—Boilers	0.3	0.3	0.3	0.3	0.4	0.3	0.4	--	--
Industry—Other	0.2	0.3	0.3	0.3	0.3	0.4	0.4	--	--
Electric utilities	0.1	0.1	0.1	--	--	--	--	--	--
Total oil consumption	1.7	1.9	1.9	1.8	2.0	2.0	2.3	--	--
World oil price assumed for national coal analysis (1979 U.S. dollars/barrel)	$20*	20	20	23	26+	29+	42+	2.5% after '85	2.5% after '85
Economic growth assumed for national coal analysis (GNP, billion 1978 dollars)	197	259	259	308	308	434	484	3.5	3.5

* Uses current price of $20/barrel (June 1979 U.S. dollars) as baseline world oil price and as floor price throughout the period.

OIL LIMITATION AND NUCLEAR MORATORIUM CASE

ASSUMPTIONS FOR WOCOL LOW COAL CASE

- Nuclear moratorium does not affect economic growth, primary energy demand or proportion of electricity in primary energy balance.
- Moratorium causes a further increase in international coal trade, which leads to the following changes for Canada as compared to the reference case (Series I).

		WOCOL Low Coal Case	
		1990	2000
		(mtce)	
Exports			
	Steam coal	+5	+10
Imports			
	Metallurgical coal	—	—4
	Steam coal	—	—4

- Coal-electricity is expanded to compensate for lost nuclear capacity.
- Nuclear capacity held at 10 GWe after 1985, reflecting slower nuclear scenario in Low Coal Case.

ASSUMPTIONS FOR WOCOL HIGH COAL CASE

- Economic growth reduced 3% over Series II estimates to reflect lower economic growth expected after 1990.
- Proportion electricity reduced in 2000 by 3% of primary energy demand.
- Coal electricity compensates for nuclear capacity lost after correcting for lower fraction of electricity in energy balance after 1990.
- Nuclear capacity held at 15 GWe after 1985 to reflect rapid nuclear scenario in High Coal Case.
- Additional energy assumed consumed in industry to offset lower proportion of electricity consumed in economy as a whole. One half of this extra energy directly consumed by industry is assumed to be supplied from coal and the other half from expanded use of natural gas.
- Higher international coal prices causes marked changes in coal trade.

		WOCOL High Coal Case	
		1990	2000
		(mtce)	
Exports			
	Steam coal	+10	+20
Imports			
	Metallurgical coal	—2	—5
	Steam coal	—2	—4

- The results of this calculation give rather unrealistic results.

Oil Limitation and Nuclear Moratorium Case

I. Coal Use, Production, and Trade	1977	1985		1990		2000		1977-2000 Avg. annual growth—%/yr.	
		A	B	A	B	A	B	A	B
Coal use in major markets (mtce)									
Metallurgical	7	9	9	11	11	15	15	–	–
Electric	17	31	28	43	57	74	91	6.6	7.5
Industry	1	4	4	7	10	11	24	11.0	14.8
Synthetic Fuels	–	–	–	–	19	19	35	–	–
Residential/Commercial	small	–	–	–	–	–	–	–	–
Total coal use	25	44	41	61	97	119	165	7.1	8.6
Distribution of coal use by market sector (%)									
Metallurgical	26	21	21	18	11	13	9	—	—
Electric	67	70	68	70	59	62	55	—	—
Industry	7	7	11	12	10	9	15	—	—
Synthetic Fuels	–	–	–	–	20	16	21	—	—
Residential/Commercial	small	neg.	neg.	neg.	neg.	neg.	neg.	—	—
Total coal use	100%	100%	100%	100%	100%	100%	100%	—	—
Coal consumption/imports (mtce) **Consumption**									
Metallurgical	7	9	9	11	11	15	15	3.4	3.4
Steam	18	35	32	50	86	104	150	7.9	9.6
Total coal consumption	25	44	41	61	97	119	165	7.1	8.6
Imports									
Metallurgical	7	7	5	8	3	5	–	–	–
Steam	6	6	5	7	3	5	–	–	–
Total coal imports	13	13	10	15	6	9	–	–	–
Coal production/exports (mtce) **Production**									
Metallurgical	10	15	17	18	23	33	38	5.4	6.0
Steam	13	33	31	52	103	114	194	10.4	12.5
Total coal production	23	48	48	70	126	147	232	8.4	10.6
Exports									
Metallurgical	10	13	13	15	15	23	23	3.7	3.7
Steam	1	4	4	9	20	14	44	12.2	17.9
Total coal export	11	17	17	24	35	37	67	5.4	8.2

Oil Limitation and Nuclear Moratorium Case

II. Coal's Role in Total Energy System	1977	1985		1990		2000		1977-2000 Avg. annual growth–%/yr.	
		A	B	A	B	A	B	A	B
Total Primary Energy Use (mtce)									
Oil, Domestic	109	97	101	95	140	137	165	1.0	1.8
Oil, Imported	23	46	46	46	15	15	8	--	--
Gas, Domestic	56	67	90	72	92	82	97	1.6	2.4
Gas, Imported	(36)	--	--	--	--	--	--	--	--
Nuclear	9	21	36	21	36	21	36	--	--
Hydro, Solar, Other	75	84	82	111	94	148	117	3.1	2.0
Coal, Domestic	12	31	31	45	91	110	165	10.1	12.1
Coal, Imported	13	13	10	15	6	9	--	--	--
Total energy use	297	359	396	406	474	522	588	2.5	3.0
Coal penetration (%)	9	12	10	14	20	23	28	—	—
Total primary energy (mtce) input to electricity									
Oil and Gas	8	7	7	5	5	5	3	--	--
Hydro, Solar, Other	74	95	83	111	95	145	118	3.0	2.1
Nuclear	9	21	36	21	36	21	36	--	--
Coal	17	31	28	43	57	74	91	6.6	7.5
Total energy input	108	154	154	180	193	245	248	3.6	3.7
Coal penetration (%)	15	20	18	24	30	30	41	—	—
Total electric capacity (GWe)									
Oil and Gas	10	10	10	9	9	7	7	--	--
Hydro, Solar, Other	43	58	58	66	66	77	75	2.6	2.5
Nuclear	5	10	-5	10	15	10	15	--	--
Coal	12	20	20	25	40	54	58	6.8	7.1
Total capacity	70	98	103	110	130	148	155	3.3	3.5
Coal Penetration (%)	17	20	19	23	31	36	37	3.3	3.4
Peak load	52	74	75	83	96	111	116	3.3	3.6
Peak reserve margin (%)	25	25	25	25	25	25	25	—	—
Total oil imports (mbd)	0.3	0.6	0.6	0.6	0.2	0.2	0.1	--	--
Total oil consumption (mbd)									
Transportation	0.8	0.9	0.9	0.9	1.0	0.9	1.1	--	--
Residential/Commercial	0.3	0.3	0.3	0.3	0.3	0.4	0.4	--	--
Industry—Boilers	0.3	0.3	0.3	0.3	0.4	0.3	0.4	--	--
Industry—Other	0.2	0.3	0.3	0.3	0.3	0.4	0.4	--	--
Electric utilities	0.1	0.1	0.1	--	--	--	--	--	--
Total oil consumption	1.7	1.9	1.9	1.8	2.0	2.0	2.3	--	--
World oil price assumed for national coal analysis (1979 U.S. dollars/barrel)	$20*	20	20	23	26+	29+	42+	2.5% after '85	2.5% after '85
Economic growth assumed for national coal analysis (GNP, billion 1978 dollars)	197	259	259	308	308	434	421	3.5	3.4

* Uses current price of $20/barrel (June 1979 U.S. dollars) as baseline world oil price and as floor price throughout the period.

DEFINITIONS: COAL RESOURCES AND RESERVES

RESOURCE TERMINOLOGY

A meaningful appraisal of Canadian coal resources can only be made in the context of a classification scheme that takes into account the wide diversity inherent in the coal deposits. The coal resource classification scheme used in this report has some similarities to the schemes used for petroleum and mineral reources but it does differ, as it must, in order to accommodate the modes of occurrence that are unique to coal. The scheme classifies coal resources according to two basic considerations: (1) the assurance of existence (accuracy of measurement); and (2) the feasibility of exploitation. The definitions of terms used in this scheme, and as presented below, are similar to those used in the United States (Averitt, 1969) but are modified to the highly variable conditions under which coal occurs in Canada.

RESOURCES

The term *coal resources* refers to concentrations of coal of certain characteristics and occurring in the ground within specified limits of seam thickness and depth from surface.

A. Level of assurance of existence

The terms "measured," "indicated," "inferred" and "speculative" denote the precision with which given quantities of resources have been determined or estimated; they are defined as follows:

Measured resources are resources for which tonnages are computed from dimensions revealed in outcrops, trenches, mine workings and boreholes. The spacing of points of observation necessary to justify confidence in the continuity of coal seams differs from region to region according to the character of the seams. In general, the points of observation should be separated by less than the following distances:

Cordillera: 1,000 feet (500 feet in severely contorted areas)
Plains: ½ mile
Maritimes: 1,000 feet

Indicated resources are resources for which tonnages are computed partly from specific measurements and partly from reasonable geological projections. In general the points of observation should be separated by less than the following distances:

Cordillera: 2,000 feet (1,000 feet in severely contorted areas)
Plains: 1 mile
Maritimes: 2,000 feet

Inferred resources are resources for which quantitative estimates are based largely on broad knowledge of the geologic character of the bed or region and for which few measurements of seam thickness are available. The estimates are based primarily on an assumed continuity of coal seams in areas remote from the points of observation used to calculate measured or indicated resources.

Speculative resources are resources for which quantity estimates are based on information from a few scattered occurrences. Resources of this description are mainly in frontier areas where coal mining or exploration have not taken place.

B.   Feasibility of exploitation

Resources of immediate interest consists of coal seams that, because of favorable combinations of thickness, quality, depth, and location, are considered to be of immediate interest for exploration or exploitation activities. The conditions set out below do not apply rigorously in each case, but they give a general indication of thickness and depth of coal seams included in this category. In all areas, coal beds are included that are thinner or deeper than listed below but are nonetheless being mined at this time.

Cordillera: Coal of all ranks in beds at least 5 feet thick that can be surface-mined.

Anthracitic and bituminous coal seams at least 5 feet thick, at depths to 1,000 feet, that are too deep for surface mining but might be mined underground.

Plains: Bituminous and subbituminous coal beds at least 5 feet thick, at depths to 750 feet. Lignite seams at least 5 feet thick that can be surface mined (generally at depths less than 150 feet).

Maritimes: For land areas, coal seams at least 3 feet thick at depths to 1,000 feet. For submarine areas, coal seams at least 5 feet thick within 5 miles from shore and with not more than 4,000 feet of vertical cover.

Resources of future interest are coal seams that, because of less favorable combinations of thickness, quality, depth, and location, are not of immediate interest but may become of interest in the foreseeable future. The following limits are applied (excluding the resources of immediate interest described above):

Cordillera: Seams at least 5 feet thick to a depth of 2,500 feet.

Plains: Seams at least 3 feet thick to a depth of 1,500 feet.

Maritimes: For land areas, coal seams at least 3 feet thick to a depth of 4,500 feet. For submarine areas, coal beds at least 5 feet thick that are either beyond 5 miles from shore or have more than 4,000 feet of vertical cover, or both.

CHAPTER 3

CHINA, People's Republic of

ENERGY CONSUMPTION

China is a developing country self-sufficient in energy. Coal remains predominant in the country's energy supply. In 1977, the total energy consumption amounted to 521 mtce, of which coal accounted for 70.6%, oil 22.2%, natural gas 3.1% and hydro-power 4.1%.

In addition to fossil energy, there has been a great quantity of agricultural wastes used as fuels in the vast rural areas, with an annual consumption of about 300 mtce. In the rural areas, straws and stalks of crops and excrements have been extensively utilized to ferment for generation of bio-gas as a new source of energy. Now, there are more than 7 million bio-gas-generating pits all over the country and the bio-gas generated can be used not only for cooking and house-lighting, but also, as cheap energy for powering small-sized internal-combustion engines and thermal power plants.

Since the founding of the People's Republic of China in 1949, the energy industry as a whole has developed rapidly, and in 1977, raw coal production reached 550 million metric tons, oil 93.64 million metric tons, and electricity 223.4 billion kWh.

In the past, all the thermal power plants in China were coal-fired, oil-fired power plants were first set up in 1970's. At present, oil accounts for one-fourth of the energy supplied for generating electricity. The Government is paying great attention to reduction of the consumption of oil as a fuel, economization of the use of oil and conversion of oil-fired boilers into coal-fired ones step by step. In the future, it will not be permitted to build new oil-fired power plants.

China has a great variety of energy resources, with abundant coal deposits and hydro resources which rank first in the world. The potential oil deposits are also considerably rich. But in consideration of the distribution, extent of exploration and techniques for development of the various energy resources, and the national economic structure as well, equal attention will still be paid to the development of coal, oil, natural gas and hydraulic power, with coal in first place in the future national energy policy. In order to meet energy requirements of economic growth, we will further expand coal production, with an estimated raw coal output of 800 million metric tons in 1985. By the year 2000, our demands for coal will reach approximately 2 billion metric tons.

Meanwhile, we will also vigorously develop hydro resources, and several large hydro-power stations are now being set up, e.g., the Gezhouba Hydropower Station in Sanxia on the Changjiang (the Yangtse) River, with a planned installed capacity of 2,700 MW.

At present, China's crude oil production has reached 100 million tons. In the future, extensive exploration of oil within the country and the continental shelf along the coast will be conducted on the basis of reconstructing the existing oil fields in order to speed up the oil industry.

Moreover, in view of the extravagance in energy utilization, the Government is now taking every possible measure to economize on the use of energy.

As everyone knows, China is now readjusting her national economy for the realization of the four modernizations of industry, agriculture, national defense and science and technology by the end of the century. Therefore, the policies and plans for the various sectors, the coal industry without exception, are being reconsidered and reformulated. So, it is impossible for us, for the time being, to give out any specific figures of projection.

The development of our national economy has been considerably fast in the 30 years since the founding of the People's Republic of China. During 1953-1978, the average annual growth of GNP was 8.2% and the average annual increment of energy consumption was 10.4%. It is to be expected that the development of our national economy will still be relatively fast after being readjusted.

COAL CONSUMPTION

In 1977, the total domestic coal consumption was 515 million metric tons (368 mtce), of which 17.5% were for electric power generation, 9.9% for coke ovens, 50.1% for other industries, 3.8% for railroads, and 18.2% for residential use.

In recent years, coal consumption for electricity generation has increased rapidly, and the increment will be even greater in the future. Apart from being a fuel for all kinds of furnaces and kilns, coal is also being used as a feedstock for producing synthetic ammonia, with an annual coal consumption of 30 million tons.

China is also interested in converting coal into synthetic fuels, especially in coal gasification. We are now planning to employ new techniques to produce urban gas, with the intention to lessen the increasingly serious problem of air pollution.

COAL PRODUCTION

China has a good variety of coal deposits which are widely dispersed over the country. At present, the country's total coal reserves (including the proven and probable reserves) as shown in geologic reports amount to nearly 600 billion tons, of which 61% are dispersed in northern China, with one-third of the national total located in Shanxi Province.

The geological conditions in the coal fields are also diversified. Of the coal seams exploited by existing mines, those with a dip angle of up to 25 degrees contribute 80% of the total output, those with a thickness of over 3.5m provide 45% and those less than 1.3m provide 13% of the total output. Geological destructions are frequently seen in the seams of most coal mines, where gas emissions are also high. All this has brought about considerable difficulties to the mechanization of coal mining.

In 1978, China's coal production was 618 million metric tons (441 mtce), of which 55% were mined by the 570 coal mines under the jurisdiction of the

Ministry of Coal Industry whose products are distributed by the State, and the remaining 45% were produced by some 20,000 locally managed small mines all over the country and consumed locally. These small mines are playing an important role in promoting the economic development of the rural areas and in reducing strains on railroad transportation.

Since the founding of the People's Republic of China, large-scale construction of coal mines has been carried out, and, so far, more than 800 large- and medium-sized coal mines have been completed, forming more than 30 principal mining areas all over the country with a daily output of more than 10 thousand tons each.

In recent years, the increase of coal output has been dependent on the reconstruction and/or expansion of older mines. The capital investment in per ton of increased capacity resulting from the reconstruction of older mines is one-third that of the newly constructed ones.

Mechanization of coal mining has been introduced step by step in the process of technical reformation of coal mines. By the end of 1978, the degree of mechanized coal mining had already contributed 34.5% of the total deep-mined coal and the number of the fully mechanized longwall faces with powered supports had reached 51.

CHINA'S POTENTIAL FOR COAL EXPORT

The increases of China's coal production are mainly to meet domestic needs, with a small amount for export. In 1978, only 3.1 million tons were exported. Since China has abundant coal reserves, however, the potential for coal export is considerably great—seen from a long-term point of view. China has been exporting the steaming coal of Datong, the coking coals of Kailuan and Zaozhuang, and anthracite, all of which are competitive on international markets.

At present, more than half of the exported coal is transported by railroads; those by ocean shipping account for only a small portion. There are now two coal ports in China: one is Qinhuangdao Coal Port in Hebei Province which has an annual ship-loading capacity of 10 million tons and can accommodate vessels of up to 25,000 tons; the other is Lianyungang Coal Port in Jiangsu Province with a ship-loading capacity of 2.2 million tons a year. These two serve mainly the transporting of coal for domestic use.

Therefore, in order to expand coal exports, it is necessary to build larger coal ports, and at the same time to build more coal preparation plants for improving coal quality.

SOME PROBLEMS RELATING TO THE EXPANSION
OF COAL PRODUCTION

It is necessary to expand the scale of coal mine construction to insure the further increase of coal production. It has been planned to expand and/or develop several large coal areas step by step, which requires a vast amount of investment and machinery and equipment. At present, a series of large- and medium-sized collieries are under construction. Today, China can, by her own efforts, design and install large-sized collieries of an annual output of more than 3 million tons; e.g., the Yanzishan Colliery in Datong Area, Shanxi Province, now under construction, will have a capacity of up to 5 million tons a year.

Meanwhile, China will also introduce foreign capital and techniques by every possible means and seek international cooperation in developing her coal resources.

Coal transportation has been a principal factor in limiting the expansion of China's coal production, as is the case in many other countries. Railroad transportation has been pressured due to the uneven distribution of coal resources. At present, there are 20,000 wagons (normally having a payload of 50 tons each) hauling out coal from the mines every day, which comprises one-third of the total volume of rail freight.

In order to solve the problem of coal transportation, China is speeding up the construction of railroad networks and, at the same time, is planning to build "mine-mouth" power plants in many mining areas.

ENVIRONMENTAL PROTECTION

With regard to the coal mines themselves, in recent years much effort has been made in mine waste disposal and prevention of adverse effects to the surface by underground operations.

In many older mining areas, a vast amount of recoverable coal is left under railroads, surface buildings and water bodies, such as rivers, reservoirs and paddy fields. After many years of research, we have succeeded in mining seams under these areas, including the seams under railroad trunks and the beaches of the Huaihe River.

CHAPTER 4

DENMARK

INTRODUCTION

In the years after World War II until the late 1950's coal gradually became the most important primary source of energy. The coal import in 1955 accounted for 56% of Denmark's gross energy consumption.

The drop in oil prices in the following years, however, led to a nearly complete stop of coal as a source of energy, and in 1972/1973 the coal consumption dropped to less than 10% of the total energy consumption.

Since the oil crisis in 1973/1974 the trend has changed again after the relation between oil and coal prices has made the use of coal economically more attractive.

A return to coal has mainly taken place within the electricity sector by converting the existing oil-fired units to coal/oil-firing and by changing the new projected oil-fired units into coal/oil-fired units. These efforts largely fall in line with the EC aim to reduce the countries' dependence on oil by changing to coal.

Within the electricity sector first of all the coal consumption can be increased during the coming years. In 1990, 85-90% of the electricity is expected to be based on coal. In 1977 the coal share only amounted to about 50%.

APPROACH FOR THE NATIONAL WOCOL ANALYSIS

The national WOCOL analysis—High Coal Case/Low Coal Case—is based on forecasts of oil prices, gross national product and electricity consumption. Furthermore, the national energy policy, as far as such has been formulated, is taken into consideration or assumptions about a possible development are made.

The WOCOL High Coal Case is based on:

- higher oil prices
- consequently a lower economic growth rate
- consequently a smaller increase in the total energy consumption
- consequently higher efforts toward energy savings and increased use of alternative sources of energy
- delayed use of nuclear energy, i.e., no nuclear power stations are expected to be in operation until 2000.

As to WOCOL High and Low Coal Cases respectively, the following assumptions have been made.

WORLD OIL PRICE

World oil price $/barrel (in real terms 1979 US $)

	1985	1990	2000
High Coal Case	20	25	40
Low Coal Case	20	20	30

The oil prices are expected constant (real terms) until 1985 to 1990 respectively, when a situation of short supply and consequently very severe price rises might occur. Until 1985/1990, it should be possible to balance supply and demand of oil based on measures to limit consumption in the oil-consuming countries and on a small increase of production within the OPEC countries.

ECONOMIC GROWTH

The oil price first of all influences the general economic growth whereas it is much more difficult to judge which of the oil-consuming sectors will be hit the most, as the various products (gasoil, heavy fuel) might be influenced differently by higher crude oil prices. The reason is the uncertainty within the future cracking capacity of the refineries and also the Danish environmental restrictions (sulphur, etc.).

Economic growth rates (growth of the gross national product in real terms) from 1977 to 2000:

| High Coal Case | 2.4%/year |
| Low Coal Case | 3.4%/year. |

The high oil prices, which are expected in the High Coal Case, not only have a direct subdued effect on the GNP, but a further effect like decrease of the energy coefficient, i.e., the ratio between increase in the energy consumption and in the GNP. It is assumed that the energy coefficient will be reduced from 0.75 to 0.60 and 0.65 in the High and the Low Coal Case respectively.

ENERGY AND ELECTRICITY GROWTH

Average growth rates of total primary energy consumption from 1977 to 2000:

| High Coal Case | 1.6%/year |
| Low Coal Case | 2.4%/year. |

Growth rates are highest at the beginning of the period, i.e., until 1985/1990, and hereafter will show a lesser rate of increase.

The electricity consumption is expected to develop according to the following rate of increase in the period 1977-2000:

| High Coal Case | 4.8%/year |
| Low Coal Case | 5.4%/year. |

The increase of electricity consumption in the High Coal Case is expected to fall from the present increase of 7%/year to 3.7%/year in 2000.

In the Sixties and Seventies a correlation between the electricity consumption in Denmark and the gross domestic product at factor costs has been noted (see Figure 4-1). The elasticity has been calculated at about 2.5. This development will probably not continue as the efforts for energy savings will show results and a more efficient use of energy will be common. On the other hand, an increased electricity consumption can be expected because restrictions on oil-based energy consumption will lead to a change to electricity which in future will be based on a very small percentage of oil.

Figure 4-1. Electricity Consumption and Gross Domestic Product (GDP)

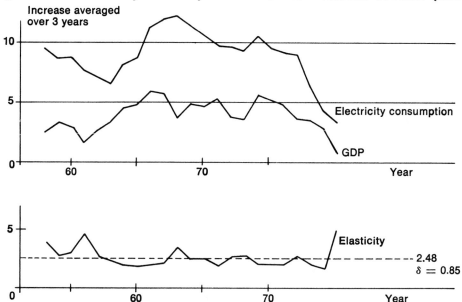

As to electricity consumption, the WOCOL national analysis is based on an elasticity between electricity consumption and GDP of 2.0 and 1.6 for High Coal Case and Low Coal Case respectively.

NUCLEAR PENETRATION

Although nuclear energy forms part of the Government's energy policy it has not yet been introduced in Denmark. Nuclear energy can only be introduced when approved by the Danish Parliament and this cannot take place until early 1981 as the Government/Parliament wants it proved that at least two suitable salt domes for disposal of nuclear waste are available in the Danish underground. Should the decision then be to introduce nuclear energy, the first nuclear power station cannot be in operation until late 1990.

The approach for the Danish WOCOL analysis is:

- High Coal Case: no nuclear energy before 2000
- Low Coal Case: the total electric power increase from 1990-2000 is based on nuclear energy (which is quite doubtful).

As to the Low Coal Case, this increase is 6,500 MW or about 600 MW a year.

Due to the cost structure for the electricity production based on nuclear energy, the nuclear power stations will enter as base load units and thereby slowly displace coal into the intermediate load area. The peak load will continue to be covered either on an oil or an electricity exchange with Sweden and Norway, which countries are based on hydro power.

The projection for construction of nuclear power stations in the Low Coal Case is expected to be:

1990	1,000 MW unit
1992	1,000 MW unit
1994	1,000 MW unit
1996	1,000 MW unit
1998	1,000 MW unit
2000	1,000 MW unit

ENERGY POLICY

Besides the basic assumptions, as stated in paragraph 2 of the national WOCOL analysis, the Danish as well as the EC political objectives are included in the national WOCOL cases.

The Danish energy policy is very widely formulated:

- to reduce the vulnerability of the country regarding energy supply and particularly our dependence on oil supply
- to build up a multilateral energy supply system, among others, aiming at the use of the indigenous sources of energy
- to limit the growth within the energy consumption.

Only a very few of the above aims are concretized in real Bills for the use of specific means; however, the following approach, which complies with the Danish energy policy, is used in the national WOCOL analysis:

- the introduction of natural gas (Bill passed)
- the introduction of nuclear power (Low Coal Case)
- combined production of electricity and district heating
- increase of the share of electricity of the total energy consumption (EC objective)
- improvement of insulation within residential areas
- restrictions within transport sectors
- promote research and development of the use of renewable sources of energy.

Some of the above-specified objectives will be described in the following paragraphs.

NATURAL GAS

In the Danish part of the North Sea there are reserves of oil, as well as natural gas, which have not yet been developed.

The Danish Parliament and Government in June 1979 decided to introduce natural gas from the Danish part of the North Sea.

An arrangement with the Danish Underground Consortium will be made to supply 2.5 billion cubic metres of natural gas per year, beginning in 1984/1985 and running until 2012.

Besides the known reserves of 100-110 billion cubic metres, there is an estimated gas potential of about 60 billion cubic metres; therefore there is a possibility to increase the supplies to 3.5 billion cubic metres, provided there is a market for the gas.

The natural gas project includes a transmission system from the gas fields in the North Sea to the Continent around Esbjerg and across Jutland, Funen and Zealand to Copenhagen (see Figure 4-2). Furthermore, a main-transmission system is planned in the southern part of Jutland which will be connected with the rest of the European gas system. In a second phase the gas system will probably be expanded to the northern part of Jutland.

The gas project (transmission and distribution system) calls for an investment of 1.2 billion US $ (1978 dollars) and it is therefore imperative to secure by legislation the necessary gas offtake.

First of all natural gas will be used within the residential area, individual as well as collective residential heating. Moreover, it will be used to generate process heat within the industry. Primarily natural gas will substitute oil, however, in areas where there are potential possibilities to use heat (produced by combined production with electricity) natural gas will compete with coal. In this case a thorough examination will be carried out in order to secure an optimum use of the sources of primary energy.

Figure 4-2. Danish Natural Gas System

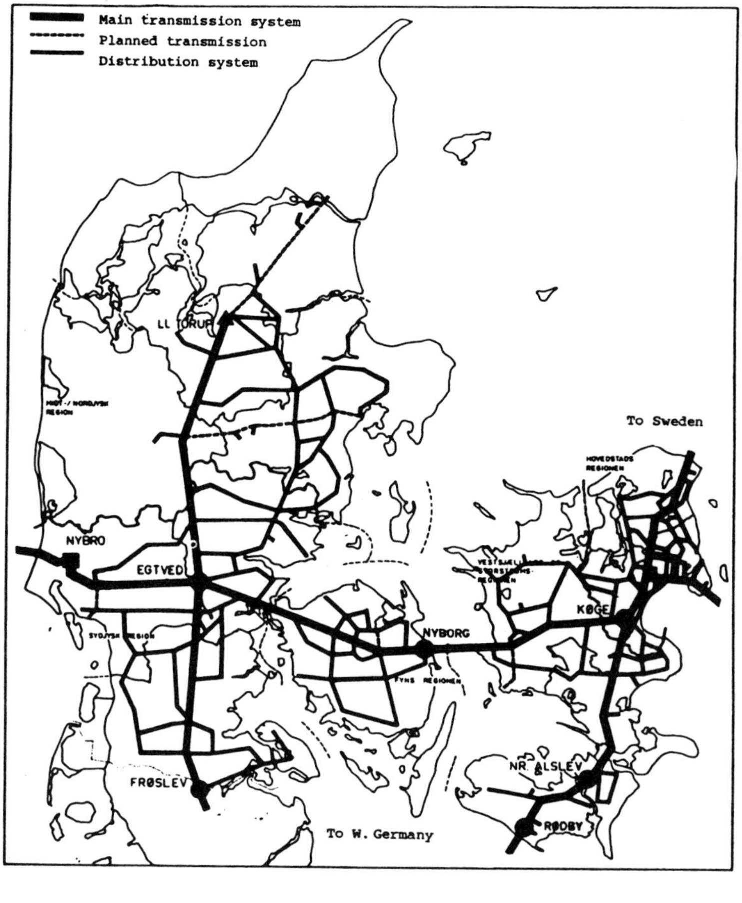

ELECTRICITY SYSTEM

The profile (age and size of the installed capacity) of the present Danish electricity system can be seen in Table 4-1. By end 1979 the total capacity will amount to about 6,500 MW, of which about 3,900 MW will be coal-fired equal to 60%.

The oldest generation within the system consists of coal/oil-fired 30-60 MW units (total, about 800 MW) which were built in the Fifties. These units—about 25 years old—have very high specific consumption and many of them are therefore shut down on a long-term basis.

The following generation consists of a series of coal/oil-fired 70 MW units built at the beginning of the Sixties.

From the mid-Sixties until the beginning of the Seventies a series of coal/oil-fired units from 100-200 MW (a total of 1100 MW) were built. Most of these units, which are now more than 10 years old and most of them having been in operation for about 100,000 hours, are still used as base load units.

At the end of the Sixties and the beginning of the Seventies the installation started of purely oil-fired units, i.e., about 1850 MW oil-fired capacity is equal to 7 units of 265 MW each. Four of these units were, however, prepared for coal-firing, and already at the end of 1979 two of these are converted to coal-firing at a cost of 50 million US $ equal to 100 US $/kW or 25% of the price for a new coal/oil-fired unit. During 1980 the last two units will be converted to coal-firing, which means that a total of about 1,100 MW of the original 1850 MW will be converted to coal/oil-firing.

The future expansion in the 1980's will exclusively consist of coal/oil-fired units. The present expansion projections are:

1980	650 MW	1 unit
1983	610 MW	units of 330 MW + 150 MW + 85 MW + 45 MW
1984	330 MW	1 unit
1985	450 MW	1 unit
1986	600 MW	1-2 units[1]
1987	130 MW	1 unit
1988	1,050 MW	2-3 units[1]

[1] Part of this capacity might be built as small combined electricity-heat (backpressure) units.

Table 4-1. Profile of Existing Power Plants
(End 1979)

Unit size / Age (years)	Below 100 MW Coal/oil	Oil	100-200 MW Coal/oil	Oil	200-300 MW Coal/oil	Oil	Above 300 MW Coal/oil	Oil	Total Coal/oil	Oil
over 30	90								90	
20 - 29	805	138	125						930	138
10 - 19	420	58	849	276	757				2,026	334
5 - 9		143	256		269	1,331[2]			525	1,474
0 - 4		87					300	560	300[1]	647
Total	1,315	426	1,230	276	1,026	1,331	300	560	3,871	2,593

[1] 600 MW unit, 50 pct. owned by SH, Denmark—50 pct. by NWK, Federal Republic of Germany.
[2] Two 270 MW units will be converted to coal during 1980.

Table 4-2. Construction Cost for New Plants
1978 Prices[1]

Unit size MW	Fuel	Built for Electricity and Heat Production	Cost $/KW		Construction Period (Years)	Possibility of Electricity Production Without Heat Production
			New site	Existing site		
600	Coal/oil	x	445	360	6-7	Yes
600	Coal/oil		440	355	6-7	Yes
350	Coal/oil	x	495	410	6-7	Yes
350	Coal/oil		490	405	6-7	Yes
80	Coal/oil	x[2]	550	—	5	No
17	Coal/oil	x[2]	565	—	2-3	No
1,000	Coal/oil	x	765	—	9-10	Yes

[1] 1 US Dollar = 5.3 kroner
[2] Backpressure turbines

COMBINED ELECTRICITY-HEAT GENERATION

EXISTING SYSTEM

Denmark has a very long tradition in producing electricity and heat for district heating in combination. In the existing plants the heat is produced by condensing cycle with reheat system. The heat production in combination with electricity production is the largest per inhabitant compared to all other countries in Europe.

Today the combined production takes place mainly in the big cities such as Copenhagen, Aarhus, Odense, Aalborg, Randers and Esbjerg, where also the largest share of the electricity is produced.

In 1979 the heat production by combined generation amounted to 13% of the electricity production based on energy output (see Figure 4-2). To obtain this heat production the extra energy input only amounted to 5%, or, to put it another way, the main part of the heat is produced by improving the efficiency compared to pure electricity production where the utilization of fuel can thus be improved from 35% to 45% on an annual basis for the total system.

FUTURE COMBINED PRODUCTION SYSTEM

Besides the combined production by condensing cycle with reheat, the future development will be construction of small backpressure units within decentralized plants built in the smaller towns. In this way the superior energy policy is considered to utilize the primary energy most efficiently. The efficiency by backpressure production can be increased up to 85% for a combined unit.

The first of these units will be built in Herning and Randers of 85 MW and 45 MW, respectively. Most of the future backpressure plants will be units ranging in size from 15 MW to 50 MW. Governmental projections regarding the Danish heating system anticipates construction of totally 600 MW combined units until 1995.

The total amount of heat from combined production, i.e., heat produced by condensing cycle with reheat as well as by backpressure production, is expected to cover 35% of the Danish heating demand in 1995. The combined production in 1978 only covered about 12%.

The combined production of heat can be increased further to cover about 45% of the Danish heating demand, but hereby part of the market for natural gas will be eliminated.

Figure 4-3. Energy Balance for the Danish Power System in 1978 (Unit TWh)

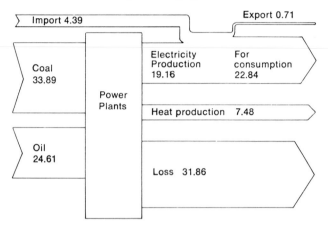

INDUSTRY AND DISTRICT HEATING

District heating from small plants covers about 20% of the total heating market. The primary energy consumption in these plants, which are today entirely covered by oil, equals 2.3 million tce. By intensifying the expansion of the combined production of heat many of these plants in future will be used as peak load plants. Another group of district heating plants will be converted to use natural gas.

Remaining is a small part of district heating plants which can be converted to coal-firing. Many district heating plants, however, are located in residential areas which will cause environmental constraints by introducing coal-firing.

This means that about a 30% maximum of the energy demand (High Coal Case), which is today covered from district heating plants, will be covered by coal in 2000 equal to 0.6 million tce.

A large quantity of coal is already used in the industry today (0.8 million tce in 1978). Coal is mainly used in the cement, sugar and paper industry. The energy consumption in these industrial branches amounts to only 20% of the total industrial energy consumption.

The use of coal will, of course, be spread within industries with a high consumption of energy, but in many cases it will be in very small units which will depress the economy by conversion to coal-firing.

In the WOCOL High Coal Case a doubling of the coal consumption is estimated to take place within the industry until the year 2000, which implies an almost steady share of coal consumption within the industry in the period 1977-2000.

COAL CONSUMPTION

The main share of coal consumed in Denmark will be used for electricity (and combined heat) production, i.e., about 90%.

The projections already described will lead to the following coal consumption within the various areas (see also table on pages 119-120):

Table 4-3. Steam Coal Consumption (Million Metric Tons)

Year Area	1977	1985 Low Coal Case	1985 High Coal Case	1990 Low Coal Case	1990 High Coal Case	2000 Low Coal Case	2000 High Coal Case
Electricity generation	4.4	11.5	11.5	15.0	15.0	10.0	22.0
Industry	0.9	0.9	1.1	0.9	1.3	0.9	1.7
Residential, commercial district heating	0.1	0.1	0.3	0.1	0.5	0.1	0.7
Total	5.4	12.5	12.9	16.0	16.8	11.0	24.4

COAL PORTS AND COAL TRANSPORTATION IN DENMARK

All existing power stations are situated near open water which means that direct supply by ocean-going ships (3,000-120,000 dwt) is possible.

The coal ports are listed below (also see Table 4-4):

Ensted (power station)
max. ship size: 120,000 dwt
max. loa   : 300 m
max. draft   : 15.0 m

Stigsnaes (power station)
max. ship size: 120,000 dwt
max. loa   : 300 m
max. draft   : 15.0 m

Kalundborg (Asnaes power station)
max. ship size: 70,000 dwt (part-loaded)
max. loa   : 300 m, max. beam: 32 m
max. draft   : 11.0 m

Studstrup (power station)
max. ship size: 60,000 dwt (part-loaded)
max. loa   : 235 m, max. beam: 33 m
max. draft   : 10.7 m (can possibly be increased to 11.9 m)

Esbjerg (power station)
max. ship size: 50,000 dwt (part-loaded)
max. loa   : 220 m
max. draft   : 9.5 m

Copenhagen (Amagervaerket, power station)
max. ship size: 30,000 dwt
max. loa   : 400 m
max. draft   : 10.0 m

111

July, 1979

Table 4-4. Danish Port Characteristics

Name	Location	Steam Coal Imports	Max draft (meters)	Max. ship (1000 tons)	Discharge Rate (tons/day)	Annual Capacity (mt./year)	(ships)	Storage Capacity (mt.)	Year
Ensted	Aabenraa	X	15.0	120 full	25,000	4.0	60	1.0	1978
" [1]	"	X	17.0	160 full / 200 part	30,000	5.5	60	2.0	1983
Stigsnaes	Skelskoer	X	15.0	120 full	25,000	4.0	60	0.5	1979
Asnaes	Kalundborg	X	11.0	45 full / 70 part	15,000	2.5	60	0.5	1977
"	"	X	12.5	60 full / 120 part	30,000	5.0	80	1.5	1980
Studstrup	Aarhus	X	10.7	40 full / 60 part	10,000	1.5	60	0.5	1977
"	"	X	10.7	40 full / 60 part	15,000	2.5	80	1.2	1982
Amager	Copenhagen	X	10	30 full / 50 part	10,000	1.5	60	0.5	Existing
Esbjerg		X	9.5	20 full / 60 part	12,000	2.0	60	0.5	1978
Aarhus[1]	[1]	X	12-13	50-60 full	12,000	2.0	60	0.5	1981-82

+ about 10 small ports for vessels up to 5,500 tons

High Coal Case:[1]

Name	Location	Steam Coal Imports	Max draft (meters)	Max. ship (1000 tons)	Discharge Rate (tons/day)	Annual Capacity (mt./year)	(ships)	Storage Capacity (mt.)	Year
Risinge or Glatved		X	22	300 full	50,000	8	40	4.0	1988
One central port for Scandinavia at same location		X	22	300 full	50,000	16	80[2]	5.0	1988

[1] Not decided
[2] Two berths

112

Aalborg (cement factory—Roerdal)
max. ship size: 40,000 dwt (part-loaded)
max. loa   : 200 m, max. beam: 20 m
max. draft   : 8.5 m

SMALL PORTS

In addition to the main coal ports as described above, there are several small coal ports in Aalborg, Aarhus, Kyndby, Copenhagen, Odense, Randers and Skaerbaek, which can only accommodate vessels between 3,000 and 5,000 dwt. These ports will mainly be supplied with coal from short-distance suppliers, i.e., Poland, USSR, FRG and UK.

The ELSAM power pool has built up a barge transportation system consisting of three 7,500 dwt barges. The barge system is mainly intended to supply Odense by transshipment from the large port at Ensted. The barge system has a capacity of 2.5 million tons/year.

TOTAL STOCK CAPACITY

The total stock capacity in the existing Danish coal ports in 1979 is between 5 and 6 million tons, which means that about 10 months' consumption of coal can be covered from stocks. Parallel to the increased consumption in the years to come, the stock capacity will also be increased.

The background for the Danish stock policy is that almost all energy used in Denmark has to be imported and in order to improve security large stocks have to be maintained.

PORT EXPANSIONS DURING THE EIGHTIES

In the Eighties the expansions in the electricity sector will be based exclusively on coal-fired units, mainly by expanding the existing power plants. Together with the increased coal-fired capacity, the port and handling facilities will be improved accordingly.

To a great extent it is general policy to use two-port-discharge in an integrated Danish system, where Ensted and Stigsnaes will be used as first-ports. After having discharged part of the cargo, the vessels will continue to one of the ports which can only accommodate part-loaded large ships.

During 1980 Kalundborg (Asnaesvaerket, power plant) will expand its port to be able to receive part-loaded 120,000 dwt ships with a draft of 12.5 m. The port can later be dredged to a draft of 16 m.

PORT EXPANSIONS IN THE NINETIES

Provided Denmark does not introduce nuclear energy at the beginning of the Nineties, the coal-fired capacity will continue to increase. If this is the case, it will be necessary to introduce new sites in addition to the existing power plant sites. Plans exist to build a new and large central port in connection with a new 2,000 MW power plant. Possible sites for this project have been investigated on the east coast of Jutland and Funen. The port will probably be built for a draught of 22 metres (300,000 dwt ships) and could, in cooperation with Sweden and Finland, be used as a central port for all of Scandinavia. The existing projection foresees a capacity of the port of 7-10 million tons/year. The port can be used as the main port for transshipment to Denmark which means that barges and small vessels can be loaded there and the small Danish ports will be supplied with coal from overseas.

Furthermore, large vessels destined for Sweden and Finland can use the port as first-discharge-port and continue part-loaded.

In principle, a port of the above size could also be built on the Swedish coast of Skagerak. It would, however, be advantageous to place this port close to a large consumer of coal such as Denmark, provided, of course, that the coal consumption increases continue during the 1990's.

INLAND TRANSPORTATION

In addition to the large central power plants, coal consumption will increase by using coal in decentralized combined district heating power plants, district heating centrals and industries. Many of these new coal consumers are characterized by being placed inland a maximum of 100 km from the nearest port because of Denmark's geography.

The consumption in this sector will probably increase to 0.5-1.0 million tons/year. The coal will be distributed from the existing ports either by railway or by truck, depending on the quantities to be transported and the environmental restrictions which will be imposed by the Environmental Protection Agency.

As an example it may be mentioned that a combined district heating power plant in Herning will come into operation in 1983 with a consumption of 0.2 million tons/year.

CONSTRAINTS TO HIGHER COAL CONSUMPTION

The increased use of coal naturally means very high investments in the power stations, ports and the industry. Based on the prevailing coal and oil prices there is a big incentive, seen from an economic point of view, to make these investments.

In this connection it should be mentioned that Denmark imports all coal at the prevailing international market price (in 1977: 30 US $/tce CIF Denmark*) and the country is therefore not hampered by an expensive indigenous coal production.

As to the coal-firing technique, there are no insoluble technical problems which could hamper a development like more coal-firing.

Since the majority of coal utilization will be in the power industry, the development will depend mainly on whether the Government or the Parliament intervenes against the rapidly increasing consumption of electricity.

In the Nineties the crucial point will be whether nuclear energy is introduced or whether the increasing energy consumption within the power industry shall continue to be covered by coal.

Legal uncertainty with regard to environmental protection might occur which could cause certain delays when building the plants. It will not prevent expansion, but at the end it can result in higher costs.

---

* 1 U.S. dollar = 5.30 kroner.

ENVIRONMENTAL, HEALTH AND SAFETY CONSIDERATIONS

In Denmark the industry has very few environmental restrictions in connection with coal-firing.

There are only regulations regarding particulate pollution (TSP), i.e., mg/Nm^3† flue gas. On the other hand, there are no direct regulations against the sulphur emission from coal-firing.

There are, however, general regulations against the quality of air for SO_2 content as well as for particles (see Table 4-5).

Regulation against SO_2 content in the air can be observed by construction of high stacks ("high stack policy").

There are, however, regulations against the sulphur emission from large oil-fired plants. The oil used in purely oil-fired plants must have a sulphur content below 2.5% (below 1% in Copenhagen). Today power stations with high stacks have dispensation from the 2.5% rule.

According to regulations, dual-fired plants can be fired by high-sulphur fuel oil in combination with coal if the sulphur content of the mixture (on an oil equivalent basis) is below 2.5%.

As far as is possible, the power stations observe the above regulations when they are 100% coal-fired, which leads to a maximum sulphur content of 1.6% in the coal.

The environmental regulations—especially in connection with coal-firing—are not expected to be tightened up in the near future because Denmark, compared to many other countries, is a low-pollution area.

---

† N means normal and refers to a standard condition of the flue gas. Nm^3 therefore means normal cubic meter.

Table 4-5. Examples of Environmental Control Standards & Local Limitations Which Impact on Coal Utilization

	National Ambient Standards[1]		Emission Limitations for Existing Sources[2]	Emission Limitations for New Sources
	Monthly Mean			ALL AREAS
	MAJOR METRO-POLITAN AREAS	RURAL		
SO_2	0.750 mg/m^3 [3]	0.350 mg/m^3 [3]	none	none
TSP	0.250 mg/m^3 [3]	0.100 mg/m^3 [4]	none	150 mg/Nm^3 (for plant above 100 MW)
NO_2	none		none	none

[1] Limits on ground level concentrations (measured as mean of month with 15 half-hour measurements per month.
[2] Limits on stack emissions for sources burning solid fuel (monthly mean value).
[3] Limit on total ground level concentration.
[4] Limit on contribution to the ground level concentration from the new source.

Table 4-6. Worksheet for Indicative Cost Estimates for Specific Environmental Measures

Coal Utilization

Environmental Measure	Cost	Comments
1. Control of Waste Heat Emissions by Use of Cooling Towers	Not applicable	Not existing in Denmark
2. Particulate Control a) ESP b) Scrubber c) Baghouse (conventional)	a) 1 $/ton coal b) not applicable c) not applicable	a) in common use b) not existing in Denmark c) only few
3. Control of SO, a) Lime/Limestone FGD b) Dry FGD	a) b) not applicable	high stack policy
4. Ash Disposal a) Conventional b) As a hazardous material	0.35 $/ton coal 0.45 $/ton coal	a) unprotected deposit b) protected deposit
5. Control of NO, a) Combustion techniques (where possible) b) Other hardware	not applicable	no government regulation
6. Wastewater Treatment a) Wet ash transport b) Dry ash transport	not applicable	a) present regulation can be observed without special treatment
7. Other Existing or Possible Future Control, such as a) Fine particulates b) POM c) Coal & ash radiation d) Cost of unit or site capacity limitations due to limits on emissions e) Add'l SO control due to sulfates & acid rain	not applicable	

DANISH ENERGY PRICES

15th July, 1979
(1 US Dollar = 5.30 Kroner)

Fuel oil:
3500 sec. 2.5 pct S	230 $/t[1]
1500 sec. 2.5 pct S	242 $/t[1]
3500 sec. 1.0 pct S	248 $/t[1]
1500 sec. 1.0 pct S	260 $/t[1]
Gasoil	343 $/m³
Gasoline	
93 octane	738 $/m³
99 octane	749 $/m³

LPG	468 $/t[2]
Coal	32.3 $/t[3]
Electricity	7.5 cents/kWh[4]

[1] Industries are excepted from VAT and energy taxes which gives a price reduction of about 45 pct.
[2] During 1979 LPG price will be increased due to new taxes (130 $/t).
[3] Average CIF price during 1st quarter 1979.
[4] Estimate.

DANISH OIL IMPORTS

Oil imports to Denmark as a result of WOCOL analysis (million barrels per day) are:

1977	*1985*	*1985*	*1990*	*1990*	*2000*	*2000*
	Low Coal Case	*High Coal Case*	*Low Coal Case*	*High Coal Case*	*Low Coal Case*	*High Coal Case*
0.30	0.27	0.27	0.27	0.22	0.29	0.18

In WOCOL Low Coal Case oil imports will be nearly constant between 1977 and 2000. In the High Coal Case oil imports will be reduced by 2.2% per year between 1977 and 2000.

A further reduction of oil import can only be achieved by:

- further restrictions on energy consumption in oil-consuming sectors
- increased domestic oil production
- synthetic oil production from coal.

None of these measures, however, seem likely.

Two Ilustrative Coal Trade Chains

Opencast Mine in Western Canada—Electric Power Plant, Denmark

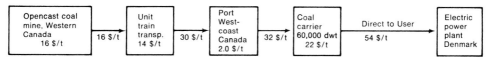

Underground Mine, South Africa—Electric Power Plant, Denmark

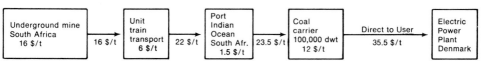

117

Illustrative Implementation Requirements For a Typical Coal Chain

| Opencast coal mine Western Canada | → | Unit train transport | → | Port West-coast Canada | → | Coal carrier | → | Electric power plant Denmark |

	Mines	Trains	Port	Ships	Power Plants	Total System
CAPACITY	3 million t/year	same	same	same	same	3 million t/year
FACILITIES Unit size	3 million t/year	1000 km/trip 100 cars 95 t 100 trips/year	15 million t/year[1]	60,000 dwt 5.5 trips/year	600 MW	
Number of units	1 mine	3.15 trains	0.2 port	9.1 ships	2.5 plants	
LEAD TIMES[2]	3 years	1 year	2 years	1 year	6 years	6 years
COSTS Total capital	60 million $	25 million $	12 million $	220 million $	675 million $	992 million $

[1] Extension of existing port.
[2] Lead times for actual project execution after all permits granted.

118

Summary Worksheet

I. Coal Use, Production, and Trade	1977	1985		1990		2000		1977-2000 Avg. annual growth—%/yr.	
		A	B	A	B	A	B	A	B
Coal use in major markets (mtce)									
Metallurgical	0	0	0	0	0	0	0	0	0
Electric	3.8	9.9	9.9	12.9	12.9	8.6	18.9	3.6	7.2
Industry	0.7	0.7	1.0	0.7	1.1	0.7	1.4	0	3.1
Synthetic Fuels	0	0	0	0	0	0	0	–	–
Residential/Commercial	0.1	0.1	0.2	0.1	0.4	0.1	0.6	0	8.1
Total coal use	4.6	10.7	11.1	13.7	14.4	9.4	20.9	3.2	6.8
Distribution of coal use by market sector (%)									
Metallurgical	0	0	0	0	0	0	0	—	—
Electric	83	93	89	94	90	91	90	—	—
Industry	15	6	9	5	7	8	7	—	—
Synthetic Fuels	0	0	0	0	0	0	0	—	—
Residential/Commercial	2	1	2	1	3	1	3	—	—
Total coal use	100%	100%	100%	100%	100%	100%	100%	—	—
Coal consumption/imports (mtce) Consumption									
Metallurgical	0	0	0	0	0	0	0	0	0
Steam	4.6	10.7	11.1	13.7	14.4	9.4	20.9	3.6	6.8
Total coal consumption	4.6	10.7	11.1	13.7	14.4	9.4	20.9	3.6	6.8
Imports									
Metallurgical	0	0	0	0	0	0	0	0	0
Steam	4.6	10.7	11.1	13.7	14.4	9.4	20.9	3.6	6.8
Total coal imports	4.6	10.7	11.1	13.7	14.4	9.4	20.9	3.6	6.8
Coal production/exports (mtce) Production (Greenland)									
Metallurgical	0	0	0	0	0	0	0	–	–
Steam	0	0	0.6	0	0.6	0	0.6	–	–
Total coal production	0	0	0.6	0	0.6	0	0.6	–	–
Exports (Greenland)									
Metallurgical	0	0	0	0	0	0	0	–	–
Steam	0	0	0.3	0	0.3	0	0.3	–	–
Total coal export	0	0	0.3	0	0.3	0	0.3	–	–

Summary Worksheet

II. Coal's Role in Total Energy System	1977	1985		1990		2000		1977-2000 Avg. annual growth–%/yr.	
		A	B	A	B	A	B	A	B
Total Primary Energy Use (mtce)									
Oil, Domestic	0.7	1.0	1.2	1.3	2.0	1.4	2.0	3.1	4.7
Oil, Imported	22.9	20.8	20.2	20.2	15.8	20.0	13.0	-0.6	-2.4
Gas, Domestic	0	2.4	2.4	4.7	4.7	4.7	4.7	--	--
Gas, Imported	0	0	0	0	0	0	0	--	--
Nuclear	0	0	0	0	0	13.2	0	--	--
Hydro, Solar, Other	0	0	0	0	0	0	0	--	--
Coal, Domestic	0	0	0	0	0	0	0	--	--
Coal, Imported	4.6	10.7	11.1	13.7	14.4	9.4	20.9	3.2	6.8
Total energy use	28.2	34.9	34.9	39.9	36.9	48.7	40.6	2.4	1.6
Coal penetration (%)	16	31	32	34	39	19	51	—	—
Total primary energy (mtce) input to electricity									
Oil and Gas	3.8	1.7	1.7	1.5	1.5	1.7	1.7	-3.4	-3.4
Hydro, Solar, Other	0	0	0	0	0	0	0	--	--
Nuclear	0	0	0	0	0	13.2	0	--	--
Coal	3.8	9.9	9.9	12.9	12.9	8.6	18.9	3.6	7.2
Total energy input	7.6	11.6	11.6	14.4	14.4	23.5	20.6	5.0	4.4
Coal penetration (%)	50	85	85	90	90	37	92	—	—
Total electric capacity (GWe)									
Oil and Gas	3.3	1.9	1.9	1.9	1.9	1.9	1.9	-2.4	-2.4
Hydro, Solar, Other	0	0	0	0	0	0	0	--	--
Nuclear	0	0	0	0	0	6.5	0	--	--
Coal	3.0	6.6	6.6	8.5	8.5	8.5	13.0	4.6	6.6
Total capacity	6.3	8.5	8.5	10.4	10.4	16.9	14.9	4.4	3.8
Coal Penetration (%)	48	78	78	82	82	50	87	—	—
Peak load	4.3	6.8	6.8	8.7	8.7	14.1	12.4	5.3	4.7
Peak reserve margin (%)	45	20	20	20	20	20	20	—	—
Total oil imports (mbd)	0.30	0.27	0.27	0.27	0.21	0.26	0.17	-0.6	-2.4
Total oil consumption (mbd)									
Transportation	0.07								
Residential/Commercial	0.13								
Industry—Boilers	0.06								
Industry—Other									
Electric utilities	0.05	0.02	0.02	0.02	0.02	0.02	0.02	-3.9	-3.9
Total oil consumption	0.31	0.29	0.28	0.28	0.23	0.30	0.20	-0.01	-1.9
World oil price assumed for national coal analysis (1979 U.S. dollars/barrel)	$20*	20	20	20	25	30	40	1.8	3.1
Economic growth assumed for national coal analysis (GNP, billion 1978 dollars)	52.1	69.1	69.1	79.6	75.5	112.4	89.9	3.4	2.4

* Uses current price of $20/barrel (June 1979 U.S. dollars) as baseline world oil price and as floor price throughout the period.

CHAPTER 5

FINLAND

INTRODUCTION

Energy use in Finland has been increasing rapidly during the last few decades and is today at a higher average level, in relative terms, than in the industrialized countries. This growing demand has been satisfied by increasing imports, mostly of oil, which currently accounts for about 50% of the total energy supply.

The degree of self-sufficiency has been constantly declining. This is partly due to the limited nature of the country's indigenous resources; there is a total absence of oil, coal and natural gas. Another cause has been the availability of abundant, inexpensive and convenient imported energy. Today, no more than a quarter of Finland's primary energy comes from indigenous sources.

Intensive energy consumption and heavy dependence on imports underline the importance of an active energy policy in Finland. The Government recently issued its first energy program, which forms the basis for the policy to be pursued in the next few years.

The cornerstones of the program are energy conservation and increased supplies of indigenous fuels. Where the latter is concerned, the Government is especially counting on peat, wood and wastes.

The program gives coal a certain priority over other imported fuels. Efforts will be made to increase its proportional share in the total energy supply, especially over the long term. Means of diversifying sources, and developing transport systems and handling and combustion technology for coal are to be examined.

Although Finland has no coal resources of her own, this fuel has played a significant role in the national energy supply for several decades. Twenty years ago it was mostly used for industrial and transportation purposes; it was also used for heating.

The major coal users at present are power and district-heating utilities. After most of the available hydro-power had been harnessed and before nuclear power stations came onstream, coal was the major primary energy source for the growing electricity generation sector. Today this sector has two major alternatives for its future expansion: nuclear and coal.

Coal is a competitive fuel for district heating, particularly in coastal areas. The Helsinki metropolitan region is mostly heated by coal-fired district-heating stations, while in the inland regions of the country, peat has become the most economical fuel.

At the end of the 1950's, coal accounted for close to 20% of the national energy supply. The percentage is now about 10 and by the year 2000 it will be between 15 and 25%, depending on the choice made between nuclear and coal.

Table 5-1. Breakdown of Primary Energy Consumption in Finland 1960-2000, %

	1960	1977	2000 Low Coal Case	2000 High Coal Case
Steam coal	18	11	15	25
Oil	23	53	37	37
Gas	—	3	3	3
Nuclear	—	3	20	10
Electricity imports	1	1	3	3
Hydro	13	13	8	8
Other	45	16	14	14
Total %	100	100	100	100
Total mtce	15	32	50	50

APPROACH FOR THE NATIONAL WOCOL ANALYSIS

The national study is based mainly on energy scenarios earlier made by government experts. Two reference cases have been studied here: Low Coal Case and High Coal Case.

Data dealing with a case in which oil supplies in the year 2000 are postulated to be 20% below the level originally projected for that year are also provided. However, this case is ignored in the subsequent discussion, as cuts in oil purchases will mainly result in energy conservation and increased use of indigenous fuels, with only minor effects on coal use.

No separate case of restricted nuclear development has been construed, since the High Coal Case already implies that nuclear expansions in this century will be limited to those plants now in operation or under construction.

Both reference cases for coal use—High Coal Case and Low Coal Case—have the same economic background. An annual economic growth rate of 3% is assumed for the period 1977-2000. The world oil price is assumed to double by the year 2000.

The scenario assumptions envisage an average annual growth rate of 2% in total energy consumption, and 3% in the case of electricity.

Capacity requirements in heat and electricity generation will be as follows: the total new electricity generation capacity needed by the year 2000 will be about 4,000 MW. About 1,000 MW of capacity will be built for cogenerating heat and electricity in industry. Another 1,000 MW of capacity will be built for cogenerating district heat and electricity. The remaining 2,000 MW will be provided by condensing power plants using either nuclear fuel or coal.

The fuel mix for industrial cogeneration will be the same in both coal cases. The same applies to district heating, and to all existing utilities as well. The difference between the two cases is the fuel choice for the new 2,000 MW condensing power plant capacity. This base-load capacity corresponds to about 10% of the national energy supply in the year 2000. In coal use, it would result in a difference of 7.7 mtce to 12.4 mtce in that year.

COAL CONSUMPTION

As indicated in the previous section, the basic assumptions concerning potential coal markets are the same for both WOCOL cases. The difference lies in the fuel choice for new condensing power plants.

Coal use in the metallurgical sector is not expected to grow significantly from the present level. This is because primary production of iron is not assumed to grow either. At present, a significant part of iron and steel output is exported and, as domestic consumption grows, exports will be adjusted to domestic use. The recoverable iron ore reserves in Finland do not allow increases from present production levels.

It is assumed that the district heating utilities in the Helsinki and Turku metropolitan areas will continue to use coal. Some other cities on the west coast are also potential coal users. All the other cities that have or will have district heating power plants are assumed to use peat, except for a few oil- or gas-fired plants. According to this model, coal would not be used for separate district-heating purposes.

Coal use for industrial steam is not expected to grow significantly. Most of the energy-intensive process industries that can use solid fuels are situated in areas where indigenous fuels such as peat and wood are more competitive.

The above assumptions of increasing coal use in larger power plants only is somewhat simplified. It is possible that coal will become a reasonable alternative to other fuels in some existing or new heating units serving industries or communities. The future development of oil prices and coal technology may support this trend.

The present coal-fired electricity production capacity implies a maximum consumption of 3.2 mtce per annum. In the High Coal Case the construction of 2,000 MW of new coal-fired capacity would increase annual coal use to 7.9 mtce.

Coal conversion into gaseous or liquid fuels is not expected to take place in Finland during this century. The most plausible energy source for a synthetic fuels industry is peat.

The choice between coal and nuclear is not assumed to influence the volume of oil consumption and imports. Oil is not used for base-load electricity generation in Finland.

Table 5-2. Consumption of Steam Coal and Coke in Finland in 1977-2000, mtce

	1977	2000 Low Coal Case	2000 High Coal Case
Condensing power plants	1.9	3.2	7.9
District heating power plants	0.9	3.5	3.5
Industry (incl. coke)	1.5	2.0	2.0
Total	4.3	8.7	13.4

COAL PRODUCTION

Finland has no coal reserves and thus no indigenous coal production. But she does have large reserves of peat, which is mainly used for industrial steam production and cogenerating district heat and electricity. Peat production at present is at a comparatively low level, but is growing fast and should reach 2 mtce by 1990.

NATIONAL COAL SUPPLY/DEMAND INTEGRATION

The integration of coal demand and supply is methodologically very simple in the case of Finland. Coal demand is estimated for each sector as described earlier; since there is no indigenous coal production, coal demand and required imports are by definition equal.

The allocation of import demand to individual coal exporters is briefly discussed under policy items in the last section of this chapter.

TRANSPORTATION

COAL FLOWS

As stated above, all of the coal used in Finland comes from abroad, mainly from Poland. A large part of it is transported by sea and only minor quantities of Soviet coke come by rail.

Polish coal is carried by vessels with maximum capacities of 20,000-30,000 tons. The distance from Poland to Finnish ports is between 700 and 1,400 kilometres. Small river boats are used mainly for Soviet imports.

Consumption is concentrated on the south coast, where the potential increase is also expected to occur. About 80% of the coal is directly used at the importing site without further transshipment.

ADEQUACY OF EXISTING INTERNAL TRANSPORT SYSTEM

The existing importing ports are rather small, serving one or a few local consumers. The major ports can take vessels with drafts of between 9 and 10 metres. Annual imports to these ports range from 400,000 to 2 million tons.

As long as coal continues to be acquired from the present sources, the existing infrastructure can, with minor expansions, handle increasing coal flows. It is, however, possible that purchases from other sources will be needed in the future. In practice, this would lead to overseas imports, which are inconceivable without a deep and large coal port being available. None of the existing ports are suitable for that purpose at present.

TRANSPORT SYSTEM EXPANSION REQUIREMENTS

A port for large-scale transoceanic imports with appropriate storage and loading facilities would be a central inlet for the whole country. It should be able to receive vessels of 120,000-150,000 dwt.

Some preliminary studies have been made with a view to siting the port. Several alternative sites have been investigated on the south coast, but so far, no final decisions have been made.

An eventual coal port in Denmark or Sweden might be a temporary or permanent alternative to a Finnish port. Such a facility could be used either as a central terminal for several Nordic countries or as a first-discharge-point for vessels continuing to Finland.

The timing of port requirements will depend heavily on policy decisions which affect the development of coal consumption and the choice between different sources. As a rough estimate, however, it can be stated that in the WOCOL High Coal Case larger ports (national or Scandinavian) would be needed in the

1980's and in the Low Coal Case in the 1990's. As long as the direction of policy measures remains undetermined, as it is today, long-term planning should envisage higher than lower cases.

ENVIRONMENTAL, HEALTH AND SAFETY CONSIDERATIONS

At present, emissions from coal burning are not considered a major problem in Finland. The coal used is mostly from Poland and its sulphur content is about 0.8%. Theoretical calculations show that sulphur emissions from coal use are only about one-fifth of those from oil use in Finland. In addition, only about half the total sulphur precipitation comes from indigenous sources. The rest is transfrontier pollution.

There are three coal-fired power stations in central Helsinki. They do not have sulphur scrubbers. The sulphur emissions in the downtown Helsinki area are, however, at a much lower level than they were twenty years ago, when most buildings had their own individual oil-fired heating systems. The change is due to the lower sulphur content of coal and to the higher smokestacks which have been built at the power stations.

It is, however, possible that current practices will have to be changed. It may not always be possible to import low-sulphur coal. Recent studies carried out in several countries also indicate that heavy metals in coal may cause harmful emissions. This is a factor that will have to be taken into account in the future. Further studies concerning the environmental impacts of coal use have been initiated in Finland.

EVALUATION OF REQUIRED POLICY ACTIONS

The Government of Finland can, to a certain extent, control the choice of fuels for increasing the energy supply. The new Electricity Act empowers the Government to consider and finally decide on the construction of all major new power stations (excluding hydro power and some industrial plants). Financial means of influencing the development of the energy supply are available through public subsidy schemes for district-heating utilities and through central bank control of foreign borrowing.

The potential increase in coal use is in the cogeneration of heat and electricity for district heating and in condensing power plants. The full-scale implementation of district-heating schemes seems to be guaranteed in the Government's energy program, and this goal will be supported by a set of financial, legislative and other measures. The adequacy of these efforts cannot be evaluated yet, but they are likely to increase coal use in coastal areas.

As for condensing power plants, coal and nuclear are alternatives. Their pros and cons should be examined within a few years, before a decision on the next major investment falls due. From the Finnish point of view, coal use involves the special drawback that it will entail a heavy burden on the balance of payments, although requiring smaller initial capital inputs.

The environmental impacts of coal also deserve attention. The management of increasing quantities of fuel wastes has not been seriously considered and the effects of heavy metal emissions are not well known.

Some diversification of coal sources is likely to be needed to secure a continuous and economic supply over the long term. This would automatically lead to transoceanic imports. The existing transport infrastructure and ports cannot handle coal flows of this magnitude. At the moment, solutions are being sought on both a national and a Nordic basis.

Increasing coal use will create a need for additional storage capacity. Up to now, the question of eventual emergency stockpiles has been ignored in Finland. This is partly due to the fact that consumers maintain fairly large operational stocks. The question must, however, be taken into account in the context of an eventual expansion of the transport system.

Summary Worksheet—Reference Case

I. Coal Use, Production, and Trade	1977	1985		1990		2000		1977-2000 Avg. annual growth—%/yr.	
		A	B	A	B	A	B	A	B
Coal use in major markets (mtce)									
Metallurgical	0.8	1.0	1.0	1.0	1.0	1.0	1.0	1.0	1.0
Electric	1.9	1.1	1.1	3.2	3.2	3.2	7.9	2.3	6.4
Industry	0.7	0.9	0.9	1.0	1.0	1.0	1.0	1.6	1.6
Synthetic Fuels	–	–	–	–	–	–	–	–	–
Residential/Commercial [1]	0.9	1.4	1.4	2.3	2.3	3.5	3.5	6.1	6.1
Total coal use	4.3	4.4	4.4	7.5	7.5	8.7	13.4	3.1	5.1
Distribution of coal use by market sector (%)									
Metallurgical	19	23	23	13	13	11	7	—	—
Electric	44	25	25	43	43	37	59	—	—
Industry	16	20	20	13	13	12	8	—	—
Synthetic Fuels	–	–	–	–	–	–	–	—	—
Residential/Commercial [1]	21	32	32	31	31	40	26	—	—
Total coal use	100%	100%	100%	100%	100%	100%	100%	—	—
Coal consumption/imports (mtce) **Consumption**									
Metallurgical	0.8	1.0	1.0	1.0	1.0	1.0	1.0	1.0	1.0
Steam	3.5	3.4	3.4	6.5	6.5	7.7	12.4	3.5	5.7
Total coal consumption	4.3	4.4	4.4	7.5	7.5	8.7	13.4	3.1	5.1
Imports									
Metallurgical	0.9	1.0	1.0	1.0	1.0	1.0	1.0	0.5	0.5
Steam	4.1	3.4	3.4	6.5	6.5	7.7	12.4	2.8	4.9
Total coal imports	5.0	4.4	4.4	7.5	7.5	8.7	13.4	2.4	4.4
Coal production/exports (mtce) **Production**									
Metallurgical	–	–	–	–	–	–	–		
Steam	–	–	–	–	–	–	–		
Total coal production	–	–	–	–	–	–	–		
Exports									
Metallurgical	–	–	–	–	–	–	–		
Steam	–	–	–	–	–	–	–		
Total coal export	–	–	–	–	–	–	–		

(1) Includes power generation in district heating plants.

Summary Worksheet—Reference Case

II. Coal's Role in Total Energy System	1977	1985		1990		2000		1977-2000 Avg. annual growth–%/yr.	
		A	B	A	B	A	B	A	B
Total Primary Energy Use (mtce)									
Oil, Domestic	--	--	--	--	--	--	--	--	--
Oil, Imported	17.1	18.5	18.5	17.0	17.0	15.5	15.5	-0.4	-0.4
Gas, Domestic	0.3	0.4	0.4	0.4	0.4	0.4	0.4	1.3	1.3
Gas, Imported	1.1	1.3	1.3	1.4	1.4	1.6	1.6	1.6	1.6
Nuclear	0.9	5.0	5.0	5.0	5.0	9.7	5.0	10.9	7.7
Hydro, Solar, Other	9.2	11.4	11.4	12.7	12.7	15.1	15.1	2.2	2.2
Coal, Domestic	--	--	--	--	--	--	--		
Coal, Imported	3.5	3.4	3.4	6.5	6.5	7.7	12.4	3.5	5.7
Total energy use	32.1	40.0	40.0	43.0	43.0	50.0	50.0	2.0	2.0
Coal penetration (%)	11	9	9	15	15	15	25	—	—
Total primary energy (mtce) input to electricity									
Oil and Gas	1.8	1.5	1.5	1.4	1.4	1.3	1.3	-1.4	-1.4
Hydro, Solar, Other	5.1	6.5	6.5	6.2	6.2	5.7	5.7	0.5	0.5
Nuclear	0.9	5.0	5.0	5.0	5.0	9.7	5.0	10.9	7.7
Coal	2.2	1.5	1.5	3.9	3.9	4.2	8.9	2.5	6.3
Total energy input	10.0	14.5	14.5	16.5	16.5	20.9	20.9	3.3	3.3
Coal penetration (%)	22	10	10	24	24	20	43	—	—
Total electric capacity (GWe)									
Oil and Gas	2.9	2.6	2.6	2.4	2.4	2.2	2.2	-1.2	-1.2
Hydro, Solar, Other	2.9	4.8	4.8	4.9	4.9	5.6	5.6	2.9	2.9
Nuclear	0.4	2.2	2.2	2.2	2.2	4.2	2.2	10,8	7.7
Coal	1.9	2.4	2.4	3.0	3.0	3.5	5.5	2.7	4.7
Total capacity	8.1	12.0	12.0	12.5	12.5	15.5	15.5	2.9	2.9
Coal Penetration (%)	23	20	20	24	24	23	35	—	—
Peak load	5.9	9.8	9.8	10.2	10.2	12.6	12.6	3.4	3.4
Peak reserve margin (%)	37	23	23	23	23	23	23	—	—
Total oil imports (mbd)	0.29	0.26	0.26	0.24	0.24	0.22	0.22	-1.2	-1.2
Total oil consumption (mbd)									
Transportation	0.06	0.07	0.07	0.08	0.08	0.08	0.08		
Residential/Commercial	0.09	0.08	0.08	0.07	0.07	0.06	0.06		
Industry—Boilers Industry—Other	0.07	0.09	0.09	0.08	0.08	0.07	0.07		
Electric utilities	0.02	0.02	0.02	0.01	0.01	0.01	0.01		
Total oil consumption	0.24	0.26	0.26	0.24	0.24	0.22	0.22	-0.4	-0.4
World oil price assumed for national coal analysis (1979 U.S. dollars/barrel)	$20*	25	25	30	30	40	40	3.1	3.1
Economic growth assumed for national coal analysis (GNP, billion 1978 dollars)	30	38	38	44	44	59	59	3.0	3.0

* Uses current price of $20/barrel (June 1979 U.S. dollars) as baseline world oil price and as floor price throughout the period.

Oil Limitation Case

I. Coal Use, Production, and Trade	1977	1985		1990		2000		1977-2000 Avg. annual growth—%/yr.	
		A	B	A	B	A	B	A	B
Coal use in major markets (mtce)									
Metallurgical	0.8	1.0	1.0	1.0	1.0	1.0	1.0	1.0	1.0
Electric	1.9	1.1	1.1	3.2	3.2	3.5	8.2	2.7	6.6
Industry	0.7	0.9	0.9	1.0	1.0	1.3	1.3	2.7	2.7
Synthetic Fuels	–	–	–	–	–	–	–	–	–
Residential/Commercial [1]	0.9	1.4	1.4	2.3	2.3	3.8	3.8	6.5	6.5
Total coal use	4.3	4.4	4.4	7.5	7.5	9.6	14.3	3.6	5.4
Distribution of coal use by market sector (%)									
Metallurgical	19	23	23	13	13	10	7	—	—
Electric	44	25	25	43	43	36	57	—	—
Industry	16	20	20	13	13	14	9	—	—
Synthetic Fuels	–	–	–	–	–	–	–	—	—
Residential/Commercial [1]	21	32	32	31	31	40	27	—	—
Total coal use	100%	100%	100%	100%	100%	100%	100%	—	—
Coal consumption/imports (mtce) **Consumption**									
Metallurgical	0.8	1.0	1.0	1.0	1.0	1.0	1.0	1.0	1.0
Steam	3.5	3.4	3.4	6.5	6.5	8.6	13.3	4.0	6.0
Total coal consumption	4.3	4.4	4.4	7.5	7.5	9.6	14.3	3.6	5.4
Imports									
Metallurgical	0.9	1.0	1.0	1.0	1.0	1.0	1.0	0.5	0.5
Steam	4.1	3.4	3.4	6.5	6.5	8.6	13.3	3.3	5.2
Total coal imports	5.0	4.4	4.4	7.5	7.5	9.6	14.3	2.9	4.7
Coal production/exports (mtce) **Production**									
Metallurgical	–	–	–	–	–	–	–		
Steam	–	–	–	–	–	–	–		
Total coal production	–	–	–	–	–	–	–		
Exports									
Metallurgical	–	–	–	–	–	–	–		
Steam	–	–	–	–	–	–	–		
Total coal export	–	–	–	–	–	–	–		

[1] Includes power generation in district heating plants

Oil Limitation Case

II. Coal's Role in Total Energy System	1977	1985		1990		2000		1977-2000 Avg. annual growth–%/yr.	
		A	B	A	B	A	B	A	B
Total Primary Energy Use (mtce)									
Oil, Domestic	--	--	--	--	--	--	--		
Oil, Imported	17.1	18.5	18.5	17.0	17.0	12.4	12.4	-1.4	-1.4
Gas, Domestic	0.3	0.4	0.4	0.4	0.4	0.4	0.4	1.3	1.3
Gas, Imported	1.1	1.3	1.3	1.4	1.4	1.6	1.6	1.6	1.6
Nuclear	0.9	5.0	5.0	5.0	5.0	9.7	5.0	10.9	7.7
Hydro, Solar, Other	9.2	11.4	11.4	12.7	12.7	16.3	16.3	2.5	2.5
Coal, Domestic	--	--	--	--	--	--	--	--	--
Coal, Imported	3.5	3.4	3.4	6.5	6.5	8.6	13.3	4.0	6.0
Total energy use	32.1	40.0	40.0	43.0	43.0	49.0	49.0	1.9	1.9
Coal penetration (%)	11	9	9	15	15	18	27	—	—
Total primary energy (mtce) input to electricity									
Oil and Gas	1.8	1.5	1.5	1.4	1.4	0.8	0.8	-3.5	-3.5
Hydro, Solar, Other	5.1	6.5	6.5	6.2	6.2	5.9	5.9	0.6	0.6
Nuclear	0.9	5.0	5.0	5.0	5.0	9.7	5.0	10.9	7.7
Coal	2.2	1.5	1.5	3.9	3.9	4.5	9.2	3.2	6.4
Total energy input	10.4	14.5	14.5	16.5	16.5	20.9	20.9	3.3	3.3
Coal penetration (%)	22	10	10	24	24	22	44	—	—
Total electric capacity (GWe)									
Oil and Gas	2.9	2.6	2.6	2.4	2.4	1.6	1.6	-2.6	-2.6
Hydro, Solar, Other	2.9	4.8	4.8	4.9	4.9	5.9	5.9	2.9	2.9
Nuclear	0.4	2.2	2.2	2.2	2.2	4.2	2.2	10.9	7.7
Coal	1.9	2.4	2.4	3.0	3.0	3.8	5.8	3.1	5.0
Total capacity	8.1	12.0	12.0	12.5	12.5	15.5	15.5	2.9	2.9
Coal Penetration (%)	23	20	20	24	24	25‧	37	—	—
Peak load	5.9	9.8	9.8	10.2	10.2	12.6	12.6	3.4	3.4
Peak reserve margin (%)	37	23	23	23	23	23	23	—	—
Total oil imports (mbd)	0.29	0.26	0.26	0.24	0.24	0.18	0.18	-2.1	-2.1
Total oil consumption (mbd)									
Transportation	0.06	0.07	0.07	0.08	0.08	0.07	0.07		
Residential/Commercial	0.09	0.08	0.08	0.07	0.07	0.05	0.05		
Industry—Boilers Industry—Other	0.07	0.09	0.09	0.08	0.08	0.05	0.05		
Electric utilities	0.02	0.02	0.02	0.01	0.01	0.01	0.01		
Total oil consumption	0.24	0.26	0.26	0.24	0.24	0.18	0.18	-1.4	-1.4
World oil price assumed for national coal analysis (1979 U.S. dollars/barrel)	$20*	25	25	30	30	40	40	3.1	3.1
Economic growth assumed for national coal analysis (GNP, billion 1978 dollars)	30	38	38	44	44	59	59	3.0	3.0

* Uses current price of $20/barrel (June 1979 U.S. dollars) as baseline world oil price and as floor price throughout the period.

CHAPTER 6

FRANCE

INTRODUCTION

Between 1950 and 1973, France's energy needs tripled, reaching at that point 262 million tons of coal equivalent. This supposes an annual growth rate of almost 5% over those twenty-three years, with a peak between 1960 and 1973 when the average rate was actually 5.7% per annum. (See Table 6-1.)

In this context, France was subject, along with the rest of the world, to an evolution which gradually substituted oil for coal in a large number of applications.

In 1950, with its 70 million tce, coal still accounted for 70% of our primary energy consumption. Today, or at least in 1978, its place has been lowered to 18% of our energy needs (48.5 out of 260 million tce). (See Table 6-2.)

This evolution has resulted in an energy dependency rate of more than 75%, which is even more pronounced than that of Europe as a whole and is primarily due to petroleum and gas imports. This shows to what extent France is one of the European countries which faces the most acute supply problems, and it explains some of her energy policy orientations, especially in the area of nuclear energy.

Throughout this period—and this is an important characteristic of the French market owing to the evolution of needs and the nature of her resources—France was forced to fill out the range of her coal production, both quantitatively and qualitatively, by importing between 17 and 21 million tons per year, reaching, in 1978, a total of 25 million tons: more than half of her coal consumption.

The short-term perspectives of the coal market are not so encouraging, although after a period of rather pronounced regression beginning in 1965 (69 million tce in 1965, 46 in 1972), consumption seems to have stabilized since 1972, with a slight tendency toward increase (48 million tce in 1978) in a general context of nearly stable energy consumption on the order of 265 million tce.

In the years from 1950 up to 1965, when France was consuming some 70 million tons of coal, up to 25 million tons were being used in industry and domestic households in approximately equal shares, with the remainder split between the iron and steel operations and electricity. This does not include the national railroad (SNCF) and gas (GdF) systems, both outlets having practically disappeared from the market in the early 1960's.

Today, consumption amounts to 48 million tce, breaking down to 15 for the iron and steel industry, 25 for electricity, with the rest divided between domestic households (5.3) and the rest of industry (2.7). Shortly before the crisis, another tightening of the market was deemed inevitable in all sectors except the iron and steel industry.

131

Table 6-1. French Energy Consumption, 1950-1978 (mtce)

	1950	1955	1960	1965	1970	1971	1972	1973	1974	1975	1976	1977	1978
Coal	65.1	70.6	70.2	68.5	57.2	52.3	46.7	45.7	47.4	41.2	48.4	47.1	48.3
Oil	15.5	28.1	40.3	74.6	131.0	141.9	159.6	174.5	168.6	152.6	163.4	157.8	160.2
Gas	0.4	0.5	4.5	7.7	13.9	16.4	19.3	22.5	24.0	26.2	28.2	30.2	31.4
Hydraulics	6.6	8.5	13.4	15.7	18.8	16.0	14.6	15.1	19.0	21.0	16.9	27.2	24.3
Nuclear	—	—	—	0.3	1.5	2.6	4.2	4.3	4.4	5.5	4.8	5.3	9.3
Primary consumption	87.5	107.7	128.4	166.8	222.4	229.2	244.4	262.1	263.4	246.5	261.7	267.6	273.5

Source: "Synthèse des bilans énergétiques"—French National Committee for the World Energy Conférence.

Table 6-2. French Coal Consumption, 1950-1978 (mt)

	1950	1955	1960	1965	1970	1971	1972	1973	1974	1975	1976	1977	1978
Production	52.5	57.4	58.3	54.6	40.6	36.7	33.5	29.1	26.8	26.8	26.5	26.1	23.9
(incl. secondary recovered products)	—	—	(0.1)	(0.5)	(0.5)	(0.9)	(0.8)	(0.7)	(1.1)	(1.2)	(1.4)	(1.7)	(1.5)
Imports													
Coal	9.8	10.8	10.1	12.0	13.7	13.6	11.7	12.5	16.4	17.4	18.8	21.4	23.5
Briquettes	0.3	0.9	0.8	0.8	0.5	0.4	0.4	0.3	0.3	0.2	0.2	0.2	0.4
Coke	3.6	5.0	5.1	4.4	3.4	2.8	3.1	3.6	4.6	2.8	2.7	2.1	1.7
Total	13.8	16.7	16.0	17.2	17.6	16.8	15.2	16.5	21.3	20.4	21.8	23.8	25.6
Exports													
Coal and briquet.	2.2	6.1	1.5	0.9	1.2	0.9	1.0	1.0	0.7	0.6	0.6	0.6	
Coke	0.2	0.3	0.1	0.2	0.9	0.6	0.6	1.0	1.1	0.7	1.0	0.9	
Total	2.4	6.4	1.6	1.1	2.1	1.5	1.6	2.0	1.8	1.3	1.6	1.4	1.3
Apparent consumption	62.9	69.6	69.4	69.2	58.2	53.0	46.4	45.7	46.7	43.2	48.0	48.0	48.7

Source: "Synthèse des bilans énergétiques français"—French National Committee for the World Energy Conference.

PERSPECTIVES 2000

At present, the question is raised in completely different terms.

In all likelihood, France will consume some 500 million tce on the average, which implies a considerable drop in energy growth with respect to the past—only 2.5% to 3% per year. The problem lies in determining whether and to what extent coal, associated with other sources, will be able to contribute to a better energy balance.

If France does not decide to set up a coal strategy on a fairly high level, hydrocarbons will continue to play an important, if not a determinant, role in her energy balance—on the order of fifty percent or more, depending on the relatively uncertain development of other sources.

Indeed, nuclear energy can only hope to cover about 30% of the energy demand, considering the programs already under way.

Hydraulic energy and new energy forms: 7% to 10%.

Local coal production: 2%.

The rest, nearly two-thirds of our supplies, is still uncertain, raising a very serious question in light of the present international energy situation.

Conversely, for a safe energy balance in the year 2000, the objectives of an overall coal strategy could be defined.

Depending on the scenarios imagined, in other words according to the levels of energy consumption, coal could account for up to 125 million tce and even more if the development of gasification is ultimately accelerated.

This is the only strategy which, in the hypothesis of high consumption, would enable us to level off hydrocarbon imports at their present level. In this way we would be headed toward a diversified, and therefore more balanced, model in which, excluding renewable energy forms, the share of each of the three other sources (hydrocarbons, nuclear energy, and coal) would be roughly equivalent.

One of the advantages of this energy setup, which attempts to take new world supply conditions into account, would be to give back to France a part of the independence which she has lost: her national resources and the resources which are controlled by French interests abroad could amount to 60% to 70% of her requirements.

This would, of course, only be a relative autonomy, but it would be quite preferable to the present situation and the risks it involves.

APPROACH FOR THE NATIONAL WOCOL ANALYSIS

THE OVERALL FRAMEWORK

As far as method goes, it seemed indispensable to relate our considerations on coal strategy and its underlying hypotheses to an overall energy design which, in turn, is placed within an economic growth model.

Considering the new world context, we have attempted to take into account the modifications which may come about with respect to the past elasticity rates between the GDP and energy consumption. Moreover, it is not certain that these new elasticity rates will be respected, for by the end of the century the energy systems we predict are relatively heavy systems which, productive as they may be, will require considerable energy consumption, even if this disadvantage can be attenuated as time goes by and technology is refined.

This general context refers back as well, for the most part, to the very hypotheses of the French Plan, with slight variations.

CASE VARIABLES

The economic growth rates selected amount to 3% yearly at the lowest estimate and at 4% for the highest, in agreement with French and European predictions.

These rates cannot be independent of the evolution of petroleum prices, as recent experience has shown. The higher the price of petroleum, the more difficult it will be to maintain a high rate of economic growth in the industrialized countries. This underlines the indetermination which weighs on these estimates, and the only thing which can alleviate this indetermination is for alternative energy models to be set up as quickly as possible to avoid the influence of an uncontrollable leading price. But it is clear that time constraints will not allow a fast and radical modification of existing industrial structures. And the evolution of petroleum prices at a rhythm of 3.2% per year, and 4.5% according to some hypotheses, is only indicative.

In connection with economic growth hypotheses and considering the computable elasticity rates, which at 0.7 to 0.8 are actually favorable, energy growth rates have been set at 2.3% and 3.1% yearly, depending on the case.

As regards electricity, we have followed the estimates of the Plan, which, considering both past evolution and a desire to have electricity penetrate further into the energy system, have set the growth differential between energy and electricity at about 2%, so that the annual rates for the period in question are 4.1% and 5.1%.

Regarding nuclear energy, its penetration in France is quite strong, given the dimensions of the program. The share of such energy in the energy balance will go from 3% in 1978 to some 30% in the year 2000, which corresponds to an annual growth rate between 13% and 14% in both installed capacities and in TWh production.

SELECTION OF VARIABLES FOR WOCOL HIGH COAL CASE AND LOW COAL CASE

Two cases, one High and one Low, have been selected. In the High Coal Case, greater economic growth, consumption of energy and coal consumption are assumed than in the Low Coal Case. However, the consumption of electricity of nuclear origin, although it continues to follow a rapid and expanding evolution, remains at the same level in both cases. It corresponds to the minimum amount mentioned in official predictions for the end of the century.

As far as hydrocarbons are concerned, consumption levels are also nearly identical in both cases; but the consumption of gas is more sustained in the High Coal Case than in the Low Coal Case, whereas petroleum consumption levels off at nearly 140 million tce in the High Coal Case and progresses slowly in the Low Coal Case in order to account for projections which have been made concerning price.

ANALYTICAL METHODS FOR THE NATIONAL ANALYSIS

As regards coal requirements, we have taken as the Low Coal Case the estimates of the VIIIth French Plan now being worked out. These might still be raised in view of developments, since the preliminary documents mention that the "least possible regret criterion" should lead an "intelligent and cautious" decision-maker to examine the advantages of a coal strategy, and that the "role played by coal within the energy balance of the year 2000 could legitimately be raised" within the framework of a voluntarist policy.

The High Coal Case is based essentially on the top goals of various estimates resulting from international or national surveys (see Table 6-3). These have been brought up to date, completed, and made more detailed so that they could be adapted to the structure of the WOCOL worksheet as far as sector distribution is concerned. This High Coal Case is obviously in no way a forecast, and even less a "program." It is based on potentialities defined by different sources, and, without aiming to influence the decisions which must be taken on the government level, its objective is to test the possibilities, implications and restrictions of a coal strategy carried out on this scale with a primary view to contain or even curb the role played by hydrocarbons in the energy scheme.

We refer you to the section on coal consumption concerning the method adopted in the sector analysis.

As far as production is concerned, we have simply used the plan worked out by Charbonnages de France, the only French producer, bearing in mind government guidelines.

This plan takes into account both deposit restrictions and cost restrictions, and even technical restrictions as well.

The calculations for import requirements have in both cases been based on the difference between demand and national production, since export possibilities are negligible or even nonexistent.

Import requirements were what led us to examine the implications as regards:

- maritime transportation, which means the creation of an ore-ship fleet,
- development of ports, and
- inland transportation, both on land and by river.

The environmental problem has been treated with reference to standards laid down by the Public Authorities. This involves estimating the cost of these standards and determining the actual situation in terms of these different demands.

The final question, which consists of determining the steps which are essential to bringing about a coal policy, may be summed up in methodological terms as a strategic approach.

COAL CONSUMPTION

POTENTIAL COAL MARKETS

One must refer to both the Low Coal and High Coal Cases in order to measure the scope of the development potential of the coal market in France.

In the first case, potential development is practically nil, since requirements remain constant at the present level. It is only the second case which points out how much is at stake as far as the coal strategy is concerned, and its full justification is shown in the sector analysis.

The most stable base is coking, which, despite cyclical fits and starts, used on the average in the final years before the crisis some 18 to 19 million tons of coal. Since then, coking coal requirements have somewhat diminished, as they were on the order of 15 million tons in 1978. But the main thing is to consider

Table 6-3. Coal Use in Final Demand Sectors

| | 1977 | | | 1985 High | | | | | | | |
| | Energy Equiv-alent Coal Use mtce/yr | % Coal Penetra-tion of Sector % | Physical Tons of Coal Used mtc/yr | Energy Equivalent Coal Use mtce/yr | | | | % Coal Penetration of Sector % | | | |
				PLAN (1)	IEA (2)	WAES (3-7)	CEREN (4)	PLAN (1)	IEA (2)	WAES (3-7)	CEREN (4)
Electricity generation	72	31	22	111	113	122	—	13	14	14	—
Industry (5)	76	22	17	89	—	160	113	27	—	18	22
Steel	19	74	14	22	—	—	23	82	—	—	83
Conversion to synthetics	—	—	—	—	—	—	—	—	—	—	—
Residential, commercial, etc. (including district heating)	59	10	6	63	—	192	115	3	—	3	5
Other (6)	51	—	—	67	—	73	—	—	—	—	—
TOTAL COAL USE	—	—	45	—	—	—	—	—	—	—	—
TOTAL ENERGY USE	258	17	—	330	—	507	—	12	—	10	—

| | 1990 High | | | | | | | |
| | Energy Equivalent Coal Use mtce/yr | | | | % Coal Penetration of Sector % | | | |
	PLAN (1)	IEA (2)	WAES (3-7)	CEREN (4)	PLAN (1)	IEA (2)	WAES (3-7)	CEREN (4)
Electricity generation	139	140	—	—	7	12	—	—
Industry (5)	102	—	—	129	26	—	—	23
Steel	22	—	—	24	82	—	—	83
Conversion to synthetics	—	—	—	—	—	—	—	—
Residential, commercial, etc. (including district heating)	64	—	—	147	3	—	—	3
Other (6)	81	—	—	—	—	—	—	—
TOTAL COAL USE	—	—	—	—	—	—	—	—
TOTAL ENERGY USE	386	—	—	—	10	—	—	—

| | 2000 High | | | | | | | |
| | Energy Equivalent Coal Use mtce/yr | | | | % Coal Penetration of Sector % | | | |
	PLAN (1)	IEA (2)	WAES (3-7)	CEREN (4)	PLAN (1)	IEA (2)	WAES (3-7)	CEREN (4)
Electricity generation	201	225	189	—	5	17	23	—
Industry (5)	127	—	248	170	28	—	24	38
Steel	24	—	—	25	79	—	—	96
Conversion to synthetics	4	—	—	—	75	—	—	—
Residential, commercial, etc. (including district heating)	77	—	199	148	5	—	—	3
Other (6)	103	—	110	—	—	—	—	—
TOTAL COAL USE	—	—	—	—	—	—	—	—
TOTAL ENERGY USE	512	—	746	—	10	—	14	—

(1) Commission de l'Energie du Plan (Plan's Energy Commission)
(2) "Steam coal—projects to 2000"—Organization for Economic Cooperation and Development—International Energy Agency (1978)
(3) Report of the Workshop on Alternative Energy Strategies (1977)
(4) Centre d'Etudes et de Recherches Economiques sur l'Energie (Economic Studies and Research Center for Energy)

FRANCE

Table 6-3. Coal Use in Final Demand Sectors (Cont.)

1985 Low

Physical Tons of Coal Used mtc/yr				Energy Equivalent Coal Use mtce/yr				% Coal Penetration of Sector %				Physical Tons of Coal Used mtc/yr			
PLAN (1)	IEA (2)	WAES (3-7)	CEREN (4)	PLAN (1)	IEA (2)	WAES (3-7)	CEREN (4)	PLAN (1)	IEA (2)	WAES (3-7)	CEREN (4)	PLAN (1)	IEA (2)	WAES (3-7)	CEREN (4)
14	16	17	—	102	113	94	—	12	14	6	—	12	16	6	—
24	—	29	25	83	—	103	103	25	—	14	21	21	—	14	22
18	15	—	19	19	—	—	22	84	—	—	82	16	15	—	10
—	—	—	—	—	—	—	—	—	—	—	—	—	—	—	—
2	—	4	6	60	—	116	115	3	—	3	4	2	—	4	4
—	14	—	—	62	—	49	—	—	—	—	—	—	14	—	—
40	45	50	—	—	—	—	—	—	—	—	—	35	45	24	—
—	—	—	—	307	—	—	—	11	—	7	—	—	—	—	—

1990 Low

Physical Tons of Coal Used mtc/yr				Energy Equivalent Coal Use mtce/yr				% Coal Penetration of Sector %				Physical Tons of Coal Used mtc/yr			
PLAN (1)	IEA (2)	WAES (3-7)	CEREN (4)	PLAN (1)	IEA (2)	WAES (3-7)	CEREN (4)	PLAN (1)	IEA (2)	WAES (3-7)	CEREN (4)	PLAN (1)	IEA (2)	WAES (3-7)	CEREN (4)
10	17	—	—	124	140	—	—	8	12	—	—	10	17	—	—
26	—	—	30	90	—	—	113	26	—	—	22	23	—	—	25
18	15	—	20	20	—	—	22	80	—	—	82	16	15	—	18
—	—	—	—	—	—	—	—	—	—	—	—	—	—	—	—
2	—	—	5	60	—	—	121	3	—	—	4	2	—	—	5
—	19	—	—	69	—	—	—	—	—	—	—	—	19	—	—
38	—	—	—	—	—	—	—	—	—	—	—	35	—	—	—
—	—	—	—	343	—	—	—	10	—	—	—	—	—	—	—

2000 Low

Physical Tons of Coal Used mtc/yr				Energy Equivalent Coal Use mtce/yr				% Coal Penetration of Sector %				Physical Tons of Coal Used mtc/yr			
PLAN (1)	IEA (2)	WAES (3-7)	CEREN (4)	PLAN (1)	IEA (2)	WAES (3-7)	CEREN (4)	PLAN (1)	IEA (2)	WAES (3-7)	CEREN (4)	PLAN (1)	IEA (2)	WAES (3-7)	CEREN (4)
9	43	43	—	166	255	160	—	6	9	7	—	10	24	11	—
36	—	60	64	108	—	231	134	29	—	4	29	31	—	10	39
19	15	—	24	21	—	—	20	81	—	—	95	17	15	—	19
3	—	—	—	4	—	—	—	75	—	—	—	3	—	—	—
4	—	—	5	66	—	169	120	6	—	—	3	4	—	—	3
—	25	—	—	86	—	72	—	—	—	—	—	—	25	—	—
52	82	103	—	—	—	—	—	—	—	—	—	48	64	21	—
—	—	—	—	430	—	632	—	11	—	3	—	—	—	—	—

(5) Industry, energy sector, self consumption and conversion losses ➔ "Plan" and "WAES"
(6) Agriculture and transport ➔ "Plan" and "WAES"
Other than Iron and Steel Sector and Electricity Generation ➔ "IEA"
(7) As for WAES estimates, only the maximum objectives by sector have been referred to in this table.

137

that France imports two-thirds of its supplies, in the form either of coke or of coking coal—in other words almost 10 million tons, of which half come from the ECSC† and half from outside countries.

Whatever our coking coal needs may be in the future—between 15 and 20 million tons in 1985 and even as much as 25 million tons in the year 2000 according to the most optimistic estimates—all of this growth will have to be met by imports, as we can hardly rely on development of national production: the latter, in fact, tends rather to decrease. France, therefore, runs the risk of being subjected to importing at least three-fourths of her supplies, with the amount coming from the ECSC being, of course, considerable. Depending on the case, High or Low, coking will represent 30% (Low Coal Case) or 15% (High Coal Case) of the coal market in the year 2000.

As regards carbonization, France has three main processes at its disposal, and they complement each other:

- preheating,
- formed coke from the Houillères du Bassin du Nord, and
- the rotary furnace of the Houillères de Lorraine (Lorraine Colliery).

In fact, these processes were developed to increase the percentage of low-coking coal. The experience acquired in Lorraine since the Second World War is most interesting in this respect: intended to solve a local problem, the use in coking of cannel coal which accounts for most of the Lorraine extraction, it turned out to be the solution of a worldwide problem of very similar nature.

To illustrate the possibilities of these processes, it may be said that under the conditions encountered in Lorraine, where demands on the quality of coke are rather severe, the classical technique makes it possible to use 30% of cannel coal. Under comparable conditions, pounding makes it possible to reach 50% and preheating to go beyond 60%. The advantage in mastering these techniques is thus clear, both for ourselves and for exporting.

The Houillères de Lorraine have also studied, over the past years, the possibility of making coke for chemical uses in an internal heating rotary furnace: this process is considerably lighter than the traditional coke furnace.

To make formed coke, conglomerates similar to household "ovoids" or briquettes are prepared for carbonization after agglomerating into the pitch a mixture composed of 85% dry coal and 15% coking bituminous. The field of possibilities has been widened now by substituting noncaking coal for the dry coal, as such coal is also nonfusible.

The second large outlet, which is to become the first if only we see to it that a coal strategy corresponding to the High Coal Case is set up, is composed of electric power plants.

In 1978, classical thermal power stations (see Table 6-4) consumed in France some 45 mtce in fossil fuels, half of which, or 21 mtce, was coal, with national production and imports providing roughly equivalent proportions. At the same time, uranium consumption accounted for not more than 7 or 8 mtce.

By 1985, coal will incontestably be of prime necessity for complementing the contribution of nuclear energy and to insure electricity supplies under the

---

† European Community for Steel and Coal.

138

Table 6-4. Age Profile of Fossil Electric Power Plants (as of December 31, 1978)

	Existing (Capacity MWe) Dec. 31, 1978	Capacity Under Construction (MWe) Dec. 31, 1978	Existing Capacity Installation Period (MWe)				
			1970-78	1960-69	1950-59	1940-49	Before 1940
Plants fired with one fuel							
coal	3,268	1,200	248.0	1,045.5	1,933.8	38.5	2.1
oil	11,729	—	8,495.4	2,182.3	829.8	160.4	61.4
gas	773	—	268.0	298.1	146.7	2.6	57.8
other	97	—	8.5	89.0	—	—	—
total	15,867	1,200	9,019.9	3,614.9	2,910.3	201.5	121.3
Plants fired with two fuels							
coal-oil and coal-gas	8,239	—	1,599.2	4,489.7	2,070.5	13.0	66.5
oil-gas	2,501	—	629.3	1,102.1	739.1	3.8	26.3
total	10,740	—	2,228.5	5,591.8	2,809.6	16.8	92.8
Plants fired with three fuels							
coal-oil-gas	1,585	—	500	468.0	507.0	110.0	—
Total	28,192	1,200	11,748.4	9,674.7	6,226.9	328.3	214.1

best possible conditions. But maintaining, or even slightly increasing, the level of coal consumption would make it possible both to:

- accelerate the penetration of electricity which would amount to 350 TWh instead of 325 TWh, and
- to reduce the share of hydrocarbons in the production of electricity.

The first two aims conform to those of the public authorities. But a further result would be to provide an insurance for the future in the event that the nuclear program cannot be completely achieved. This is supposing that the number of coal power stations in use is raised from 13 to 16 GWe, which implies an effort on the order of 600 to 700 MW per year.

Beyond this horizon, two courses of events can be envisaged.

The first is based on the almost exclusive development of nuclear energy tending to eliminate all other forms of energy, except for a few very special purposes. Coal, in particular, would be eliminated. This is an absolute choice which involves a certain number of risks, as the project must be a total success not only in timing, but also in its technical, financial, ecological and sociological implications, not to mention the problems which could arise in obtaining uranium supplies which would have to be mostly imported.

The other course aims at loosening all constraints without threatening the primacy of nuclear energy and insuring its future by providing an alternative in case of failure of any nature. By introducing an element of diversification and flexibility, it favors optimal supply conditions both in price and in safety and availability. Coal and uranium geopolitics are actually not fundamentally different, and their respective advantages on the level of use are complementary. As of mid-1979, it seems that the coal kWh is no more expensive than the nuclear kWh, and the cost of either is probably about one third less than that of the petroleum kWh.

In the final analysis, the electrical balance can be secured by the combined development of nuclear energy and coal.

Under these conditions, the estimates relating to coal consumption in the electricity sector, set between 40 and 50 million tons based on studies by the International Energy Agency and WAES, would suppose that the present number of classical thermal power stations be maintained and renewed by supplying them mainly with coal. This represents a construction effort of one thousand MW per year between 1985 and 2000. This stock could at first be a base, at least partially, and later be used to cover peak needs estimated roughly at 20% of the total electricity consumption.

The technological improvements which are expected to facilitate the use of coal in power stations can only reinforce the choice in favor of the second course of events described above.

In the industrial sector, coal covered 77% of energy requirements in 1950, 54% in 1960, and about 5% in 1978. This is doubtless the sector in which the consensus is strongest, both on the political and on the industrial levels, in favor of the development of coal consumption. The cement manufacturers have already expressed their preference for this fuel, and the question is now under study in other industries. Considering this, the CEREN and WAES estimates to which we referred in the High Coal Case and which set consumption at 40 mtce at the end of the century (40% of the energy requirements in this sector), no longer appear at all exaggerated. The CEREN actually reached this potential by taking into account the evolution of the present number of boilers as well as possible substitutions. The latest French Plan emphasizes a desirable coal consumption in industry of almost 10 mtce by the years 1985-1990.

In any event, beyond the political and industrial consensus which has been strengthened by the acuteness of the petroleum crisis, a breakthrough by coal can only be definitely secured if its price remains clearly lower than that of petroleum. We must, in fact, take into account the additional burdens which coal consumption implies on the levels of transportation and investments.

In the domestic household sector, France has undergone an evolution resulting in the fact that this outlet now represents only 12% of coal consumption, which covers 10% of total household energy needs today as compared with 88% in 1950. For the future, it does not seem reasonable to predict an expansion of coal except for centralized heating systems, which could raise coal's share in this market to at least 15%.

One outlet remains, and its size is indeterminable: this is synthetic conversion producing either oil or gas. We have selected a purely hypothetical bracket of 3 to 10 mtce. In fact, the dimensions of this market will depend on how and under what conditions imported gas contracts can be renewed in the period from 1985 to 1990. Thus it is the evolution of the world gas and petroleum market which will condition the size of this outlet. The evolution of technology will also play its role, and in this respect France has set up a program of research for the next four years, combining French know-how, not only in nuclear gasification, but also in on-site combustion. These perspectives constitute a further justification for setting up a wide-scale coal strategy. The quantities of coal which at first would be going to electricity and to industry could, in the early nineties, be increased to satisfy gas needs and this will be even more probable as the gas produced from coal could sooner or later make up the main of the raw material of chemistry.

Considering the ratio of the present prices, coal, through its transformation into gas, is in a particularly good position for becoming again the principal raw material used in the chemical industry.

In view of the energy demand in 2000 which will approach 25 mtce, one can be aware of the importance of the market created even by a gradual substitution of synthetic gas for naphtha in chemical processes.

PROJECTIONS OF COAL CONSUMPTION FOR WOCOL HIGH COAL AND LOW COAL CASES (See Tables 6-3 and 6-5)

IMPLICATIONS FOR REQUIRED OIL IMPORTS

Import requirements and consumption may be taken as one and the same, since domestic production will remain virtually nonexistent.

It is to be noted that oil consumption, and therefore imports, are maintained at their present level in the Low Coal Case, and even reduced in the High WOCOL case (see Table 6-5). This is, in fact, the government's primary objective.

The more stringent energy policy toward which we seem to be turning out of necessity would reduce the relative share of petroleum, if not of gas, in the French energy balance by the year 2000. The development of synthetic hydrocarbons could also significantly change the picture.

COAL PRODUCTION

RESOURCES

Coal deposits in France are generally deep, jagged, and difficult to mine. For the most part, usable deposits are located between 700 and 1,250 meters and in three general basins, as shown in the table below. In comparison, the German Ruhr Valley deposits are mined at 700 meters, Russia's between 300 and 500 meters, and Great Britain's between 300 and 400 meters.

French Coal Reserves
(million tons)

BASINS	Exploitable Reserves	January '79 Predictable Reserves Estimate
North Pas-de-Calais	460	30
Lorraine	800	310
Center-Midi:		
—Bottom	102	110
—Discoveries	8	
Total CdF	1,370	450

Source: Charbonnages de France

Local resources were reassessed after the crisis, and the above estimates are drawn from this study. The so-called "predictable reserves" which, according to the new assessment, have increased slightly, are reserves which may be exploited under certain technical and economic conditions.

The volume of these potential reserves is based on the estimate of technically exploitable reserves. It is obtained by applying to the latter abatement coefficients, using an appropriate weighting, to take into account the probability of the existence of these reserves on the one hand, and on the other hand the economic possibilities

Table 6-5. Summary Coal and Energy Projections for France

Summary Worksheet

I. Coal Use, Production, and Trade	1977	1985		1990		2000		1977-2000 Avg. annual growth—%/yr.	
		A	B	A	B	A	B	A	B
Coal use in major markets (mtce)									
Metallurgical	14	16	17	16	18	17	20	0.8	1.4
Electric	22	12	25	10	30	10	45	-3.5	3.2
Industry	3	5	12	7	19	14	40	6.9	11.9
Synthetic Fuels	–	–	–	–	–	3	10	–	–
Residential/Commercial	6	2	5	2	7	4	10	-1.6	2.1
Total coal use	45	35	59	35	74	48	125	0.3	4.5
Distribution of coal use by market sector (%)									
Metallurgical	31	46	29	46	24	36	16	—	—
Electric	49	34	42	28	11	21	36	—	—
Industry	7	14	20	20	26	29	32	—	—
Synthetic Fuels	–	–	–	–	–	6	8	—	—
Residential/Commercial	13	6	9	6	9	8	8	—	—
Total coal use	100%	100%	100%	100%	100%	100%	100%	—	—
Coal consumption/imports (mtce) Consumption									
Metallurgical	14	16	17	16	18	17	20	0.8	1.6
Steam	31	19	42	19	56	31	105	–	5.4
Total coal consumption	45	35	59	35	74	48	125	0.3	4.5
Imports									
Metallurgical	10	11	12	11	13	12	15	0.8	1.8
Steam	14	11	34	14	51	26	100	2.7	8.9
Total coal imports	24	22	46	25	64	38	115	2.0	7.0
Coal production/exports (mtce) Production									
Metallurgical	8	5	5	5	5	5	5	-2.0	-2.0
Steam	13	8	8	5	5	5	5	-4.2	-4.2
Total coal production	21	13	13	10	10	10	10	-3.3	-3.3
Exports									
Metallurgical	2*	–	–	–	–	–	–	–	–
Steam	–	–	–	–	–	–	–	–	–
Total coal export	2	–	–	–	–	–	–	–	–

* Coke in terms of coking coal.

Table 6-5 (cont.)

Summary Worksheet

II. Coal's Role in Total Energy System	1977	1985		1990		2000		1977-2000 Avg. annual growth–%/yr.	
		A	B	A	B	A	B	A	B
Total Primary Energy Use (mtce)									
Oil, Domestic	1	1	1	1	1	1	1		
Oil, Imported	149	136	136	135	135	147	134		
Gas, Domestic	9	5	5	5	5	5	5		
Gas, Imported	20	44	47	52	57	62	73		
Nuclear	5	62	58	90	85	137	140		
Hydro, Solar, Other	26	24	24	25	28	33	45		
Coal, Domestic	21	13	13	10	10	10	10		
Coal, Imported	24	22	46	25	64	38	115		
Total energy use	255	307	330	343	385	430	520		
Coal penetration (%)	18	11	18	10	19	11	24	—	—
Total primary energy (mtce) input to electricity									
Oil and Gas	20.4	13	14	12	10	10	7		
Hydro, Solar, Other	25.3	21	21	21	23	23	25		
Nuclear	5.7	62	58	90	85	137	140		
Coal	22.0	12	25	10	30	10	45		
Total energy input	73.7	108	118	133	148	180	217		
Coal penetration (%)	29	11	21	8	20	6	21	—	—
Total electric capacity (GWe)									
Oil and Gas	18.9	15	17	15	12	14	9		
Hydro, Solar, Other	17.5	20	20	22	23	25	31		
Nuclear	4.6	36	34	48	50	78	80		
Coal	10.3	14	16	10	20	13	30		
Total capacity	51.3	85	87	95	105	130	150		
Coal Penetration (%)	20	16	18	11	19	10	20	—	—
Peak load	37								
Peak reserve margin (%)	38							—	—
Total oil imports (mbd)	2.1	1.9	1.9	1.9	1.9	2.1	1.9	–	-0.4
Total oil consumption (mbd)									
Transportation	0.66								
Residential/Commercial	0.56								
Industry—Boilers)	0.69								
Industry—Other									
Electric utilities	0.19								
Total oil consumption	2.1								
World oil price assumed for national coal analysis (1979 U.S. dollars/barrel)	$20*	20	25	25	30	30	40	3.2	4.5
Economic growth assumed for national coal analysis (GNP, billion 1978 dollars)	381	483	521	560	634	756	939	3.0	4.0

* Uses current price of $20/barrel (June 1979 U.S. dollars) as baseline world oil price and as floor price throughout the period.

of exploitation. The present estimate of these reserves seems adequate: since the idea has been applied, the decrease in "predictable reserves" noted over a period of several years is roughly comparable to the cumulative production over the same period, whereas former estimates led to a "combination" of reserves much higher than cumulative production.

The new estimate is higher than the preceding one only by approximately a hundred million tons. This is not surprising, since the production costs of coal in France, even after the massive increase in oil prices, are not very far below the new prices on the energy market. Since no change in production costs is to be expected, a change in the estimate of economically exploitable reserves can be ruled out as well.

Nevertheless, in accordance with the Houillères cutback plans, it was impossible to produce much more than 200 million tons of coal in cumulative tonnage. Insofar as the aim from now on would be to exhaust the potentially usable reserves as much as possible, it is evident that the recovery of French resources could at least be doubled.

This short study on the deposits, and on the difficult conditions of exploitation, throws a light on the cut-back course which was followed, even though the crisis appreciably affected this course.

PRODUCTION

Even before the obvious signs of this renewal of interest in coal appeared on the international market, France had already asked the French Coal Board (Charbonnages de France) to look into the problem. This consisted of preparing a program to stabilize or even increase national production while at the same time examining the possibilities of additional supplies from foreign markets. In addition to this, Charbonnages de France was to look into the opportunities for increasing industrial demands and perhaps those of electrical power stations. This coal revival program has resulted in a pronounced reduction in the rate of decline of national coal production, which has diminished from 3 millions tons per annum decline to approximately 500,000 tons per year decline. At this rate, French production, which at the moment is slightly over 20 mtce, will decline only to 10 million tons in the year 2000.

PROJECTIONS OF COAL PRODUCTION FOR WOCOL HIGH COAL AND LOW COAL CASES (See Table 6-6, Coal Supply)

Indicative Economics of Coal Supply

Levels 1978	Costs of Production FF/t.	FF/Kthermie*
Average for France	330	52
Surface mines	165 to 200	30 to 35
Lorraine	270	42
Provence (lignite)	160	35

Developments

The costs of production in Lorraine and Provence, the only collieries remaining after 1985, will increase by 1 or 2% yearly in constant currency.

* 1 $ = 4.30 FF.

1 BTU: 0.000252 thermie = 0.252 × 10⁹ Tcal.

144

Table 6-6.   Coal Supply

Coal Category: 1 = Hard Coal (surface)
                2 = Hard Coal (deep-mined)
                3 = Brown Coal

		1985	1990	1995	2000	2005	2010
Total Resource							
—Million metric tons	1	5	0	0	0	0	0
	2	1,200	1,100	1,050	1,000	950	900
	3	70	60	50	40	35	25
—Million tce	1	4	0	0	0	0	0
	2	1,110	1,020	980	930	880	840
	3	48	41	34	27	24	17
Economically Recoverable Reserves							
—Million metric tons	1	1	0	0	0	0	0
	2	320	200	150	120	85	55
	3	50	40	30	20	15	5
—Million tce	1	1	0	0	0	0	0
	2	300	190	140	110	80	50
	3	34	27	21	14	10	3
Potential Production 1978 Costs							
—Million metric tons	1	1	0	0	0	0	0
	2	12	10	10	10	10	10
	3	2	2	2	2	2	2
—Million tce	1	1	0	0	0	0	0
	2	11	9	9	9	9	9
	3	1	1	1	1	1	1
Expected Annual Production 1978 Costs							
—Million metric tons	1	1	0	0	0	0	0
	2	12	8.5	6.5/8	5.5/8	4.5/8	3.5/8
	3	2	1.5	1.5/2	1.5/2	1.5/2	1.5/2
—Million tce	1	1	0	0	0	0	0
	2	11	8	6/7	5/7	4/7	3/7
	3	1	1	1	1	1	1
Potential Production 1978 Costs + 50%							
—Million metric tons	1	1	0	0	0	0	0
	2	12	10	10	10	10	10
	3	2	2	2	2	2	2
—Million tce	1	1	0	0	0	0	0
	2	11	9	9	9	9	9
	3	1	1	1	1	1	1
Expected Annual Production 1978 Costs + 50%							
—Million metric tons	1	1	0	0	0	0	0
	2	12	10	10	10	10	10
	3	2	2	2	2	2	2
—Million tce	1	1	0	0	0	0	0
	2	11	9	9	9	9	9
	3	1	1	1	1	1	1

NATIONAL COAL SUPPLY/DEMAND INTEGRATION
See Table 6-5, Summary of WOCOL Cases.

REQUIRED COAL IMPORTS FOR
WOCOL HIGH COAL AND LOW COAL CASES
Once French production has been set in any event at some 10 million tons, France will have to rely mainly on imports to cover most of its needs both in steam coal and in coking coal.

But it is clear that the volume of imports will vary considerably, depending on the case.

If a decision is taken not to increase present consumption rates, depriving us at the same time of the energy stakes implied in the coal strategy, imports will increase by only 50%, reaching 38 million tons at the end of the century—12 million tons in coking coal and 26 in steam coal.

If, on the other hand, a coal strategy is decided upon to secure the energy balance, we will have to contemplate a fivefold increase over the present volume of imports.

COAL TRANSPORTATION
Due to the waning of the Western European coal mines and the arrival on the world market of new big producers, the recent development of imports, essentially steam coal, has been carried out by sea over growing distances. This tendency will continue.

PORT EQUIPMENT (See Table 6-7)
The taking delivery of coal in the French ports increased from 5.1 million tons in 1972 to 17.2 million tons in 1978.

The present port capacities are over 25 million tons and within the framework of the existing plans they might exceed 80 million tons. The accomplishment of these plans would allow to enter deep-draft ships, since the maximum depth in le Havre and Dunkirk will be increased to 23 meters and in Fos to 20 meters.

The imports, according to the Low Coal Case, approaching the present situation, would require little or no new port installations.

For the High Coal Case, in addition to the accomplishment of the existing plans, it would be necessary to create new ports or to have recourse to the transit through foreign ports, especially Rotterdam. The coal carrier fleet required for meeting the 1985 import would be of 5.6 million dwt, of 8.4 million dwt for the 1990 import and of 16.7 million dwt for the 2000 import (in 1978 the fleet under French colors accounted for 1.3 million dwt).

DOMESTIC TRANSPORTS

RAILROADS
The transport by rail is carried out mainly in high-capacity, multipurpose rail cars (40 to 60 tons, limited to 20 tons per axle) for coal and coke and even for coal and ore. Within a period of 30 years the capacity has grown from 250,000 tons to 650,000 tons. The existing stock includes about 13,000 rail cars of a

Table 6-7. Port Characteristics

Name	Year	Imports S: steam M: met.	Max. Draft (m)	Max. Ship (dwt)	Loading/ Discharge Rate (t/working day)	Annual Capacity mt/year	Storage Capacity mt	ha
Dunkirk	current	S/M	14.20	110,000	35,200	8/9	0.6	7.5
	1985	S/M	23	250,000	112,200	18/21	2.3	28.75
Le Havre	current	S	16	140,000	68,200	9	0.17 (1)	2.125
	1985	S	17	180,000	143,000	15	0.49	6.125
	1990	S	23	250,000	222,200	24	1.21	15.125
	2000	S	23	250,000	301,400	33	"	"
Rouen	current	S	10.10	35,000	37,400	5	0.6/0.8	7.5/10
	1982	S	11.50	40,000	56,100	6.5	1.1/1.3	13.75/16.25
	1990	S	11.50	40,000	78,100	8.5	"	"
Fos	current	M	20	160,000	33,370	3	0.35	40
(Marseille)		S	16.50	100,000	27,000	(2)		53
	1981	S	17.50	140,000		2.5 (3)		
	1985	S	19/20	200,000		10 (3)		
Montoir (Nantes)	1982	S	16	120,000	48,000	5	0.25/0.5	
Bordeaux—Bassens	1981	S	11	35,000	32,000	1.5	0.23	5.1
Bordeaux—Le Verdon	1985	S	14.50	75,000	40,000	5	0.4	10
			17.50	140,000	40,000	"	0.6	10

(1) Storage capacity of the central power-station not included (0.4 mt)
(2) Not used for coal at present
(3) Total capacity (M+S): 5.5 mt (1981); 13 mt (1985)

147

capacity of 600,000 tons (220,000 tons of which for coal and coke).

The per annum tonnage is 90 tons per ton of capacity, which corresponds to an average rotation of 4 days. In 1978, the transport of coal and coke by rail reached 24 million tons, i.e., half of the French coal consumption.

The only constraint on the increase of the traffic is the time necessary for adapting the rolling stock of high-capacity rail cars. A growth of the sea import would not require such an important increase of the domestic traffic, taking into account the consumer's equipment near the discharging ports.

WATERWAYS

In 1978, nearly 10 million tons of coal and coke had been transported by waterway.

As long as the planned Rhine-Rhone link is not achieved, the waterway network open to high-capacity barges is limited to:

- the Rhine and the Moselle (up to Neuves-Maisons near Nancy)
- the linkage from Dunkirk to the Scheldt (Valenciennes)
- the Seine up to Montereau (at 90 km upriver from Paris)
- the linkage between the Seine and the North via the river Oise and the canal of the North (for middle-capacity barges).

The last developments of the Rhone and Saone rivers and the construction of a canal between the port of Fos and the Rhone are programmed for the near future. The development of coal transport in accordance with the High Coal Case might promote a decision on the Rhine-Saone link.

ENVIRONMENTAL, HEALTH & SAFETY CONSIDERATIONS

It is extremely difficult to be precise about the effects which a strict application of current regulations would have on the use of coal, because coal is little used at present by industry. Moreover, where coal is used, it is, as a matter of preference, low-sulfur coal. For the time being, there is no industrial market for dust-removal or desulfurizing equipment.

Thus, we must confine ourselves to general observations on two sectors: power stations and industry.

In thermal power stations there is no desulfurizing problem, because the coal used there is usually low in sulfur content (less than 1%). There is, however, a problem for sulfurous fuel oils.

If, in the future, we had to use sulfurous coal, the cost of desulfurizing would increase investment per kW by some 20% to 25% at most—an increase on the order of $100 per installed kW.

The cost of water cooling (using atmospheric refrigeration) would be below 3 or 4% of installed kW.

The cost of dust removal would not exceed 5% per installed kW.

In other words, under present circumstances the extra costs incurred by observing environmental regulations should not increase the kWh cost by more than 10 to 15%.

We should also remember that new technology such as the fluidized bed reduces the release of sulfur and ash, and, according to several different estimates, should, at the same time, lower the cost of installed kW.

Concerning coal' consumption in industries using boilers; the problem of desulfurization can be left aside, bearing in mind the widespread availability of low-sulfur coal on the market. The essential problem is the investment necessary to reduce coal dust. If the requirements remain as they are at present, or become even more severe under ecological pressure, mere mechanical dust-removal will not suffice. Recourse to an electrostatic dust-removing process, reducing dust to almost nothing, would no doubt lead to an investment increase of about 30% which, depending on payback time, could lead in turn to an increase of about 50%, in the best of cases, in the price of the thermal unit. Moreover, it is known that this problem does not arise when coal is used in cement factories, since the ashes are incorporated during the manufacturing process.

It seems, therefore, that environmental problems are not an insurmountable obstacle for the extension of the use of coal and, as such, cannot be a reason for putting off the decision to use this fuel.

At current energy prices, it would not seem that the rough costs mentioned above are a limiting factor for the use of coal as opposed to other sources which very often involve higher costs in this area.

IMPLEMENTING ACTIONS REQUIRED FOR THE TOTAL COAL SYSTEM

Extracting and preparing coal do not cause any particular problems in this respect as far as France is concerned. The production regression is scheduled keeping deposit limitations and economic and social restrictions in mind. Means are available for this scheduling to be carried out.

France has two research programs concerned with the conversion of coal. One, over five years, deals with nuclear gasification and combines the know-how of the main organizations involved in this research: Gaz de France, the Atomic Energy Commission of France, and Charbonnages de France (the French Coal Board). The other program concerns on-site combustion and covers a period of four years, with an initial experiment in the "Bassin du Nord-Pas-de-Calais" region.

Beyond such programs, the capital, equipment, and work force required will depend upon the results of research and the evolution of the market. In other words, it is impossible at present to estimate these quantities.

For coal-power thermal stations, the required capacities are shown in the appended tables for the High Coal and Low Coal Cases. The financial and technical means that would be involved in either case can be easily procured. Remember that the investment cost of one "installed coal kW" is between 2,000 and 2,500 French francs (i.e., some 500 US dollars in 1979). From an environmental point of view, the legal standards can also be easily respected. The sites, too, which would be required to implant the planned capacities, can be found without difficulty, particularly in the electrically deficient areas along the Atlantic coast.

In the final analysis, it would appear that France is probably quite able to build up the infrastructure required for a coal strategy in both the cases studied.

OBSTACLES AND RESTRAINTS IN THE EXPANSION OF COAL USE

In conclusion it might be said, as the International Energy Agency unhesitatingly did, that the problems of market, availability, cost, infrastructure and environment, although not negligible, are actually secondary compared to the main obstacle that could be created by the absence of political determination and industrial consensus.

All necessary conditions seem to be present to justify adopting a coal strategy on a rather wide scale. But certain initiating factors depend on public authorities, not only for the choice of the whole, but also for the specific measures needed to ensure the development of the use of coal in the main sectors examined above.

France is fully aware of the international context which favors setting up a coal strategy as a means of answering the oil challenge.

She is also aware of the need, from now on, to consider the coal problem in its two intrinsically bound and complementary aspects:

- the preservation of national, economically justifiable potential,
- joining or participating in the international coal market where she naturally has a role to play.

On the other hand, it is obvious that France must open up to the international market if she wishes to preserve, even develop, and in any case utilize under the best possible conditions, the technical know-how which she lays claim to.

The latest government recommendations (from the July 1977 interministerial committee) tend, as far as coal is concerned, to be based on the oil setup which has long been operating in the best interests of the country.

There is a possibility that a large part of the market will be reserved for national operators, and bearing this in mind, it is envisaged that those operators who are asked to cooperate should control foreign coal resources corresponding to French import needs which will roughly correspond in the future to the whole of our national requirements.

It seems that this is the only strategy likely to restore to the French market a relative degree of autonomy.

Table 6-8. Hypothetical Coal Trade Flows

WOCOL   Country: _France_____

                Units: ___mtce_____

Trade Flows (indicated importer preferences)		1977	1990		2000	
			Low Coal	High Coal	Low Coal	High Coal
Australia	—Steam	1	4	12	5	25
	—Metallurgical	1	2	2	2	3
Canada	—Steam	–	1	9	2	17
	—Metallurgical	–	–	2	1	2
Germany, Federal Republic of	—Steam	2	1	1	–	–
	—Metallurgical	5	5	5	5	5
United Kingdom	—Steam	1	–	–	–	–
	—Metallurgical	–	–	–	–	–
United States	—Steam	–	–	8	2	21
	—Metallurgical	2	2	2	2	3
(Subtotal, OECD)	—Steam	(4)	(6)	(30)	(9)	(63)
	—Metallurgical	(8)	(9)	(11)	(10)	(13)
China, People's Republic of	—Steam	–	–	1	1	1
	—Metallurgical	–	–	–	–	–
Colombia	—Steam	–	–	–	1	2
	—Metallurgical	–	–	–	–	–
India	—Steam	–	–	2	2	5
	—Metallurgical	–	–	–	–	–
Indonesia	—Steam	–	–	–	1	2
	—Metallurgical	–	–	–	–	–
Poland	—Steam	3.5	2	5	3	5
	—Metallurgical	1.5	2	2	2	2
South Africa, Republic of	—Steam	5	6	12	8	20
	—Metallurgical	–	–	–	–	–
USSR	—Steam	1	–	1	1	1
	—Metallurgical	–	–	–	–	–
Other Countries	—Steam	–	–	–	–	1
	—Metallurgical	–	–	–	–	–
(Subtotal, Non-OECD)	—Steam	(10)	(8)	(21)	(17)	(37)
	—Metallurgical	(2)	(2)	(2)	(2)	(2)
Total Required Imports	—Steam	14	14	51	26	100
	—Metallurgical	10	11	13	12	15
	—Total Coal	24	25	64	38	115

Table 6-9. Illustrative Unit Coal Costs for a Typical Coal Trade Chain—South Africa to France (cement industry)

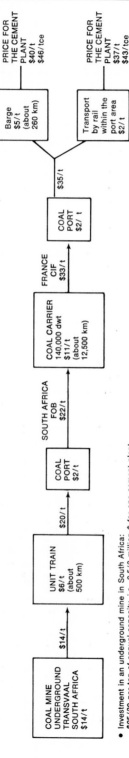

- Investment in an underground mine in South Africa: $25/30 per ton of annual capacity, i.e., 2.5/3 million $ for one cement plant.
- Combined transport by big coal carriers for EDF, steel industry and cement industry. Cost of a 140,000 dwt vessel: 30/35 million $. Annual capacity: 1 mt. Part of the cost for one cement plant: 3/3.5 million $.
- Investment in the French port extension: 60 million $ per 4 million tons of annual capacity, i.e., 1.5 million $ for one cement plant. One 2,000 t barge required for the cement plant on the river.

152

CHAPTER 7

GERMANY, Federal Republic of

The following have cooperated in this study as participants and associates:

Dr. H.B. Giesel, Essen
Dr. H.D. Schilling, Essen
Dr. D. Schmitt, Cologne
Prof. Dr. H.K. Schneider, Cologne
Dipl.-Ing. D. Wiegand, Essen

With additional cooperation by:

Dipl.-Ökonom G. Dach, Dortmund
Dr. U. v. Fricken, Brühl

INTRODUCTION

The Federal Republic of Germany (FRG) presently depends on oil imports for about 50% of its energy needs. To cope with the increasing shortage of this energy source and to reduce the potential risk inherent in reliance on oil imports from OPEC countries, the primary task for energy policy should be to reduce the role of oil from its hitherto dominating function as a source of energy supply.

If this is to be successful, the consumers must be taught to use energy more efficiently. At the same time, however, the use of alternative energy sources should be promoted, since energy demand will be increasing in the coming decades—even though at a slower rate than previously and even if potential conservation is largely practiced.

Renewable energy sources are not expected to make major contributions toward the solution of the energy problem within the next two decades. They will, however, gain importance after the turn of the century. Therefore, any efforts which have been initiated to promote and commercialize relevant technologies should be continued and intensified if necessary.

As far as natural gas is concerned, it is expected to make a considerably increasing contribution during the coming decades, although its potential to supply a large share in covering the energy demand growth and to substitute for imported oil will remain limited.

Due to this, the Federal Republic of Germany will have to promote the use of coal and nuclear energy if oil consumption is to be prevented from increasing above current levels, i.e., if consumption is to be stabilized and then decrease in the medium and long term. To arrive at this goal, the issue of acceptance of nuclear energy, and especially of nuclear waste disposal, will have to be settled because only then will nuclear energy be able to fully contribute to future energy supply.

153

Without making any extreme assumptions, coal demand in the Federal Republic of Germany may increase by as much as 70% in the year 2000, in comparison to 1977. The demand for coal for electricity generation and for industrial fuel use will increase substantially, whereas the demand of coking coal by steel mills will remain more or less stable. In the long run, there will presumably be important new markets for coal going into gasification and liquefaction. Any actions taken by consumers, producers, and government have to bear in mind this line of development at the present.

The Federal Republic of Germany has an important coal mining industry. As far as lignite is concerned, actions were decided upon and initiated with a goal to stablize present production. As to hard coal, it was decided after the first oil crisis of 1973/74 that the production capacity should not be cut back further, but instead be maintained at its present level as far as possible. Such maintenance of capacity required strong efforts which have to be supported, at least for the time being, by adequate political measures.

The rapidly increasing demand for hard coal which is expected to occur during the second half of the 1980's, and especially in the 1990's, requires an evaluation of the potential for expanding hard coal production in the Federal Republic of Germany. There is a fair chance of expanding the production potential by some 15 mtce by the year 2000, which would bring the total production up to 105 mtce. Coal deposits in the Federal Republic of Germany will support such expansion; further relevant conditions will have to be settled as early as possible.

However, notwithstanding increasing domestic coal production, additional quantities of coal will have to be imported to meet all of the expected future coal demand. Here again actions will have to be taken in the foreseeable future, ensuring not only the utilization of this potential, but, furthermore, a reasonable timing of coal imports.

In view of the considerable lead time, research and development in the fields of preparation and utilization of coal in a way which is acceptable to the environment should be expanded immediately in order to be able to use such technologies on a large scale rather soon. In the Federal Republic of Germany some key decisions have been made recently; the important thing to do now is to implement the actions needed to achieve the goals.

If all these measures are implemented in time and without delay, the primary energy consumption in the Federal Republic of Germany can be fundamentally restructured within the coming 20 years, thus leading to a considerably improved security of energy supply. In this case, coal and nuclear energy would account for around 50% of the total energy supply, while oil consumption could be reduced by about one-third from present consumption levels.

The Federal Republic of Germany has large deposits of hard coal and lignite which, until the 1960's, were the primary source of energy supply. On the other hand, oil and gas resources in the Federal Republic of Germany are comparably limited.

Since the end of the 1950's the primary energy mix has been changing as oil increased its share of the markets. In spite of a considerably increased total energy consumption (1960: 211.5 mtce, vs. 1977: 372 mtce), the use of coal decreased so that domestic hard coal production had to be reduced from 143 mtce in 1960 to 86 mtce in 1977. At the same time, the production of lignite (which is produced by lower cost strip mining) increased from 25 mtce to approx. 34 mtce.

154

Rapid expansion in the use of oil, approximately 45 mtce in 1960; 194 mtce in 1977, and, later on, of natural gas (1 mtce in 1960 against 56 mtce in 1977) combined with lower coal consumption led to an increasing dependence on imported oil, since the domestic production of oil (8 mtce in 1977) and natural gas (1977: 21 mtce) was capable of meeting only a small proportion of energy needs. The dependence on energy imports rose from one-fourth in 1960 to approximately two-thirds of the total energy consumption in 1977/78. Oil, 96 percent of which is imported, presently accounts for more than 50% of the total primary energy consumption. Although accounting for no more than 15% of the total primary energy consumption, two-thirds of the natural gas is imported. At present, the majority of these gas imports are supplied from West European countries.

The following facts

- no sizeable domestic oil and gas reserves
- a high proportion of oil supplies must be imported, and most from OPEC countries,
- an increasing share of gas imports must be obtained from non–European, mostly OPEC countries

make it obvious since the oil crisis of 1973, and even more so since the Iranian crisis in 1979, that coal must be assigned a much more important role in the energy future of the Federal Republic of Germany. If nuclear energy is not permitted to grow as expected, then coal's role will have to be expanded even more.

The first energy program issued by the Federal Government in the fall of 1973 specifically highlighted the hazards of the continued reliance on imported oil, and the continuation of the program promotes the preferential utilization of coal as a domestic energy source as well as a limited expansion of nuclear energy.

The inherent chances of these programs become obvious if one bears in mind how important domestic coal is in major energy markets; more than 50% of electricity production is based on bituminous coal and lignite. In addition, metallurgical coal from the Federal Republic of Germany mines supplies the majority of the needs of the European Community's steel industry.

In the future, there are also good prospects for coal to be used as a raw material for the manufacture of synthetic fuels. Consideration is given to this in German energy policy.

The policy issues to be dealt with in the near future include:

- To ensure availability of more power plant capacity to enable hard coal to make the expected increasing contribution to meet the rising electricity demand.
- To increase the utilization of hard coal in the general heat market, which at present is mainly supplied by oil and gas.
- To complete the development work concerning processes for the manufacture of coal-based synthetic fuels by the construction of numerous demonstration plants, utilizing a variety of processes.

The size of the future potential coal demand—as much as 175 mtce by 2000 —may require increased coal imports during the 1990's. Even if domestic coal production is increased substantially, coal imports might reach 40 mtce/year by the year 2000.

Such a quadrupling of the present level of coal imports raises a number of policy issues, including the following:

- How can German companies participate in the exploration for, and the production of, coal in other countries as a means of securing needed imported coal?
- How can the required coal imports be assured even in periods of potential supply interruption?

These issues must be resolved so that the replacement of oil by the expanded use of coal does not result in trading one hazard (i.e., dependence on OPEC oil) with another (i.e., dependence on imported coal).

APPROACH FOR THE NATIONAL WOCOL ANALYSIS

Forecasts of energy consumption for the Federal Republic of Germany under various assumptions have been prepared (following the evaluations carried out) by three research institutes and serve as the basis to the second update of the energy program issued by the Federal Government in December 1977.* Taking into account the changes which have occurred, substantial modifications have been made concerning both the total future energy consumption as well as the energy mix. The earlier predicted rate of growth in oil consumption through 1985 was reduced and the absolute level of oil consumption after 1985 was predicted to decline even faster than previously estimated towards the end of the century. Contribution of nuclear energy was reduced, whereas the contribution of coal was assumed to increase considerably.

In forecasting future energy consumption, the energy mix was altered and higher energy prices, especially oil prices, were assumed. In addition, the following parameters were considered:

- Future economic growth
- Effects of energy-saving measures (i.e., energy conservation)
- Future expansion of nuclear energy
- Potential for the utilization of alternative energy sources, including renewables

Two scenarios, "Low Coal Case," and "High Coal Case" were delineated as follows:

High Coal Case as opposed to Low Coal Case assumes:

- a distinctively higher oil price ($30/bbl. v. $24/bbl. in 2000)† and, thus, a generally higher energy price level,
- henceforth a lower economic growth (2.8% against 3.3%/year),
- slower development of nuclear energy,
- forced measures of energy conservation and development of alternative energy sources.

---

* DIW/EWI/RWI: Future development of energy demand/supply in the Federal Republic of Germany, prospects until 2000. Essen, 1978.

† In 1977 dollars.

156

Concerning the level and structure of energy consumption, the following conclusions may be drawn from the above:

High Coal Case against Low Coal Case:

- lower total energy consumption specifically at the expense of oil and nuclear energy,
- considerable increase in the use of coal

The details on level and structure of primary energy consumption are shown in Table 7-1.

Table 7-1. Total Primary Energy Consumption

WOCOL

Country: Germany, Federal Republic of

Units: mtce

Energy Source	1977	1985 Low Coal	1985 High Coal	1990 Low Coal	1990 High Coal	1995 Low Coal	1995 High Coal	2000 Low Coal	2000 High Coal
Domestic Oil —Conventional	8	5	5	4	4	4	4	3	3
—Unconventional									
Imported Oil	186	218	207	219	207	198	176	157	127
Oil Subtotal	194	223	212	223	205	202	180	160	130
Domestic Gas —Conventional	21	20	20	20	20	18	18	15	15
—Unconventional									
Imported Gas	34	68	65	72	67	77	72	80	75
Gas Subtotal	55	88	85	92	87	95	90	95	90
Hydro/Geo/Solar	9	11	11	16	16	25	25	40	40
Nuclear	12	37	34	55	50	84	72	125	105
Domestic Coal	93	110	115	111	116	120	125	130	135
Imported Coal	9	9	11	18	26	19	33	20	40
Coal Subtotal	102	119	126	129	142	139	158	150	175
Total Primary Energy Use	372	478	468	515	500	545	525	570	540
Coal Penetration (%)	27.4	24.9	26.9	25.0	28.4	25.3	30.1	26.3	32.4

COAL CONSUMPTION

Coal consumption in the Federal Republic of Germany is concentrated in the electricity and steel sectors.

The lignite consumed comes almost exclusively from domestic mines. Out of total lignite production of 34 mtce in 1977 (equivalent to 123 million metric tons), almost 90%, or 31 mtce, were used in power plants all of which are located in the immediate neighborhood of the mines in order to eliminate the need for costly transportation of these low-rank coals. The major part of remaining raw lignite is briquetted and sold mainly to households and small consumers (1977: 2.4 mtce or 3.5 million metric tons), plus smaller amounts to industry.

Consumption of such lignite briquettes has been declining for some years, and this trend is expected to continue into the future. On the other hand, larger amounts of lignite could be used—although regionally limited—in industrial burning systems as far as volumes out of the domestic production are available for the purpose. Finally, lignite could be used in the future for manufacturing synthetic gases.

Hard coal consumption in the Federal Republic of Germany is mainly supplied by domestic mines; imports from nonmember countries of the EC, which are restricted by a quota system, are used to supply mostly traditional customers (mainly power plants) of imported coal which are located near the coast. In 1977, total sales from the domestic production of 79.5 mtce went into the following sectors:

- 28 mtce (35%)—electric power plants,
- 19.7 mtce (25%)—domestic iron and steel industry,
- 9.7 mtce (12%)—households, industries, and small consumers,
- 22.1 mtce (28%)—exports, including 11.7 mtce coal to iron and steel industries in EC member countries.

Considering exclusively domestic sales, the concentration on the electricity-generation and steel sectors becomes still more obvious.

In 1977, 57.4 mtce of domestic sales from domestic production went into the following sectors:

- 28 mtce or 49% to power plants,
- 19.7 mtce or some 34% to the iron and steel industry,
- 9.7 mtce or some 17% to other industries, households and small consumers.

Prospects for hard coal sales in the Federal Republic of Germany are expected to grow. In the power generation sector, a ten-year contract was concluded in 1977 between the mining industry and the power-generating industry, whereby an average of 33 mtce/year of domestic steam coal would be used in power plants between 1978 and 1987, in addition to the approximately 4 mtce per year of imported coal. Since then, the estimate of total demand for steam coal for use in power plants in 1985 has been increased to 45 mtce and the latest forecast of steam coal demand for power plants in 2000 is 66 mtce/year.

With regard to the steel industry, future sales are expected to remain strong since coking coal is relatively scarce due to the conditions of deposits. With regard to the other markets, i.e., the general heat and raw material market, the potential for stopping and possibly reversing the previous decline in coal consumption in these markets by using new technologies, e.g., fluidized bed combustion, district heating, and conversion to gaseous or liquid fuels, will be of critical importance. Although the general heat and raw material markets account for some 50% of total energy consumption in the Federal Republic of Germany, hard coal's share of these markets is only 8%. At present, this market is supplied mainly by oil and gas.

Based on the assumptions used in the High Coal Case and Low Coal Case scenarios, coal consumption in the Federal Republic of Germany is expected to show an appreciable increase between 1977 and 2000 (for details please refer to Table 7-2):

- Total coal consumption is to increase from 102 mtce up to 175 mtce, bituminous coal from 67 to 130 mtce, lignite from 34 to 45 mtce.
- Electricity generation: increase from 61 mtce to 106 mtce, thereof: bituminous coal from 30 to approx. 66 mtce, lignite from 31 mtce to 40 mtce.
- Steel industry: from 23 mtce up to 26 mtce (hard coal) by 1985, followed by a slow decline through 2000.
- Production of synthetic fuels: increase from 0 to 25 mtce, thereof: bituminous coal more than 20 mtce, lignite less than 5 mtce.

The considerably increasing use of coal for power generation and production of synthetic fuels requires the construction of large amounts of new capacities and

Table 7-2. Coal Use in Final Demand Sectors

WOCOL

Country: _Germany, Federal Republic of_

Units: ___mtce___

Coal Market Sector	1977	1985 Low Coal	1985 High Coal	1990 Low Coal	1990 High Coal	1995 Low Coal	1995 High Coal	2000 Low Coal	2000 High Coal
Electric	61	76	79	84	89	92	100	99	106
Industry	5	6	8	6	9	7	10	8	12
Metallurgical	23	26	24	25	23	25	23	25	22
Synthetic Fuels	–	1	3	5	10	7	15	10	25
Residential/Commercial	13	10	12	9	11	8	10	8	10
Total Coal Use	102	119	126	129	142	139	158	150	175
Total Primary Energy Use	372	478	468	515	500	545	525	570	540
Coal Penetration (%)									
Total Energy	27.4	24.9	26.9	25.0	28.4	28.3	30.1	26.3	32.6
Electricity	55.5	46.6	49.7	44.9	49.4	42.2	47.8	38.7	44.2
Industry	1.3	1.3	1.7	1.2	1.8	1.3	1.9	1.4	2.2

—as far as synthetic fuels are concerned—economic and financial guarantees for these capacities under the conditions presently prevailing.

- The hard coal-based power plant capacity has to be nearly doubled, i.e., raised from approx. 26 GWe (as of 1977 including coal burnt in dual firing) to 47-49 GWe by the year 2000. The amount of hard coal to be used by these plants would increase sharply to 60-66 mtce as against approx. 30 mtce used in 1977.

- The lignite-based power plant capacity has to be increased from the present 14 GWe to approximately 18 GWe; the use of lignite in these plants by 2000 would amount to 40 mtce as against 31 mtce in 1977.

- Concerning the 25 mtce going into the production of synthetic fuels by 2000 (High Coal Case) it was assumed that it would require the construction of three large coal conversion facilities, each requiring 6 mtce per year plus several smaller plants.

The resubstitution of oil in industrial and associated sectors, by means of developing improved technologies of coal utilization, e.g., fluidized bed combustion, and supporting their introduction in the market, if necessary, would lead to increasing sales of coal in these markets.

The decrease of direct coal consumption in the residential/commercial sector does not by itself mean a loss of market share for coal, if intensified use of coal for district heating and for the production of coal gas and coal oil is promoted.

Table 7-3. Total Electricity Balance

WOCOL

Country: <u>Germany, Federal Republic of</u>

Units: mtce/yr. fuel input

Power Plant Type	1977	1985		1990		1995		2000	
		Low Coal	High Coal	Low Coal	High Coal	Low Coal	High Coal	Low Coal	High Coal
Nuclear	12	37	34	55	50	84	72	125	105
Hydro/Pumped Storage	7	10	10	10	10	10	10	10	10
Gas Turbines/Combined Cycle									
Geothermal/Solar/Other	5	7	7	7	7	8	8	9	9
Fossil Steam[1]									
Oil Steam	8	9	7	9	6	7	5	3	3
Gas Steam	17	24	22	22	18	17	14	10	7
Coal Steam	67	76	79	84	89	92	100	99	106
Total Primary Fuel Input	110	163	159	187	180	218	209	256	240
Coal Penetration (%)	55.5	46.6	49.7	44.9	49.4	42.2	47.8	38.7	44.2

[1] Includes gas turbines/combined cycle

COAL PRODUCTION

The Federal Republic of Germany has large lignite and hard coal deposits which had formerly been the basis of industrialization and which will also continue to be the most important domestic source of energy for the future. The resources of lignite total some 55 billion tons, of which some 35 billion tons (10.5 billion tce) are considered to be economically and technically recoverable reserves. Reserves are concentrated in the Rhenish coal field west of Köln (Cologne) where 88 percent of the lignite was produced in 1977.

Earlier planning of the mining companies provided an annual production of 130 million (metric) tons corresponding to approximately 35 mtce, the higher calorific value of coal from deeper deposits bringing in the year 2000 the mtce value to approximately 38. Both cases anticipate a production of 45 mtce (corresponding to over 150 million tons) toward the end of the century, since lignite is the cheapest domestic energy source and, secondly, an increased use of lignite as the base load in electricity generation is economically indicated, assuming restricted prospects for nuclear energy.

In the Hambach Forest where new mine development started during the fall of 1978, production is to be given in 1983 to reach full production of 40 to 50 million tons/year (15 to 17 mtce) by 1990. This new mine is essentially a replacement for nearly exhausted mines. A production increase appears feasible, however, by intensified winning operations. The development of this new mine is estimated to require an investment of some 5 billion DM during the first decade.

Hard coal resources amount to some 230 billion tons, of which some 24 billion tons are economically and technically recoverable.* Reserves are concentrated in the Ruhr District where 81 percent of the production in 1977 occurred. All production came from deep mines.

---

*According to a survey carried out by the Commission of the EC and based on following economic criteria: —over 60 cm seam thickness   —down to 1500 m depth

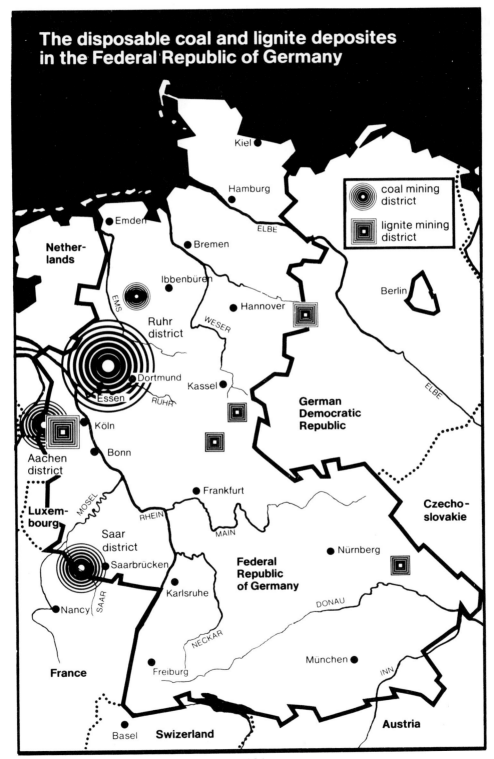

The disposable coal and lignite deposites in the Federal Republic of Germany

In 1977, the production was approximately 86 mtce against a capacity of more than 90 mtce which could not fully be utilized because of the then still prevailing excess of energy supply. 1979 is the first year where a production increase by 2 mtce (up to 87 mtce) against the previous year has been attained.

Both WOCOL cases assume that potential production after 1990 will be significantly larger than present capacity. Such an intermediate-term production increase seems feasible if technical bottlenecks are eliminated and if labor-recruiting programs are instituted. Over the longer term, new mines will have to be developed to replace depleted mines and to increase production. With the present price relationship between domestic hard coal and imported coal, such a production increase will not be possible without protective policies. It cannot yet be appreciated definitively whether the competitive situation will change substantially in favor of German hard coal so that government support measures can be dispensed with, which may be conceivable—particularly supposing the High Coal Case—on the background of the worldwide rising demand for coal involving the construction of new production and transport installations or, alternatively, in case of cost increases. When determining the potential import coal demand, production was assumed to increase. From the viewpoint of recoverable reserves, there is no limitation on increasing hard coal production to the projected levels.

Mining operations in the Federal Republic of Germany are concentrated in just a few coal fields.

Approximately three-fourths of the hard coal production in the Federal Republic of Germany is mined by Ruhrkohle AG in the Ruhr District. The rest is supplied by five other smaller mining companies as shown below:

Mining Company	District(s)	% Production 1977
Ruhrkohle AG	Ruhr	74.1
Saarbergwerke AG	Saar	11.0
Eschweiler Bergwerksverein AG	Ruhr, Aachen	7.5
Gewerkschaft Auguste Victoria	Ruhr	3.2
Preussag AG	Ibbenbüren	2.2
Gewerkschaft Sophia-Jacoba	Aachen	2.0
		100.0

Lignite is produced by four companies as follows:

Mining Company	% Production 1977
Rheinische Braunkohlenwerke AG	87.7
Bayerische Braunkohlen-Industrie AG	6.2
Braunschweigische Kohlen-Bergwerke	3.7
Preussische Elektrizitäts-AG	2.4
	100.0

NATIONAL COAL SUPPLY/DEMAND INTEGRATION

Even with increasing consumption, in the future coal supplies for the Federal Republic of Germany would be assured mainly by domestic production.

Practically all of the lignite produced in the Federal Republic of Germany will be consumed in the country, mainly for power generation, but later on also for the production of gas. No sizeable export trade in lignite or lignite briquettes is foreseen.

If actual production is increased to the level of potential production, then both imports and exports will remain constant through the year 2000 under the WOCOL Low Coal Case. However, in the WOCOL High Coal Case, imports will increase and might reach the level of 40 mtce by the year 2000.

Coal going into export is mainly coking coal, whereas imports are exclusively steam coals. Due to the fact that the worldwide availability of coking coal is restricted because of more limited deposits, and coking coals command premium prices, higher export volumes in coking coal are possible. The import demand for power plant coal would, therefore, increase accordingly.

Table 7-4. Coal Supply/Demand Integration Summary (mtce)

	1977	1985		1990		1995		2000	
		Low Coal Case	High Coal Case	Low Coal Case	High Coal Case	Low Coal Case	High Coal Case	Low Coal Case	High Coal Case
Coal Consumption	102	119	126	129	142	139	158	150	175
Potential Coal Production									
Hard Coal	86	93	93	96	96	100	100	105	105
Lignite	34	35	35	35	35	40	40	45	45
Potential Coal Exports[1]	22	18	13	20	15	20	15	20	15
Required Coal Imports[1]	9	9	11	18	26	19	33	20	40

[1] Hard coal only.

COAL TRANSPORTATION

The Federal Republic of Germany has a well-designed, efficient and dense network of railroads and waterways. The infrastructure of transport systems would allow a substantial increase of coal shipments without requiring extensive new investments.

Since lignite is used almost exclusively in power plants situated near mines, railroad or conveyor belt transport is provided for by the mining companies.

Hard coal, too, is mainly consumed in the coalfields or in their neighborhood. Electricity generation and steel mills are concentrated in these areas so that no additional transportation facilities are required. Since hard coal exports from the Federal Republic of Germany are not expected to increase, no substantial problems are expected.

ENVIRONMENTAL, HEALTH & SAFETY CONSIDERATIONS

COAL CONSUMPTION

The Bundesimmissionsschutzgesetz (Federal Immission Control Law) of March 15, 1974, contains regulations on air quality and noise suppression. The act allows positive action in those cases where harmful effects on the environment by emissions (air pollution, noise, vibrations, light, heat, radiation, etc.) must be remedied. And also, the act includes a preventative concept according to which industrial plants have to be equipped with emission-controlling devices complying with the most recent state of the art.

The act includes comprehensive procedural regulations, from approval procedures through air quality programs and emission for a particular area to the nomination of an officer in charge of protection against emissions.

Basic requirements with regard to air quality control are contained in the Technische Anleitung zur Reinhaltung der Luft (TA Luft) (technical instructions for air purity of August 28, 1974. To prevent harmful effects on the environment, these instructions define maximum threshold limits for the emission of more than 50 substances and of more than 120 gaseous substances, all of which are classified in three groups according to their environmental impact. As a further prerequisite for approval, "TA Luft" requires industrial plants to be equipped with emission-control devices complying with the most recent state of the art. As far as the eight most significant types of air pollution are concerned, additional air quality standards have been defined which may not be exceeded within the area of any industrial plant.

| | Mass Concentration | |
Type of Emission	mg/m³ IW 1*	mg/m³ IW 2*
Chlorine	0.10	0.30
Hydrochloric acid —expressed as inorganic gaseous chlorine compounds	0.10	0.20
Hydrofluoric acid —expressed as inorganic gaseous fluorine compounds	0.0020	0.0040
Carbon monoxide	10.0	30.0
Sulphur dioxide	0.140	0.40
Hydrogen sulphide	0.0050	0.010
Nitrogen dioxide	0.10	0.30
Nitrogen monoxide	0.20	0.60

* IW 1 = long-term value; IW 2 = short-term value

The emission limits contained in "TA Luft" have been established on the basis of medical experience. According to the Federal Emission Control Law, new plants applying for approval may be erected and operated only at total sites where concentrations will not exceed these standards after the plant has started operating. The emission control, according to the most recent state of the art, is also compulsory in areas where atmospheric concentrations are far below the emission limits.

"TA Luft," with its associated air quality standards, governs approving authorities only, without being binding for any court or for individuals since approval procedures involve a high degree of legal uncertainty. Therefore, attempts are being made to integrate these emission values into the act so that they will become legally effective.

By an edict issued by the authorities of North-Rhine Westphalia in 1977, the emissions of coal-fired power plants must not exceed 2.75 kg SO_2 per MWh.

Other federal districts (Länder) are integrating this requirement into their approval procedure.

The "Wasserhaushaltsgesetz" (Water Administration Act) of 1976 requires that the volume and toxity of water discharged into a river shall be kept to the minimum achievable by applying the appropriate treatment according to the generally accepted controls.

In addition to this, the law on the discharge of residual waters provides an economic stimulus for minimizing the discharge volumes of toxic residual waters, by raising levies depending on the volume and the degree of toxicity of discharged waters.

The European Community is elaborating emission standards for substances and groups of substances considered dangerous and of which, consequently, restricted volumes only may be discharged into the surface waters.

With regard to expenditures for remedial actions, equipment for flue gas desulfurization is particularly onerous. The cost of electricity generation is significantly increased by the capital and operating costs associated with the control of particulate emissions, noise abatement and flue gas desulfurization.

COAL PRODUCTION

Substantial increase of lignite production from additional opencast workings is restricted by environmental barriers. Opencast mining seriously affects the landscape, which is particularly aggravating as far as the Federal Republic of Germany is concerned, since about 90% of the lignite is produced within the densely populated Rhine area in the immediate proximity of the big cities of Cologne, Düsseldorf, and Aachen. All these drawbacks are no obstacles to increased production by intensified mining methods. This assumption is made for the end of this century.

For bituminous coal, which is produced exclusively by deep mining, there are no comparable problems.

No significant obstacles dictated by health and safety standards are expected to impede an increase in production; these operations are already at a high technical level, thanks to the utilization of machinery and hydraulic supports of high performance. However, with increasing use of machinery, miners are exposed to higher dust and noise levels than previously.

Increasing mining depths involve higher temperatures, and thus, deteriorating mine conditions. These conditions, however, are not unusual for the German coal mining industry. Safety standards issued by the mining companies, as well as the mining inspectorates regulations, take this situation into account by mine air cooling and shorter work time, in combination with scrupulous medical controls.

IMPLEMENTING ACTIONS REQUIRED FOR THE TOTAL COAL SYSTEM

The increased use of coal will necessitate substantial investments in production and consumption. As far as we can see there are, however, no unsolvable technical or financial obstacles ahead and the labor problem, too, seems solvable.

There are two facts which have affected investments during recent years:

- a too-low price level being in contradiction to the shortage expected in the long run, and
- legal uncertainty with regard to environmental protection which has considerably delayed the construction of power plants.

165

Consumption of primary energy fell after 1973 and the level of that year was only regained in 1978. The growth rate of electricity was also lower than expected and with excess supply capacity no shortages have as yet resulted from the obstacles to investment referred to above.

The heavy investments already made in the lignite production is sufficient to maintain the present capacity. The lignite-based power station capacity of approximately 14 GWe is supposed to be increased according to the development of nuclear energy; however, new power plants are predominantly supposed to replace obsolete capacities. New investments are also planned, for new technologies, in particular lignite gasification.

Complete utilization of existing bituminous coal production capacity was not achieved in 1979. If, however, the supply contribution by domestic hard coal is to be increased to the extent predicted, more extensive investments are required which must aim at eliminating technical bottlenecks. After this, extensions of existing mines and, finally, the construction of new mines, will be necessary.

Extensions to existing mines would cost some 300 to 500 DM per ton/year, whereas for the construction of new mines at least 500 DM per ton/year would have to be invested. New mines would have a design capacity of about 3 million tons/year.

The construction of new coal-fired power plants has been delayed considerably, due to the prevailing legal uncertainty concerning environmental protection. The power industry and the hard coal-mining industry have more than 35 GWe of new coal-fired power plant capacity either under construction or decided upon or in the design stage which will cost 45 billion DM at the present price level.

If part of the existing capacity, which will be technically and economically outdated in the 1980's, is to be replaced in time and if a net additional capacity, required even in case of an unrestricted expansion of nuclear energy, is to be provided, these projects have to be started without undue delay.

When evaluating the prospects of the conversion of coal to gaseous and liquid products, one has to take into account the presently available technologies and technical development potentials. Coal gasification and liquefaction were already implemented on a large scale before and during World War II, and it may therefore be assumed that a sound technological basis will be available, at least in part, in these fields. Due to the changed energy situation, the technological development and plant design and construction must proceed at an accelerated pace.

The development of coal liquefaction to products including light fuel oil and gasoline will require greater technological efforts and larger financial investment to reach commercialization than is the case with coal gasification. In the long run, a combination of coal gasification with a high-temperature reactor would be economically attractive, since this combination may lead to a substantially improved utilization of coal reserves as well as to a cost reduction for producing gas.

In summary, action has to be taken first of all in the power plant sector in order to ensure the implementation of projects. With regard to coal production, measures of exploration and development have to be taken quickly, since lead times of at least 10 years have to be reckoned with.

Considering the necessity to complement and, later on, to replace oil products and natural gas by coal products, the feasibility of industrial-scale application of the processes developed in recent years needs to be demonstrated. In this sense the Federal Government, the Government of the mining provinces of North-Rhine

Westphalia and Saarland have expressed interest. In addition to this, organizational, financial, and economic questions, besides pollution control problems, need to be brought to solution.

OBSTACLES AND CONSTRAINTS TO EXPANDED COAL USE

Two facts which have obstructed expanded use of hard coal from domestic production in recent years have been:

- the unfavorable price situation of coal
- disadvantages of coal with regard to handling and ease of use.

In the power generation sector these drawbacks—in relation to heavy fuel oil —have been compensated for since 1965 by a complex of three legal acts favoring coal-based power generation. These also reduced the use of oil and gas for power generation by subjecting the use of these fuels to an approval procedure. As a result of these measures, the proportion of fuel oil going into the electricity supply of the Federal Republic of Germany was cut down to 9% of total generation.

Sales of domestic hard coal to power plants were guaranteed some 31 million tce/year within the past decade. Hard coal and lignite now account for more than 50% of total electricity generation.

Any further replacement of oil for electricity generation appears to be difficult in the near future. Toward the end of 1978, the total installed power plant capacity of the Federal Republic of Germany amounted to 84.5 GWe, of which 14.5 GWe, or 17%, was accounted for by single fuel oil-based power plants. The substantially reduced proportion of oil (9%) used for power generation is a result of the operation of plants within the lower medium-load range so that their degree of utilization is quite low. Power plants used only some 5% (8.8 mtce) of the total oil consumption of the Federal Republic of Germany.

Since the construction of oil-based power plants became subjected to approval in 1975, virtually no large-scale oil-fired power plants were allowed to be built anymore. According to a statement by the Federal Government, this policy is not only to be maintained, but beyond this, efforts are to be made to substitute oil completely in the power-generating sector. At this juncture, an examination must be made as to if, and to what extent, existing oil-fueled power plants can be transformed to coal-fueling.

A revival of coal in the residential/commercial and in the industrial sectors may stimulate new technologies.

- With regard to industrial burning equipment, this could include fluidized bed combustion, which is in the trial stage or, depending on the total demand volume, combined electricity/heat generation.
- For households and smaller consumers, an expansion of coal-based district heating systems, followed by the use of coal gas and coal oil, may be considered.

Furthermore, synthetic products (synthesis gas, methanol, coal-based petrol) will open up new and hitherto inaccessible outlets for coal.

Recently, however, the price relationship between coal and oil products has moved in favor of coal, a trend which may be predicted to continue providing a strong incentive for the industrial sector to look for substitution opportunities even before the introduction of new technologies.

Table 7-5. Hypothetical Coal Trade Flows

WOCOL   Country: <u>Germany, Federal Republic of</u>

Units: <u>   mtce   </u>

Trade Flows (indicated importer preferences)		1977	1990 Low Coal	1990 High Coal	2000 Low Coal	2000 High Coal
Australia	—Steam	0.6	6	8	6	12
	—Metallurgical	–	–	–	–	–
Canada	—Steam	0.3	1	2	1	2
	—Metallurgical	0.1	–	–	–	–
Germany, Federal Republic of	—Steam					
	—Metallurgical					
United Kingdom	—Steam					
	—Metallurgical					
United States	—Steam	1.0	4	6	5	10
	—Metallurgical	0.3	–	–	–	–
(Subtotal, OECD)	—Steam	(5.2)*	(11)	(16)	(12)	(24)
	—Metallurgical	(0.8)	(–)	(–)	(–)	(–)
China, People's Republic of	—Steam	–	1	2	2	4
	—Metallurgical	–	–	–	–	–
Colombia	—Steam					
	—Metallurgical					
India	—Steam					
	—Metallurgical					
Indonesia	—Steam					
	—Metallurgical					
Poland	—Steam	2.0	2	3	2	4
	—Metallurgical	–	–	–	–	–
South Africa, Republic of	—Steam	0.8	3	4	3	5
	—Metallurgical	–	–	–	–	–
USSR	—Steam	–	–	–	–	–
	—Metallurgical	0.2	–	–	–	–
Other Countries	—Steam	–	1	1	1	3
	—Metallurgical	–	–	–	–	–
(Subtotal, Non-OECD)	—Steam	(2.8)	(7)	(10)	(8)	(16)
	—Metallurgical	(0.2)	(–)	(–)	(–)	(–)
Total Required Imports	—Steam	8.0	18	26	20	40
	—Metallurgical	1.0	–	–	–	–
	—Total Coal	9.0	18	26	20	40

* Includes imports from EC-Countries

168

Table 7-6. National Environmental Control Standards & Limitations Which Impact on Coal Utilization

		AMBIENT STANDARDS				EMISSION LIMITATIONS	
		PRIMARY		SECONDARY		(lbs. per million Btu)*	
		ANNUAL MEAN	MAX.—once Per year	ANNUAL MEAN	MAX.—once Per year	MAJOR METROPOLITAN AREAS	RURAL
SO₂	IW 1:*** IW 2:****	0.14 mg/m³ .40 mg/m³				2.75 g/kWh (heat input 4 TJ/h, $\eta = 0.378$)	
TSP	IW 1: IW 2:	0.2 mg/m³ 0.4 mg/m³				100 mg/m³ (util. of lignite)** 150 mg/m³ (util. of hard coal) (flue gas flow up to 500,000 m³/h	
NOₓ	NO₂: NO:	IW 1: IW 2: IW 1: IW 2:	0.1 mg/m³ 0.3 mg/m³ 0.2 mg/m³ 0.6 mg/m³			State of the art is to be taken into account	
Etc.	CO:	IW 1: IW 2:	10 mg/m³ 30 mg/m³			250 mg/m³	

* In Germany SO₂ emissions are commonly related to energy produced, not to heat input.
** measure m³ is related to 0°C (273 K), 1.013 bar, dry base (normal conditions) 5-6% O₂ content of flue gas permitted.
*** IW 1 short-term, ground-level standard limitation.
**** IW 2 long-term, ground-level standard limitation country North Rhine-Westphalia.

Table 7-7. Indicative Cost Estimates for Specific Environmental Measures

Coal Utilization

ENVIRONMENTAL MEASURE	COST ($/tce 1978)	COMMENTS
1. Control of Waste Heat Emissions by Use of Cooling Towers	0.8-0.9	wet cooling tower
2. Particulate Control a) ESP b) Baghouse (conventional)	a) 2-3 b) Not applicable	a) In common use b) Today in Germany unusual
3. Control of SOₓ a) Lime/limestone FGD b) Dry FGD	13-25	
4. Ash Disposal a) Conventional b) As a hazardous material	Not applicable	a) Utilization for building materials, blasting b) No government regulation
5. Control of NOₓ a) Combustion techniques (where possible) b) Other hardware	Not applicable	a) Flue gas recirculation, burner adjustment b) No government regulation
6. Wastewater Treatment a) Wet ash transport b) Dry ash transport	Not applicable	not applicable
7. Other Existing or Possible Future Control, such as a) Fine particulates b) POM c) Coal & ash radiation d) Cost of unit or site capacity limitations due to limits on emissions e) Add'l SOₓ control due to sulfates & acid rain	Not applicable	a) Max. 100 mg/m³ b) No government regulation c) No problem d) Depending on special sites conditions e) Not required

Summary Worksheet

I. Coal Use, Production, and Trade	1977	1985		1990		2000		1977-2000 Avg. annual growth—%/yr.	
		A	B	A	B	A	B	A	B
Coal use in major markets (mtce)									
Metallurgical	23	26	24	25	23	25	22	0. 4	0. 2
Electric	61	76	79	84	89	99	106	2. 1	2. 4
Industry	5	6	8	6	9	8	12	2. 1	3. 9
Synthetic Fuels	–	1	3	5	10	10	25	–	–
Residential/Commercial	13	10	12	9	11	8	10	-2. 1	-1. 1
Total coal use	102	119	126	129	142	150	175	1. 7	2. 4
Distribution of coal use by market sector (%)									
Metallurgical	22	22	19	19	16	17	13	—	—
Electric	60	64	63	65	63	66	61	—	—
Industry	5	5	6	5	6	5	7	—	—
Synthetic Fuels	–	1	2	4	7	7	14	—	—
Residential/Commercial	13	8	10	7	8	5	5	—	—
Total coal use	100%	100%	100%	100%	100%	100%	100%	—	—
Coal consumption/imports (mtce) Consumption									
Metallurgical	23	26	24	25	23	25	22	0.4	-0.2
Steam	79	93	102	104	119	125	153	2.0	2.9
Total coal consumption	102	119	126	129	142	150	175	1.7	2.4
Imports									
Metallurgical	1	–	–	–	–	–	–	–	–
Steam	8	9	11	18	26	20	40	4 .1	7 .2
Total coal imports	9	9	11	18	26	20	40	3.5	6.7
Coal production/exports (mtce) Production									
Metallurgical	40	44	37	45	38	45	37	0.5	-0.3
Steam	80	84	91	86	93	105	113	1.2	1.5
Total coal production	120	128	128	131	131	150	150	1.0	1.0
Exports									
Metallurgical	17	18	13	20	15	20	15	0.7	-0.5
Steam	5	–	–	–	–	–	–	–	–
Total coal export	22	18	13	20	15	20	15	-0.4	-1.7

Summary Worksheet

II. Coal's Role in Total Energy System	1977	1985		1990		2000		1977-2000 Avg. annual growth-%/yr.	
		A	B	A	B	A	B	A	B
Total Primary Energy Use (mtce)									
Oil, Domestic	194	223	212	223	205	160	130	−0.8	−1.7
Oil, Imported									
Gas, Domestic	55	88	85	92	87	95	90	2.4	2.2
Gas, Imported									
Nuclear	12	37	34	55	50	125	105	10.7	9.9
Hydro, Solar, Other	9	11	11	16	16	40	40	6.7	6.7
Coal, Domestic	93	113	115	111	116	130	135		
Coal, Imported	9	9	11	18	26	20	40	3.5	6.7
Total energy use	372	478	468	515	500	570	540	1.9	1.6
Coal penetration (%)	27.4	24.9	26.9	25.0	28.4	26.3	32.4	—	—
Total primary energy (mtce) input to electricity									
Oil and Gas	25	33	29	31	24	13	10	−5.2	−7.3
Hydro, Solar, Other	12	17	17	17	17	19	19	3.6	3.6
Nuclear	12	37	34	55	50	125	105	10.7	9.9
Coal	61	76	79	84	89	99	106	2.1	2.4
Total energy input	110	163	159	187	180	256	240	3.7	3.5
Coal penetration (%)	55,5	46.6	49.7	44.9	49.4	38.7	44.2	—	—
Total electric capacity (GWe)									
Oil and Gas	36.3	39	36	37	33	32.5	30	−0.9	−1.5
Hydro, Solar, Other									
Nuclear	7.4	19	17	28	25	62.5	53	9.7	8.9
Coal	40.0	50	52	55	57	65	67	2.1	2.3
Total capacity	83.7	108	105	120	115	160	150	2.9	2.6
Coal Penetration (%)								—	—
Peak load									
Peak reserve margin (%)								—	—
Total oil imports (mbd)	2.58	3.0	2.84	3.02	2.77	2.16	1.75	−0.8	−1.7
Total oil consumption (mbd)									
Transportation	0.69	0.75	0.74	0.81	0.79	0.72	0.69	0.2	−
Residential/Commercial	0.90	1.03	1.00	0.94	0.86	0.62	0.46	−1.6	−2.9
Industry—Boilers	0.70	0.86	0.79	0.88	0.82	0.62	0.39	−0.5	−2.5
Industry—Other									
Electric utilities	0.11	0.13	0.10	0.13	0.08	0.04	0.04	−4.3	−4.3
Total oil consumption	2.69	3.10	2.94	3.10	2.85	2.22	1.81	−0.8	−1.7
World oil price assumed for national coal analysis (1979 U.S. dollars/barrel)	$20*	21.3	23.0	22.2	25.2	24	30	0.8	1.0
Economic growth assumed for national coal analysis (GNP, billion 1978 dollars)	514.1	667	641	784	736	1085	970	3.3	2.8

* Uses current price of $20/barrel (June 1979 U.S. dollars) as baseline world oil price and as floor price throughout the period.

CHAPTER 8

INDIA

INTRODUCTION

India has a multifuel energy scenario in which as much as 46% is covered by noncommercial fuel, such as firewood, vegetation waste and animal dung, while commercial fuels, like coal, oil and nuclear energy cover 54% of the total energy demand. The noncommercial energies are steadily being displaced by commercial energies and it is assessed that by 2000 the share of noncommercial energy will go down to 29% of total energy. One-third of commercial energy growth will go to substitute noncommercial energy. Coal is adopted as the prime source of commercial energy in India.

During 1977, India produced 101 million metric tons (72 mtce) of coal and 3.7 million metric tons (1.32 mtce) of lignite. Average energy of Indian coal is 5 million kilocalories per metric ton. Indian lignite has about 2.5 million kilocalories per metric ton. To obtain figures of coal equivalents as adopted in the WOCOL study, the coal and lignite tonnage figures are multiplied by 5/7 and 2.5/7 respectively. During 1977, oil consumption was 26.5 million metric tons. 17.5 million metric tons crude oil and petroleum products were imported and 10.2 million metric tons were supplied from indigenous production. During 1977, 2.5 billion cubic meters of natural gas was produced. During 1977, 23.77 million kWh of electricity was consumed in the country from an installed capacity of 26,000 MW, of which thermal power covered 55.1%, hydro generation covered 42.2% and nuclear power covered only 2.7%. Nuclear power station capacity totals only 600 MW. It is said that animal energy is equivalent to about 30,000 MW of power though only a part may be available for effective use.

India has an ambitious program of coal development to produce 160 million tons (114 mtce) by 1985, 220 million tons (157 mtce) by 1990 and, finally, 400 million tons (286 mtce) by 2000. Assuming an economic growth rate of 5.1% per annum and commercial energy growth at 6%, projected demand of oil will be on the order of 75 million tons (107 mtce) by 2000. If the country produces indigenously about 30 million tons (43 mtce), the import of oil will be on the order of 45 million tons (64.3 mtce) by the end of the century. Nuclear energy has a projected expansion to 1400 MW of power-generation capacity by 1983. Installed capacity of nuclear stations by 2000 will be between 5,000-10,000 MW. Its major growth can take shape after introduction of fast breeder technology.

Coal in India is well established, produced from most of the 54 coalfields and transported by rail network throughout the length and breadth of the country. 75% of the coal appears in thick seams above 4.8 meter thickness. Maximum

173

thickness is 138 meters. Mining conditions are substantially shallow, permitting extensive opencast and shallow underground mining. Opencast mines have a maximum depth of about 60 meters, but plans are in the working to extend to depths of about 200 meters. Underground mines with entries by inclines or shafts are commonly worked at depths to 300 meters, though the deepest workings extend to 800 meters. Mining of thick seams underground has its problems of mining technology, spontaneous heating, monsoon water and the effects on ground surface. It also has the advantages of low capital investment with bord and pillar mining.

Coal has established itself as a dependable commercial energy, although it faces problems of transportation from time to time. To some extent it suffers from a high ash content varying between 15 and 45%, although Indian coal is very low in sulphur; less than 1% for most of the production. Coal resources admit a life of 150-200 years depending upon growth of demand. Pithead prices of raw marketable coal vary between US $6 and $20, depending upon quality, location, etc.

APPROACH FOR THE NATIONAL WOCOL ANALYSIS

Indian energy policy was developed by a Fuel Policy Committee in 1974, after the international oil price hike of October 1973. This policy framework identified coal as the prime source of energy and had adopted the following points as the energy strategy:

- Oil will be substituted, wherever technologically and economically possible, by other forms of energy.
- The exploration, exploitation and utilization of coal will be programmed according to the policy, while indigenous production of oil will be maximized.
- The energy policy will require production of electricity from water, coal and nuclear sources.
- High priority will be given for the fulfillment of rural energy needs.
- Optimization of energy and other inputs of the system will be attempted.
- A pricing pattern will be evolved which will give an adequate return at a reasonable level of operating efficiency.

National economic growth realized in the country earlier averages 3.2% per annum. The five-year period of 1978-83 projects economic growth at an average of 4.7%. The economic growth till the end of the century has been projected at 5%. In relation to this, the growth of primary energy between 1977 and 2000 has been projected at 6% and the growth of coal is projected at 6.1% per annum, or doubling every 10 years.

World oil prices will have an impact on the economic growth of the country, although realistic evaluation till 2000 has not yet been done. In October 1979 it is assessed that international oil prices in 1985 may be about $25 (1979 dollar per barrel) ex-Middle East. By the end of the century, the oil price may be anything between today's $35 and $50 per barrel. It is generally felt that whether the price of oil increases or not, the growth of coal in India will remain maximized subject to the parallel chain growth of transportation and consumption sectors and will not be so dependent on the price of oil, unless an abnormal situation comes up.

Electricity consumption has grown at the rate of 10% compound per annum for the last 28 years. It is expected that till 1985, electricity will grow at a rate of

10%, whereafter the rate may come down to 6.5% till 2000. As already mentioned, the nuclear power generation growth will remain low till the end of the century, whereafter fast breeder technology based on thorium can give high nuclear power growth to the country. The energy picture reflects that apart from domestic and imported oil, the main impact on commercial energy will have to be borne by coal, as the contribution of nuclear power will be small till 2000. Oil import is still projected at a growth of 4% to a figure of 45 million tons, or 900,000 barrels per day by 2000.

During 1977, coal used for generating industrial steam amounted to about 24 mtce followed by electricity generation at 20 mtce and metallurgical use as 16 mtce, commercial locomotive boilers at 9.5 mtce and residential use at 2.85 mtce. The share of electricity is moving up fast and locomotive boiler coal use is steadily going down, estimating 5.89 mtce in 2000. In locomotive transport coal is steadily being displaced by oil and electricity. The consumption of coal for electricity generation is having a significant increase and will go up to about 152 mtce, followed by metallurgical and industrial steam accounting for 51 mtce and 50 mtce, respectively. Synthetic coal products are also expected to take a share of at least 10.7 mtce and even go up if coal liquefaction projects are taken up.

In the area of substitution of oil by coal products, the commissioning of the first low-temperature carbonization plant at Ramakrishnapur, with an input capacity of 900 tons per day of sized raw coal, has taken place during 1979, since the first plant based on lignite was built in Neyvelli in 1966. Planning of additional LTC plants are progressing at four other city centers. These plants produce smokeless solid domestic coke and various by-products of tar distillation. Two major coal gasification plants with a raw coal input of one million tons per annum each for production of fertilizer have been commissioned at Talcher and Ramagundem in 1979. A feasibility plan has been prepared for a high-pressure coal gasification unit to be located within a steel plant complex for substituting oil. An Expert Group has completed a study on the feasibility of conversion of coal into one million tons of liquid fuel per annum. The cost estimate found the economics of coal oil plant operations competitive to imported oil costs, on the basis of Indian coal prices. However, capital costs were very high and not encouraging a decision for investment during 1977. Presently, the situation appears different and the scope for a coal liquefaction project has improved substantially.

RESEARCH IN COAL UTILIZATION

Coal research in India is well established since the creation of the Central Fuel Research Institute in 1948. A process of coal quality upgrading by an oil agglomeration technique has been successfully established in a two-tons-per-hour pilot plant. Finely pulverized coal is homogenized with oil in a controlled pH bath, where coal oil agglomerates are formed with low ash content. Another process of chemical demineralization of coal has also been tried successfully in small pilot plants. Fluid bed combustion techniques are being pursued successfully under pressurized conditions. Various techniques of making pellet coke, coal fine briquettes, are also being developed in pilot plants. A new process of making fertilizer from coal has been established in laboratory tests and field trials of fertilizer have been completed. Several simple processes of making smokeless coal blocks, improved domestic oven design, etc., is being developed for domestic application.

175

Extensive work on the carbonization of coal has been done successfully, permitting the blending of substandard caking coals with coking varieties for metallurgical use. A solvent extraction process has resulted in almost ashless coal in laboratory investigations.

Summary charts for WOCOL cases are at the end of this chapter and show coal use in major markets, coal production, and coal imports/exports.

The charts show that total primary energy use is expected to grow at 6% per annum, to contribute to an economic growth of 5.1%, calculated on the price of oil at $20 per barrel fixed. It is already based on highest coal growth, at 6.1% per annum. Any increases in the price of oil, which could be $35-50 per barrel in 2000, will mean a reduction of economic growth, which has not yet been calculated. A small export of 1 mtce steam coal and a small import of metallurgical coal between 1-3 mtce is shown.

IMPLICATIONS FOR REQUIRED OIL IMPORTS

With economic growth projection at 5.1% per annum, and the energy scenario of all forms of commercial and noncommercial energies to be deployed, the anticipated oil import will go up from the 1977 level of 17.5 million metric tons to 45 million metric tons by 2000. The trend indicates that economic growth will be dependent upon energy growth and oil imports.

COAL RESOURCES

A total of 85,444 million metric tons (61,174 mtce) of coal resources of various types and grades under different categories, with an ash content between 15 and 45%, have been estimated for seams of 1.2 meters and above in thickness and generally down to a depth of 600 meters. This consists of 4,956 million tons of prime coking coal, 9,340 million tons of medium coking coal, 3,615 million tons of semi to weakly coking coal and 67,533 million tons of noncoking coals. Of the total resource, 24,604 million tons are in a "proved" category, 37,585 million tons are in the "indicated" category and 23,255 million tons are in an "inferred" category.

It is also estimated that if coal seams of a thickness of 0.5 meters and to a depth of 1,200 meters are considered, a further resource of 26,184 million tons (18,702 mtce) can be expected. Besides these, a total resource of 3,200 million tons (1,143 mtce) of lignite has been estimated. Over 75% of coal resources occur in thick seams of 4.8 meters and above. All data here are furnished in metric tons of Indian coal (and in coal equivalent).

The coal resources mentioned above are the total geological resources of hard coal. For the extent of coal reserves which can be considered as feasible for economic mining under prevailing prices, a rough indication of the proportion will be 15.3% of all hard coal resources, i.e., 17,079 million tons of a 1,200-meter depth (12,199 mtce) and 20% of lignite resource, i.e., 640 million tons (228 mtce).

PRODUCTION

Coal mines in India are generally shallow, with depths to within 300 meters, but the deepest coal mine is of a depth of about 800 meters. There are 400 coal mines in India. Shallow seams are worked by opencast methods, contributing about 26% of total production. Most Indian coalfields have multiple coal seams varying in thickness from 2.4 meters to 30 meters, though quite a few thinner and thicker seams are also mined.

The gradients of seams are generally less than 20 degrees to horizontal, except in the coal seams of Assam and a few places in the Jharia coalfields, where the gradient is high at 70-85 degrees. The coal is generally hard and the roofs and floors are strong. Seams, by and large, are low in gas emission, though four of the mines are highly gassy. Due to shallow, thick and multiple seams, the effects of underground mining on the ground surface are considerable.

Geological features and working conditions determine the types of technologies and methods of working to be adopted. The mining conditions, coupled with an abundance of unskilled manpower, have encouraged continuance of labor-intensive methods of bord and pillar mining with a minimum of capital investment and quick returns on capital. However, during the last two decades necessary research and development have resulted in the trial of various systems of mining, both for underground and opencast mines. Longwall contribution is only about 2% of total production, but this will increase rapidly.

After the nationalization of the mines in 1971 and 1973, when reconstruction started in a big way, new and modified techniques were considered for adoption. Many new underground mines will now have mechanized longwall faces, including power supports. Better techniques are also being applied to improve the performance of the mines with bord and pillar methods of working. These are: uses of scrapers/slushers, side/front discharge loading machines, extraction of developed pillars by longwall method with flight loaders, knife-edge caving and partial extraction. In the areas of longwall mining, various combinations of single- or sublevel caving with solid blasting in coal, winning by shearers with single steel props, and central power packs or power supports are being introduced. For drivage/galleries, road-headers, side-loaders, scrappers, etc., in conjunction with conveyors, are being added.

Thrust on opencast mining will increase the share from the present level of 26% of opencast coal to 45% by 1988. This will increase by 2000, when half the production may come from opencast. Some of the mines now being developed have an ultimate capacity of 10 million metric tons (7 mtce) per annum.

PROJECTIONS OF COAL PRODUCTION FOR WOCOL HIGH COAL AND LOW COAL CASES

The main coal deposits in India are located in a triangle, of which the western edge is in the center of the country and the eastern corner is 150 kilometers west of Calcutta. The oldest coalfields of Raniganj and Jharia are in the east, producing the best-quality metallurgical and nonmetallurgical coals covering half of the country's total production. The trend for the last 5 years is toward more development in the western part of the triangle of the coal belt in India. Coal development projections are already made on the highest growth of 6.1% per annum.

INDICATIVE ECONOMICS OF COAL SUPPLY

Coal prices are controlled in India. After a wage hike, new prices have come into effect from July 1979. Along with taxes, pithead prices vary between Rs. 45 (US $6) and Rs. 160 (US $20) per metric ton, depending upon quality. Coal qualities vary between 15 and 45% ash. Since coal is transported by rail network over distances as far as 500-1500 km, the cost of transport is often more than the pithead price of coal.

NATIONAL COAL SUPPLY/DEMAND INTEGRATION

The country exports about 600,000 metric tons per annum from the eastern ports of Calcutta, Haldia & Paradip. At one time it used to export about 3 million metric tons (2.1 mtce). Recently, as a trial, the import for one year of one million metric tons of coking coal from Australia and Canada has been arranged. Long-term import of coking coal is being debated, based mainly on quality and conservation needs.

COAL TRANSPORTATION

Transporting coal to all parts of a large country like India has been a major problem. India, having the third largest railway network in the world, obviously depends more upon rail transport, with roadway trucks being the second most important carriers. Conveyors, coastal shipping and river transport are also contributing small volumes of transport in their respective fields. The possibility of pipeline transport is also being explored, but chances are very little. Up to now, not even one case of pipeline location could be located. Nearly 80% of coal is transported by railways, 16% by road and the rest by other means. Railways are the most important and economical mode of transport of coal for all long distances, even for 10 kilometers or more. Whenever rail operations go down for any reason, or when very small lots of coal are to be transported, the truck transport of coal goes up. Road transport is used particularly for carrying coal to the interiors of the country away from the railheads. There are fixed rational directions of coal movement from different coalfields to linked power stations, and the program is coordinated regularly. Few power plants are located close to mines, where coal is transported directly by belt conveyor, aerial ropeway or private rail systems. Most of the power stations are located in consumer areas. Recently, 4 large power stations of 2000 MW capacity have been taken for construction close to coalfields and coal transport are being arranged by private rail system.

ENVIRONMENT

Coal mining is generally concentrated away from urban establishments and so attracts small attention from an environmental viewpoint. But as mining activities grow, such areas become urbanized over a period of time and pollution increases. Efforts are under way to keep the problem of pollution to a minimum for the areas where large-scale mining is planned in the immediate future. One of the major problem areas being studied is the old coking coalfield of Jharia, where 21 contiguous thick seams are being developed and are awaiting final extraction. Shallow mining causes ecological disturbances, especially when the mining of thick seams is undertaken, as has happened with the old coalfield of Raniganj. Studies are being made to evolve environmental guidelines for future opencast and underground mining practices.

IMPLEMENTING ACTIONS REQUIRED FOR THE TOTAL COAL SYSTEM

Since the nationalization of the coal mines in India in 1971 and 1973, the industry has been working under the Holding Company of Coal India Limited,

178

producing about 88% of total coal in the country. This company has 4 subsidiaries for coal production and one design company, known as the Central Mine Planning & Design Institute Ltd. Another State-cum-Central Sector Undertaking produces about 9%, the remaining 3% being contributed by mines under a private steel company. Development of coal production is projected within a framework of a National Five-Year Plan, where all chain investments are also finalized.

During the last 5 years, about Rs.10,000 million (US $1,250 million) has been invested by the Government in the coal mining industry as a whole. This amount was spent mainly in reorganizing and expanding existing mines, in the replacement of old machinery, the construction of residential and industrial infrastructures, and large-scale geological exploration in lieu of construction of new mines. The Government has planned to invest another Rs.18,500 million (US $2,312 million) during the Sixth Five-Year Plan (1978-83). This will permit the opening up of new opencast and underground mines, the setting up of coal washeries and the construction of a few coal utilization plants.

Normally, it takes about 3-5 years for the construction of small opencast mines and 5-8 years for the construction of large opencast or underground mines. The deep underground mines are taking a much longer time; up to 7-12 years. The major problems that face most developing countries, including India, are getting capital for large-scale development, adaptation of foreign technology to suit local techno-economic situations, development of appropriate technology (apart from training in industry), management of large organizations, installation of suitable infrastructures, import of machinery and spare parts, quality manufacture of indigenous machinery, expert supervision, design support, etc. However, there are plenty of trained engineers, technicians and skilled workmen, and, at the present, foreign exchange is available. The manufacturing capacity of mining and general machinery has already increased.

The current trend of thermal power generation shows that the country is moving from the concept of 400 MW stations in various parts of the country to the construction of large thermal power stations of 2,000 MW each at various coalfields.

Apart from supplying coal to the large power stations, the dependence of coal transport on the railways continues both as a means of progress and sometimes as a constraint. Rail capacity improvement is an infrastructure need, especially in the next decade, when road transport will be very costly and will have the constraint of oil availability.

Haldia port, on the east coast, is considered the main port for the exporting of coal, with a capacity of 3.5 million metric tons per year. Small quantities are shipped in small vessels from Calcutta port. Another east coast port at Paradeep also handles a small amount of coal for export and import in vessels of 60,000 tons dwt.

EVALUATION OF CAPABILITY TO MEET INFRASTRUCTURE REQUIREMENTS

Coal use is growing in the area of conversion of low-grade coal into power. A high ash content, a maximum of 45%, which is controlled only by strict vigilance in the quality of dispatches from mines and in the proper designing of boilers of consumers, pose some problems in coal use. Ash content in metallurgical coal is tending to increase, even after washing, and the ash content in raw coal is causing some problems in coal washing plants, as the ash in Indian coal is fully disseminated. Normal ash content in clean coal is kept at 17-18%.

One good feature of Indian coal is that it is almost free from sulphur and its price per unit of energy is still very low compared to the alternative fuels or coals abroad.

Coal is being utilized in conventional usage such as metallurgical, power, steam locomotive, industrial boilers, domestic usage, etc., and also as feedstock for fertilizer and low-temperature carbonization plants. Extensive research is being conducted for developing new coal conversion processes to give thrust to this area of coal use during the 1980's. Introduction of low-temperature carbonization plants to supply domestic and industrial solid fuel and also coal gas are making headway. Techno-economic studies indicate that coal liquefaction is an economic venture, provided high capital is assured.

In the end, it is stated that coal mining and coal usage in India has come of age and is going to play a major role as a supply of energy for the country till 2000 and also for the next century.

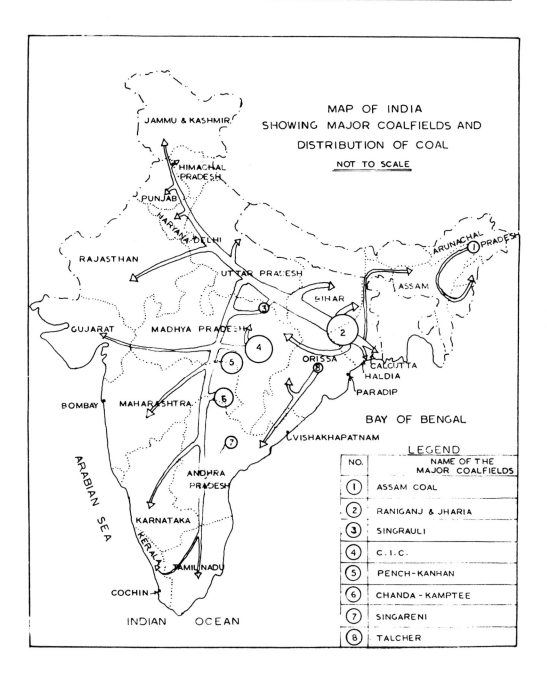

MAP OF INDIA
SHOWING MAJOR COALFIELDS AND
DISTRIBUTION OF COAL
NOT TO SCALE

LEGEND

NO.	NAME OF THE MAJOR COALFIELDS
1	ASSAM COAL
2	RANIGANJ & JHARIA
3	SINGRAULI
4	C.I.C.
5	PENCH-KANHAN
6	CHANDA - KAMPTEE
7	SINGARENI
8	TALCHER

Summary Worksheet

I. Coal Use, Production, and Trade	1977	1985		1990		2000		1977-2000 Avg. annual growth—%/yr.	
		A	B	A	B	A	B	A	B
Coal use in major markets (mtce)									
Metallurgical	16.35	–	30.68	–	38.82	–	50.41	–	4.9
Electric	20.37	–	52.79	–	80.68	–	152.29	–	9.1
Industry	24.28	–	29.36	–	35.45	–	50.69	–	3.3
Synthetic Fuels	–	–	–	–	7.14	–	10.71	–	4.2
Residential/Commercial *	12.35	–	21.27	–	15.11	–	21.91	–	2.4
Total coal use	73.35	–	134.1	–	177.2	–	286.07	–	6.1
Distribution of coal use by market sector (%)									
Metallurgical	22.29	–	22.87	–	21.90	–	17.62	—	—
Electric	27.77	–	39.36	–	45.53	–	53.24	—	—
Industry	33.10	–	21.89	–	20.00	–	17.72	—	—
Synthetic Fuels	–	–	–	–	4.02	–	3.74	—	—
Residential/Commercial	16.83	–	15.86	–	8.52	–	7.66	—	—
Total coal use	100%	100%	100%	100%	100%	100%	100%	—	—
Coal consumption/imports (mtce) **Consumption**									
Metallurgical	16.35	–	30.68	–	38.82	–	50.41	–	5.0
Steam	57.00	–	103.42	–	138.38	–	235.60	–	6.4
Total coal consumption	73.35	–	134.1	–	177.2	–	286.07	–	6.1
Imports									
Metallurgical	–	–	1.0	–	1.0	–	1.0	–	–
Steam	–	–	–	–	–	–	–	–	–
Total coal imports	–	–	1.0	–	1.0	–	1.0	–	–
Coal production/exports (mtce) **Production**									
Metallurgical	17.00	–	30.68	–	38.82	–	50.41	–	4.3
Steam	54.78	–	103.32	–	137.60	–	235.30	–	6.5
Total coal production	71.78	–	134.0	–	176.42	–	285.71	–	6.2
Exports									
Metallurgical	–	–	–	–	–	–	–	–	–
Steam	0.5	–	1.0	–	1.0	–	1.0	–	–
Total coal export	0.5	–	1.0	–	–	–	–	–	–

*includes coal for loco boilers – 9.50, 7.73, 6.88, 5.89 mtce in 1977, 1985, 1990, 2000 respectively

Summary Worksheet

II. Coal's Role in Total Energy System	1977	1985		1990		2000		1977-2000 Avg. annual growth–%/yr.	
		A	B	A	B	A	B	A	B
Total Primary Energy Use (mtce)									
Oil, Domestic	15.38	–	18.90	–	23.24	–	28.57	–	2.7
Oil, Imported	20.62	–	24.72	–	46.48	–	64.28	–	5.1
Gas, Domestic	–.	–	–	–	2.0	–	26.46	–	26.0
Gas, Imported	–	–	–	–	–	–	–	–	–
Nuclear	1.32	–	3.04	–	8.22	–	24.60	–	12.9
Hydro, Solar, Other	9.23	–	11.34	–	18.36	–	28.52	–	5.5
Coal, Domestic	73.35	–	134.1	–	177.2	–	285.07	–	6.1
Coal, Imported	–	–	1.0	–	1.0	–	1.0	–	–
Total energy use	119.9	–	193.1	–	274.5	–	459.5	–	6.0
Coal penetration (%)	63.84	–	69.44		64.55		62.25	—	—
Total primary energy (mtce) input to electricity									
Oil and Gas	0.73	–	0.73	–	0.73	–	0.73	–	–
Hydro, Solar, Other	9.23	–	11.34	–	18.36	–	28.52	–	5.5
Nuclear	1.32	–	3.04	–	8.22				
Coal	26.0	–	41.75	–	59.1	–	104.3	–	6.3
Total energy input	37.38	–	56.86	–	86.41	–	158.15		7.5
Coal penetration (%)	69.35	–	70.1	–	68.2	–	65.9	—	—
Total electric capacity (GWe)									
Oil and Gas	0.18	–	0.18	–	0.18	–	0.18	–	–
Hydro, Solar, Other	10.47	–	11.78	–	20.93	–	30.61	–	5.0
Nuclear	0.56	–	1.29	–	3.50	–	10.47	–	12.9
Coal	15.47	–	24.27	–	28.94	–	58.18	–	4.5
Total capacity	26.68	–	37.52	–	53.55	–	99.44	–	5.9
Coal Penetration (%)	58.0	–	64.63	–	54.04	–	58.50	—	—
Peak load									
Peak reserve margin (%)								—	—
Total oil imports (mbd)	0.28	–	0.40	–	0.72	–	0.90	–	5.2
Total oil consumption (mbd)									
Transportation	0.32	–	0.44	–	0.67	–	0.97	–	4.9
Residential/Commercial	0.12	–	0.17	–	0.26	–	0.37	–	4.9
Industry—Boilers ⎤ Industry—Other ⎦	0.03	–	0.04	–	0.06	–	0.09	–	4.9
Electric utilities	0.03	–	0.03	–	0.05	–	0.07	–	3.7
Total oil consumption	0.50	–	0.68	–	1.04	–	1.50	–	4.9
World oil price assumed for national coal analysis (1979 U.S. dollars/barrel)	$20*	–	$20	–	$20	–	$20	–	–
Economic growth assumed for national coal analysis (GNP, billion 1975 dollars)	85.0	–	126.1	–	157.7	–	268.1	–	5.1

* Uses current price of $20/barrel (June 1979 U.S. dollars) as baseline world oil price and as floor price throughout the period.

CHAPTER 9

INDONESIA

INTRODUCTION*

Occurrences of coal in Indonesia have been known for many centuries and utilization of coal from outcrops and near-surface deposits in a number of places by local inhabitants might have been started long before the arrival of the coal age. Organized coal mining in this country, however, did not start until the middle of the 19th century and from then on up to the outbreak of the war in the Pacific in 1942, there was a steady increase in coal mining activities in Sumatra and Kalimantan. Total coal production in Indonesia in 1941 amounted to 2,028,875 tons, while coal exports to neighboring countries in 1940 amounted to 690,600 tons.

After the war, coal mining in Indonesia faced difficult times. Cheap oil and a continuously shrinking domestic market have made coal mining increasingly uneconomic. Production rapidly declined, especially in the period from 1966-1973. Lacking new capital input and operating continuously at a loss, the few remaining coal mines continued to deteriorate. Indonesian coal production in 1973 reached an all-time low of only 148,800 tons. But the "oil crisis" in 1973 has generated renewed interest in coal since then, and the Indonesian Government has decided to rehabilitate the two remaining state-owned coal mines Ombilin in West Sumatra and Bukit Asam in South Sumatra. Starting in the early 1980's and over the next decades coal will most probably become one of Indonesia's major energy resources.

Attached to this brief report on coal in Indonesia are some vital data on Indonesia's coal reserves, production figures, coal marketing and utilization, and a projection of energy development in Indonesia's Five-Year Development Plan.

The history of coal mining in Indonesia in the last 40 years is best illustrated by the following table of coal production, Table 9-1.

DISTRIBUTION AND GEOLOGY OF THE COAL DEPOSITS

Coal-bearing sediments, ranging in age from Permo-carboniferous to Pliocene, are quite widespread throughout the Indonesian archipelago. Coal deposits of economic significance, however, are confined only to the Tertiary sediments in the western part of Indonesia, viz. on the islands of Sumatra and Kalimantan (see Figure 9-1).

Eocene coals are found in nonmarine sediments deposited in intramontane basins, while Young Tertiary coals occurred in the regressive sequence of the Neo-

---

*Compiled by S. Sigit, Department of Mines and Energy, Jakarta, Indonesia, in April 1979 as a contribution to the World Coal Study.

185

Table 9-1. Coal Production in Indonesia
(in metric tons)

Year	Coal Mines[1]			Total
	Ombilin	Bukit Asam	Others	
1939	590,743	631,663	558,231	1,780,637
1940	577,616	847,835	575,229	2,000,680
1941	537,738	863,706	627,431	2,028,875
—				
1966	100,655	185,040	34,288	319,983
1967	66,697	121,834	20,042	208,573
1968	68,253	91,407	16,356	176,016
1969	69,281	112,701	8,232	190,214
1970	77,285	90,985	4,082	172,352
1971	89,730	108,526	—	198,256
1972	87,971	91,269	—	179,240
1973	81,841	66,985	—	148,826
1974	78,804	77,349	—	156,153
1975	76,095	130,295	—	206,390
1976	60,151	132,759	—	192,910
1977	81,020	149,607	—	230,627
1978	87,115	177,065	—	264,180

[1] From 1958 on all coal mines in Indonesia are controlled by the Government, and since 1972 only two state-owned coal mines, i.e., Ombilin in West Sumatra and Bukit Asam in South Sumatra, continued production.

gene back-deep basins and—in the case of coal deposits in East Kalimantan—also in deltaic basins.

The Eocene coals in the intramontane basins are limited in extent, but they are generally more intensely ameliorated; these coals are hard, black and lustrous, and resemble bituminous coals of pre-Tertiary age.

The Young Tertiary coals in the regressive sequence are extensively distributed, but they are in general of lower rank; unless locally ameliorated by intrusive igneous activity, these coals are essentially lignites with a moisture content of 30% and higher.

Although numerous coal finds have been recorded in geologic mapping and prospecting reports, systematic coal exploration activities in the past were very limited. From existing documentation on the principal coal deposits in Sumatra and Kalimantan, one can infer the measured reserves of hard black coal and lignitic black coal in Sumatra and Kalimantan respectively amounting to 200 million and 100 million metric tons. Estimates of possible and probable coal reserves, consisting mainly of lignitic hard coal and lignites, range from 10 to more than 15 billion tons for Sumatra, and in excess of 500 million tons for Kalimantan.

COAL MINING

Since 1958 all coal mining activities in Indonesia are controlled by the Government. At present, the State coal mining enterprise PN Batubara is the only organization engaged in coal mining in Indonesia. It operates two production units: the *Bukit Asam Coal Mine* in South Sumatra and the *Ombilin Coal Mine* in West Sumatra.

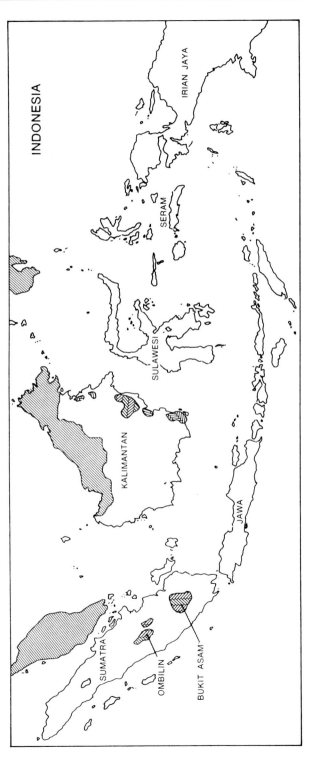

Figure 9-1. Principal Coal Deposits of Indonesia

BUKIT ASAM COAL MINE

Coal mining in the region of Bukit Asam was started by the Netherlands Indies Government in 1919. Until 1942 both open pit as well as underground systems were applied, but the latter was discontinued since then. The coal beds mined at Bukit Asam are of Miocene age.

Prewar coal production reached 847,835 tons in 1940 and 863,706 tons in 1941; compared to those prewar figures, present coal production is only one-fifth, amounting to 177,065 tons in 1978.

The Air Laya opencast mine, from which the bulk of the prewar production was derived, remains until today the most potential coal field. Recent studies based on drilling results indicated that there is still a reserve of close to 100 million tons of hard lignitic coal in this field, contained in the so-called A and B seams which have a cumulative thickness of up to 15 meters.

The coal in the region of Bukit Asam is essentially lignitic, but thermal heating from post-Pliocene andesitic intrusives has ameliorated it into a variety of ranks, from lignite through bituminous, sub-bituminous to anthracitic coal and anthracite.

Besides hard lignitic coal produced from the Air Laya field, anthracite coal is mined in a small scale in the Suban field, located close to the andesite intrusive body.

The average proximate analyses of the various coals presently produced in Bukit Asam are as follows:

Air Laya lignitic hard coal

Moisture + Water	: 18.0% to 23.2%
Ash	: 4.4% to 8.9%
Fixed Carbon	: 36.1% to 44.0%
Sulphur	: 0.16% to 0.41%
Volatile Matter	: 29.4% to 32.1%
Calorific Value	: 6,000 to 6,500 cal/gr.

Suban anthracitic coal and anthracite

Moisture + Water	: 0.5% to 1.2%
Ash	: 3.6% to 4.4%
Fixed Carbon	: 75% to 80%
Sulphur	: negligible
Volatile Matter	: 15% to 19%
Calorific Value	: 8,000 to 8,200

THE OMBILIN COAL MINES

The Ombilin coal mines are located in the region of Sawahlunto, West Sumatra. Coal mining was started here by the Netherlands Indies Government in 1892.

The Ombilin coal, which is of Eocene age, is a hard, bituminous to sub-bituminous coal. It is excellent steam coal with mild coking properties, with a swelling index varying from 1.0-1.5.

The Ombilin mines have achieved maximum production of 665,000 tons in 1931, and output in the last years before the outbreak of the Second World War amounted on the average to slightly less than 600,000 tons per year. The coal was mined underground from the "lower A" and the "upper C" seams. The A seam averages 1.5 to 2.0 meters in thickness, while the "upper C" seam is 6 to 8 meters thick.

At present, coal is produced from the Sawah Rasau field by underground methods, and also from small opencast sites in the area of Tanah Hitam. Production from the Ombilin mines in 1978 amounted to 87,115 tons, or only about 15 percent of prewar average annual production.

Total coal reserves in the Ombilin coal basin have been estimated at 450 million tons, but detailed explorations carried out so far in some parts of the basin have indicated only 35 million tons of mineable coal reserves.

The proximate analysis of a typical Ombilin coal sample is as follows:

Moisture	: 6.0%
Ash	: 1.5%
Fixed Carbon	: 49.9%
Sulphur	: less than 0.5%
Volatile Matter	: 42.5%
Calorific Value	: 7,500 cal/gr.

COAL DEVELOPMENT PROSPECTS

Domestic commercial energy generation in Indonesia at present is overdependent on oil. Out of a total of 29.6 million tce (tons of coal equivalent) domestic commercial energy consumption in the year 1978, about 84% is provided by oil.

Although Indonesia at present is still exporting some 75% of its oil production, an optimal development strategy for Indonesia requires reduced dependence on oil resources for domestic primary energy generation. This strategy is not only evident, but it is also becoming more urgent now since the rate of new indigenous oil discovery within these last few years is not keeping pace with the growth of domestic demand. Unless alternative sources of energy are developed, Indonesia will be compelled to reduce its oil exports, which at present account for some 70% of the country's foreign exchange earnings.

So far, the subsidized price of oil in Indonesia has concealed the potential competitiveness of coal. But steadily increasing oil prices in international markets in these last few years has not only improved the competitive position of coal, but also amplified the role of oil as foreign exchange earner. This has led to the issuance of a Presidential instruction in 1976 aiming at the maximum possible utilization of coal for future domestic electric power generation and industrial uses.

A rehabilitation/expansion project of the state-owned coal mine in Bukit Asam, South Sumatra, is currently under evaluation. This project, which is under study by the World Bank, consists of the expansion of the mine's production capacity from the current 200,000 tons per year to 3 million tons per year by 1983-1984, the construction and acquisition of transportation facilities and equipment and the construction of two 375-MW power plants in Suralaya, West Java.

Studies are also being undertaken on the magnitude of coal deposits in the area of Ombilin, West Sumatra, and in East and Southeastern Kalimantan. The state-owned coal mining enterprise PN Batubara is negotiating with foreign companies for the exploration and exploitation of these coal deposits.

It is obvious from Indonesia's development planning that coal is going to play a steadily increasing role in the domestic commercial energy supply in the future. In 1978, coal's contribution to the domestic commercial energy generation, which amounted to 29.6 million tce, was only 0.5 percent. By 1984, out of an estimated total of 52.78 million tce domestic commercial energy requirement, coal is anticipated to contribute 1.25 million tce, or 2.4 percent. The Government has taken the principal policy decision that priority should be given to the use of coal in future thermal systems for electricity generation.

In conclusion, coal has certainly the potential to become Indonesia's major source of energy in the years to come. Although its own prospect for export is rather limited, as an alternative to oil for domestic primary energy generation, coal can maintain and enhance the role of oil as a foreign exchange earner for the country.

INDONESIA—COAL DATA

Table 9-2. Principal Coal Reserves

Island	Area/Region		Reserves*
Sumatra	1. West & Central Sumatra	M	50,000,000 ton
		P	400,000,000 ton
	2. South Sumatra	M	150,000,000 ton†
		P	15,000,000,000 ton‡
Kalimantan	East and Southeastern	M	100,000,000 ton
	Kalimantan	P	500,000,000 ton

* M = Measured reserves   P = Possible & probable reserves
† Lignitic hard coal, partly metamorphosed to anthracitic coal and anthracite
‡ Mainly brown coal/lignite.

Table 9-3. Operating Mines & Production

Mine	Region	Coal Production (metric tons)		
		1976	1977	1978
Ombilin Mine	West Sumatra	60,151	81,020	87,115
Bukit Asam Mine	South Sumatra	122,759	149,607	177,065
		182,910	230,627	264,180

Table 9-4. Coal Utilization/Marketing
(metric tons)

	1976	1977	1978
Power Generation	21,650	24,520	24,000
Cement Industry	33,160	50,609	47,219
Railway	43,257	43,052	30,748
Metal processing	10,073[1]	16,411[1]	22,240[1]
Small industries	5,015	5,109	7,009
Mine Operation	58,257	64,085	67,100
Export	7,000[2]	18,650[2]	24,018[2]
Total	178,412	222,436	222,334

[1] anthracite from Bukit Asam Mine.
[2] mainly anthracite from Bukit Asam Mine.

Table 9-5. Coal Quality

	Ombilin Mine Hard Coal	Bukit Asam Mine	
		Lignitic hard coal	Anthracitic coal and anthracite
Fixed carbon	49.9%	36.1%-44.0%	75.0%-80.0%
Ash	1.5%	4.4%- 8.9%	3.6%- 4.4%
Volatile Matter	42.5%	29.4%-32.1%	15.0%-19.0%
Moisture	6.01%	18.0%-23.2%	0.5%- 1.2%
Cal. Value (cal/gr)	7,500	6,000-6,500	8,000-8,200
Sulphur	traces	0.16%-0.41%	negligible

Table 9-6. Energy Resources Development In Indonesia

	1978		1979		1984	
	mtce	(%)	mtce	(%)	mtce	(%)
Oil	24.760	(83.5)	26.710	(84.1)	42.088	(79.7)
Natural Gas	4.408	(14.9)	4.395	(13.8)	8.339	(15.8)
Coal	0.159	(0.5)	0.255	(0.8)	1.254	(2.4)
Hydropower	0.310	(1.1)	0.398	(1.3)	1.084	(2.1)
Geothermal	—	—	—	—	0.015	(0.0)
Total	29.637	(100.0)	31.378	(100.0)	52.780	(100.0)

mtce = million tons of coal equivalent.

CHAPTER 10

ITALY

A BRIEF HISTORY OF COAL CONSUMPTION IN POSTWAR ITALY

Coal has never played as important a role in the Italian energy economy as in other industrialized countries. Though its share in all primary energy sources rose to as high as 77% between 1905 and 1909, this occurred in a period when the economy had not yet taken off into sustained industrial growth and when coal consumption was mostly limited to a handful of industrial activities and rail transport. The maximum prewar level of coal and lignite consumption was reached in 1925 at around 11 mtce (66% of primary energy consumption) and, all told, has not since changed very significantly from these levels, remaining stable at about 10 to 13 mtce/yr. throughout the subsequent half century or so, ending in 1972.

In sharp contrast to most other industrialized countries, coal has in fact not been the major energy source behind the drive to industrial maturity which can be said to have reached its fullness in Italy only after World War II on the crest of the oil and gas era. Coal's share in total primary energy consumption was barely greater than 25% even as early as 1953, and in relative terms coal has played in Italy, as in most other countries, a rapidly declining role in fueling the energy economy as oil and later, natural gas became the dominant fuels (Table 10-1).

Table 10-1. Coal Share in Overall Primary Energy Consumption in Italy: 1953-72 (mtce)

	Coal	Total	% Coal
1953	11.1	43.4	25.6
1959	10.3	68.5	15.0
1965	13.4	134.1	10.0
1972	12.4	221.7	5.6

The country's limited coal resources, the secondary role that coal has played in the most important phases of industrial development and the long time that

The following have been involved in preparing and reviewing this report:

Participants

Marcello Colitti
Umberto Colombo

Associates

Oliviero Bernardini
Eugenio Nardelli

Acknowledgments are due to Paolo Caropreso of ENI for assistance given during the course of the study.

has, in any case, elapsed since coal was a significant element of the energy picture, all these factors have left Italy with very little technical, commercial, engineering and scientific experience in this fuel, and the Italians altogether culturally alien to the idea of a coal economy.

UP TO THE EVE OF THE ENERGY CRISIS OF 1973-74

Coal use in postwar Italy has been concentrated in industry, but a fairly large portion of overall consumption during the earlier part of this period occurred in transport and residential sectors, particularly space heating (Table 10-2).

Table 10-2. Distribution of Coal Consumption Among Principal Sectors[1]
(%, primary energy terms)

	Industry	Transport	Residential and Commercial	Electricity Generation	Total
1953	50.9	14.7	29.4	5.0	100.0
1959	46.5	9.4	32.0	12.1	100.0
1965	51.8	3.9	31.2	13.1	100.0
1972	66.5	1.6	16.6	15.3	100.0

[1] Includes agriculture

In the transport sector, coal consumption, confined largely to steam locomotives, was quite important immediately after the war but declined very rapidly even in absolute terms, with increasing electrification of the railway system and increasing automobile travel, and has now become quite negligible (Table 10-3).

Table 10-3. Consumption of Coal and Basic Derivatives
in Final Use Sectors[1] (mtce)

		1953	1959	1965	1972
industry	coal	4.3	3.8	5.0	5.3
	total	12.4	18.9	34.5	53.1
	% coal	34.9	20.0	14.4	10.1
transport	coal	1.6	1.0	0.5	0.2
	total	5.2	7.9	15.5	25.5
	% coal	31.2	12.3	3.4	0.8
residential/	coal	2.0	2.5	3.1	1.7
commercial	total	9.1	13.0	20.1	44.0
	% coal	21.7	19.1	15.5	3.8
total	coal	8.1	7.2	8.6	7.2
	total	26.7	39.8	70.2	122.6
	% coal	30.4	18.1	12.3	5.9

[1] In terms of final energy

In the residential and commercial sector, by contrast, coal consumption actually increased in absolute terms, at least up to the mid-sixties, with increasing residential space-heating using coal boilers. In relative terms, substitution of coal

194

was slow until fuel oil, and later gas oil, became more abundant in the residential market during the Sixties. In 1972 consumption of coal and basic coal derivatives in the residential and commercial sector was down to 1.7 mtce (3.8% of the overall sector consumption) and rapidly declining.

Since the late Fifties coal consumption in industry has been increasing in absolute terms, albeit slowly. Two basic (but opposite) forces account for this slow increase. On the one hand, nonmetallurgical sectors have experienced a continuing decline in coal consumption throughout the postwar period as fuel oil, the principal oil substitute, became increasingly dominant. On the other hand, coal consumption in metallurgical uses has been increasing very strongly in direct relation to the rapid expansion of basic steel production during the Sixties (Table 10-4). Coal consumption, which was for the most part concentrated in nonmetallurgical sectors in 1953, was largely confined to metallurgical uses in 1972 (Table 10-5).

Table 10-4. Consumption of Coal and Basic Derivatives in Manufacturing and Mining Industries[1] (mtce)

	Nonmetallurgical			Metallurgical		
	Coal	Total	% Coal	Coal	Total	% Coal
1953	3.2	9.9	32.0	1.1	2.5	46.5
1959	2.3	15.0	15.4	1.5	3.9	37.9
1965	1.5	26.6	5.5	3.5	7.9	44.2
1972	0.8	42.6	1.9	4.5	10.5	43.3

[1] In terms of final energy

Table 10-5. Consumption of Coal and Basic Derivatives in Metallurgical and Nonmetallurgical Industries[1] (mtce)

	Nonmetallurgical	Metallurgical	% Metallurgical
1953	3.2	1.1	26.4
1959	2.3	1.5	38.9
1965	1.5	3.5	70.4
1972	0.8	4.5	85.0

[1] In terms of final energy

In no period in history has coal occupied anything more than a marginal position in electric power production in Italy (Table 10-6). This distinctive feature is connected to the very dominant role that hydropower played in the Italian economy well into the Fifties. As late as 1953 over 85% of electricity production came from hydropower. When the hydropower potential began to be exhausted in the Sixties, coal was no longer the dominant fuel in world markets and most thermal power necessary to cope with rapidly increasing demand for electricity was based on petroleum. The major increase in coal and lignite generation took place in the late Fifties and consumption of these fuels had stabilized to about 1.2 mtce within a decade. However, existing plans in the early Seventies indicated that coal and lignite burning capacity would soon be closed down or converted.

195

Table 10-6. Coal and Lignite Consumption in Electricity Generation (mtce)

	Coal and Lignite	Total Input[1]	%
1953	0.5	15.6	3.2
1959	1.0	18.4	5.4
1965	1.3	31.8	4.1
1972	1.1	42.6	2.6

[1] Assuming equivalent thermal power plant efficiency of the time

On the eve of the energy crisis of 1973-74, it could be safely concluded that coal was a rapidly vanishing energy commodity in all sectors of the Italian economy excepting, of course, metallurgy. The only coal mine of significance, the Sulcis brown coalfield of Sardinia, was closed down late in 1972. Although some lignite mining continued in connection with local electric-generating capacity in central Italy, the country had, to all intents and purposes, settled down to an oil economy.

THE MARKET RESPONSE TO THE OPEC OIL PRICE RISE

The fourfold increase in oil prices, which occurred in 1974, brought coal suddenly and unexpectedly back into the economic picture. There was, however, no immediate response in the market. Coal consumption continued to decline in absolute and relative terms in all Italian energy markets in both 1974 and 1975. Clearly no immediate turnover was possible. The depression of the economy in 1974-75 and the uncertain international climate held back possible thoughts of turning over to coal. But Italy did respond more slowly than other countries to the new situation. Despite the proliferation of authoritative assessments on impending tensions in international oil markets, the general feeling, or hope, was that there was still plenty of oil around and that oil prices would soon enough drop back down to reasonable levels.

Since 1974, OPEC has proved strong enough to prevent oil prices from decreasing substantially in real dollar terms and, especially after the price increases occurring during 1979, accompanied by effective limitations in oil supply, most industrial operators in Italy were accepting the idea that the "high" oil price and tight oil markets were here to stay. But it was too late to avoid seriously compromising Italy's flexibility to possible future situations of scarcity in oil supplies. Massive installations in new oil-fired electric generating capacity were in fact committed immediately after the energy crisis of 1973. This choice was moreover compounded by adverse events in the nuclear field in Italy, as well as in other countries. It is in the wake of these events that coal has been emerging in the last two years as a major source to bridge the anticipated energy gap over the coming decades and Italian energy policy is now being increasingly directed to promoting its use.

In a developed industrial economy experiencing slow population growth and reduced economic growth, additions to productive capacity will tend to be small in relation to existing capacity, and the scope for promoting fuel substitution through the vehicle of industrial growth is limited. Coal can also enter the industrial market through capacity replacements, but there is a major problem of turnover in capital stock which will have to be faced before any really significant increase in coal consumption can occur. To start with, much industrial capacity in Italy is relatively recent. Moreover, in the short term only such industries can convert quickly back to coal, as still have the basic receiving, stockpiling and handling facilities and adequate coal-burning equipment. The ease with which a given plant can go back to coal varies inversely with the time that its coal-using facilities have been out of service. Some plants have maintained coal burning on standby service, or functioning at reduced rates. These plants clearly are in a position to respond rapidly to changes in the market price structure. The vast majority of Italian plants have either never had coal-handling and burning equipment, or have discarded it many years back. These enterprises will be, in general, much slower to respond to changes in the market structure, requiring turnover times as long as, or longer than, the average lifetime of their oil-burning capital stock.

Similar arguments also hold for the residential and commercial final use markets which have become increasingly geared to oil and gas and would now find it very cumbersome and very costly to make a quick turnaround.

Coal consumption in basic thermal use sectors effectively touched a minimum of 1.4 mtce in 1975 and then began increasing consistently thereafter (Table 10-7). Government policy related to coal has come rather late and remains still rather weak, being based on guidelines and stated preferences. This increase has therefore been largely market-determined and, to be sure, longer term perceptions of future energy markets have played an important role, particularly in the electric sector. It is interesting to note from Table 10-7 that this market response was actually able to check the substantial decrease in metallurgical uses due to declining steel production since 1974, so that for the economy as a whole, coal consumption decreased only slightly in this period.

Table 10-7. Coal Consumption in the Years After the Energy Crisis (mtce)

	1974	1975	1976	1977	1978
Metallurgical uses	12.4	11.7	11.5	11.1	10.6
Thermal uses	2.0	1.4	1.9	2.4	2.9
power plants	1.3	1.0	1.5	1.8	2.2
cement industries	0.03	0.03	0.04	0.17	0.31
others[1]	0.44	0.40	0.40	0.40	0.40
Total coal	14.4	13.1	13.4	13.5	13.5
Total primary energy	199.2	190.0	201.7	200.7	206.7
Total primary input to electricity production	46.8	46.3	51.4	52.4	54.9
Share of coal in total primary energy consumption (%)	7.1	6.9	6.6	6.7	6.5
Share of coal in electricity production (%)	2.1	2.1	2.9	3.4	4.0

[1] Includes other manufacturing industries (~40%), transport (~10%) and residential and commercial uses (~40%). Excludes gaseous coal derivatives.

Coal and lignite consumption in electricity generation reached a minimum of 1.0 mtce in 1975, barely 2.1% of total primary energy input to electricity generation. The inversion in trend in this sector was quite marked. In 1976 consumption was up to 1.5 mtce. Two years later it had reached 2.2 mtce, more coal and lignite than has ever before been consumed in this country for electricity generation. Official plans to continue this trend into the future are quite optimistic. By 1983, Enel, Italy's electric power authority, plans to achieve an overall coal consumption of 5.7 mtce, essentially by converting existing coal facilities that are presently burning oil. Official and semiofficial estimates for 1990 range from 10 to 20 mtce burned in coal-fired plants.

Cement industries have also responded quite rapidly to the more favorable relative coal prices. This sector had been a fairly substantial coal user in earlier days and many plants have maintained coal-burning equipment on standby or at reduced activity. A substantial part of the cement-production capacity is located in the north of Italy, close to the major coal-receiving ports, a fact which allows relatively favorable transport costs. Coal consumption in cement production reached a minimum of 0.03 mtce in 1975. Within three years it had increased tenfold to 0.31 mtce, about 7% of the industry's overall primary energy consumption. These are still very low levels of activity, but the increasing trend is quite definitely real. The cement industry is generally very optimistic about expanding coal use in the future if the present price differential remains, and particularly if it increases.

This is generally not true for other industrial sectors, and the residential and commercial sector, which continues to show declining trends as coal-burning central heating equipment is progressively displaced. There is, of course, substantial potential for increasing coal use in many industrial sectors as basic underboiler fuel, but leaving aside the very particular case of cement, perhaps some other mineral products, iron and steel, paper and board, and a few chemicals, the energy component in overall factor cost of production is still relatively minor (smaller than 5%) even at current energy prices, so that there seems to be no real market incentive favoring investments in coal substitution over and above alternative uses of capital, promising higher rates of return. Manufacturing industries as a whole have simply not been in a position to respond to the market situation and, short of coercion, will probably not be allured into doing so until the present oil-burning stock of capital equipment has been sufficiently depreciated and then only in anticipation of a much greater price differential between oil and coal, or outright shortages of hydrocarbon fuels.

The major problem to increased coal consumption in Italian industry is, however, the lack of adequate infrastructure for internal transportation, amplified by the problem of subsequent distribution to the very highly fragmented industrial sector. The problem, which is clearly aggravated for small users in the residential and commercial sector, exists quite apart from the other major problem of lack of adequate importing terminals and facilities. These problems are not in themselves insurmountable, but quite apart from the costs involved, there is clearly a limit of coal consumption in the manufacturing and other end-use sectors of the economy, beyond which the energy market cannot respond without major public investments in terminals and port handling facilities, in internal infrastructure and distribution networks. Over and above these issues, extensively distributed uses of coal pose, moreover, major environmental problems related to coal transport, distribution and use, which by themselves play a potentially dominant role in identifying the limits of a coal strategy for Italy.

FRAMEWORK OF THE STUDY

STRATEGIC POLICY OPTIONS

A basic obstacle to rapid expansion of solid coal use in Italy is represented by the lack of adequate logistic infrastructures for coal transport within the country. The freight-carrying capacity of the Italian railway system has been at about 18×10^9 ton-km/yr for almost a decade. Substantial investments would be required in order to significantly expand this or to develop alternative means of overland transport. Italy's extensive coastline, its narrow elongated peninsular form divided as it is by a long mountain chain, its few internal waterways, are geographic features peculiar to the country which might be expected to abnormally inflate economic costs of internal logistic infrastructure expansion related to solid coal transport. The country's high population density, particularly in the industrial North, is a further element aggravating problems relating to land use and the environment.

In seeking the boundaries of an optimal strategy for coal use in Italy it is important to consider existing infrastructure systems, based on oil and gas, which have been developing over the past three decades and which have incorporated within them conspicuous investments in capital and human resources. In the case of gaseous fuels, the present pipeline network has reached 16,000 km and is expected to grow to 20,000 km by 1985 and even more beyond this date. This basic infrastructure is developing essentially as part of pre-existing natural gas supply expansion programs aiming at a strategic policy of oil substitution. By the same token, the liquid transport and distribution network, which presently copes with some 16×10^9 ton-km/yr is already in existence and is expected to continue to evolve and adapt to changing conditions of liquid fuel demand and supply sources.

Given the existence of a well developed and growing transport and distribution system for liquid and gaseous fuels in Italy, there is scope for very seriously considering gasification and liquefaction as long-term strategic policy alternatives to solid coal use since these do not involve dramatic investments in logistic infrastructures for internal transport and distribution. Of course, capital investments and processing costs involved in gasification and liquefaction may be so high, particularly when coupled with the relatively high cost of imported coal feed, that these options will need to be carefully assessed from an overall economic standpoint.

The synthetic fuels option, however, is unlikely to make major inroads in the overall energy scene before the next century, while substitution of coal for oil will be of crucial importance in the period before the year 2000. The available technological options in this period confine coal basically to its solid uses, including fluidized bed combustion, when it becomes fully commercial, and possible complementary solutions such as coal/oil suspensions, if this proves feasible.

It is clearly important to set strategies for coal development in solid uses during the next two decades, against the background of a possible long-term future for coal in Italy based on gasification and liquefaction. If the long-term option is one of gasification and liquefaction, infrastructure expansion for inland coal transport and distribution during the next two decades, should clearly be kept at a minimum level, while it will be necessary to go ahead with expansion in coal-importing infrastructures which will continue to fulfill an irreplaceable role into the next century as coal is progressively diverted from solid uses to synthetic fuels production. If the long-term option is based predominantly on solid uses of coal, this cannot be decided with certainty before the technologies for gasification and liquefaction are fully commercial and before other questions, such as the status of nuclear power, the level of natural gas imports and the question of solar energy, are fully resolved. It would therefore be unwise to set out prematurely on a generalized strategy based on solid fuel uses, which involved extensive inland transport.

While adopting this active "wait-and-see" approach with respect to the long-term strategy for coal, it cannot be ignored that coal synthetics are almost certain to imply greater overall energy losses (and inevitably also greater costs) than coal combustion as a solid, say in a fluid-bed combuster or smokeless domestic burners. In a general situation of energy shortages, this fact will need to be balanced against all the other contributing factors that have been mentioned and it is not possible to discount entirely the possibility of substantial coal deployment as a solid in industry and even in the residential and commercial sector (say in district heating), beyond the year 2000.

In order to balance decisions related to coal-use strategy in the intermediate period, it would seem necessary, in any event, to avoid levels of fixed infrastructure expansion for inland transport, which could become binding, or which might just not be utilized soon after the turn of the century. As a consequence of all these constraints, there seems presently to be no choice but to concentrate coal uses in the next two decades in electricity generation in power plants located either at importing terminals or at coastal ports. Such a solution allows the possibility of achieving relatively high levels of coal consumption by the year 2000 without prematurely committing the country to significant infrastructure expansion for inland transport. At the same time, it keeps open the possibility for diversifying into synthetic fuels production as those coal-fired plants, which bear the burden of the most critical part of the transition away from oil, are phased out during the early decades of the next century.

A last important reason for limiting most coal consumption to highly centralized uses such as electricity generation and synthetics production, is related to the security of consumption, given the extended planning horizon that a sustained coal import strategy involves. The importation of large quantities of coal requires far-reaching long-term commercial commitments related to mining and impressive infrastructure expansion in ports and terminals, a very large undertaking, which presumes the existence of a small number of firm customers rather than a very large number of uncertain consumers.

These considerations have led to excluding from the present analysis, ending in 2000, possible coal-use strategies requiring extensive substitution in sectors other than electricity generation, synthetic fuels production at the end of the period, and cement production. It is well to recognize that in no case can coal substitution, as underboiler fuel in industry or in the residential and commercial sector, be considered in the sense of a strategic energy policy option for the next two decades, though it would be technologically feasible and it might even be economically favorable. Only in the event that there was unlimited scope for coal expansion, might it be possible to embark immediately on an all-out strategy of coal substitution which embraced all final use sectors of the economy, including industry and the residential and commercial sector.

However, as will be emphasized later in this study, there are severe limits on the coal-carrying capacity of the country, posed by environmental constraints, population density, and competing uses of land and seashore which exist quite apart from logistic problems and security of coal supplies. The choice of a coal strategy for Italy restricted to centralized uses requiring little or no inland infra- structure expansion for transport and distribution, is indeed dictated as much by considerations related to environmental constraints as to considerations related to commercial relations, logistics of movement and technology of coal use. It must in fact be remarked as compelling that both these lines of reasoning lead to the same conclusion.

THE SCENARIOS

Having outlined the limits and the general nature of a coal strategy for Italy in the next two decades, this section enters into the question of what form this strategy might take in the context of plausible combinations of intervening events. The specific scenarios are chosen not only to provide a concrete basis for analysis, but with the main aim of exploring the sensitivity of a coal strategy to the full range of variation of the most critical development variables involved. A primary purpose of the analysis is to determine the amount of steam coal that would have to be imported into the country in the period between now and 2000, in a situation which presents uncertainties related to the extent of economic growth, the level of oil price and oil availability on international markets and the degree of nuclear energy development.

Coal consumption strategies have very important implications for public policy decisions related to commercial relations with exporter countries, port development and maritime transport as well as other infrastructures, not to speak of environ- mental and social questions, which all have relatively long characteristic lead times. It is common to speak of substituting coal for oil without taking into sufficient consideration the final uses to which this coal might be put, the quantity of coal movement that could be involved and the producing countries that might provide it in an international market situation that could be quite strained, and, last but not least, the political and public arbitrage and prior planning at the national, regional and local levels that will be required to achieve the necessary degree of substitution.

Replacing oil with coal in the Italian energy economy as it develops toward the year 2000, involves efforts at all levels which are considerably more con- spicuous than the quantity of oil displaced might at first sight suggest. This sce- nario analysis, by linking the level of coal consumed on the one hand with the basic development variables, and on the other with the degree of commitment in international coal markets, in transport infrastructures and in public policy, is aimed at offering a practical appraisal of the most critical aspects of coal substi- tution for oil in Italy.

REFERENCE SCENARIOS

The main scope of this section is to identify the Low Coal Case and High Coal Case reference scenarios which are used as a basis for the subsequent analysis. These scenarios are identified in terms of three basic variables, the rate of growth of gross domestic product (GDP), the international price of oil and the extent of commitment to nuclear power development, defined over three intervals of time in the period 1977 to 2000.

The basic variable considered is the *rate of growth of GDP*. Low growth and high growth scenarios are specified. In the period 1977-85 the annual rate of growth of GDP is assumed to take on a value of 3.2% per annum in both low and high growth cases. This value is somewhat higher than the average growth of 2.8% experienced in Italy in the period 1972-78 and much closer to current thinking on the potential of the Italian economy over the next five years in the uncertain international situation conditioned by a tight oil suppliers' market. The low and high GDP growth rates diverge significantly in the period 1985 to 2000 but remain both relatively low growth by pre-1970 standards. This lower growth can be justified in part by intervening factors such as a slower rate of population growth and a reduced productivity growth as the country approaches industrial maturity, but will also largely be conditioned by constraints on energy supplies necessary for driving economic growth which may be expected to induce a shift from quantity of growth to quality of growth. During the first part of this period, up to 1990, the growth rates are 2.8% and 3.5% per annum, respectively. In the last decade of the century both low and high GDP growth rates decline very slightly from the previous five-year trend, to 2.5% and 3.3% per annum, respectively.

This difference in growth rates between the scenarios over a relatively short period of time may appear rather insubstantial, but it does lead to a still fairly pronounced difference in overall GDP by the year 2000, respectively 423 and 472 billion US dollars at 1978 prices, up from 231 billion US dollars in 1978, and as will be clear later, to a quite appreciable difference in electricity consumption.

The second basic scenario variable is the *international price of oil*. This is assumed to increase steadily (and never discontinuously) between 1978 and the year 2000. Two possibilities are considered for the year 2000, a low price of $25/bbl (in 1979 prices) and a high price of $40/bbl, which compare with an average price in 1979 of something above $20/bbl. The low price is linked with the low economic growth assumption, while the high price is linked with the high economic growth assumption. The rationale behind this linkage is that tensions in oil markets, leading to higher prices, will be greater in the case of higher economic growth, because oil is used up faster and is more difficult to replace quickly enough. While this rationale is by no means absolute, it does provide a more comprehensive systems description than the rather partial view, that increases in the price of oil are independently set from outside the system and only induce economic growth penalties without experiencing any feedback effects resulting from the system response. In the case of the low price, the underlying assumption is that OPEC, which is the main supplier and price leader in the market, is able to maintain average prices at about the same levels as today or not much higher, while, in the case of the higher price, an actual doubling in real terms, takes place by the year 2000 in response to declining oil availability and increasing tensions on the international market.

The third basic scenario variable is the *extent of commitment to nuclear power*. This is given two values in the reference scenarios, a low value and a high value, where the terms low and high are not absolute values but refer to the potentialities of the related economic assumption. Since the impact of this variable is felt exclusively in solid-coal consumption for electricity generation, its precise specification will be postponed to the section dealing with electricity generation. Since the terms high and low are relative to the scenario potentialities, it is possible to link low nuclear development with both high and low GDP growth and vice versa (see Figure 10-1). For the purpose of this study high nuclear development has been associated with low GDP growth and low nuclear development with high GDP growth. It is stressed that there is no functional rationale behind this linkage which has been suggested predominantly in order to explore low and high coal futures for the year 2000, since nuclear energy is the principal alternative fuel to coal in electricity generation. Combining this linkage with the oil price linkage gives the reference scenarios outlined in Table 10-8.

Figure 10-1. Pictorial Representation of High and Low Coal Scenario Couplings

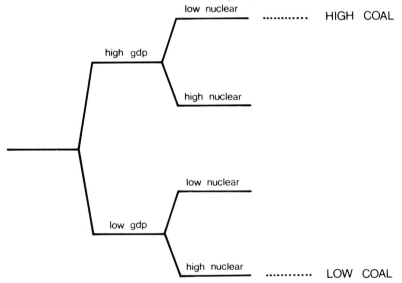

Table 10-8. The Reference Scenarios

	Low Coal Case	High Coal Case
1977-85[1]		
GDP growth (% per annum)	3.2	3.2
oil price ($/bbl)	20	20
nuclear commitment	low	low
1985-90		
GDP growth (% per annum)	2.8	3.5
oil price ($/bbl)	20 +	30
nuclear commitment	high	low
1990-2000		
GDP growth (% per annum)	2.5	3.3
oil price ($/bbl)	25	40
nuclear commitment	high	low

[1] Since GDP growth was 2.6% in 1978, then this hypothesis corresponds to an average growth of 3.3% in 1978-85.

The Low Coal Case and High Coal Case scenarios thus specified should not be considered as most likely development paths. They have been chosen for analysis because they provide a full breadth of scope in coal futures and *not* because they correspond to most reasonable or most desirable situations. For this reason, it would be unwise to seek special compatibilities between the combinations of variable values used in the scenarios. A source of misunderstanding, which has already been discussed, might be the apparent incompatibility between high GDP growth and high oil prices.

As another example, it might be expected that high nuclear development would be more compatible with high GDP growth than with low growth, because of the rather large investments involved. This is, however, only a question of degree. GDP in the high growth scenario is barely 12% higher in 2000 than in the low growth scenario and there is generally significant space for maneuver as to how investments are allocated to different sectors of the economy. Moreover, the high growth reference scenario (High Coal Case) does have considerable coal-fired electric generating capacity with unit costs that are not much lower than for nuclear plants. Applying fairly standard cost figures to the coal- and nuclear-based capacity additions between 1985 and 2000 indicates that investments in this sector are about 11% higher in the high GDP growth scenario, so that there is no inconsistency.

Yet another example is the question of compatibility between oil price and the extent of nuclear commitment. It might be expected that a higher oil price would induce a higher nuclear commitment while, instead, the choice of scenario coupling is exactly the opposite. The point here is that nuclear power and coal are alternatives in substituting oil for electricity generation and the choice between the two should be relatively indifferent to increasing oil prices.

All in all, the scenario choices appear to be quite compatible in the light of what is known about the Italian and the world energy/economy system. In the present state of knowledge it does not seem possible to advance that these scenarios are any more likely or unlikely than any other, and they do have the advantage that they identify a bread spectrum of coal futures for Italy.

EXCURSION SCENARIOS

A number of excursions from the reference scenarios have been studied to further test the sensitivity of steam coal demand to the two most critical system variables: oil availability and nuclear power development.

a. *Oil limitation scenarios.* The reference scenarios assume there are no problems of oil availability in international markets. A comparison between the supply and demand of oil on a world level shows, however, that notwithstanding substantial levels of coal penetration, the demand for oil in the year 2000 is appreciably greater than the most plausible available supply even at prices in the order of $35-40/bbl. Given this circumstance, it becomes important to study how the Italian energy system might respond, given sufficient foresight, by increasing its dependence on coal to make up for the shortfall in oil, assuming there are no repercussions on the economic picture. The additional scenario variable in this case is the decrease in the level of oil dependence relative to the reference scenario. For the purpose of analysis it is assumed that Italy's oil dependence, which is almost 100% import dependence, drops by 20% relative to the reference scenarios. This occurs through substitution of coal and nuclear energy for oil in electric power generation and through increased conversion to synthetic fuels.

b. *Nuclear delay scenarios.* A nuclear delay relative to the assumptions embodied in the reference scenarios remains a distinct possibility. Italy's nuclear program is experiencing great difficulty in getting off the ground, and only 2 $\times$ 1,000 MW of new capacity has been ordered and localized. The extended public and political debate on nuclear power, as well as financing and technical problems, have slowed development almost to a standstill. Since oil can no longer be seriously considered a substitute for coal and nuclear power in new electric capacity, a shortfall in nuclear power, maintaining the same level of electricity consumption, inevitably results in an increased demand for coal. Thus the case of an extended slowdown acquires critical importance in this analysis. A nuclear delay is here defined as a 30% reduction in nuclear capacity in place in the year 2000, relative to the reference scenario assumptions. This replaces the "low" and "high" nuclear assumptions of the reference scenarios, while the rest of the picture remains unchanged.

c. *Nuclear delay and oil limitation.* If public and political debate, as well as financing and other technical problems result in an extended slippage in the nuclear programs, it then becomes critical to study how and to what extent the energy economy might respond through increased coal use, in the event of concurrent limitations in oil availability toward the end of the century. The scenarios studied are a direct combination of the variable assumptions in the separate oil limitation and nuclear delay excursions. However, they cannot be directly compared with the reference scenarios since, as will be discussed in a later section, the combination of oil limitation and nuclear delays are likely to provoke changes in the economic picture.

THE SCENARIO PROJECTIONS

A complete overview of the scenario projections is given in the summary tables at the end of this chapter. This section outlines the methodology behind the projections, gives some of the principal assumptions and results, and identifies the most important sensitivities relating to coal and oil dependence that emerge out of the analysis of the various scenarios. This study focuses principally on coal use, the importation and movement of coal, environmental, social and political constraints limiting coal use. Since it is the gross magnitudes of coal, rather than the fine details of the energy system that are of most interest, the methodology employed for the energy projections has been kept relatively unsophisticated. It is sketched out in Figure 10-2, as an aid to the following discussion.

ENERGY/ECONOMY RELATIONS

Projections of overall energy demand and electricity demand are consistent with the energy/economy relations illustrated in Figure 10-3. These relations already include the depressing effect, particularly on overall energy demand, consequent to increases (actual and anticipated) in oil price and energy prices in general. This is apparent from the fact that the energy/GDP ratios decrease more slowly in the low oil price case than in the high oil price case. Such decreases in energy consumption, at a given level of economic achievement, are expected to occur through a more thrifty use of energy induced by higher prices, through the develop-

Figure 10-2. Methodology of Energy Projections

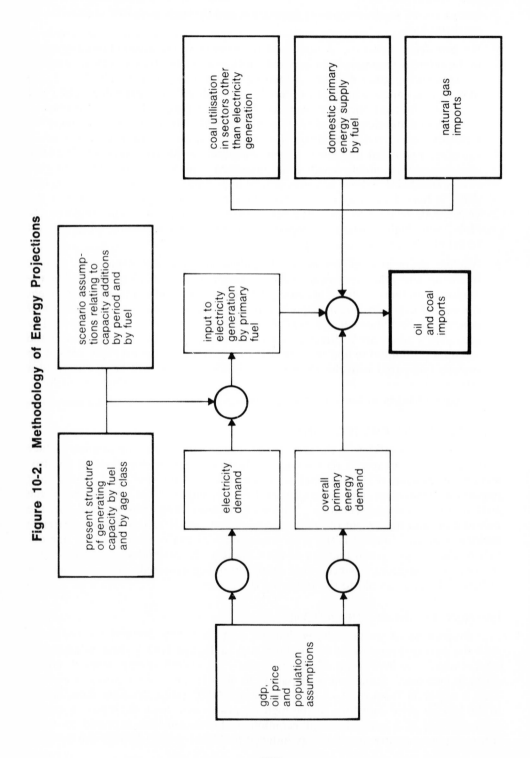

Figure 10-3. Energy/Economy Relations

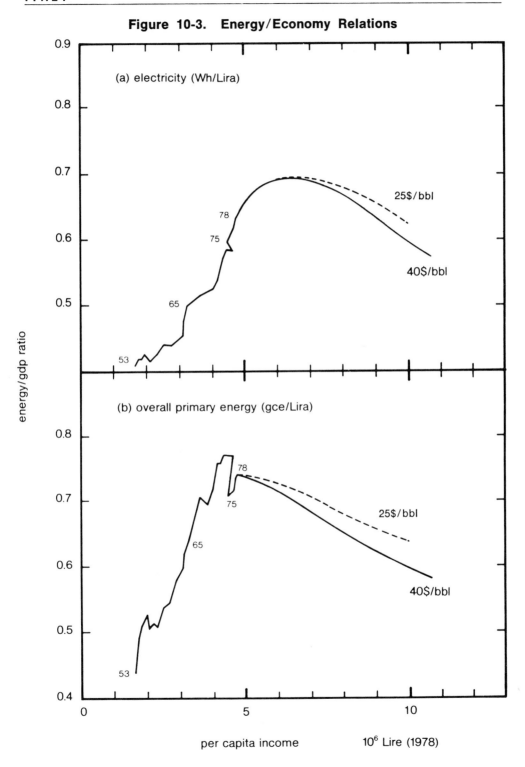

energy/gdp ratio

(a) electricity (Wh/Lira)

25$/bbl

40$/bbl

78

75

65

53

(b) overall primary energy (gce/Lira)

78

75

25$/bbl

65

40$/bbl

53

per capita income   10⁶ Lire (1978)

207

ment and diffusion of energy-sparing technologies, and through policy measures aimed at saving energy.

The energy/GDP ratio turns out to be much lower in the high economic growth scenario partly because of a more advanced degree of development, because of the depressing effect of higher prices and because of higher investments in conservation rendered possible by a higher rate of investment.

The implied price elasticity of demand in the range $20 to $40/bbl oil prices, and through an induction period of 10 to 20 years, is about −0.08 for overall primary energy and −0.05 for electricity. The income elasticities of demand also show a strong decrease relative to historic trends independent of the effect of increasing energy prices. This is due to multiple saturation effects in most energy end uses, as well as to changes in the mix of economic activities. In the high growth scenario for example, the "pure" income elasticity of demand for primary energy (overall) decreases from a very high average level of 1.61 in the period 1960 to 1972, to 0.95 in the period 1978 to 1985, and to 0.72 in the period 1985 to 2000. The "pure" income elasticity of demand for electricity follows a somewhat different path, increasing at first from 1.44 in the period 1960 to 1972, to 1.49 in the period 1978 to 1985 and then decreasing to 0.92 in the period 1985 to 2000.*

Notwithstanding the implied strong decrease in energy growth rates relative to historic trends, it is well to notice that the overall increase in demand can still be quite substantial in the period between 1978 and 2000. In the high GDP growth scenario, the increase amounts to 75% for overall primary energy and to 125% for electricity. This growth is sufficiently appreciable that even major efforts at substituting oil with coal and nuclear energy have relatively minor effects in the overall energy picture. The limitations in energy supply that seem likely to come to the fore toward the last decade of the century will clearly act as inhibitors of economic growth, unless the nature of this growth changes markedly in regard to its implications for energy consumption. The fairly drastic reduction in the income elasticities of demand implied in these projections is also a reflection of the impossibility of otherwise verifying a satisfactory level of economic growth.

The rather aggregate methodology underlying the energy demand projections does not easily allow fine tuning with respect to conversion losses from primary to secondary energy and other possible effects related to energy technology, issuing from within the economy. It can be estimated, however, that differences in conversion losses arising from an alternate mix of technologies, particularly in electricity production, have only a second order effect on energy demand in these scenarios. As a result, overall primary energy demand and electricity demand tend to be insensitive to most effects other than the rate of growth of GDP and oil price (Table 10-9).

There is a minor exception to this in the case of the oil limitation scenarios in which some of the oil shortfall is assumed to be made up by resorting to coal synthetics (with an implied 40% conversion loss). The increase of about 2%

---

* This discussion is based on the very simple econometric specification:

$$E = G^\alpha P^\beta$$

where E is energy consumption, G is GDP, P is the price of oil, and α and β are elasticities.

Table 10-9. Primary Energy Demand and Electricity Demand

	Total Primary Energy (mtce)			Electricity (10⁹ kWh)[1]		
	Reference	Oil Limitation	Nuclear Delay	Reference	Oil Limitation	Nuclear Delay
1977	201			171		
1985						
Low Coal Case	252	252	252	248	248	248
High Coal Case	250	250	250	248	248	248
1990						
Low Coal Case	286	286	286	277	277	277
High Coal Case	284	284	284	303	303	303
2000						
Low Coal Case	342	350	342	352	352	352
High Coal Case	352	358	352	384	384	384

[1] Electricity refers to production

in overall primary energy demand in 2000 is, however, barely appreciable. It may appear strange that in an oil-limited scenario there should be an increase in energy consumption, albeit slight. However, the increase is entirely due to coal and is an inevitable consequence of the conversion to synthetics, all else remaining equal. Limitations in oil supply in international markets are likely to lead to average oil prices higher than the $40/bbl envisaged for the reference scenario, so that it might be expected that further energy savings could be squeezed out of the system than occurs in the reference scenario. This must remain conjectural, but it seems difficult to believe that the Italian energy economy could present sufficient slack to allow an even more drastic decrease in energy/GDP ratios (in the time available) than is indicated in Figure 10-3, without impacting on the model of growth itself.

An altogether different situation arises in a combined oil limitation/nuclear delay scenario in which the energy constraints on the system are quite likely to impose negative effects on economic growth and therefore induce substantially different levels of energy demand. This case is so particular in its possible negative feedback on the economy that it is singled out for more detailed consideration in a subsequent section.

THE ELECTRIC-GENERATING MIX

Most of the electric-generating capacity in 1978 was oil based and quite recent, as can be seen from Table 10-10, so that it will be some time before existing stock can be substituted significantly by other fuels. Most of the potential for replacing oil in the electricity sector must therefore be sought in new capacity additions. In the future these will need to be concentrated in coal and nuclear power, to a certain extent in hydropower and geothermal energy and to a minor extent in natural gas. But in the coming five years or so, there seems to be no way that further capacity expansions in oil-fired plants can be avoided, primarily because over 10,000 MW are presently in various phases of construction. In considering the allocation of new capacity additions, it is useful to divide the period up to the end of the century into three parts:

209

Table 10-10. Existing Electric-Generating Capacity by Fuel and by Age Class in 1978 (MW)

Plant Type	Existing Capacity Dec. 31, 1977	Capacity Under Construction Dec. 31, 1977	Existing Capacity Installation Period				
			1970-77	1960-69	1950-59	1940-49	Before 1940
fossil steam	19,900	14,750	10,000	7,800	2,100	—	—
coal	300[1]	—	—	—	300	—	—
oil	19,600[2]	14,750	10,000	7,800	1,800	—	—
gas	—	—	—	—	—	—	—
gas turbines	800	2,200	540	170	90	—	—
hydroelectric	14,000	5,500	2,000	2,000	10,000	—	—
nuclear	500	3,000	—	350	150	—	—
geothermal	400	50	40	100	180	80	—
total	35,600	25,500	12,580	10,420	12,520	80	—

[1] Lignite
[2] Oil-fired capacity of which:
- 10,500 MW has dual-fired design for coal
- 3,500 MW has dual-fired design for gas

1978-1985

There are no differences between scenarios in this period since the assumptions are identical. No contributions above existing nuclear capacity are considered possible by 1985 on account of delays in power station siting. Moreover, no new coal capacity additions are envisaged before 1985, but only conversion, or more coal-intensive utilization, of some dual-purpose plants which have been burning largely fuel oil in the past. The total coal capacity assumed in service in 1983 amounts to 6,320 MW, compared to 2,040 MW in 1978, and breaks down as indicated in Table 10-11. This does not include lignite capacity located in Tuscany at the Santa Barbara and Pietrafitta lignite mines (a total of 218 MW) which, though quite old, are expected to be maintained in service up to 1985. Although these small plants have up to recently provided the principal contribution to solid-fueled power production in Italy, their role in 1985 will doubtless be quite marginal.

Minor increments are also expected from natural gas while additions to hydropower and geothermal capacity are unlikely to exceed 1,500 MW. Most of the increase in electric power capacity during the period to 1985 will inevitably be made up by oil-fired plants which are already licensed and under construction. Thus, notwithstanding some retirements in oil-fired capacity, and the increased use of coal, the contribution of oil to electric power production cannot help but increase between 1978 and 1985, albeit only slightly: from 51% to 52% in terms of primary energy input.

1985-1990

No new oil capacity additions are expected after 1985 and all new base capacity will need to come from either coal or nuclear power. This period is singled out since it is during these five years that significant differences begin to emerge between the scenario cases either in the actual capacity in service, or in perceptions about the future leading to modifications in plans for capacity additions.

Table 10-11. ENEL Program for Coal Conversion to 1983: Capacity Partly or Completely Running on Coal (MW)

	1978	1985
Genova	1 × 160	1 × 160
	2 × 70	—
La Spezia	2 × 320	2 × 320
	—	2 × 600
Fusina	2 × 160	2 × 160
	1 × 320	2 × 320
Monfalcone	2 × 160	2 × 160
Vado Ligure	—	4 × 320
Porto Marghera	2 × 70	—
Brindisi	—	4 × 320
Sulcis	—	2 × 240
total	2,040	6,320

a. *Reference and oil limitation scenarios.* At least a part of the capacity specified in the Italian nuclear program approved by Parliament (8,000 MW), is expected to be in place and producing electricity by 1990. At present, preliminary clearing activities have begun at Montalto di Castro (2 × 1,000 MW) but the siting procedures for the remaining 6,000 MW of the nuclear program are going ahead very slowly indeed. New additions to nuclear capacity in service by 1990 are assumed to total 4,000 MW, of which 2,000 MW are represented by Montalto di Castro, leading to a total of about 5,500 MW. This figure can be considered independent of high and low GDP growth as discussed below. The difference in capacity requirement after retirements is assumed to be made up by coal-fired plants and to a minor extent by natural gas, some hydropower and geothermal energy (~1,000 MW). Practically all dual-purpose power plants will have been converted to coal by 1985 and further increases in coal consumption will be dependent on new coal-based capacity.

Clearly it is not possible to know at the beginning of a long licensing and construction period (~10 years for nuclear power, 7 years for coal) whether economic growth will be high or low, and it may be questioned that the capacity mix in place by 1990 will be significantly different in the low and high GDP scenarios. The difference is real however, and is consolidated by the fact that the Low Coal Case (low growth) scenario assumes a policy choice distinctly in favor of nuclear energy while the High Coal Case (high growth) scenario assumes a choice that is more in favor of coal. In the low growth scenario, adjustments in new capacity additions to the lower electricity growth in 1985-90, can be expected to take place by slowing down construction in new coal-fired plants. Considering that 600 MW are retired, coal capacity in service actually declines in this scenario. These effects also explain why oil input to electricity generation is higher in the low GDP scenario. Even in this scenario however, the contribution of oil to electricity generation has started a marked decline by 1990, when it reaches 44%.

b. *Nuclear delay scenarios.* In this scenario it is assumed that slippage in the nuclear program decreases new additions to capacity by 1,000 MW relative to the reference scenarios. Thus, only 3,000 MW of new nuclear capacity can be considered available by 1990 in both high and low GDP growth scenarios, which include the 2 × 1,000 MW plants already ordered and under construction at Montalto di Castro. The difference in required capacity is assumed made up entirely by coal.

1990-2000

This is the period when very large differences open up between all scenarios considered.

a. *Reference scenarios.* The contribution of nuclear power in this period is the key variable in determining coal-fired capacity additions. The assumptions for nuclear capacity in service by 2000 are 21 GW in the Low Coal Case (high nuclear) scenario and 14 GW in the High Coal Case (low nuclear) scenario. All new capacity additions necessary to fill the gap between peak demand (including reserves) and existing supply (detracting retirements), are assumed coal-based except for a small quantity of natural gas capacity and some, by now minor, increments from hydropower and geothermal energy (~1 GW). Oil input to electricity generation, as might be expected, drops markedly in this period, reaching around 25% in the year 2000, in both scenarios.

b. *Oil limitation scenarios.* Over half of the 20% oil shortfall occurring in the period 1990 to 2000 is assumed to be made up in electricity generation by early retirement or standby use of base oil-fired plants. Specifically, annual oil input to electricity generation is assumed to drop by 18 mtce in both high and low GDP scenarios. New coal and nuclear capacity required to make up for the difference, are taken as 6 GW and 5 GW in the High Coal Case (low nuclear) scenario and respectively 5 GW and 6 GW in the Low Coal Case (high nuclear) scenario. In principle, further increments in coal consumption for power production could come from burning coal/oil mixtures in existing oil-based power plants without the need for new capacity additions and correspondingly high investments. Suspensions of up to 50% coal in oil could substantially relieve demand for fuel oil and provide an important instrument for easing the transition to alternative energy systems in periods of oil shortages foreseen for the future. This possibility is not presently incorporated in the projections since its technological feasibility is yet to be demonstrated. In any event, it would not make any substantial difference to the additional quantity of coal required in these scenarios.

c. *Nuclear delay scenarios.* It is assumed that slippage of nuclear programs during the Eighties carries its delaying effect over into the Nineties. Nuclear power capacity installed in 2000 is reduced to 30% below that in the reference scenario in both High and Low Coal Cases, leading respectively to 15 and 10 GW in this year. All nuclear capacity that does not materialize under a nuclear delay is assumed made up by coal-fired plants, on the grounds that these have shorter licensing and construction times.

212

COAL UTILIZATION IN SECTORS OTHER THAN ELECTRICITY GENERATION

SYNTHETIC FUELS

In the case of a country like Italy, without extensive coal resources, it could be argued that the very high transport component of landed costs, coupled with the uncertain and probably increasing prices of coal, could make the synthetic fuels option uneconomic even under increasing oil prices. This is left as an open question since the answer depends on the technology for conversion as well as the availability and price of alternative fuels, but clearly the synthetic fuels option in Italy might be somewhat penalized relative to countries with ample coal resources and low transport costs. In any event, it can be safely assumed that even for technological reasons alone, there will not be any gasification or liquefaction capacity in place in Italy before the 1990's.

Some gasification may be expected to occur by the end of the century, at least in the more intensive coal use scenarios. The underlying assumption is that high Btu gasification technology will be commercial by 1990. This is probably a good assumption, given the increasing prices of oil and natural gas foreseen around this time. The market for gasified coal naturally extends to all markets competing for natural gas. Since these markets are quite large, the technical limit to the amount of coal that can be introduced into the economy through gasification is set by the supply expansion capacity of synthetic natural gas plants and coal importing terminals.

It also seems possible to assume that the combined interaction of technology and increasing oil price will make coal liquefaction an economic option during the course of the 1990's. However, plants will probably not have been scaled up as much as in the case of the more advanced gasification technology. It can be argued that the prospects for coal liquefaction in Italy are not as good as for gasification. It would, in fact, be cheaper to liquefy the coal at minemouth and transport the liquid, rather than transport the solid and liquefy it in Italy. In the case of gasification, there is generally no choice but to transport the solid because of the very high cost of liquid gas transport. Against this argument is the fact that liquefaction abroad implies large foreign investment flows which raise problems of security and opportunity in the allocation of capital resources.

These considerations, though important, are not critical to this study, however, since the actual assumptions on coal requirements for synthetic fuels production and accompanying oil substitution in Italy, are relatively insensitive to the mix between liquefaction and gasification.

a. *Reference and nuclear delay scenarios.* Synthetic fuels from coal are assumed to be produced only in the high GDP growth scenarios, which are also High Coal Case scenarios. Specifically, 8 mtce of coal are employed for this purpose in 2000, which could be distributed in three facilities, say two for gasification consuming 3 mtce/yr each, and one for liquefaction consuming 2 mtce/yr. Assuming 60% conversion efficiency gives a total production of 25×10^{12} kcal/yr of synthetic natural gas and about 8×10^{12} kcal/yr of coal liquids, which contribute together less than 7-8% of oil and gas consumption in 2000. A significant part of this synthetic fuels capacity could be located at the Sulcis brown coalfield in Sardinia. This field, the only coalfield of importance in Italy, is presently awaiting reopening. One of the economic options under discussion

213

is gasification of its high-sulphur, low-Btu coal. Maximum production from this field (total proved reserves about 400×10^6 t brown coal) is about 4×10^6 t/yr (about 3 mtce/yr) so that part of this could in principal provide the input for a gasification plant.

b. *Oil limitation scenarios.* A significant part of the shortfall in oil is assumed to be made up by recourse to synthetic fuels from coal. Specifically 19 mtce are input for gasification and liquefaction in the low GDP scenario and 22 mtce in the high GDP scenario in 2000. These quantities correspond to about 6 to 7 full-sized plants and cover respectively 38% and 41% of the oil shortfall.

INDUSTRIAL HEAT

In recent times there has been awakening interest on the demand side to the potentialities of solid coal combustion for industrial heat. As discussed elsewhere in this study, this potential demand has yet to come to terms with problems of costs and availability on the supply side, as well as environmental problems in general. There are few industrial sectors for which increased solid coal consumption would be an economic option over the next two decades. This is mainly because of the relatively small parcel quantities of coal involved to satisfy Italy's typically dispersed industrial heat demands, and the correspondingly very high infrastructure and transport costs involved. There is, in fact, only one sector, cement production, for which solid coal seems to have a promising future in the coming years. This is because of the relatively high quantities of coal that would be involved up to the last phase of distribution (see the section on coal transportation) and the high component cost of energy in the total factor cost of production.

Cement production is expected to increase at a decelerating rate with respect to GDP, at an elasticity averaging 0.6 over the period from 1978 to 2000. The assumption is made that 50% and 40% of new capacity is based on coal respectively in the higher and lower oil price scenarios, independent of other scenario conditions. Most of the coal penetration (between 60% and 70%) however, is expected to occur gradually over time through replacement of existing oil-burning capital stock. Payback times for conversion presently range from 3 to 6 years, with the lower value applying to locations close to the main points of entry of steam coal into the country. The economics, however, appear more attractive in the light of anticipated increases in oil price which could reduce payback times to 2 or 3 years. Coal contribution to cement production increases from 7% in 1978 (up from less than 1% in 1976), to 20% and 30% in 1985 in the low and high GDP scenarios, and to 40% and 45% respectively in 2000.

METALLURGICAL COAL

On account of slower growth in basic demand sectors and substitution from other materials, steel requirements are expected to increase considerably slower than GDP, specifically with an elasticity averaging 0.6 over the period 1978 to 2000. Moreover, substitution of coal in metallurgy is expected from electricity through increased recycling via the electric furnace. Coal substitution in the iron and steel industry will also be occurring indirectly through increasing imports of basic steel (particularly in the form of sponge) for later reworking. Taking these various factors into account results in annual metallurgical coal consumption showing only a small increase to 11.5 mtce in 1990 and 12 mtce in 2000, from today's level of 11.1 mtce.

OIL AND COAL DEPENDENCE

The oil and coal dependence that emerges from the scenario assumptions out-lined in the previous pages is detailed in Table 10-12. Increase in oil demand is reasonably contained even in the reference scenarios, where it rises to between 11% and 18% above the 1978 levels. The 20% shortfall assumed to occur in the oil limitation scenarios actually leads to lower levels of oil consumption than in 1977. Oil consumption results somewhat higher in the low growth scenarios, but this must be attributed to use in sectors other than electricity generation and may be accounted for, at least in part, by the greater quantities of synthetic fuel substituting for oil in the high GDP scenarios. The share of oil in overall primary energy consumption decreases steadily from a high of 68% in 1977, to 64% in 1985, to 58% and 54% in 1990 respectively in the low and high GDP scenarios. In 2000 the share drops further to 47% and 43% respectively in the low and high GDP reference and nuclear delay scenarios, and to 37% and 34% in the oil limitation scenarios.

Table 10-12. Oil and Coal Dependence (mtce/yr)

	Oil			Steam Coal		
	Reference	Oil Limitation	Nuclear Delay	Reference	Oil Limitation	Nuclear Delay
1977	136			3		
1985						
Low Coal Case	162	162	162	11	11	11
High Coal Case	159	159	159	12	12	12
1990						
Low Coal Case	164	164	164	12	12	13
High Coal Case	153	153	153	21	21	23
2000						
Low Coal Case	162	130	162	20	47	30
High Coal Case	151	121	151	49	73	56

The figures include domestic production, about 3 mtce/yr, for both oil and coal.

The reason for studying a number of different basic cases is to obtain a feeling for the sensitivity of coal consumption with respect to the most important under-lying variables. Metallurgical coal can conveniently be excluded from this discus-sion because it does not increase markedly above 1978 levels and any problematique related to its importation and use should not be substantially different from today. Steam coal use, on the other hand, increases substantially in all scenarios and in some cases quite dramatically. There is a fairly big jump in coal use between 1978 and 1985 which corresponds to existing plans for conversion of dual-purpose oil plants and there is thus very little difference between Low and High Coal Case scenarios in this time scale. Between 1985 and 1990, however, the effect of new coal-fired capacity coming on line as part of a preconceived strategy makes itself clearly felt. In the high GDP scenario, steam coal consumption increases from 12 to 21 mtce/yr (23 mtce/yr in case of a nuclear delay) in these five years, while it remains unchanged in the Low Coal Case scenario, tendentially a high nuclear scenario, except in the event of a nuclear delay, and even then it increases by only 1 mtce.

Most of the increase in steam coal consumption takes place in the last decade of the century and this is why it becomes so important to focus on this period, given that it is only 10 years away. Even in the Low Coal Case reference scenario, steam coal consumption increases to 20 mtce/yr by 2000. In all other cases it is higher than 30 mtce/yr. The highest level of consumption (73 mtce/yr) would be occurring in the high GDP oil limitation scenario. As evidenced by the scenarios considered, it is therefore possible to imagine a substantially increased role for steam coal in the Italian energy economy. From a low level of 1.5% of overall primary energy consumption achieved in 1978, steam coal can increase its share to about 5% in 1985, to as much as 9% in 1990, and to as much as 21% in 2000. Even in the lowest coal scenario considered, steam coal imports in 2000 amount to about 20 mt (assuming an average heat content of 6000 kcal/kg) and this will require no mean effort in planning and development of transport infrastructures and related topics. In the highest coal scenario, steam coal imports in 2000 amount to 82 mt, and this will require an exceptional amount of planning and development, and above all, a high degree of private and political voluntarism.

THE CASE OF AN EXTENDED NUCLEAR DELAY COMPOUNDED WITH LIMITATIONS IN OIL SUPPLY

This section briefly describes the type of response that is open to the Italian energy system in a situation in which an extended nuclear delay were compounded with oil supply limitations toward the end of this century. This description leaves aside all manner of transition problems which would arise if an oil gap of the implied dimensions were suddenly to open up in the course of a few years, and assumes smooth adjustments in the internal structure of the Italian energy economy. Clearly these are optimistic assumptions, given the very short time scale available for action, so that the real situation is likely to be more dramatic than suggested here.

The shortfall in nuclear power is felt directly in electricity production. If all the unavailable nuclear power were replaced by coal, and if, over and above this, steam coal were to replace oil in electricity generation to the extent required in the oil limitation scenarios, then the quantity of steam coal required to maintain the same level of electricity consumption in 2000 would be 69 mtce in the low GDP scenario and 89 mtce in the high GDP scenario. These levels of steam coal consumption correspond to an actual tonnage imported in 2000 of respectively 77 and 100 mt.

Leaving aside the purely ecological and economic aspects, which might by themselves designate such a response as infeasible, there would also be a serious problem of lead times. While the coal import requirement of a nuclear delay by itself might conceivably be manageable with sufficient advanced planning, the combination of a nuclear delay with limitations in oil supply (assuming no change in demand) would create a large surge in steam coal consumption, of a further 39 and 34 mtce/yr respectively in the low and high GDP scenarios, in the space of less than a decade. This is over and above the already substantial levels of 30 and 56 mtce/yr of a nuclear delay scenario and would require deciding, locating and building 2 to 3 additional coal terminals in less than 10 years, together with a host of other infrastructure and power plant conversion problems. Adding to this the difficulties that would be encountered in finding sufficient coal on the international market, and the probably very high prices that this would command, makes this type of response seem totally unmanageable.

The compounding of a nuclear delay with limitations in oil supply toward the end of this century would almost certainly lead to a lower rate of economic growth relative to the original scenarios. It is possible to obtain a rough estimate of the maximum drop in GDP growth by making the simple assumption that there would be no increase in coal consumption above the nuclear delay scenario levels, and that the oil shortfall would be allocated to consumption sectors in direct proportion to potential demand. In this case there would be a 17% and a 19% shortfall in electricity consumption in the year 2000, respectively, in the high and low growth scenarios, which is consistent with an 0.3% to 0.4% drop in the rate of GDP growth. The actual drop in GDP growth would depend on the amount of extra coal that could be brought into the economy, beyond the nuclear delay levels without advance planning. It seems unlikely that this could increase beyond another 10 mtce/yr, which would allow containment of the drop in GDP growth to less than 0.2% to 0.3%.

THE TRANSPORT COMPONENT OF A SUSTAINED COAL IMPORT SCENARIO

Coal imports to Italy in 1978 amounted to 13.1 mtce, equivalent to about 14.9 mt. Of these, 10.6 mtce were metallurgical coal. The remaining 2.5 mtce, consisting of steam coal, were imported in roughly equal portions from Poland and South Africa. Already in 1979, however, imports from South Africa represented two-thirds of the whole. Transport was directly to the Enel power plants burning the coal, or through the port of Savona for inland distribution (Table 10-13). Polish coal has normally been landed in the Northern Adriatic ports, while South African coal has generally gone to the Northern Tyrrhenian ports. Overland distribution to cement plants and to the residential and commercial sector occurs mostly through the rail junction at San Giuseppe di Cairo Montenotte, located 328 meters above sea level, and connected to Savona by funicular (maximum capacity 2.2 mt/yr). On a weight basis, however, about twice as much coal presently travels by road than by rail, mostly on account of the final distribution stage after rail transport.

Table 10-13. Steam Coal Imports by Port in 1978

Port/Power Plant	Coal Imports (mtce)	Draft Restrictions on Ship Size (thousand dwt)
Fusina	0.52	24
Monfalcone	0.44	8 — 9
Porto Marghera	0.17	16
La Spezia	0.47	45 — 50
Genova	0.07	24
Vado Ligure/Savona	0.11	45 — 50
total	1.78	

Steam coal importation and distribution does not pose any significant logistic problems today because of the relatively small quantity of coal involved and its dilution over space and in time. The levels of coal use projected in the scenarios for the year 2000 are, however, considerably higher, with coal playing a more strategic role in the energy economy. This will undoubtedly require an extensive overhaul in transport infrastructures if there are to be no bottlenecks in the provisioning and distribution of coal. The most critical feature of this change, in the case of Italy, is related to the importation and landing of coal. This could not be carried out efficiently and cheaply using the relatively small carriers (20 to 50 thousand dwt) that are normally possible under present draft restrictions in ports (Tables 10-13 and 10-14) and without considerable changes in layout, installations and other characteristics of the ports themselves.

Table 10-14. Existing Draft Restrictions in Ports by Length of Approach (km)

Port Location	Depth (m)							
	<8	8/10	10/12	12/14	14/16	16/18	>18	total
upper Adriatic	24.0	23.8	4.0	—	1.6	3.0	—	56.4
lower Adriatic	12.8	3.9	1.3	0.3	—	—	—	18.3
Jonian	8.9	7.8	3.5	3.4	0.8	1.1	2.4	27.9
lower Tyrrhenian	20.8	10.1	1.7	1.1	—	—	—	33.7
upper Tyrrhenian	20.0	22.8	6.5	1.3	0.7	—	—	51.3
total	86.5	68.4	17.0	6.1	3.1	4.1	2.4	187.6

Includes industrial and oil tanker dry-dock approaches.

The high levels of throughput projected imply that even as early as 1990, shipments from coal-producing countries could be effected more cheaply—and even at somewhat lower investment costs—by transshipment through large terminals provisioned by bulk carriers in the order of 100 thousand dwt and greater. In the case of Italy, which will have to import its coal from generally very great distances, the transshipment option offers the possibility of taking advantage of the considerable savings on long-distance ocean transport available through economies of scale, where the ports of final destination cannot be adapted—except at very high costs—to receive large carriers.

It is estimated below that the overall cost difference between transshipment from large bulk carriers and transport in small carriers would be in the order of $18/tce which contributes 1.1 billion US $/yr in the case of a 60 mtce/yr import scenario. While this may seem small in the overall economic picture, amounting to less than 0.6% of today's GDP, it is not so small in terms of unit costs since it is equivalent to something in the order of a 60% increase in the transport contribution to the CIF costs of landed coal calculated for 2000.

Another merit of bulk transshipment terminals is that they avoid the irregularity of supply due to large distances of transport, given the possibility of a large enough coal storage area. In effect, a large transshipment terminal importing 20 mt per year with a 20% (4 mt) continuous storage capacity, can be thought of as

218

a local coal mine combining strategic stockpiling functions of all the power plants it provisions, at lower overall average stock and hence lower total stockpiling costs. In the case of Italy, with generally limited land area, this aspect of the transshipment option assumes considerable importance.

While most of the coal imported into Italy will be consumed in power plants situated on the seacoast, there will be some opportunity, and even some strategic space, for extending coal use inland through waterways and overland travel by road and rail. These possibilities are therefore also investigated in the following assessment of transport systems and economic costs. It is emphasized that the main aim of this exercise is not to propose a solution to the problem of sustained coal imports to Italy. This would require enormously more extensive analysis than has been possible in this study. An attempt has instead been made to provide estimates for the economic cost and other critical parameters of transport systems, to use as a basis for an overall assessment of energy strategy. For this reason the analysis will be very vague with regard to the territorial pattern of coal consumption, the location of transshipment terminals and ports of final destination, the overland distribution of coal and other assumptions. Although specific locations have had to be used as proxies in the rather detailed calculations underlying this study, only in those cases where plans are already fairly firm is there any attempt to actually identify the sites involved.

The estimates rely, moreover, on critical assumptions about unit investment costs, capacity utilization, operation and maintenance, etc. Clearly, the detailed results will be sensitive to all these specific assumptions, particularly at the local level. The more aggregated results seem, however, to be relatively insensitive so that it is possible to be confident in the principal result of the analysis which is that economic costs of transport infrastructures should not provide a constraint on even very sustained levels of coal use in Italy.

The level of steam coal imports chosen for the analysis is 60 mtce/yr, higher than both the low and high reference assumptions of respectively 16.5 and 45.5 mtce/yr imported steam coal consumption in the year 2000, but lower than the very high import level which obtains under a nuclear delay or oil limitation in these projections. It is not necessary to consider metallurgical coal imports, which increase only very slightly to around 12 mtce/yr by 2000, since the related infrastructures are already in existence, vertically integrated into the iron and the steel industry. The high starting assumption should not be taken as implying that a very sustained coal import scenario is either favored or the most likely. However, it is only by referring to a relatively high coal import and transport scenario, that it is possible to develop all the transport systems involved to beyond a critical mass necessary for a minimal analysis, and hence obtain a significant measure of the nationwide logistics and cost. The unit cost parameters obtained from this analysis for all the many elements of the transport system can be extended fairly generally to other scenarios and have indeed been used in the study to estimate the transport costs in the various scenario cases.

BASIC TERRITORIAL ASSUMPTIONS

The basic territorial assumptions relate specifically to the demand centers (power plants, coal synthetics plants and cement plants) where the coal is finally consumed, to the supply centers (terminals) where the coal is originally imported into the country, and to the redistribution centers (coastal ports or inland ports) which sometimes provide a necessary intermediate logistic stage between supply and final consumption. Clearly, the choice of all these elements of the picture represents the result of a compromise between the many factors that enter into the complex decision process which frequently takes the form of repeated iterations between variable supply, redistribution and consumption configurations. The following basic reasoning and assumptions have entered into the simulated decision-making process.

THE LOCATION OF DEMAND CENTERS

The sectoral distribution of coal consumption in this assessment is not tied to any particular one of the scenarios treated in the previous sections. The sustained level of coal use assumed, however, places it conceptually in the class of higher GDP, oil limitation or nuclear delay scenarios. The level of coal use in cement production and in industrial underboiler uses has been assumed at 3 mtce/yr, the same as in the High Coal Case scenario. Similarly, 11 mtce/yr have been assumed input to gasification and liquefaction, somewhat more than in the High Coal Case reference scenario. The difference, 46 mtce/yr, has been assumed input to electricity generation, which compares with the low and high nuclear delay scenario levels of 47 and 56 mtce/yr.

The location of demand centers used in the calculations is indicated in Table 10-15. Half of the 3 mtce/yr employed in cement production are assumed located in the Po Valley within easy reach of the Po River and canal system, and the remaining 1.5 mtce/yr distributed elsewhere around the Peninsula. The distribution

Table 10-15. Regional Distribution of Imported Coal Consumption by Final Use Sector in 2000 (mtce/yr)

Region	Industrial Heat	Synthetics	Electricity	Total
Piemonte	0.2	—	4.2	4.4
Val d'Aosta	—	—	—	—
Lombardia	0.5	—	4.2	4.7
Trentino—Alto Adige	—	—	—	—
Veneto	0.3	—	0.7	1.0
Friuli—Venezia Giulia	—	—	8.4	8.4
Liguria	—	—	2.2	2.2
Emilia—Romagna	0.5	—	—	0.5
Toscana	0.5	—	4.2	4.7
Umbria	—	—	—	—
Marche	—	—	4.2	4.2
Lazio	—	—	—	—
Abruzzi	—	—	4.2	4.2
Molise	—	—	—	—
Campania	—	—	4.2	4.2
Puglia	0.5	—	5.3	5.8
Basilicata	—	—	—	—
Calabria	0.3	11.0	4.2	15.5
Sicilia	0.2	—	—	0.2
Sardegna	—	—	—	—
Total	3.0	11.0	46.0	60.0

Consumption of coal in Veneto, Liguria and Puglia includes contributions from presently existing power plants located respectively at Fusina (0.7 mtce/yr), Vado Ligure (2.2 mtce/yr) and Brindisi (1.1 mtce/yr).

by plant size is chosen similar to the existing situation, while distribution by distance is assumed rapidly falling with distance as indicated in Table 10-16. The final stage of coal delivery to cement plants is assumed to take place invariably by road. This is because it is generally short-distance, low-volume distribution.

Table 10-16. Coal Distribution for Cement Production by Plant Consumption and by Distance (10^3 tce/yr)

Distance from Point of Distribution (km)	Plant Consumption (10^3 tce/yr)				
	<30	30/70	70/100	>100	total
<50	160 (8)	400 (8)	360 (4)	560 (4)	1480 (24)
50/100	180 (9)	200 (4)	540 (6)	280 (6)	1200 (21)
>100	40 (2)	100 (2)	180 (2)	—	320 (6)
total	380 (19)	700 (14)	1080 (12)	840 (10)	3000 (51)

Figures in parentheses refer to number of plants. Average distances used in the assessment of road transport requirements are 30, 80 and 155 km respectively, for the three distance classes.

All coal synthetics capacity is assumed concentrated in one large complex located in Southern Italy and, to minimize transport costs, this has been assumed located in close proximity to the lower Tyrrhenian terminal (see below). Although major load centers for high Btu gas consumption are in the North, a Southern location for gasification was chosen in order to give a better match to potential terminal import capacities, space availability, and industrial overload in general. This should not involve any logistic problems, given the existence of pipeline transport from South to North, and indeed provides a lower cost solution under the import terminal constraints, since it is cheaper to transport gas than coal.

The regional location of electric-generating capacity has been based on most plausible development of load centers within the year 2000, existing capacity and most probable plans for capacity retirement. In all cases except for existing power plants, it has been assumed that generating capacity will take the form of 4 units by 640 MW (about 4.2 mtce/yr steam coal consumption).

In most cases, generating capacity has been assumed located in the close neighborhood of terminals or coastal ports in order to minimize transport costs. There are three basic exceptions to this, in particular the power plants in Friuli, Lombardia, and Piemonte, which assume an inland location from coastal ports. It is emphasized that while these inland locations are possible candidates for power plant sites, they are not necessarily the most likely, nor the most convenient, and owe their choice to purposes of illustration. In the case of Friuli and Piemonte, this choice was suggested in order to include in the analysis the logistics and costs of rail transport, while in the case of Lombardia, where the power plant is located on the Po River, the purpose was to evidence the logistics and costs of river and canal transport.

THE LOCATION OF SUPPLY CENTERS

Steam coal is assumed to be imported by sea through four transshipment terminals located on the Peninsula as follows, reading clockwise: the first in the northernmost reaches of the Adriatic, the second close to the heel on the Southern

Adriatic, the third above the southernmost tip on the Tyrrhenian, and the last in the North-Central Tyrrhenian.

This choice represents the least cost of delivery solution, taking into account:

- the clustering of coal consumption in four broad centroids which can be identified from the demand analysis,
- the physical and territorial characteristics of potential terminal locations, and
- the lower cost of ocean transport relative to transport by feeder ship.

Four broad coal consumption centroids can be recognized, on the basis of the demand assumptions, consisting in 19.0 mtce/yr located around the upper Adriatic basin, 9.5 mtce/yr along the lower half of the Adriatic, 19.4 mtce/yr on the lower Tyrrhenian, and 10.6 mtce/yr converging on the upper Tyrrhenian basin. While in principle a number of other terminal locations could have been identified, perhaps with some regrouping of the load centers, there are severe limitations in terminal potentialities which discount most other solutions on the Peninsula. These relate to deep-water facilities beyond 16 meters, that can be developed at reasonable cost to accommodate tankers carrying beyond 100 thousand, and as much as 200 thousand dwt, sufficient storage space availability to allow storage of up to 20-25% of yearly throughput on a continuous basis (requiring about 0.2 km² for each mtce stored), adequate protection from adverse sea conditions and, last but not least, possible congestion from other sea-going traffic.

One of the major problems relates to draft restrictions in ports. Presently, only 4% of all dock approaches could accommodate carriers holding 100 thousand dwt and only 1% carriers holding 150 thousand dwt. Only one dock can presently accommodate 200-thousand dwt carriers. Extensive dredging and port reconstruction will clearly be necessary in order that the specified transshipment terminals may materialize. This will add very noticeably to their cost and maintenance.

It would also have been conceivable to assume location of a large terminal in Sardinia. Local steam-coal demand would not easily have justified this, however, particularly in view of appreciable local brown coal supply from the Sulcis mine which in the reference scenarios has been assumed to be exploited at the rate of 3 mtce/yr in 2000. Such a solution also appears to involve substantially higher transshipment costs, since onward transport by large tankers carrying more than 100 thousand dwt is almost an order of magnitude cheaper than transport by 10-20-thousand dwt feeder ships. A location on Sardinia, however, cannot be totally discounted because of the very favorable characteristics of possible terminals, particularly in view of future steam-coal potential that might develop beyond 2000.

For similar reasons it seems difficult to justify a large transshipment terminal in the Jonian Sea, although port characteristics might favor this location, except by going possibly to giant sizes of 30 mt/yr import capacity and more to take the place of the postulated lower Adriatic and lower Tyrrhenian terminals together. An argument strongly in favor of such a location is the existence of deep-water reaches in the Jonian Sea, of which Taranto is, of course, the prime example, while the waterline along the whole of the Southern Adriatic is relatively shallow and would require extensive dredging solutions.

While there are still some economies of scale in fixed-investment costs to be reaped by going to extra-large terminals, a comparison of overall delivery costs under alternative terminal sizes and locations, assuming the given territorial distribution of coal consumption, indicates that four intermediate- and large-size terminals, approximately located around the coastline, provides a considerably more economic solution than one or two super-sized terminals. Here again, however, the difference is not so great that such an alternative solution could be altogether discounted, particularly if other noneconomic or nontechnical factors are included in the assessment.

This study considers only current coal transport technologies. It may be expected, however, that developments in new technologies will permit alternative terminal import solutions on the shallow coastlines of the Adriatic and elsewhere that do not require extensive dredging. Restricted draft design bulk carriers allow for a reduction in deep-water requirements by as much as 15% to 20%. While capital costs of transport equipment involved may increase by 10% due to the broad beam design, the cost of dredging, which is in large part a running cost, is very significantly reduced, so that this technology could provide, overall, a more economic way of importing coal. Slurry ships, as another example, offer the advantage that they can be unloaded from an offshore buoy if there are draft limitations at the port, although there are serious downstream problems of environmental nature which have to be solved, and added costs associated with dewatering of the coal slurry. These and other possible solutions have not been investigated in this study, also because they are not presently available on a commercial scale and are unlikely to become important before the last decade of this century.

The level of coal consumption in the demand centroids specified above, the physical and territorial characteristics of the chosen terminals and a consideration of the trade-offs between transport by ocean carriers and transport by feeder ships, suggest the level of steam coal imports according to terminal given in Table 10-17. These have been used in the transport analysis as a basis for estimating terminal planning capacities, also indicated in the table, employed later in the estimates of investment costs. These terminal capacities may appear large by some conventional standards. If, however, the level of coal imports aimed at for the year 2000 is anywhere near the figure of 60 mtce/yr, the choice is inescapably in the range of 5 to 6 small-size terminals at one extreme and 2 or 3 super-sized terminals at the other, so that the choice of 4 intermediate-size terminals appears to represent a balanced compromise.

Table 10-17. Coal Imports by Terminal and Terminal Capacity in 2000

	Imports (mtce/yr)	Capacity (mt/yr)
upper Adriatic	17.1	20
lower Adriatic	11.9	15
lower Tyrrhenian	19.9	25
upper Tyrrhenian	11.1	15
total	60.0	75

Average heat content of imported coal taken as 6000 kcal/kg.

Twenty years may be a long enough planning time to achieve this. At present, however, only the lower Tyrrhenian terminal can be identified with some certainty. The Italian Government, in fact, has recently indicated in Gioia Tauro, located some 30 km above the Straits of Messina, the probable site of a first transshipment terminal in Italy. This is a new port begun in 1974 originally to serve a large steel complex—a project which has more recently been abandoned—and construction of port facilities and preparation of ground area is already well under way.

THE LOCATION OF REDISTRIBUTION CENTERS

According to the demand specifications, almost 45 mtce/yr, or 75% of all imported steam coal is consumed in the immediate vicinity of transshipment terminals or coastal ports and therefore require no further transport. The location of these receiving centers presents no further problem since they are identified with the demand centers (power plants or synthetics plants, and to some extent, cement plants) which they represent.

There are, however, also receiving centers that owe their existence to the necessity of transmitting coal from terminals or coastal ports on to inland final consumption centers, with minimal overland travel, though there may actually be no local consumption. The location of these redistribution centers has been established by minimizing the cost of delivery between terminals and final consumption centers. The minor of the two coastal redistribution centers postulated, handling some 5.7 mtce/yr, is conditioned by the existence of a potentially high-volume river and canal system reaching up to 250 km inland (as the crow flies) with an outlet into the sea in the Northern Adriatic basin. All the coal landed in this port, assumed located in Emilia-Romagna, is required on the Po River either to feed the power complex situated about 350 km upstream on the river itself in Lombardia, or to be further distributed from river ports for cement production (see Figure 10-4).

Figure 10-4. Coal Delivery to Inland Final Consumption Centers (mtce) (circles identify river tract)

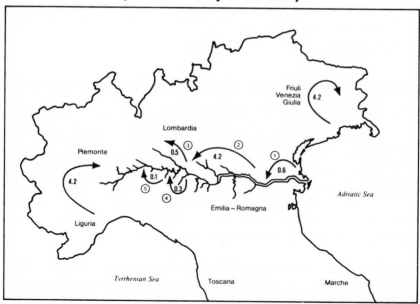

The major coastal redistribution center located in the northernmost arch of Liguria, and handling about 6.4 mtce/yr, serves the purpose of feeding the existing power plants at Vado, located on the coast, and of providing a landing for coal to be consumed at the power complex located inland in Piemonte. The only other redistribution centers are the small river ports already mentioned above, ranging from 0.1 to 0.6 mtce/yr throughput capacity and identified in Figure 10-4.

The level of coal consumption in the proximity of terminal and coastal ports and the level of coal in transit through redistribution centers, results in the levels of coal throughput by coastal and river ports given in Table 10-18. These have been used as a basis for estimating port planning capacities, also indicated in the table, and are necessary in the ultimate assessment of investment costs.

Table 10-18. Coal Landed by Port and Port Capacities in 2000

	Coal Landed (mtce/yr)	Port Capacity (mt/yr)
coastal ports	38.0	
Venezia Giulia	4.2	5.0
Veneto	0.7	0.8
Emilia-Romagna	5.7	7.0
Marche	4.2	5.0
Abruzzi	4.2	5.0
Puglia	4.2	5.0
Campania	4.2	5.0
Toscana	4.2	5.0
Liguria	6.4	8.0
river and canal ports	5.7	
Emilia-Romagna	0.6	0.7
Lombardia	4.2	5.0
"	0.5	0.6
"	0.3	0.4
"	0.1	0.2

Average heat content of coal taken as 6000 kcal/kg.

It will be evident from the above description that substantial feedback is involved in the choice of location of demand, supply and redistribution centers, and this seems natural in view of the many participating decision centers. Describing the major features of the related decision process is not so straightforward a matter, because of the many iterations and reassessments that are involved in balancing the many variables with the constraints. It is inevitable that the results of the assessment described below will be somewhat sensitive to the territorial assumptions. While the analysis does not rule out other territorial configurations it seems unlikely, however, that the differences in unit costs obtained could be significantly greater than the uncertainties due to all the many other assumptions that need to be made, and certainly not great enough to alter the basic conclusions of the study.

BASIC TRANSPORT ASSUMPTIONS

This section focuses on the operating characteristics and magnitude of the transport systems required to deliver steam coal from producing countries to final consumption centers, given the territorial configuration outlined in the previous section. As already indicated, the territorial configuration has been obtained, in part, through a consideration of related transport systems and costs and the separate treatment of the two topics has been suggested in the interest of clarity of presentation. There are five basic systems to be taken into consideration: ocean transport, coastal transport, river and canal transport, and overland transport by road and rail.

OCEAN TRANSPORT

Required infrastructure in ocean carriers is based on the following assumptions:

a. *Trade flows.* Coal trade flows to Italy have been established on the principle of maximum diversification of sources within expected supply expansion capacity of producing countries, and perceptions of competing diversification strategies from other importing countries. Imports to the various transshipment terminals by country of origin (Figure 10-5) are determined by applying a simple criterion of least cost shipping route, which usually amounts to least distance. Shipping distances have been established by assuming for simplicity the following ports of origin:

Australia:	Newcastle
China:	Lu-ta
Colombia:	Cartagena
India:	Calcutta
Indonesia:	Jakarta
Poland:	Gdansk
South Africa:	Richards Bay
United States:	Hampton Roads

and that coal imports from the Far East and Australia pass through the Suez Canal, while imports from other regions pass through Gibraltar.

Figure 10-5. International Coal Trade Flows to Italy in the Year 2000 (mtce/yr)

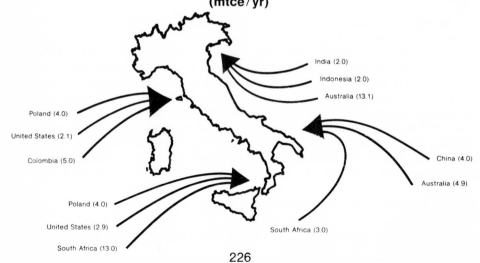

Some doubt may be expressed as to the possibility of 200 thousand dwt tankers passing through the Suez Canal. Presently only 60 thousand dwt tankers can use this route. The canal is, however, in the process of being deepened to accommodate up to 100 thousand dwt carriers, probably by 1982. Existing plans to bring the capacity to 150 thousand dwt seem to be stalling for lack of demand. If coal trade does build up to the levels assumed for Italy and the rest of the world in this study, then there would be every justification to deepen the canal to take 150 thousand, and even 200 thousand, dwt carriers, so that these assumptions can be considered internally consistent. On the other hand, if the Suez Canal is not deepened sufficiently, then coal trade from the Far East and Australia would either have to occur in smaller ships, or would have to pass around the Cape of Good Hope, determining in turn either poor economies of scale or greatly increased distances. Both of these alternatives lead to considerable increases in capital and running costs that can be estimated in the order of 50%.

Clearly, canal charges would increase substantially, and may be so high relative to some trading routes that the preferred choice might be around the Cape of Good Hope. In the case of exports from Richards Bay in South Africa, for example, the shorter distance through the Suez Canal is offset by the higher canal charges, which is the reason why a route through Gibraltar has been preferred as the trading assumption. In the case of coal trade from Australia, on the other hand, the alternative through the Suez Canal provides the cheaper route even assuming the very high canal charges (up to $4/t) that would accrue in the event that the canal had to be deepened to take 150 thousand dwt and greater tonnage.

b. *Carrier size.* Three basic ship sizes are assumed, depending on shipping distance:

100 thousand dwt   up   to 16 thousand km round trip
150   "   " from 16 to 24   "   "   "   "
200   "   " over   24   "   "   "   "

The criterion for this choice is related to economies of scale in maritime transport and logistic considerations related to the level and rate of coal throughput.

c. *Operating characteristics.* An average ocean speed of 13 knots (about 560 km/day) has been assumed throughout the calculations. This is substantially lower than the typical speed of about 16 knots current today and reflects the increasing cost of fuel foreseen in the scenarios for the year 2000. The average number of days in port per round trip for loading/unloading has been assumed to increase with carrier size from 6 days for 100 thousand dwt, to 8 days for 150 thousand dwt and to 10 days for 200 thousand dwt. These figures are typical of the situation today and it might be expected that they would decrease substantially with improving coal loading and discharging technology. Considering entrance into ports, docking time and other dead periods, they correspond today to a coal-handling capacity of about 2000 t/hr for each carrier in port. Though this could double or even treble by the end of the century, it seems unlikely that an increased handling rate would substantially reduce time in port. There are, in fact, other rate controlling steps which take over as loading and discharge times decrease. For example, congestion in ports due to increasing coal traffic would prolong time of entrance into ports and could in principle become so serious as to actually increase average time in port relative to today. Time in dock for maintenance is taken as 20 days/yr.

COASTAL TRANSPORT

    Required infrastructure in feeder ships is based on the following assumptions:

a. *Transshipment flows.* The assumed transshipment flows (Figure 10-6) are based on the territorial location of supply, demand and redistribution centers and obtained using the criterion of minimizing overall transshipment costs.

Figure 10-6.   Coal Transshipment in Italy in the Year 2000 (mtce/yr)

b. *Feeder ship size.* Since the terminals are well distributed around the coastline, average round-trip distance is inferior to 400 km, with only 27% of coal transport effected over round-trip distances greater than 600 km. Under the circumstances, a feeder ship size of 20 thousand dwt represents a good match for most routes. This figure is used throughout to simplify the assessment, even though on some of the shorter low-flow routes (for example, transshipment of 0.7 mtce/yr to Fusina over a round-trip distance of less than 100 km) a carrying capacity of 10 thousand dwt might represent a somewhat better solution.

c. *Operating characteristics.* An average coastal speed of 12 knots (about 22 km/hr) has been assumed throughout the calculations. This is somewhat low by present standards and reflects the effect of increasing costs of fuel. The average time spent in port per round trip for loading/unloading has been taken as 2 days throughout. Considering queuing and docking times, and other periods in port when the ship is not loading or unloading, this corresponds to an average round-trip coal-handling capacity not much greater than 3,000 t/hr for each vessel in port. Most advanced technology corresponds today to about 10,000 t/hr for self-discharging ships which, when averaged with slower loading rates, gives an overall round-trip rate in the range of 5,000 t/hr. While faster coal handling is more critical to short-distance coastal trips than to ocean journeys (to balance the ratio of time in port to time en route), there is even here a limit above which other rate-controlling steps take over. It seems that an average of 2 days in port per round trip is an acceptable figure for estimating purposes. Time in dock for maintenance is taken as 15 days/yr.

RIVER AND CANAL TRANSPORT

Distribution of coal along the Po River and canal system is defined by the territorial assumptions as already indicated in Figure 10-4. The infrastructure requirements in tugs and barges is based on the following assumptions:

a. *Characteristics of tugs and barges.* Barges are assumed to carry a maximum load of 1,200 mt, while maximum pulling capacity of tugs is equivalent to two fully laden barges.

b. *Operating characteristics.* The en route average round-trip speed is taken as 12 km/hr on the river and 7 km/hr on canals. The average time spent in port per round trip for loading/unloading is taken as 1 day. This requires coal-handling capacities in the order of 200 t/hr. Yearly operation is assumed to occur over a period of 180 days, since the Po River is not everywhere navigable during the summer months. Two barges to each tug are assumed throughout the assessment.

OVERLAND TRANSPORT: RAIL

Under the territorial specifications, coal transport by rail occurs exclusively to serve inland power stations located in Piemonte and in Friuli. In the case of Piemonte, the railway link is assumed to be from the coastal port situated in Liguria, as already explained, after a possible funicular connection to overcome the first steep mountain range. In the case of Friuli, the railway link is assumed to be directly from the upper Adriatic terminal, bypassing any form of transshipment. Railway connections covering these tracts amount to about 130 and 80 km, respectively, and an important question was to investigate whether or not their capacity is presently great enough to provide for a coal throughput of almost 5 mt/yr in the presence of other heavy rail traffic. As will be discussed below, competing traffic appears not to present a real problem, only if one considers the possibility of concentrating coal transport during off-peak hours.

Required infrastructure in wagons and locomotives is based on the following assumptions:

a. *Characteristics of locomotives and wagons.* Wagons are assumed to carry a maximum load of 60 t, while maximum pulling capacity of locomotives is taken as 1,600 t. Considering that each empty wagon weighs 20 t, this is equivalent to a maximum of 20 wagons per locomotive.

b. *Operating characteristics.* The en route average round-trip speed of coal trains is taken as 30 km/hr. The average time spent in station for loading/unloading is taken as 5 min. for each round trip for each wagon. This implies use of the hatch technology, which is particularly suited to rail transport. Operating time, excluding Sundays and other festivities, amounts to 305 days/yr. This is considered as 9 or 18 hrs/day average according as coal transport is or is not concentrated during off-peak hours in competing rail traffic. Overall infrastructure requirements in locomotives and wagons are clearly greater, using larger coal trains because train loading/unloading time is roughly proportional to the number of wagons per coal train. The decision on train length, however, depends also on the logistics of movement, since time between passages increases with increasing length of train. A satisfactory compromise is attained at a total train length of 60 wagons, pulled by 3 locomotives, which is the figure used later in the economic assessment.

OVERLAND TRANSPORT: ROAD

As previously described, the final stage of delivery of coal to cement plants (and other distributed industrial facilities) is assumed to occur exclusively by road. Such deliveries amount to a total of 3 mtce/yr and occur from 7 point sources (3 terminals and 4 river or canal ports), with the distribution by plant consumption and distance outlined in Table 10-16.

Required infrastructure in trucks is based on the following assumptions:

a. *Truck size.* Although optimum truck size will vary somewhat according to annual throughput and distance from the point of distribution, the market for these specialized trucks will be somewhat limited and it seems reasonable to conclude that a single size of truck will be most common. The carrying capacity used in the assessment is 40 t.

b. *Operating characteristics.* Average round-trip road speed is taken as 40 km/hr. Average time spent for loading/unloading, including rest for truck drivers, is taken as 1 hr for each round trip. Operating time is assumed to be 250 days/yr, and 12 hrs/day.

A CONSIDERATION OF TRAFFIC VIABILITY

An argument that is frequently advanced against the opportuneness of developing high levels of coal consumption in Italy relates to the problem of bottlenecks in coal transportation, and more generally, the coal transport capacity of the country as a whole, given the rather high population density, the competing uses of land and seashore, and of existing infrastructures. Certainly, these features aggravate the problem of high levels of coal deployment in Italy, but probably no more than in the case of oil, which is even somewhat less dense than coal, and therefore occupies a slightly smaller volume.

The principal difference in the transport of oil and coal lies in their physical state; the one liquid, the other solid. While travel speed can be as high for coal as for oil, transfer times can be an order of magnitude higher in the case of coal. This circumstance could, in principle, cause critical problems, because of the possibility of crowding in ports and rail junctions due to longer unloading and clearing times and stochastic purturbations in flow, and there is a legitimate question of feasibility at acceptable costs that has to be answered.

As this assessment suggests, problems in the management of coal movement should not by themselves provide limitations on coal use, at least for the throughput levels contemplated in the scenario projections. However, smooth operation in coal movement will require very considerable upgrading and extension of all facilities even beyond the levels suggested, to encompass, through redundance, the many possible unforeseen events of stochastic nature. This can be seen with reference to some of the critical fixed infrastructure requirements within the major receiving facilities and the logistics of movement involved, that emerge as a direct consequence of the assumptions outlined in the foregoing pages.

TERMINALS

Assuming land area requirements of 0.20 km² for each mt of coal stored and a continuous storage capacity equivalent to 20% of annual throughput to provide a security stockpile, then land area requirements for storage amount to 0.8 and 0.6 km² at the upper and lower Adriatic terminals and 0.5 and 0.9 km² at the upper and lower Tyrrhenian terminals. These land area requirements are not in themselves large, except in the context of competing uses of land. It seems, in fact, that there might be problems in identifying sites in the four areas in the proximity of existing ports that are large enough for coal storage without cutting seriously into other local activities.

Terminal traffic is substantial, as might be expected, given also the fact that much of the coal is transshipped to other coastal ports, but it cannot be considered unduly heavy (Table 10-19). The average number of yearly passages of ocean

Table 10-19. Indicators of Coal-Related Traffic in Terminals

Terminal	Coal Imports (mtce/yr)	Number of Yearly Passages		Average Number of Carriers Present Simultaneously	
		ocean carriers	coastal vessels	ocean carriers	coastal vessels
upper Adriatic	17.1	215	1,530	1.39	2.09
lower Adriatic	11.9	151	1,197	0.97	1.64
lower Tyrrhenian	19.9	363	480	1.77	0.66
upper Tyrrhenian	11.1	224	1,249	1.03	1.71

carriers either entering or exiting harbors is between 151 for the lower Adriatic terminal and 363 for the lower Tyrrehnian terminal, which still amounts, on average, to only one passage per day. Feeder ship traffic varies from a low value of 480 passages a year for the lower Tyrrhenian terminal to a high value of 1,530 passages a year for the upper Adriatic terminal. But even this high figure still amounts to an average of less than 5 passages per day of 20-thousand dwt carriers, which should be well within terminal capabilities.

Terminal crowding, on the other hand, may pose a more serious problem, requiring in some cases a significant expansion of fixed infrastructures and loading/unloading capabilities. The figures in Table 10-19, giving the average number of ocean carriers present in a given terminal unloading at the same time, indicate that at least in the case of the two larger terminals, facilities would have to be in place to process two ocean carriers concurrently at least part of the time. These figures reflect the assumption of equilibrium flow, with coal carriers coming and going at equally distributed intervals of time. Considering the stochastic nature of the real life process, it will probably be necessary to dispose of two berths for the lower Adriatic and upper Tyrrhenian terminals, and as many as three berths for the upper Adriatic and lower Tyrrhenian terminals. The numbers obtained are, of course, sensitive to the carrier size specifications (and thus to the trade flows assumed), but not significantly, since the shorter unloading time of smaller carriers is offset by a larger number of carriers present in the terminal unloading at the same time.

Crowding is less severe, but still significant, in the case of feeder shiploading facilities, as appears in the last column of Table 10-19. Here again, the heaviest feeder ship traffic is in the upper Adriatic terminal, which shows the continuous presence of more than two 20-thousand dwt vessels loading at the same time.

These measures of terminal traffic are not intended as an indication of congestion in coal deployment, though clearly, bottlenecks could occur as a result of a mismatch between supply and demand of facilities. They do, however, indicate the magnitude of the facilities that would have to be set up in order that coal arriving from producing countries may be promptly delivered and transshipped to coastal vessels. Anything falling shorter than the implied facility requirements will clearly lead to the impossibility of verifying the assumed coal scenario. This picture, moreover, has to be set against the background of unforeseeable events during maritime transport and onshore in Italy, such as port strikes and other stochastic events downstream, which can only be allowed for by increasing redundance. The level of coal imports, however, is still some way from reaching the physical limitations of the terminals involved.

COASTAL PORTS

Traffic indicators for coastal ports, given in Table 10-20, suggest that problems of congestion due to coastal vessels unloading coal, should be easily manageable in every case. Only for the redistribution centers in Emilia-Romagna and in Liguria are facilities required to handle, on average, more than one shipload concurrently. However, in the case of the Adriatic redistribution port, which caters exclusively to upriver distribution, provision will need to be made for extensive docking area to accommodate barges for coal loading and related 200 t/hr loaders. It can be calculated that, on average, 15 barges, each about 80 meters in length, will be simultaneously unloading in this port.

Table 10-20. Indicators of Coal-Related Traffic in Coastal Ports

Coastal Port Location	Coal Received (mtce/yr)	Number of Yearly Passages	Average Number of Carriers Present Simultaneously
Venezia Giulia	4.2	495	0.68
Veneto	0.7	96	0.13
Emilia-Romagna	5.7	676	0.93
Marche	4.2	480	0.66
Abruzzi	4.2	485	0.66
Puglia	4.2	496	0.68
Campania	4.2	480	0.66
Toscana	4.2	499	0.68
Liguria	6.4	750	1.03

RIVER AND CANAL TRAFFIC

The volume of traffic on the Po River and the related canal system is well within the capabilities of the inland waterway system. In none of the five river tracts considered is the average separation between convoys going in opposite directions shorter than 6 km, or half an hour of travel time (Table 10-21). However, on the downstream tracts where traffic is heaviest, it will almost certainly be necessary to expand existing facilities to avoid bottlenecks in lock crossings.

Traffic in river and canal ports is generally light, with less than 2 barges (one convoy) simultaneously in port for unloading. At the power plant, on the other hand, facilities will have to be in place to accommodate as many as 12 barges (6 convoys) simultaneously.

Table 10-21. Indicators of Coal-Related River and Canal Traffic

	Number of Convoys	Separation (km)	Separation (hr)	Coal Landed (mtce)	Average Number of Barges Present Simultaneously in Port
tract 1	23.5	6	0.5	0.6	1.6
tract 2	25.8	7	0.6	4.2	11.3
tract 3	1.3	49	4	0.5	1.4
tract 4	1.1	120	10	0.3	0.8
tract 5	0.3	(420)	35	0.1	0.3

Tracts 1 to 5 are identified in Figure 10-4. Coal landed, and average number of carriers, refer to port upstream of related tract.

RAIL TRAFFIC

Movement of coal trains may not pose a basic problem under off-peak utilization of existing track facilities, but seems otherwise more difficult to imagine without additions to the existing track. Assuming 18 hours' daily operation and 80 wagons per coal train (train length about 1 km), the distance between trains going in opposite directions is between 35 and 45 km, according to the route, or over one to one and a half hours' separation. Rail junctions are occupied by coal trains loading (or unloading) about 11 hrs/day. There is normally sufficient slack in these figures to allow reduction of both train length and operating time (limiting it to only night traffic and off-peak hours) without amplifying the existing track. While the latter of these would require a proportionate increase in rolling stock, the former permits, instead, a reduction, because of the shorter train loading/ unloading times. The optimum solution would appear to lie somewhere in between, concentrating most coal movement during night hours using shorter coal trains (Table 10-22).

Table 10-22.   Logistics of Coal Transport by Rail (average yearly values)

	Friuli Number of Wagons Per Coal Train				Piemonte Number of Wagons Per Coal Train			
	20	40	60	80	20	40	60	80
operating time 18 hrs/day								
number of coal trains	5.4	3.3	2.6	2.3	7.8	4.5	3.4	2.9
distance between trains (km)	31	50	64	72	34	59	78	91
time between trains (min)	31	50	64	72	34	59	78	91
passage time (min)	0.5	0.9	1.4	1.8	0.5	0.9	1.4	1.8
junction occupancy (hrs/day)	11	11	11	11	11	11	11	11
operating time 9 hrs/day								
number of coal trains	10.7	6.6	5.2	4.5	15.5	9.0	6.8	5.8
distance between trains (km)	16	25	32	40	17	29	39	46
time between trains (min)	16	25	32	40	17	29	39	46
passage time (min)	0.5	0.9	1.4	1.8	0.5	0.9	1.4	1.8
junction occupancy (hrs/day)	11	11	11	11	11	11	11	11

Distance between trains refers to trains going in the same direction. Time between trains refers to time between passages in opposite directions. Passage time refers to time for an entire train to pass a fixed point en route.

However, solutions that contemplate any extensive degree of night transport will need to sustain increased capital costs due to the necessity of introducing automatic controls and viaducts, or increased running costs associated with night operation of level crossings.

Assuming, instead, that coal movement by train is constrained to occur only during daylight hours (say 9 hrs/day as a year-round average), then there may be considerable interference with other heavy rail traffic. As a working day average over the whole State railway, the distance between trains going in the same direction during daylight operations is today between 5 and 14 km, which amounts to an average time of between 4 and 16 minutes between trains going in opposite directions. These values, of course, vary considerably over the railway network, but they already indicate the type of interference which heavy coal traffic might create if constrained during daylight hours. In most of the heavier traffic lines it would severely reduce the distance and the time between trains, making the logistics dangerous, if not altogether unmanageable, particularly considering perturbations of a stochastic nature. Moreover, the situation is likely to aggravate with increasing rail traffic expected by the year 2000.

To be on the safe side, it can be assumed that a level of coal movement by rail much higher than about 2 mt/yr would normally require additions to the existing track. This would vary with the circumstances, and there are a number of rail routes which are sufficiently free to accept greater traffic today without track extensions. Particularly in the case of rail linkages between high load centers and ports, which are the most likely candidates for high levels of coal throughput, it seems difficult to avoid doubling the track, unless operations were limited to night traffic. There is also the fact that over two-thirds of the railway system is single-track, which puts a further stringent limit on the use of existing facilities.

In the particular case examined in the scenarios, competing traffic is sufficiently intense that it would seem impossible to deliver the steam coal without either doubling the track or limiting all transport to night hours. The 10 mt of coal that have to be delivered correspond to about 10^9 t/km, compared to a present freight traffic over the whole State railway of just 18×10^9 t/km: around 5% of railway freight (almost 20% of the total tonnage transported) concentrated on barely 1% of the network.

ROAD TRAFFIC

Under the assumptions of the study, that is, relatively low overall throughput (3 mtce/yr) distributed from 7 point sources to over 50 different plants, transport by road should not pose any serious problem of logistics. The only critical area might be the road network immediately around the points of distribution, since thereafter the coal routes diverge and the traffic becomes rapidly diluted. It can be shown, however, that even at the coal port where the trucks are loaded and the coal traffic is heaviest, the underlying assumptions imply an average of only 7 truck passages per hour in opposite directions, which is very low and does not require particular investments in road infrastructures. Clearly, this conclusion depends heavily on the logistic assumption. If, for example, all the coal were distributed from a single-point source instead of 7, then the number of truck passages in opposite directions becomes 25 every hour, which, considering stochastic effects and competing traffic, would very likely require additional investments in roads.

THE ECONOMIC COSTS

Required investments in fixed infrastructures and transport equipment, and the system operating costs, can be estimated from the above logistic analysis, which furnishes all the operating elements—together with their sizes and other characteristics—that need to be in place by the year 2000 to deliver 60 mtce annually to final consumption centers.

Unit investment costs of each of the single elements of this picture have been obtained mostly from industry experts, while factor contributions to total annual costs are based on fairly standard assumptions discussed in a subsequent section. Though the unit values employed can be considered quite firm today (with an uncertainty usually smaller than 10% either way), it is difficult to say how the picture could develop over the next one or two decades. The assumption has been made for simplicity, that inflation in coal transport infrastructures and in operating costs (making an exception for the cost of energy) will proceed at the same rate as the general price indicator of the economy. That is, the same unit costs at constant 1978 prices have been assumed for the year 2000 as apply today. This simplifying assumption should not detract significantly from the general conclusions, though it may affect the actual numbers obtained. For example, if the rate of inflation in transport equipment is 1% greater than the rate of inflation of the general price indicator, then unit costs are underestimated by about 20% in 2000, and of course the rate of inflation could be lower rather than higher. While a considerable element of uncertainty is inevitable at this stage of the assessment, the figures used are outlined in sufficient detail that alternative assumptions may be tested as desired.

INVESTMENTS IN FIXED INFRASTRUCTURES

Physical infrastructure requirements and their unit costs are given in Table 10-23, together with total investments required. Overall investments in fixed infrastructures that have to be laid down by 2000, amount to about 3.3 billion US dollars at 1978 prices. The major item in this investment, as might have been imagined, comes from the four terminals which contribute together about 1.5 billion US dollars, or almost 50% of the fixed investments. Investments required for upgrading and expansion of coastal ports and the creation of coal-handling infrastructures do not lag far behind, however, contributing 1.0 billion US dollars, or

Table 10-23. Investments in Fixed Infrastructures

Infrastructures	Magnitude (mt/yr)	Unit Cost (US $/t)	Total Cost (10^6 $)
terminals			1554
upper Adriatic	20.0	20.0	400
lower Adriatic	15.0	22.5	338
lower Tyrrhenian	25.0	19.1	478
upper Tyrrhenian	15.0	22.5	338
coastal ports			1037
Venezia Giulia	5.0	24.3	122
Emilia-Romagna	7.0	21.0	147
Marche	5.0	24.3	122
Abruzzi	5.0	24.3	122
Puglia	5.0	24.3	122
Campania	5.0	24.3	122
Toscana	5.0	24.3	122
Liguria	8.0	19.7	158
river ports			135
Emilia-Romagna	0.7	27.7	19
Lombardia	5.0	16.2	81
Lombardia	0.6	28.2	17
Lombardia	0.4	29.7	12
Lombardia	0.2	31.0	6
inland waterways			359
river	469	0.5×10^6	235
canal	78	1.2×10^6	94
locks	10	3.0×10^6	30
railway			228
track	210	0.9×10^6	190
yards	2	19×10^6	38
total			3275

For inland waterways (river and canal) and railway tracks, magnitude refers to km; for locks and rail yards it refers to number, otherwise it refers to throughput capacity. Rail yards at the receiving end are assumed incorporated in the power plant costs. Unit costs are average values.

33% of the fixed investments. Strong economies of scale in civil works determine a smaller contribution to unit costs in the large transshipment terminals than in the generally much smaller coastal ports, notwithstanding the sometimes considerable degree of dredging that is necessary in the former. On the other hand, costs of installations for loading/unloading and for storage charging/discharging, which contribute 40% to 60% to port facility costs, depending on coal throughput, are relatively insensitive to economies of scale beyond 4 to 5 million mt/yr handling capacity.

River ports are a minor item of the overall investment picture, accounting for only 4% of the total costs. Considerably larger investments will however be required for upgrading and extension of inland waterways (about 11% of the total investment). Although this would not be imputed entirely to coal transport, the size of canals and locks will be largely conditioned by the requirements of coal carriers. In many cases lock capacity needs to be doubled in order to accommodate coal transport relative to other traffic requirements alone.

Similarly in the case of coal transport, the investment cost (which assumes daylight operation and amounts to about 6% of the total) will most likely be shared by other economic activities, but would probably not have been necessary in the absence of coal transport of the levels in question. Thus although costs indicated for inland waterways and rail track must be considered very much as upper bounds, since in practice they would be normally shared by economic activities other than just coal transport, in actual fact, it is possible to impute a substantial part, even as much as 50%, to this activity.

INVESTMENTS IN TRANSPORT EQUIPMENT

Transport equipment required operating in 2000 and related unit costs are given in Table 10-24, together with total investments. It is emphasized that no allowance is yet made in these figures to take account of unforeseen events of stochastic nature, such as the possibility that a larger-than-average portion of the equipment is simultaneously under repair or in maintenance. Moreover, the figures do not include cumulative investments in equipment that is acquired, used, and

Table 10-24. Investments in Transport Equipment

	Number	Unit Cost (10³ $)	Total Cost (10⁶ $)
ocean carriers			3712
100 thousand dwt	14	40000	560
150 " "	24	55500	1332
200 " "	26	70000	1820
coastal vessels	25	25000	450
barges	114	700	80
river tugs	57	900	51
locomotives	20	900	18
wagons	390	60	23
trucks	142	115	16
total			4350

replaced in the period before 2000. Such investments, occurring during the transition in infrastructures, refer essentially to short-lived equipment such as trucks, with a 6- to 8-year lifetime. As can be seen from an examination of the coal consumption buildup over time, available from the demand projections, most of the surge in investments may be expected to occur during the last decade of the century. Thus, ignoring the investments in short-lived equipment depreciated during the transition phase, should not contribute more than a few percent downward bias in total investment costs. Clearly, if the analysis were extended beyond 2000, it would be necessary to include depreciation of longer-lived equipment, such as ships, tugs, locomotives, etc., and replacement investments would become the dominating element.

Here again, as in the case of fixed infrastructures, the major contribution to total investment requirements is related to the import phase of coal transport. The 3.7 billion US dollar investment appearing in Table 10-24, however, assumes that all ocean carriers represent home investments, whereas, in reality, a substantial number of carriers will normally be chartered on the international market. If 60% represent home investments, a very reasonable assumption, considering the need for security of supplies, then total investment in ocean carriers is 2.2 billion US dollars. Except for coastal vessels, which contribute 0.5 billion US dollars, all other investments are relatively minor.

UNIT INVESTMENTS BY TRANSPORT PHASE

Overall investments in fixed infrastructures and transport equipment are compared in Table 10-25. The overall figure, corrected to allow for multiple uses in inland transport, amounts to 5.8 billion US dollars, almost equally distributed between transport equipment and fixed infrastructures. Considering that this allows importation and distribution of 60 mtce of coal each year, it corresponds to an overall unit investment of $96/tce.

Table 10-25. Overall Investments in Fixed Infrastructures and Transport Equipment (10⁶ US $)

	Fixed Infrastructures	Transport Equipment	Total
ocean transport	1554	2227	3781
coastal transport	1037	450	1487
river and canal transport	207	131	338
rail transport	114	41	155
road transport	—	16	16
total	2912	2865	5777

Assuming 60% home investment in ocean carriers and attributing 20% of inland waterway and 50% of rail investments to coal transport.

By separating the transport system into its basic phases, and dividing the related investment costs by the related coal throughput, it is possible to derive average values for unit investment costs by transport phase. These figures, given in Table 10-26, are of some importance, since they are additive and therefore, in principle, allow quick estimates of investment costs for any transport chain of interest. Clearly, the values given can be considered applicable only for the specific logistic assumptions characterizing the transport scenario. As benchmark values, however, they can be used to estimate the investment costs of transport systems for any reasonable coal scenario with a confidence better than 20% either way, as long as the level of coal throughput is sufficiently large and transport distances in the different phases are not markedly different from those of the basic transport scenario. This is likely to be true if the terminals are well spaced, because of Italy's peculiar geographical shape, defining relatively short maximum transport distances after the coal import phase.

Table 10-26. Unit Investments by Transport Phase (US $/tce annual throughput capacity)

Transport Phase	Unit Investment
up to the terminal	*63.0*
fixed infrastructures	25.9
transport equipment	37.1
from terminal to coastal port	*39.1*
fixed infrastructures	27.3
transport equipment	11.8
from coastal port to river or canal port	*59.3*
fixed infrastructures	36.3
transport equipment	23.0
from port inland by rail	*18.5*
fixed infrastructures	13.6
transport equipment	4.9
distribution by road	*5.4*
fixed infrastructures	—
transport equipment	5.4
overall	*95.9*
fixed infrastructures	48.1
transport equipment	47.8

Ocean carriers calculated, assuming 60% are home investments and attributing 20% of inland waterway and 50% of rail investments to coal transport.

As in most situations, however, unit investment costs will tend to be higher for smaller scale capacity. This will be particularly true during the initial buildup phases of large coal-importing infrastructures when throughput capacity is small. If, for example, yearly coal throughput is relatively low, say 15 mtce, then this would probably justify only one terminal. Average distances to final demand centers would increase substantially in such a situation, leading to greater requirements for coastal vessels and a correspondingly greater investment per mtce throughput. Since average coastal distances can double relative to the base scenario, the increase in unit investments in transport equipment in this phase would be lower than $10/tce (corresponding to the increase in the number of ships required). The overall increase in the terminal to coastal port phase of transport would be at most from $44 to $54/tce.

A striking characteristic of the results in Table 10-26 is the different weight of transport equipment in unit investments. It is particularly high in the case of ocean carriers because of the great distances involved and the consequently lower number of yearly round trips per ocean carrier. It is still high in the case of barges, because of the low speed of movement, which also implies a low number of yearly round trips per barge. It is intermediate in the case of coastal vessels, which combine greater speed with shorter distances. It is relatively low for rail, and particularly road transport, notwithstanding the low capacity of trucks, because of the shorter distances involved and the greater speed.

An Estimate of Total Annual Costs

Total annual costs of the various coal transport systems have been estimated by direct reference to the four basic component factors: capital, labor, fuel, and miscellaneous inputs. While there are undoubtedly shortcomings in this approach, it seems difficult and, above all, arbitrary to make a comprehensive projection of market prices of transport services over two decades. By the way they are obtained these figures reflect only the long-run economic costs of production and bear no direct relation either to short-term market prices or to accounted costs. Generally the long-run average price will tend to be higher than the actual factor cost, and comparison with short-run prices, which are determined by the market forces of supply and demand, can be quite misleading. These estimates of factor costs have moreover the advantage that they are directly anchored to the transport system defined in the logistic analysis.

a. *Capital charges.* The capital input to the coal transport system has already been discussed in the previous sections. Annualization of these investment costs is made on the basis of a 7% fixed charge rate for terminals, ports and other fixed infrastructures, 12% for seagoing vessels, 15% for barges and rolling stock, and 18% for trucks. In the case of ocean-going carriers, total annual costs include capital charges coming from that fraction of transport equipment outlays made by foreign operators. As rent on property, this should include an item of return on investment. This has, however, been ignored, treating the foreign-owned ships as if they represented home investments.

b. *Labor costs.* The labor input estimated to be required for the operation of the various components of the transport system is given in Table 10-27. The annual cost imputed to labor is calculated assuming $130/man-day for ocean transport and $90/man-day for domestic activities at 365 days/yr.

c. *Fuel costs.* Energy requirements in transport and auxiliary activities used in the estimates of fuel costs are given in Table 10-28. The cost of liquid fuels and electricity is estimated from a primary energy input price of $40/bbl, assuming today's industrial cost structure in refining and electricity production. These result in $37/Gcal for oil products and $115/Gcal for electricity.

d. *Other costs.* This includes the cost of land, materials, repairs, insurance, etc. Except for the land in auxiliary activities, these costs are generally a minor element of operating costs. These vary between 5% of total annual costs for ships and 20% for trucks, while in the case of auxiliary activities, a value of 25% has been used throughout. For ocean transport this item also contains canal charges estimated assuming $4/t passing through Suez in 2000.

The total annual costs obtained in this way are attributed entirely to coal transport, while in actual practice, return cargoes can substantially lower the price paid for a coal shipment.

240

Table 10-27. Labor Requirements of a 60-mtce/Yr Coal Transport System

	Number	mt/yr	Man yr/t	Man yr/yr
fixed infrastructures				*1,833*
terminals				*910*
	2	15	14	420
	1	20	12	240
	1	25	10	250
coastal ports				*795*
	6	5	18	540
	1	7	17	119
	1	8	17	136
river or canal ports				*128*
	1	0.2	20	4
	1	0.4	20	8
	1	0.6	20	12
	1	0.7	20	14
	1	5.0	18	90
transport equipment				*3,896*
ocean carriers				*2,555*
100 thousand dwt	14	1.08	37	559
150 " "	24	1.22	33	966
200 " "	26	0.99	40	1,030
coastal vessels	18	2.10	12	*454*
river convoys	57	0.117	43	*287*
trains	6	1.63	18	*176*
trucks	142	0.247	121	*424*
total				*5,729*

Table 10-28. Direct Energy Requirements of a 60-mtce/Yr Coal Transport System

	Activity	Specific Energy Consumption	Overall Energy Consumption
fixed infrastructures			*102.9*
terminals	70.0	1,100	77.0
coastal ports	44.3	500	22.2
river and canal ports	6.7	250	1.7
rail yards	9.8	200	2.0
transport equipment			*12,332*
ocean carriers			*11,783*
100 thousand dwt	209	8.3	1,735
150 " "	558	7.3	4,073
200 " "	866	6.9	5,975
coastal vessels	19.3	18	347
river convoys	4.4	25	110
trains	2.11	35	74
trucks	0.24	75	18
total			*12,435*

Activity in 10^6 t/yr for fixed infrastructures and in 10^9 t.km for transport equipment. Specific energy consumption in kcal/t and kcal/t.km. Overall energy consumption is 10^9 kcal/yr.

The breakdown in overall annual costs between production factors and between the different elements of the transport system are given in Table 10-29. Overall annual costs incurred in the transport and delivery of 60 mtce of steam coal in 2000 amount to 1.7 billion US dollars, of which 78% are directly related to ocean transport, 14% to transshipment to coastal ports of final destination, 3% to river and canal transport, and the remaining 5% to overland transport by road and rail. As an overall average, the cost of importing, landing and distributing coal translates into $28/tce.

Table 10-29. The Overall Annual Costs (10^6 $/yr)

	Capital Charges	Operating Costs			Total Annual Costs
		Labor	Energy	Other	
fixed infrastructures					
terminals	109	29.9	13	51.8	204
coastal ports	72.8	26.1	3.9	37.2	140
river and canal ports	14.5	4.2	0.3	6.3	25
rail yards	8.0	3.3	0.4	3.9	16
transport equipment					
ocean vessels	445	121	440	95.3	1,101
coastal vessels	54	14.9	13.0	8.0	90
river convoys	15.8	9.5	4.1	2.6	32
train	8.0	5.9	16.8	3.3	34
truck	2.9	14.0	0.7	4.4	22
total	*730*	*229*	*493*	*213*	*1,665*
fixed infrastructures	204	64	18	99	385
transport equipment	526	165	475	114	1,280

However, the average cost varies considerably according to final destination. As in the case of investment costs, it is instructive to consider the implied unit operating cost in each of the different transport phases. These are brought out in Table 10-30. Coal delivered to power plants located in the immediate vicinity of import terminals, incurs an average transport cost of about $22/tce. This result cannot be compared directly with the costs that are incurred today, which average on the order of $12/t (in 1978 prices). As pointed out above, the figures obtained reflect only the long-run economic costs of production and bear no direct relation either to short-term market prices or to accounted costs. The current figures, moreover, reflect the relatively shorter sea-going distances from Poland and South Africa, while in the estimates obtained here, much of the coal imported in 2000 will need to come from considerably further afield. Another important point is that no allowance is made for reductions in transport costs coming from return cargoes. These are likely to be less important in 2000 than today because of the difficulty of matching return cargoes at the very much higher level of coal throughput involved, but they would tend to lower the transport cost somewhat from the values given here.

The average transport cost rises to $28/tce if the coal has to be transshipped to other seaports for local use. The cost of coal delivered by river and canal rises sharply above $38/tce according to the distance along the waterway. Finally, the

Table 10-30. Unit Costs According to Transport Phase ($/tce)

Transport Phase	Unit Costs
up to terminal	*21.8*
transport	18.4
auxiliary charges	3.4
from terminal to coastal port	*6.1*
transport	2.4
auxiliary charges	3.7
from coastal port to river or canal port	*10.0*
transport	5.6
auxiliary charges	4.4
from port inland by rail	*5.9*
transport	4.0
auxiliary charges	1.9
distribution by road	*7.3*
transport	7.3
auxiliary charges	—
total	*27.8*
transport	21.3
auxiliary charges	6.4

average cost of transporting and distributing coal for inland use, after unloading at a river port, can rise to above $45/tce. The distribution of average costs by final destination in the scenario in question is shown in Figure 10-7.

Figure 10-7. Transport and Distribution Costs of Coal (US $/tce, average values)

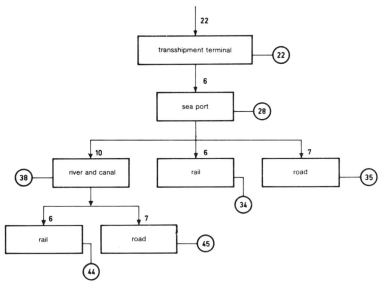

ENVIRONMENTAL AND SOCIAL ASPECTS OF COAL USE IN ITALY

The environmental aspects of coal use seem certain to play a pivotal function in Italian energy policy making over the coming years. Increasing reliance on coal will be creating environmental problems that have never before been faced in this country and are beyond the practical experience of the energy and related industries, the scientific community, the political establishment, and the population at large. The first impact of a return to coal in Italy has been essentially negative, as local environmentalists have effectively halted coal utilization in at least one dual-purpose electric facility that is being gradually reconverted specifically to burn coal. There is also, as in other countries, an ongoing debate on the environmental and social externalities of coal and nuclear energy which is likely to significantly slow down recourse to either of these fuels. There is, finally, the problem of the siting of coal-burning facilities which, in this densely populated country, is frequently seen as a question of local interests sacrificed to national objectives. This may indeed provide the main stumbling block of a future coal strategy, much as it is now doing for nuclear power.

It is beyond the scope of this brief exposé to consider some of the intricate social and political issues affecting the decision process in local and national government and the energy industry. Excepting the relatively small quantities of high-sulphur brown coal that may be mined in Sardinia, increased coal utilization in Italy has environmental implications only for coal transportation and storage, and coal conversion and use. This section deals with a few of the more critical aspects of coal transport and use, at the interface with the environment as it refers specifically to the Italian case: air quality control, the question of solid by-products, water quality and land resources, and public health.

PERSPECTIVES AND UNCERTAINTIES OF EMISSION CONTROL

The basis of Italian emission control legislation was laid down in 1966. Regulations provided at this time effectively limited coal burned in large plants to a sulphur content lower than 1%, while the corresponding figure for fuel oil was 3-4%, according to the circumstances. The same law provided that maximum ground-level concentrations of pollutants should not exceed 0.30 ppm in any half hour and 0.15 ppm as an average over a whole day. These last regulations were superseded by legislation issued in 1973, applying to new capacity additions only, which set limits for ground-level emission concentrations of 0.25 ppm in any half hour and 0.10 ppm as an average over the whole day. These new regulations, moreover, limited stack gas emissions to 2,000 ppm, to counter distributed pollution phenomena such as occur in windy areas. Finally, they set a minimum stack gas exit temperature of 90°C.

Provisions for maximum sulphur content of coal burned in large plants are among the strictest enforced in any country. Under such rules, sulphur emissions from coal-fired plants generally comply with current air quality standards without the need for additional abatement measures. This implies considerable savings in capital account and in operating costs to the industry or utility concerned, but may lead to problems in the event of difficulties in provisioning low-sulphur coal on the international market, particularly in the longer term. A part of the historical rationale behind such strict regulations can be sought in the marginal importance of coal already in the mid-Sixties when there were absolutely no anticipations that coal might play a role of any significance in the foreseeable future. Indeed, as coal began to come back into the picture immediately after the energy crisis of 1973-74, it became clear that there might be, at least temporarily, short-term problems in securing adequate quantities of low-sulphur coal on the international market, and the 1966 law was amended in 1975 in order to allow utilizing coal with up to 2% sulphur in electric utilities over short periods of time, with authorization from the Ministers of Industry and Health. The same law allows utilization of Sardinian brown coal, despite its high sulphur content, specifically in power plants sited in the Sulcis basin.

The fact that Italy is basically an importing country is another reason why there have been no preoccupations about setting low sulphur limits on steam coal burned in power plants and other industrial facilities. But clearly, future developments in environmental legislation and in pollution abatement related to coal in Italy will need to come to terms with international competition for limited supplies of low-sulphur coal and increasing demand from consuming countries which, like Italy, must rely largely on imported coal and therefore have today more freedom to set very low sulphur limits.

Particularly in the High Coal Case scenarios developed in the preceding pages, the quantity of low-sulphur coal available on the market will almost certainly be much lower than overall demand. In this perspective there are a number of possible responses, each characterized by different actors, different lead times, costs, manageability, and risk:

a. Italy could negotiate long-term leasing agreements, joint ventures in mining, or other contracts with producing countries for their low-sulphur coal. Although the price difference between low- and high-sulphur coal is not very great today, it seems certain, however, that this will increase substantially in the future, given the greater demand for low-sulphur coal. It is quite possible that this might even increase to, or above, a level set by the current cost difference of flue gas desulfurization technology in the consuming country (in the order of $10-20/tce, depending on the input/output conditions), so that economic considerations alone might not necessarily favor this solution.

b. Another possibility which would not involve relaxing today's strict environmental standards, is that of laying the onus of desulfurization at the producer's end. Coal-cleaning technologies are, however, still quite costly, and this solution, assuming it could be generalized sufficiently in producing countries, would lead to increased f.o.b. prices of coal (even above $3/tce) both on account of the coal-cleaning cost and the cost of disposal of the residues produced, minimizing leaching and other adverse effects. It is not at all clear that it would always be possible to import the coal, leaving the environmental problem with the exporting country, which might well apply environmental levies, so that even this cannot be wholly counted upon to provide the cheapest solution.

c. Finally, environmental legislation could be modified to allow intermediate- and high-sulphur coals to be employed more regularly in power plants and other industrial equipment, including synthetic fuels facilities. Emission control, in this case, could pass through a number of different routes.

    • Flue gas desulfurization and other abatement systems currently in existence can be applied to existing combustion technologies. The added costs in this case depend on the sulphur content of the coal and on the environmental standards, but tend to be quite high and will need to be compensated by lower f.o.b. prices of coal (up to as much as $20/tce lower when compared to low-sulphur coal not requiring desulfurization). To these must be added the cost of disposal of the waste slag produced, which can be estimated to be in Italy in the order of $1-3/tce burned, according to sulphur content and disposal area. A solution to the problem of disposal is offered by regenerative flue gas desulfurization technology. Another basic problem with this solution is that the overall energy efficiency decreases by 10-20%.

- Fluid-bed technology, when it becomes applicable, has a number of distinct advantages, among which are the possibility of utilizing generally any type of coal, with very little or no emissions of sulphur and nitrogen oxides. While the costs of this technology promise to be potentially attractive, it has, to date, been applied only on a pilot plant scale (up to 30 MW) and will involve problems with slag disposal or regeneration, as in the case of flue gas desulfurization.

- Conversion to low Btu gas prior to combustion in power plants is another important route which would allow utilizing higher sulphur coals with little SO_x emission. But this route involves the formation of hydrogen sulfide, ammonia, cyanides, and other products which will need to be removed with significant added costs.

- Similar uncertainties are also inherent to other conversion processes, such as high Btu gasification and liquefaction, which may become important in the longer term, even by virtue of environmental considerations. These processes seem to have reasonably low SO_2 emissions, but involve release of other organic substances whose effect on health is not yet well understood, and will likewise need to be removed.

These various possible responses do not all imply greatly increased costs of coal utilization. However, it is quite clear, even from this very brief discussion, that the question of increased coal use in Italy will soon be raising very complex issues related to environmental legislation, technological and industrial opportunities, all inextricably related to international policy.

THE QUESTION OF ASH DISPOSAL

The question of ash disposal is presently a central theme of debate in relation to increased use of coal for power production in Italy, causing disproportionately more attention and concern than emission pollution. This is due possibly in part to the fact that, under existing environmental legislation and under the currently loose market conditions for low-sulphur coal, emission control is not an immediate problem. However, an important aspect of the ash disposal quandary in Italy seems to be explainable in terms of the relatively small quantities of ash that are presently involved, no more than some 300,000 t/yr. These quantities are sufficiently small that they have not posed any great disposal problem in the past, and are currently removed through simple landfill, or dumping or similar practices. Their smallness and territorial distribution has, however, the disadvantage of not having attracted more than marginal by-product utilization. It is clearly incorrect to view the problem of ash disposal in Italy as simply one of where to deposit the ashes produced in power plants and at what costs. If large quantities of coal are burned in central power plants producing correspondingly large quantities of ash, it is reasonable to conceive that an important by-products market might result thereby in which most, if not all, of the ash found economic use.

Considering only power plants, the ash which can be estimated to be produced in Italy in the High Coal Case reference scenario (a total of 37.5 mtce of coal input to electricity generation) amounts to about 4.5 mt/yr. This would certainly be an unmanageable quantity of ash in the basically distributed utilization that occurs today, and in the absence of an organized market. But these conditions cannot be projected to hold two decades hence, when coal use will be more centralized than has been the case, and ash transport will be, as a consequence, less costly. It is comforting to find, for example, that countries such as France and Germany, which today produce more ash than Italy is likely to produce in the oil-limitation scenario in 2000 (about 5.7 mt/yr), are able to find economic use for large quantities of their ash in activities such as cement production, bricks and other mineral products, in road building, and as a filler in other uses. A possible important use for ash in Italy during the transition to the type of coal future depicted in these scenarios is in the construction of ports and terminals requiring huge quantities of standard-quality cement, which could be produced in large part utilizing ash originating in existing coal-fed power plants.

The remaining ash would have to be disposed of at costs that run as high as $1-3/tce, since there are problems of finding adequate sites for ash disposal in a densely populated country such as Italy. The situation in 2000, however, is not really worse than in France, Germany and other countries today, in relation to overall land availability and population density. Moreover, ash residue is less of a problem in fluid-bed combustion and in synthetic fuels where it is disposed of as a slag, and usually no problem at all in the cement industry, where the ash can be incorporated in the clinker. And finally, in the medium term, research and development in this area, in which Italy is now participating, promises the possibility of employing ash in other products, including ceramics, etc.

WATER QUALITY AND LAND RESOURCES

A serious, though not necessarily insoluble problem to high levels of coal use in Italy, must be sought specifically in its impact on water and land resources. Italy is a densely populated country and its land and water resources, including coastline, are severely limited.

One of the largest single impacts on the environment can be identified probably in the importation and transshipment phase. The 60 mtce/yr import scenario used for reference in this study involves four intermediate- to large-size terminals and 8 large to very large coal ports located around the Italian coastline. The large land area requirements behind the ports are not in themselves prohibitive, as discussed previously, but they are substantial, and in some cases would involve major changes in existing landscape and urban structure, frequently at the expense of existing activities. Moreover, the existence of unsightly coal yards and coal docks might very well interfere with nearby economic activities related to free time and particularly tourism, one of Italy's major industries.

Dust control, particularly during the loading and unloading of coal, is not especially costly (about $1/tce), but would have to be strictly enforced so as to avoid the soiling of whole cities adjacent to the ports and terminals, not to speak of the coastline, and endangering the local population's health. Maintaining stockpiles of millions of tons of coal also leads to water pollution from acid leaching. Particularly in a low-latitude country such as Italy, there is, moreover, an increased danger of spontaneous combustion. These and other problems are not insoluble, but they do imply very strict control, increases in the cost of imported coal, and frequently economic losses due to displaced competing activities.

Coal transport by river and canal and unloading at river ports has similar problems to maritime transport and importation. It is aggravated, however, by the danger of polluting the whole river with coal dust and coal fragments, thus endangering the balance of the river ecosystem. The analysis indicates that a coal-fired power plant located on the river implies as many as 10 and more coal barges continually unloading coal. Irreversible impacts on the environment in such situations can be avoided only by taking extreme control measures at added costs.

Reference has already been made to the viability of inland transport by river, road and rail. Traffic congestion is not a problem, as has been illustrated, except possibly in the case of rail transport. In this case, safety can be improved, and other negative repercussions avoided, by concentrating coal transport during night hours. Resulting noise disturbance from the passage of trains every half hour or so should not be unacceptable, and is not expected to lead to substantial opposition from the villages and towns that lie along the railway line. A daylight solution to coal transport by rail generally implies doubling the track, which is not only very costly, but also cuts into competing uses of land in a country where land is already scarce. Another problem with rail transport, which is independent of either of these solutions, is the damage to civil works lying along the track, that might be provoked by the passage of 5,000 t trains 4 to 5 times a day. The costs of repairing the possible damage have not been included in this assessment, but should not be very significant.

Environmental externalities related to water and land resources are generally localized and local communities in Italy have today a very important role in the decision-making process that leads to the siting of transport infrastructure and energy conversion systems. In Italy, it is the local authorities that have almost complete control over decisions regarding alternative uses of land and water. Given the serious environmental and social repercussions that can result from high levels of coal use in Italy, it may be expected that the territorial deployment of a coal-carrying and converting infrastructure will require extensive and time-consuming discussions between local and central authorities. This environmentally related factor is an important element of the overall picture, since it protracts lead times and may thus provide the principal stumbling block of a coal strategy in Italy.

THE QUESTION OF PUBLIC HEALTH

Technologies have improved considerably since the 1940's, when living in a city like Milan meant breathing heavy smog much of the year-round, and particularly during the winter months. Perceptions of environmental and social costs have changed since those days and the new technologies that have been developed as a consequence are able to greatly reduce environmental pollution. These technologies are highly costly, however, and they need to be applied to much greater quantities of coal than have ever before been known in this country.

Particularly in valleys and plains, and also close to the sea, heavy use of coal without very severe environmental abatement measures can aggravate the phenomenon of thermal inversion, or the formation of a reflecting high-density layer close above the land. Combination of fine particulate matter with fog in these circumstances leads to thick smog. Electrostatic precipitators are most effective on high-sulphur coals, where they can remove 99% of the particulate matter at a cost of $2-3/tce. More refined electrostatic techniques and Venturi scrubbers are needed for low-sulphur coals at costs in the range of $4-6/tce, but the problem remains that the very finest particulates are still freed into the atmosphere in concentrations which could be harmful to the human health. Moreover, they are not particularly effective in removing radioactive traces, whose effect on health has still to be fully investigated, and may be significant.

Because of the high levels of population density that are attained over much of the Italian territory, it can be expected that the most severe environmental standards would be enforced in the case that high levels of coal consumption were reached during the coming years. The strictest standards now in existence apply to Japan, which has a similar population density to Italy. In this country it can be estimated that environmental controls will add more than $35/tce burned in an electric power plant. Such added costs, and perhaps even higher costs, are not altogether unlikely in Italy as a response to the probable social opposition to using coal that will develop in the coming years.

STRATEGIC ISSUES RELATED TO COAL USE IN ITALY

In this concluding section an attempt will be made to bring together all the major findings of this study, which are mostly of a technical and economic nature, and examine them in the more general framework of Italian energy policy, with the aim of singling out the principal problem areas that lie in the path of a strategy of increased levels of coal use in Italy. But before embarking on such a strategy it might be questioned that there are no other alternatives to increased levels of dependence on solid coal imports, even given the necessity of rapidly substituting oil products in end-use sector of the economy. This matter is briefly set against the background of medium- and long-term energy policy in the first part of this section, which attempts to illuminate such matters as why it is considered important to examine the possibility and implications of sustained levels of coal use in Italy, and why, in particular, such coal use should be confined largely to electricity generation in the time horizon of this study.

Although the main aim has been to study the rationale and implications of a sustained solid-coal import scenario, it would have been shortsighted to ignore alternative sources of energy and technologies in the different end-use sector of the economy. A plausible case can be made for a strategic option of reintroducing coal into the Italian economy through electricity generation in the short and medium term. But already in the last decade of this century, perhaps just ten years from today, it can be foreseen that new technologies may begin to provide other uses for coal of more strategic consequence for Italy than power production. This type of development has been taken into consideration by assuming that a certain quantity of imported coal is deviated to gasification, and possibly liquefaction, by the year 2000, for conventional energy uses. This study does not attempt to give an answer to the question of whether it is more convenient to import coal synthetics produced abroad or to produce them at home from imported solid coal.

One of the most promising technologies for coal conversion is through transformation to synthesis gas, which provides an intermediate step in many of the

249

more sophisticated coal-conversion sequences. In this relation it becomes natural to ask questions about coal and coal products as feedstocks for the Italian chemical industry of the future and how this type of development might tie into the rest of the framework of this analysis. This topic is briefly treated in the second section on the future of chemical uses of coal products in Italy.

But such developments are still some time away, and if coal is to play a significant role in Italy's economy over the coming two decades, it will have to be through electricity generation. This can be seen as a transitional integrative option, or as an energy strategy of major significance. In either case, the level of steam-coal consumption in Italy will need to increase very substantially above the levels achieved today.

In the case of Italy, unlike many other industrialized countries, it is possible to speak of a return to coal in an absolute sense, despite the fact that coal consumption (steam plus metallurgical) has been regularly increasing throughout the postwar period even relative to the highest levels ever reached in prewar times. This increase, in fact, has been slight and due only to the very exceptional expansion of the steel industry, while future strategies envisage very substantial increases in consumption due instead to steam-coal use in sectors such as electricity production, direct heat uses principally in industry, and feedstock for synthetic fuels production.

Estimates of future coal use in Italy generally stop far short of the year 2000 and therefore do not recognize the large increases of coal that might be necessary to sustain economic growth for the rest of this century.

The problem of coal imports to Italy is generally written off as a problem of increasing ship sizes to some 120 thousand dwt, improving a few of the major ports, the making of long-term agreements with producing countries, finding some economic form of disposal for the ash produced in burning the coal, etc. By focusing on the period 1990 to 2000, this study attempts to bring out the problems that emerge and have to be managed, beginning today, in a sustained coal dependence scenario. A ten- to twentyfold increase in steam-coal use over a period of 20 years, in a country such as Italy, without significant coal resources, with severe logistic problems due to its narrow elongated shape, long coastline and high mountain ranges, with a high population density, and above all, with little cultural, psychological and technical preparation in steam-coal use, is likely, by any estimate, to create immense problems in planning and social acceptability that are today frequently underestimated.

Planning times presently involved in relation to coal use in Italy, are generally in the order of 8 years or so. These are sufficiently long to cope with the type of problems most frequently encountered in the conversion of a limited number of dual-fired plants to coal use, on which short-term coal policy in Italy is presently based, and it may be long enough to cope with some minor additions in new coal-fired capacity. They involve converting capable power plants from oil to coal, preparing existing facilities for landing and handling of imported coal, they involve securing adequate quantities of coal, frequently in an on-the-spot market, increasingly so through commercial agreements (generally short-term), they involve charting shipping to transport the coal. The longest technical step in this picture, the conversion of plants to coal use, takes 2 to 4 years. Any further delays in the overall chain may come from environmentalists, but the planning time for such a system is certainly short.

It is not expected that this type of situation can survive for long. For one thing, much lower coal prices and much greater security of supply can be guaranteed through mining activity which, due to the scarcity of national resources, must be carried out abroad, and through long-term commercial agreements. In the case of the former, ENI is already in the process of undertaking a mining activity which should cater to a major portion of future national requirements. As regards the latter, mining capacity in producing countries clearly cannot be expected to respond promptly to greatly increased levels of coal demand in consuming countries unless firm agreements have been placed long enough in advance. And in relation to this, adequate capacity to meet demand may be expected to keep down coal export prices. But attractive export prices may not in themselves be very useful if transport costs remain high. The third section briefly examines the rationale behind a coal import scenario based on large maritime bulk carriers and identifies some of the major problems and lead times involved in reducing the transport costs of coal.

However, maritime transport is not the only way to import coal into Italy. A good case can be made for importing coal from Northern Europe by slurry pipeline. It is doubtful that it could ever be possible to achieve a level of steam-coal imports greater than 10 mt from this area, so that, even quite apart from political strategic aspects, a slurry pipeline might provide only a partial solution to coal imports, depending on the total quantity of coal consumed. It does, nevertheless, become important at some point to make a technical, economic and political strategic assessment of the choice between slurry pipeline and maritime transport from Northern Europe. The elements for such a comparison are briefly illustrated as relates to pipeline transport in the fourth section.

The last section considers the planning problems and economic costs of solid-coal imports in the general framework of energy policy over the next two decades. In examining the whole chain of coal transport from the mine in a producing country to end-use facility in Italy, fundamental planning and organizational problems emerge which, quite independently of other constraints on the coal picture, may well pose some upper limit to what is a plausible level of solid-coal dependence for Italy in the year 2000 and beyond.

WHY COAL IN ITALY?

It has not been the purpose of this study to examine the potential role of coal in a long-term view of energy strategy for Italy. This would have required broadening the study to encompass many other aspects of the energy system and energy policy, including a comparison with alternative energy sources and technologies (energy savings included) in relation to economic and environmental costs and social acceptability, as well as time scales for development. Rather, the scope has been much more modest and precisely, to investigate the logistic, environmental and economic implications of a sustained recourse to coal over the coming decades, also with a view to identifying possible limits to coal use in this country.

To this more limited end, it might have been sufficient to examine these three aspects of coal use for a number of different levels of consumption. In making this assessment, it has, instead, been found more useful to tie assumptions about coal use directly to the developing economic and social system, to the energy demanded by this system, and in particular to electricity, with the intention of giving a concrete feeling for the circumstances under which the different levels of coal demand might materialize.

Technological, environmental, and socioeconomic constraints discussed in the body of this work, confine coal use in Italy mostly to electricity generation over the next two decades. In this sector, coal is sometimes considered as a substitute for nuclear power under circumstances in which this source is unable, for one reason or another, to take the place of oil in the short and medium term. Italy, in fact, has no domestic coal supplies of significance and coal has generally to be imported from very great distances at substantial costs. Under these circumstances, the most logical choice for central station electricity generation during the transition to the post-oil era would appear to be nuclear power, which does not require the planning and construction of huge infrastructures to allow the fuel to be imported into the country.

Seen from this strictly technical and economic angle, the choice of a sustained steam coal import scenario to take the place of nuclear power may appear rather abnormal. There are, however, reasons in the nature of social, political and lead time constraints, both past and present, which may be adduced to justify increasing recourse to coal over the coming two decades. These have been touched upon earlier in the section on strategic policy options in an attempt to tie coal use in Italy as realistically as possible to the various economic and policy variables involved. The most important justification behind increasing coal use in electricity generation during the transition period is, however, the question of diversification of energy supplies both between energy sources and between trading areas. A major lesson that has been learned from previous experience with oil is to avoid relying too heavily on one primary resource, and this applies to electricity production as well as to other uses of energy.

Seen from another angle, the partial replacement of coal for nuclear power over the next two decades could provide a possible policy instrument for introducing coal into the Italian energy economy while alternative technologies for coal utilization are still in an intermediate state of development. Set against the framework of increasingly scarce hydrocarbon resources, this medium-term policy can have important long-term strategic implications. If, indeed, such a policy is followed to its ultimate consequences, then the infrastructures for coal importation and transport will already be in place or in an advanced state of development, as alternative technologies for coal utilization evolve to economic and technical maturity.

It is in harmony with this long-term view that coal utilization as underboiler fuel in the industrial sector may not generally be considered feasible as a medium-term policy. Most industrial sector uses are sufficiently small scale and dispersed over the territory as to require an extensive and very costly infrastructure for transport and distribution, which could become quickly obsolete as alternative technologies for coal use come onto the market.

Even set against this background of rapidly depleting oil and gas resources, there still remains the important question of whether Italy should prepare itself for importing coal as a solid for use as such and for conversion to other energy vectors at home, or rather, if it should not adopt a less active strategy, relying in the first place on new developments in the field of coal conversion technology, and in the second place on readjustments in international trade patterns consequent to increasing recourse to coal as a substitute for oil in those countries, such as the United States, that are blessed with abundant coal resources. It might indeed be more logical and cheaper for Italy to import coal in the form of coal liquids when the technology for conversion is mature and economically accessible, than to lay down massive infrastructures to import solid coal in order to transform it to synthetic liquids at home.

The trouble with this approach is that it assumes a fairly loose situation in which there is plenty of time to respond to changes on the energy scene as technologies develop to maturity. Above all, it assumes that the principal energy sources fueling the economy, oil and gas, will not be in short supply over the coming two decades. In fact, there are serious doubts that oil supplies to Italy will increase very significantly above today's levels and the possibility that they might even decrease toward the horizon date of this study cannot altogether be discounted. Even increasing the supplies of natural gas involves major problems of a political and financial nature which make this option less certain than might be supposed.

The projections in this study have been fairly severe with the question of oil availability, while they have been more optimistic with natural gas (Table 10-31). The Low Coal and High Coal Case reference scenarios assume, respectively, a 31% and a 37% increase in oil and natural gas counted together, between 1978

Table 10-31. Primary Energy Mix (mtce)

	1978	Low Coal Case			High Coal Case		
		1985	1990	2000	1985	1990	2000
reference							
coal	13.5	22.3	23.0	31.5	22.9	32.5	60.5
oil	142.2	161.7	164.5	162.0	159.1	153.0	151.0
natural gas	32.1	44.5	63.0	77.0	44.5	63.0	77.0
nuclear	1.4	2.5	9.5	36.5	2.5	9.5	24.5
hydro/geo	16.1	18.0	20.0	21.5	18.0	20.0	21.5
renewables	1.4	3.0	6.0	13.5	3.0	6.0	17.5
total	206.7	252.0	286.0	342.0	250.0	284.0	352.0
oil limitation							
coal	13.5	22.3	23.0	59.0	22.9	32.5	84.5
oil	142.2	161.7	164.5	130.0	159.1	153.0	121.0
natural gas	32.1	44.5	63.0	77.0	44.5	63.0	77.0
nuclear	1.4	2.5	9.5	47.0	2.5	9.5	33.0
hydro/geo	16.1	18.0	20.0	21.5	18.0	20.0	21.5
renewables	1.4	3.0	6.0	15.5	3.0	6.0	21.0
total	206.7	252.0	286.0	350.0	250.0	284.0	358.0
nuclear delay							
coal	13.5	22.3	24.5	42.0	22.9	34.0	67.5
oil	142.2	161.7	164.5	162.0	159.1	153.0	151.0
natural gas	32.1	44.5	63.0	77.0	44.5	63.0	77.0
nuclear	1.4	2.5	8.0	26.0	2.5	8.0	17.5
hydro/geo	16.1	18.0	20.0	21.5	18.0	20.0	21.5
renewables	1.4	3.0	6.0	13.5	3.0	6.0	17.5
total	206.7	252.0	286.0	342.0	250.0	284.0	352.0

Renewables include wood

and 2000. Natural gas contributes a 140% increase in the same period. Even in the oil limitation scenarios in which oil availability is assumed to drop by 20% relative to the reference scenarios, the amount of natural gas assumed available is sufficient to allow an increase of 14% and 19%, respectively, in the oil and gas component of energy supply.

These increases are, however, still relatively small compared to the demands of a growing economy. Notwithstanding fairly substantial increases in nuclear power and renewables, it would not be possible to continue on a path of satisfactory and smooth economic growth without a major contribution from energy savings and fairly radical changes in the way energy is consumed. The amount of energy savings incorporated in the projections which form the basis of this study is very substantial, as already discussed earlier (see also Figure 10-3).

This does leave coal. In the reference scenarios, coal is assumed to enter mainly into electricity generation. Under the respective assumptions on oil and gas availability and energy savings, steam coal can play an already important role, together with nuclear power, in meeting increasing demands of electricity. However, if the availability of oil and gas turns out to be lower than expected (oil limitation scenarios), there seems to be no other way that the economy can continue growing at a satisfactory rate without major contributions from steam coal for basic heat uses, either as a solid or through gasification and liquefaction.

The solid combustion option can be largely discounted on economic, environmental, and even strategic grounds, as described previously, which leaves only gasification and liquefaction. The choice is therefore between synthetic fuels production abroad followed by imports on the one hand, and solid coal imports for synthetic fuels production in Italy on the other. While the latter option could appear illogical (particularly in the case of liquids) in a long-term equilibrium view of the economy, in a short- and medium-term transitional phase, it may be the only viable alternative. In either case, it is clearly not possible, in a period of mounting energy shortages, to rely only on other nations to develop the necessary infrastructures for coal conversion and to hope that some of this would be available for consumption in Italy, either as such or as displaced oil and gas. This country would have to play a more active role in order to secure synthetic fuels from coal.

Such a strategy would clearly involve identifying coal supplies through long-term leasing and commercial agreements and investing in synthetic fuels conversion capacity either in producing countries close to mine mouth, or at home close to import terminals. The latter option is generally cheaper and more convenient in the case of gasification, while the former option might be preferred in the case of liquefaction. Even in this case, however, the tradeoff between costs and benefits over the short term is debatable because of the very extensive foreign investments involved, which it might be desirable to keep at home for both economic and political reasons.

THE FUTURE OF COAL AS A CHEMICAL FEEDSTOCK IN ITALY

Despite anticipation of increasing tensions in oil markets over the coming decades, oil is far from being a dwindling resource today. If oil were to be limited to its presently unsubstitutable end uses, transport and petrochemicals, it could probably last for a century at accessible prices. Unfortunately this cannot happen in the short term, and there is a chance that tensions in oil markets will make themselves felt over the coming years, on both the nature of the feedstocks used in the chemical industry as well as, more generally, on the geographical pattern of chemical sector activity. In the medium term of the next two or three decades, giant steps will, of necessity, have been taken in most countries to substitute oil out of all nonessential uses, liberating it for transport and feedstock. But by this time, alternative feedstocks may have been developed to take the place of scarce oil. Quite generally, it can therefore be said that the potential for coal as a feedstock for the chemical industry exists both in the medium term as a consequence of adjustment to increasing tensions in oil markets, and in the very long term as oil becomes unequivocably depleted.

However, the problem is very much a dynamic one, and it is complicated by other aspects such as the possibility of biomass as an alternative feedstock where large quantities of agricultural waste are available or, conceivably, the outright substitution in some uses by natural or other materials and, moreover, by great diversities of geographical order. Ultimately it is important to remember that oil-based chemicals will frequently continue to be competitive with many substitute materials as energy prices increase, because the energy content of many petrochemicals is lower. For these reasons it is difficult to generalize on the question of coal as a feedstock for chemicals over the next two decades. Some estimates have nonpetroleum feedstock contributing substantially to production around the year 2000, but this possibility cannot be considered uniformly across all geographical boundaries.

In the case of Italy, great uncertainties are introduced due to the fact that this country has little or no coal resources to speak of. At 1979 oil prices, it is only when secure long-term supplies of coal are available locally, priced for one reason or another, at around $20/tce or less, that one begins to look at coal-based chemical operations. At present, Italy has no secure long-term supply of coal, if one excludes the marginal contribution from Sardinian brown coal, and import prices for steam coal run today on the order of $50-60/tce.

It is conceivable that this situation may change substantially in the course of the next two decades. Toward the end of the century, under the High Coal Case scenario price of $40/bbl of Arabian light crude marker, the upper limit at which coal would be of interest as a general feedstock might be in the order of $40-50/tce, and therefore still only marginally within reach of Italian-based operations. As estimated in this study, transport costs alone are expected to contribute some $22/tce or more. But if tensions in the oil market are not quite so severe, and the prevalent oil price does not rise substantially above 1979 levels as in the Low Coal Case scenario, then coal as a feedstock would remain well out of economic reach of Italy's chemical industry.

This situation, however, is not likely to be uniform across the whole slate of chemical intermediaries. At one extreme, synthetic petroleumlike liquids from coal could never hope to compete as feedstock because of their high costs, while they will have an important role in easing the use of petroleum for feedstock through substitution of oil and gas in basic energy-use sectors. On the other hand, ammonia and methanol from coal could well be competing with their oil-based production at prices that may be prevailing in the last decade of the century. Synthesis gas is today the basis for these products and synthesis gas from coal could possibly begin providing some feedstock for ammonia and methanol-based chemicals in the range of coal prices that might be prevailing in Italy toward the end of the century in a high oil price scenario.

The basic intermediate feedstock for the large majority of petrochemicals is, however, ethylene. Catalysts to convert synthesis gas directly to ethylene are not yet practicable and dimerization of methanol followed by dehydration is still quite far into the future. However, direct synthesis to ethylene glycol is already possible today using rhodium catalyst, so that where it is cost-effective, ethylene glycol could already join the ranks with ammonia, methanol and acetic acid of bulk commodity intermediates that could be based on synthesis gas from coal.

As has been briefly outlined, fundamental uncertainties in technology, oil and coal prices, and in availability of coal, do not presently add up to a very favorable planning environment for an eventual substitution of coal for some of Italy's petrochemical feedstocks. It is, moreover, unlikely that this could even begin to happen before a coal strategy of greater proportion gathers momentum in this country.

It should not be imagined, however, that a change in the prospects of coal in Italy accompanying a favorable price and supply development over the next few years means that the chemical industry could automatically turn over to carbochemical intermediates. There are in fact a number of factors which are likely to strongly limit the contribution of coal to Italy's chemical feedstock over the next two decades, quite apart from problems of uncertainty in prices and in supply:

- Parcel sizes for the chemical industry tend to be relatively low by comparison with the electric power industry. The lower levels of throughput mean much higher infrastructure costs for transport and distribution and generally high transport costs unless the chemical plant is situated directly at a coal port. From this study it can be estimated that investments in infrastructures contribute in the order of $60-100/tce yearly throughput capacity for a large power complex situated at a port and consuming about 4 mtce/yr. However, distribution to a small- or medium-size complex such as a chemical plant with a yearly throughput of 100-300 thousand tce might require additional investments in the range of $40 to $80/tce or higher. These infrastructures would often need to substitute existing networks for oil distribution. The larger investment costs and larger operating costs accompanying smaller scale throughput also drive up transport costs, decreasing coal's competitivity with respect to oil. Relative to the cement industry, which has similar parcel sizes and for which coal is competitive with oil, the chemical industry has to bear an additional technological cost and, associated to it, a very much higher energy share in the factor cost of production.

- The question of price is ultimately tied to the question of availability. As is emphasized in an earlier section of this chapter, coal is likely to be available in sufficient quantities at accessible prices only if long-term agreements are made with producing countries at least some 5 to 10 years in advance and if the necessary importing infrastructures (terminals and ports) are in existence. Here it is unlikely that the chemical industry could rely on vast quantities of coal bought on the Italian market, but rather it would probably have to enter itself into some form of long-term agreement with an Italian importer. This can be seen to imply much more foresight than can be hoped for in a situation of very considerable uncertainty today.

256

- Finally, low coal prices, low enough to allow thinking of coal as a plausible substitute, are not likely to last for very long, particularly after coal has effectively ousted oil out of its more easily substitutable end uses. At this time oil uses will be confined largely to transport and petrochemical feedstocks so that lower tensions in international markets could result, upsetting the prior equilibrium reached between oil and coal as feedstocks. In the meantime, the price of coal will tend to increase to levels approaching those of oil, particularly if the seller's market turns out to be tight. Such a prospect is likely to mitigate thoughts about changing to a coal-based feedstock 10 or 15 years from now, even as oil prices reach higher and higher levels, also because of the decade-long research and development activity that would be involved.

These considerations, moreover, should be set against the background of a comeback of natural products and biomass as chemical feedstock, beginning with the last decade of the century. All in all, it seems unlikely that coal could displace oil as a chemical feedstock more than marginally over the next two decades in Italy. If coal does make some headway in feedstock uses, this will most probably occur in connection with gasification of either imported coal or Sulcis brown coal, since part of the intermediate or final gasified product could be deviated to ammonia and methanol production with overall economic convenience.

ECONOMIES OF SCALE IN OCEAN TRANSPORT

Maritime transport presently contributes about 50% to the cost of steam coal landed in Italy. In 1978 almost all steam coal imported to Italy came in roughly equal quantities from Poland and South Africa, that is, over seagoing distances of about 6 and 10 thousand km. These distances would already justify the use of large carriers of 100 thousand dwt and greater. Draft restrictions in Italian ports, however, presently limit the ship size to 45-50 thousand dwt at the very most. The increase in costs coming from these diseconomies of scale is probably not a serious problem while the quantity of coal imported is marginal, but would almost certainly not be acceptable once steam coal became a sizeable contributor to the energy system. In the longer term, transport distances will also be increasing as coal is increasingly imported from Australia. In the transport hypothesis of this study, the average transport distance is about 12,000 km, with maximum transport distances of up to 18,000 km. If this coal were transported with small bulk carriers of 20 to 50 thousand dwt, in most use today, transport costs could become very high indeed.

In order to estimate the nature of the economic advantages of going to large-capacity carriers, a 60 mtce import scenario was investigated, assuming that only 40-thousand dwt tankers were used for maritime transport. Since these ships require only an 11-meter draft and can therefore go directly to all of the coastal ports, this solution avoids the need to build large terminals for large-carrier imports, though it would still require considerable adaptation in the form of dredging and restructuring of existing ports. These are indeed the two major changes that occur from the scenario described in the earlier section on transport. Since large terminals are no longer necessary in this type of solution, it might be expected that investment costs would drop dramatically. But this is not so. The number of ships required to import the coal increases from 64 in the base scenario to 250. Moreover, since these ships are smaller, their unit costs, referred to tonnage transported, is considerably larger (about $800/dwt compared to $400/dwt for 100-thousand dwt tankers). Coastal receiving ports also usually need some further upgrading to receive 40- rather than 20-thousand dwt tankers. Moreover, coal yards need to be provided, together with related coal-handling equipment, which will generally tend to be larger than in the case of transshipment, where the major stockpiling function occurs at the terminal. These factors all contribute to increasing capital costs. The outcome is that the overall investment in maritime transport infrastructures actually increases in the case of a 40-thousand dwt tanker import scenario, precisely from 6.7 to 9.9 billion US dollars (Table 10-32).

Table 10-32. Comparison of Investment Costs Between Transshipment and Nontransshipment Solutions (10⁶ US $)

	Terminals	Ports	Vessels	Total
transshipment	1,554	1,037	4,162	6,750
non-transshipment	—	1,897	7,994	9,891

Assumes all vessels represent home investment for ease of comparison.

Small-carrier transport is also considerably more expensive in terms of operating costs. The unit capital charge is more than 2 times greater than for large-capacity carriers. Specific fuel consumption is also considerably higher, about 13 kcal/t.km for 40-thousand dwt carriers as against about 8 kcal/t.km for 100-thousand dwt carriers and 7 kcal/t.km for 200-thousand dwt carriers. The unit labor input referred to the tonnage transported is also very much higher, reflecting the poor match between small-capacity carriers and long-distance, high-throughput transport. Specifically, it comes to 143 man-year/t for 40 thousand dwt, which compares, for example, with 33 man-year/t for 150 thousand dwt. This implies a total labor force on ocean-going vessels of 10,000 man-yr/yr, compared with only 2,555 in the case of large-carrier transport. Taking all these factors into account, the cost difference in the ocean transport phase is about $21/t (about $25/tce) in favor of large-capacity carriers. To this must be added the cost difference for port dues and loading and unloading, which come to about $1/t, still in favor of large-capacity carriers. These figures do somewhat overstate the real cost difference, since they do not account for the fact that a small-carrier solution avoids transshipment. The cost reduction due to this effect, however, comes to less than about $7/t. Collecting all the cost differentials, the overall cost difference between small-carrier transport and large-carrier transport with transshipment comes to about $15/t (about $18/tce) in favor of the latter (see Tables 10-29 and 10-33 for the breakdown in costs). Considering that the estimate of maritime transport cost by large carriers with transshipment amounts to $28/tce (see Table 10-30), a large-carrier solution represents a 40% cost saving over a solution based on small carriers.

While use of large carriers does imply very important savings in investment and transport costs, they are not themselves exempt from major problems. To start with, coastal approaches deep enough to take carriers as large as 150 to 200 thousand dwt are not easy to find in either exporting or importing countries.

Australia, for example, has practically no deep-water ports, and would probably be required to dynamite a way through its coral reefs before extensive coal transport could be based on large carriers.

Table 10-33. Total Annual Costs of Maritime Transport Assuming 40-Thousand DWT Carriers (10⁶ $)

	Capital Charges	Operating Costs			Total Annual Costs
		Labor	Energy	Other	
ocean vessels	960	475	780	244	2,459
coastal ports	133	40	8	64	245
total	1,093	515	788	308	2,704

For a comparison with operating costs using large ocean carriers, see Table 10-29.

Adding to the problems of large-carrier use are the cumulative lead times along the entire decision chain for creation of deep-water ports and, in particular, the necessity for firm long-term commitments at high-capacity throughput before exporting countries can even start to think of providing the necessary infrastructures.

THE COAL SLURRY PIPELINE ALTERNATIVE

An assessment of the prospects for solid coal as an energy resource for Italy cannot be complete without some reference to the possibility of importing coal from Northeastern Europe by slurry pipeline. In recent times this has been discussed as an alternative to a more conventional transport solution and it will be useful to examine the circumstances and costs under which it could contribute to Italy's import requirements.

The slurry pipeline concept, recently studied by a Polish-Italian working group, would take steam coal from Silesia in Poland over a distance of about 800 km to an arrival point on the Northern Adriatic coast of Italy. A number of alternative routes are available through Czechoslovakia and either Austria or Hungary and Yugoslavia. A detailed analysis of investment and operating costs was carried out for each of these routes and for three different levels of coal input (5, 7.5, and 10 mt/yr), as well as for a number of alternative technologies for slurry preparation and deslurrying after arrival. The results indicate that investment costs related to the whole transport operation, including coal treatment and dewatering, amount to between 450 and 700 million US dollars, according to which configuration is adopted. The transport costs involved vary between $17.5/t for the lower throughput to $14.5/t for the higher throughput, with minor variations around these values reflecting the diverse logistic and technological choices.

These estimates of investment and overall transport costs are in the same range as those for maritime transport obtained in the present study, and the question of economic costs related to transport cannot therefore be adduced alone to establish the most convenient solution. The choice of one or another technology also depends on the end use to which the coal is put. It is expected that most of the coal arriving by slurry pipeline would be utilized directly at the pipeline terminal in a number of large centralized facilities (power plant or gasification complex). In this way the coal could be used as a sludge or wet powder without the need for extensive drying. If it were instead required to transport and distribute the coal further afield, it would be necessary to dry it and pelletize it, increasing the costs so significantly as to seriously discredit the pipeline option.

Another major problem is the environmental aspect of coal slurry transport. The above estimates do not include the cost of water treatment after dewatering to comply with water-quality standards. Present technology for dewatering consists in water reduction by centrifugation or filtration, which would add about $1.5-1.8/t to the costs. Other more extreme forms of water treatment such as drying, which require extended use of fuels, would increase costs more significantly.

The principal advantage of pipeline transport relative to maritime transport is the high capital cost component in total costs (about 70% compared to 30-40%), which makes transport less sensitive to inflation. Energy consumption is also much lower. The transport is invisible and practically noiseless, since it occurs underground and is nonpolluting. It is true that fairly large quantities of water are involved (about 1 m³ for each t transported), and in the particular case in consideration, this seems to be a major problem that is presently under study.

As a means of overland transport, the coal slurry pipeline appears to be preferable to the rail alternative in terms of both capital costs and total transport costs, as well as environmental externalities.

Pipeline transport implies a fixed, single-use linkage to a producing country and this can present undesirable aspects of a political nature. In deciding between the various alternatives, it is, above all, important that coal slurry transport by pipeline should not represent a major fraction of overall import requirements, say less than 15-20%. On these grounds the pipeline option would probably need to be ruled out in the Low Coal Case scenario, in which steam coal imports amount to little over 16 mtce/yr. A low throughput pipeline of about 5 mt/yr might begin to be acceptable at a total import requirement of about 25 mtce/yr, while at the higher throughput level of 10 mt/yr it might not be considered a good choice below a total import level of 50 mtce/yr or so.

LEAD TIMES AND UNCERTAINTIES IN A COAL STRATEGY FOR ITALY

One of the most serious problems that has to be faced in a coal strategy, as for many other countries, is related to the question of lead times and uncertainties, both on the side of demand and on the side of supply. The greatest uncertainty in people's minds is presently related to the question of price. The argument that there is no incentive to use coal in Italy, because the present price coupled to the convenience cost of utilization still does not make it significantly more attractive than oil in most uses is, however, very shortsighted. It is true that in the short term coal is frequently priced on the basis of fuel oil prices in consumer markets and that coal prices may eventually increase if there are problems of supply following demand. In the longer term, however, as supply capacity increases to meet demand, coal prices should in principle settle down closer to the marginal cost of production. The real problem is availability of oil. Replacing oil with coal presently has to take place in anticipation of limitations in oil availability, accompanied by unstable and increasing oil prices. Clearly there are contradictions in the existing situation, particularly as it relates to an importing country such as Italy, buying in what is essentially a supplier's market, which lead to great uncertainties.

While not frequently recognized, uncertainties and lead times on the supply side have, however, a much more legitimate cause for concern than uncertainties on the demand side. This relates particularly to the question of long-term agreements with the supplier countries and the opening of coal mines, as well as the creation of importing infrastructures. It may take as long as 8 years between the conclusion of an agreement and bringing a new coal mine and allied infrastructures up to capacity. Experience with large ports in Italy indicates that construction of a large terminal to import coal may take anywhere from 5 to 7 years, or possibly longer.

It can be assumed quite optimistically that it takes about 5 years to technically localize, build, and bring up to regime, each incremental coal import capacity of 5 mt/yr. Assuming transshipment as the most economic solution to the problem of coal imports, then the results of this study indicate that 1.6 t/yr of port capacity (terminals plus coastal ports) are necessary for each t/yr of steam coal effectively landed in Italy. Applying these assumptions to the coal import schedules developed earlier (see also the Summary Tables at this end of this Chapter) leads to the results given in Table 10-34. This table indicates the coal-port capacity that needs to be under construction during the next two decades so that the specified levels of coal demand may be met on time. It has been constructed assuming that there is no further coal development after 2000 which explains the sudden drop in coal capacity under construction in the last five years of the period.

As an average over the entire twenty-year period, the capacity under construction varies between a minimum of 7 mt/yr throughput for the Low Coal Case reference scenario to a maximum of 33 mt/yr in the case of the High Coal Case oil limitation scenario. An even higher average level of 40 mt/yr under construction would need to be attained in order to achieve the higher level of economic growth if there are delays in nuclear power development and limitations in oil supply. However, figures of 20 and 30 mt/yr continually under construction over two decades seem already very high to be manageable. During the first half of the 1990's, the capacity under construction in this scenario needs to average almost 70 mt/yr throughput (as high as 80 to 90 mt/yr in some years), and this can be ruled out on technical grounds alone.

Under these circumstances (nuclear delay combined with limitations in oil supply), it would seem impossible to achieve even the lower level of economic growth, which also needs to average an unbelievably high capacity under construction (about 50 mt/yr) during the first half of the Nineties. With this type of criterion, the high-growth oil limitation scenario would also seem unmanageable, since it does require a peak capacity under construction as high as 55 mt/yr as an average during the same critical first five years of the Nineties.

Anything higher than an average rate of about 30 mt/yr during any five years (about 4 to 5 times the present coal-port capacity under construction) can probably be considered as an upper maximum of what can be planned and achieved realistically in Italy, particularly under the existing conditions of uncertainty. It should be pointed out, in fact that the time profiles indicated in Table 10-34 assume that the coal port capacity buildup is initiated immediately in 1980, which is difficult to believe in the case of the Higher Coal Case throughput scenarios. Any delays would simply increase the steady state level of capacity needed under construction during the peak period of the early Nineties. Indeed, if the uncertainties related to the siting and planning of a coal import system of the magnitude implied are coupled to the lead time problem, then even borderline cases such as the Low Coal Case oil limitation scenario and the High Coal Case nuclear delay scenario would probably need to be ruled out as well, and, even conceivably, the High Coal Case reference scenario.

It must be emphasized that the problem is not one of economic costs. On the contrary, the financing of all the systems depicted in Table 10-34 should be well within the range of Italian economic potential in the scenarios considered. To see this, it is sufficient to look at the implied rates of investment in new transport infrastructure. Total investments of the Italian economy in the 15-year period, 1985 to 2000, can be estimated as 1,275 and 1,400 billion US dollars, respectively, in the low and high economic growth scenarios.

Table 10-34. Coal-Port Capacity Under Construction (mt/yr throughput)

	Reference		Oil Limitation		Nuclear Delay		Combination[1]	
	Low Coal Case	High Coal Case	Low Coal Case	High Coal Case	Low Coal Case	High Coal Case	Low Coal Case	High Coal Case
1980/85	9	22	12	26	17	30	30	30
1985/90	6	23	14	26	12	25	29	29
1990/95	9	30	37	55	16	36	51	69
1995/2000	4	10	17	23	5	9	15	32
1980/2000 average	7	21	20	33	13	25	31	40
coal throughput in 2000 (mtce/yr)	19.5	48.5	47.0	72.5	30.0	55.5	69.0	89.0

[1] Nuclear delay combined with limitations in oil supply

Assuming the historic ratio of about 10% total investments going to the energy sector, then total energy investments will amount to about 128 and 140 billion US dollars between 1985 and 2000. Investments in infrastructures for importing and distributing steam coal in 2000, obtained in this study, are between 1.8 billion US dollars in the Low Coal Case reference scenario and 8.3 billion US dollars in the high economic growth, nuclear delay scenario with limitations in oil supply, which might increase to between 2.5 and 11.5 billion US dollars, considering the need for safety margins in operation of transport infrastructures. These figures represent, respectively, 2% and 8% of total energy-related investments, a relatively small percentage, and certainly not such as to provide, by itself, a constraint to sustained levels of coal development.

Seen another way, if all this coal were to be used for electricity generation and the total infrastructure investment were attributed entirely to this sector, then additional capital costs for coal-fired generation would amount to about $150/kW. This is a significant increased over base-plant capital costs, but still within acceptable range for the country as a whole, considering the longer term aspects of a coal-based strategy. Moreover, it is considerably smaller than the capital cost contribution which might be coming from environmental technologies in the case of very strict ambient quality standards: in the order of $300 to $400/kW.

These costs, however, may be somewhat underestimated for another reason. The assessment of capital requirements related to the importation of coal has assumed that Italy will be involved only in those investments that are related to coal transport from country of origin to end-use facility in Italy. It has not taken into account the amount of investments abroad in mining ventures and related transport infrastructures. This may not generally be a problem if Italy is one among many buyers. However, in comparing Italy's high coal trade assumptions with the expected available supply in each of the producing countries, it becomes quite clear that in some cases Italy would be claiming a large portion of the available export potential: over 30% in the case of South Africa, about 25% in the case of Australia, and just under 20% in the case of Poland. Under such conditions, entire coal mines would need to be opened just to satisfy Italian demand. In these circumstances, it is logical to expect that Italy would be participating to a substantial degree in mining-related capital expenditures. An upper estimate of the added costs can be obtained by assuming that Italy participates in about 50% of the investment related to mining and 30% of the investment related to transport infrastructures from mine to port. In this case a 60 mtce/yr steam-coal import scenario, for example, would imply added investments abroad amounting to as much as 1.5 billion US dollars, which would need to be added to the 5.6 billion US dollars previously estimated.

Other long lead times in the coal chain are related to the siting and construction of coal-fired plants. In terms of coal throughput, these have construction times in the same range as coal terminals and ports and can therefore be set up more or less concurrently with the importing infrastructures. Working back along the chain, a major delay arises in the definition of long-term contracts for steam coal from exporting countries. This is probably the most critical step in the whole sequence, since it may take 4 to 8 years between conclusion of negotiations and bringing a mine up to full regime. Unless one is willing to buy coal in the on-the-spot market and run the risk of incurring rapidly inflating prices, then it will be necessary to firm up long-term leasing and commercial agreements for coal exports to Italy within a few years from today, at very most. In this respect, ENI has already initiated mining activity abroad which is expected to lead to a major share of future Italian steam-coal requirements.

This brings up the problem of nonequilibrium situations during the buildup in mining and transport infrastructures. This study has limited itself to looking at the year 2000 as an arrival point, ignoring short-term adjustment problems in supply and demand related to availability of coal carriers, deep-water ports, both in producing and consuming countries and coal supply on the different trading routes. During the intervening two decades, importing terminals and ports will be under construction, mines will not yet be opened, and ships of the desired characteristics will not always be available as required. These sectors of the economy move at different rates and react in different measure to varying stimuli of economic, political and international nature. During the transition period their dynamics will very likely be out of phase with one another, with supply probably lagging behind demand and leading to higher prices both for exported coal and for transport services.

Uncertainties in the decision process on the demand side (siting of power-conversion schemes and synthetic-fuel facilities) and on the supply side (establishing long-term contracts and opening of mines) are clearly going to protract lead times and increase the difficulties of providing enough coal at the right time, and at acceptable prices. The type of sequence described above allows very little slack, given the short time available. Yet is is difficult to believe that an electric utility would begin constructing a power plant before securing enough coal on a long-term contract. On the other hand, it may not be advisable to negotiate a long-term contract for coal before the plant has been definitely sited, and the siting process is becoming a lengthy and complicated procedure.

This circular uncertainty is also aggravated by other uncertainties, such as the outcome of the controversy on nuclear energy, the question of oil availability, the picture for natural gas imports, the rate of increase in energy and electricity use, oil and coal prices, the position of environmentalists and environmental policy, and, in the longer term, new developments in technology. These uncertainties can combine together to make the picture even more uncertain. For example, will the import price of coal be sufficiently low as to permit competitive costs for synthetic fuels produced in Italy? Will advances in coal/oil mixtures allow using coal with relatively minor changes in existing oil plants? How soon will developments in fluid-bed combustion permit a different view of the environmental problem? What will environmental standards be like in the last decade of the century? What will be the social response to greatly increased levels of coal use?

ITALY

Summary Worksheet—Reference Case

I. Coal Use, Production, and Trade	1977	1985		1990		2000		1977-2000 Avg. annual growth—%/yr.	
		A	B	A	B	A	B	A	B
Coal use in major markets (mtce)									
Metallurgical	11.1	11.0	11.0	11.5	11.5	12.0	12.0	0.3	0.3
Electric	1.8	10.0	10.0	9.3	18.8	17.0	37.5	–	–
Industry	0.2	1.0	1.5	2.0	2.0	2.5	3.0	–	–
Synthetic Fuels	–	–	–	–	–	–	8.0	–	–
Residential/Commercial	0.4	0.3	0.4	0.2	0.2	–	–	–	–
Total coal use	13.5	22.3	22.9	23.0	32.5	31.5	60.5	3.7	6.7
Distribution of coal use by market sector (%)									
Metallurgical	82.2	49.3	48.0	50.0	35.4	38.1	19.8	—	—
Electric	13.3	44.9	43.7	40.4	57.8	54.0	62.0	—	—
Industry	1.5	4.5	6.6	8.7	6.2	7.9	5.0	—	—
Synthetic Fuels	–	–	–	–	–	–	13.2	—	—
Residential/Commercial	3.0	1.3	1.7	0.9	0.6	–	–	—	—
Total coal use	100%	100%	100%	100%	100%	100%	100%	—	—
Coal consumption/imports (mtce) Consumption									
Metallurgical	11.1	11.0	11.0	11.5	11.5	12.0	12.0	0.3	0.3
Steam	2.4	11.3	11.9	11.5	21.0	19.5	48.5	9.5	–
Total coal consumption	13.5	22.3	22.9	23.0	32.5	31.5	60.5	3.7	6.7
Imports									
Metallurgical	11.1	11.0	11.0	11.5	11.5	12.0	12.0	0.3	0.3
Steam	2.0	10.3	10.9	10.5	20.0	16.5	45.5	9.6	–
Total coal imports	13.1	21.3	21.9	22.0	31.5	28.5	57.5	3.4	6.6
Coal production/exports (mtce) Production									
Metallurgical									
Steam	0.4	1.0	1.0	1.0	1.0	3.0	3.0	9.1	9.1
Total coal production	0.4	1.0	1.0	1.0	1.0	3.0	3.0	9.1	9.1
Exports									
Metallurgical									
Steam									
Total coal export									

265

Summary Worksheet—Reference Case

II. Coal's Role in Total Energy System	1977	1985		1990		2000		1977-2000 Avg. annual growth-%/yr.	
		A	B	A	B	A	B	A	B
Total Primary Energy Use (mtce)									
Oil, Domestic	1.6	3.6	3.6	4.3	4.3	5.5	5.5	1.8	1.8
Oil, Imported	135.5	158.1	155.5	160.2	148.7	156.5	145.5	0.3	0.3
Gas, Domestic	14.3	14.0	14.0	14.0	14.0	14.0	14.0	-	-
Gas, Imported	16.7	30.5	30.5	49.0	49.0	63.0	63.0	5.9	5.9
Nuclear	1.0	2.5	2.5	8.0	8.0	26.0	17.5	-	-
Hydro, Solar, Other	18.1	21.0	21.0	26.0	26.0	35.0	39.0	2.9	3.4
Coal, Domestic	0.4	1.0	1.0	1.0	1.0	3.0	3.0	9.1	9.1
Coal, Imported	13.1	21.3	21.9	23.5	33.0	39.0	64.5	4.8	7.2
Total energy use	200.7	252.0	250.0	286.0	284.0	342.0	352.0	2.3	2.4
Coal penetration (%)	6.7	8.8	9.2	8.5	11.9	12.3	19.2	—	—
Total primary energy (mtce) input to electricity									
Oil and Gas	31.5	44.5	44.5	46.2	44.7	33.5	34.0	0.3	0.3
Hydro, Solar, Other	18.1	19.0	19.0	20.0	20.0	21.0	22.0	0.6	0.8
Nuclear	1.0	2.5	2.5	8.0	8.0	26.0	17.5	--	--
Coal	1.8	10.0	10.0	10.8	20.3	27.5	44.5	--	--
Total energy input	52.4	76.0	76.0	85.0	93.0	108.0	118.0	3.2	3.6
Coal penetration (%)	3.4	13.1	13.1	12.7	21.8	25.5	37.7	—	—
Total electric capacity (GWe)									
Oil and Gas	18.3	30.2	30.2	32.3	32.3	28.0	28.0	2.8	1.8
Hydro, Solar, Other	14.4	16.5	16.5	17.5	17.5	18.0	20.0	0.9	1.4
Nuclear	0.5	1.5	1.5	4.5	4.5	15.0	10.0	-	-
Coal	2.4	6.6	6.6	7.0	12.7	16.8	27.0	8.8	-
Total capacity	35.6	54.8	54.8	61.3	67.0	77.8	85.0	3.4	3.8
Coal Penetration (%)	6.7	12.0	12.0	11.4	18.9	21.6	31.8	—	—
Peak load	28.3	45.7	45.7	51.0	55.8	64.8	71.0	3.7	4.1
Peak reserve margin (%)	20.5	20.0	20.0	20.0	20.0	20.0	20.0	—	—
Total oil imports (mbd)	1.89	2.21	2.17	2.24	2.08	2.19	2.04	0.6	0.3
Total oil consumption (mbd)									
Transportation	0.61	0.69	0.69	0.71	0.67	0.91	0.87	1.7	1.5
Residential/Commercial	0.45	0.45	0.44	0.44	0.38	0.37	0.29	-0.8	-1.9
Industry—Boilers	0.33	0.39	0.36	0.37	0.32	0.26	0.20	-1.0	-2.1
Industry—Other	0.13	0.17	0.18	0.23	0.24	0.32	0.35	4.0	4.4
Electric utilities	0.40	0.56	0.56	0.55	0.53	0.40	0.40	-	-
Total oil consumption	1.92	2.26	2.23	2.30	2.14	2.26	2.11	0.7	0.4
World oil price assumed for national coal analysis (1979 U.S. dollars/barrel)	$20*					25	40		
Economic growth assumed for national coal analysis (GNP, billion 1978 dollars)	223.8	287.9	287.9	330.5	341.2	423.0	472.1	2.8	3.3

* Uses current price of $20/barrel (June 1979 U.S. dollars) as baseline world oil price and as floor price throughout the period.

Oil Limitation Case

I. Coal Use, Production, and Trade	1977	1985		1990		2000		1977-2000 Avg. annual growth—%/yr.	
		A	B	A	B	A	B	A	B
Coal use in major markets (mtce)									
Metallurgical	11.1	11.0	11.0	11.5	11.5	12.0	12.0	0.3	0.3
Electric	1.8	10.0	10.0	10.8	20.3	27.5	44.5	–	–
Industry	0.2	1.0	1.5	2.0	2.0	2.5	3.0	–	–
Synthetic Fuels	–	–	–	–	–	–	8.0	–	–
Residential/Commercial	0.4	0.3	0.4	0.2	0.2	–	–	–	–
Total coal use	13.5	22.3	22.9	24.5	34.0	42.0	67.5	5.0	7.2
Distribution of coal use by market sector (%)									
Metallurgical	82.2	49.3	48.0	46.9	33.8	28.6	17.8	—	—
Electric	13.3	44.9	43.7	44.1	59.7	65.5	65.9	—	—
Industry	1.5	4.5	6.6	8.2	5.9	5.9	4.4	—	—
Synthetic Fuels	–	–	–	–	–	–	11.9	—	—
Residential/Commercial	3.0	1.3	1.7	0.8	0.6	–	–	—	—
Total coal use	100%	100%	100%	100%	100%	100%	100%	—	—
Coal consumption/imports (mtce) **Consumption**									
Metallurgical	11.1	11.0	11.0	11.5	11.5	12.0	12.0	0.3	0.3
Steam	2.4	11.3	11.9	13.0	22.5	30.0	55.5	–	–
Total coal consumption	13.5	22.3	22.9	24.5	34.0	42.0	67.5	5.0	7.2
Imports									
Metallurgical	11.1	11.0	11.0	11.5	11.5	12.0	12.0	0.3	0.3
Steam	2.0	10,3	10.9	12.0	21.5	27.0	52.5	–	–
Total coal imports	13.1	21.3	21.9	23.5	33.0	39.0	64.5	4.8	7.2
Coal production/exports (mtce) **Production**									
Metallurgical Steam	0.4	1.0	1.0	1.0	1.0	3.0	3.0	9.1	9.1
Total coal production	0.4	1.0	1.0	1.0	1.0	3.0	3.0	9.1	9.1
Exports									
Metallurgical Steam									
Total coal export									

267

Oil Limitation Case

II. Coal's Role in Total Energy System	1977	1985 A	1985 B	1990 A	1990 B	2000 A	2000 B	1977-2000 Avg. annual growth–%/yr. A	1977-2000 Avg. annual growth–%/yr. B
Total Primary Energy Use (mtce)									
Oil, Domestic	1.6	3.6	3.6	4.3	4.3	5.5	5.5	1.8	1.8
Oil, Imported	135.5	158.1	155.5	160.2	148.7	124.5	115.5	-0.4	-0.7
Gas, Domestic	14.3	14.0	14.0	14.0	14.0	14.0	14.0	–	–
Gas, Imported	16.7	30.5	30.5	49.0	49.0	63.0	63.0	5.9	5.9
Nuclear	1.0	2.5	2.5	9.5	9.5	47.0	33.0	–	–
Hydro, Solar, Other	18.1	21.0	21.0	26.0	26.0	37.0	42.5	3.2	3.8
Coal, Domestic	0.4	1.0	1.0	1.0	1.0	3.0	3.0	9.1	9.1
Coal, Imported	13.1	21.3	21.9	22.0	31.5	56.0	81.5	6.5	8.2
Total energy use	200.7	252.0	250.0	286.0	284.0	350.0	358.0	2.4	2.5
Coal penetration (%)	6.7	8.8	9.2	8.0	11.4	16.8	23.6	—	—
Total primary energy (mtce) input to electricity									
Oil and Gas	31.5	44.5	44.5	46.2	44.7	15.0	15.5	-3.2	-3.0
Hydro, Solar, Other	18.1	19.0	19.0	20.0	20.0	21.0	22.0	0.6	0.8
Nuclear	1.0	2.5	2.5	9.5	9.5	47.0	33.0	--	--
Coal	1.8	10.0	10.0	9.3	18.8	25.5	48.0	--	--
Total energy input	52.4	76.0	76.0	85.0	93.0	108.5	118.5	3.2	3.6
Coal penetration (%)	3.4	13.1	13.1	10.9	20.2	23.5	40.5	—	—
Total electric capacity (GWe)									
Oil and Gas	18.3	30.2	30.2	32.3	32.3	28.0	28.0	1.8	1.8
Hydro, Solar, Other	14.4	16.5	16.5	17.5	17.5	18.0	20.0	0.9	1.4
Nuclear	0.5	1.5	1.5	5.5	5.5	27.0	19.0	–	–
Coal	2.4	6.6	6.6	6.0	11.7	15.8	29.0	8.5	–
Total capacity	35.6	54.8	54.8	61.3	67.0	88.8	96.0	4.0	4.4
Coal Penetration (%)	6.7	12.0	12.0	9.8	17.5	17.8	30.2	—	—
Peak load	28.3	45.7	45.7	51.0	55.8	64.8	71.0	3.7	4.1
Peak reserve margin (%)	20.5	20.0	20.0	20.0	20.0	37.0	35.0	—	—
Total oil imports (mbd)	1.89	2.21	2.17	2.24	2.08	1.74	1.62	-0.4	-0.7
Total oil consumption (mbd)									
Transportation	0.61	0.69	0.69	0.71	0.67	0.91	0.87	1.7	1.5
Residential/Commercial	0.45	0.45	0.44	0.44	0.38	0.26	0.19	-2.3	-3.7
Industry—Boilers	0.33	0.39	0.36	0.37	0.32	0.19	0.14	-2.4	-3.7
Industry—Other	0.13	0.17	0.18	0.23	0.24	0.28	0.31	3.4	3.8
Electric utilities	0.40	0.56	0.56	0.55	0.53	0.18	0.18	-3.4	+3.4
Total oil consumption	1.92	2.26	2.23	2.30	2.14	1.82	1.69	-0.2	-0.5
World oil price assumed for national coal analysis (1979 U.S. dollars/barrel)	$20*					25	40		
Economic growth assumed for national coal analysis (GNP, billion 1978 dollars)	223.8	287.9	287.9	330.5	341.2	423.0	472.1	2.8	3.3

* Uses current price of $20/barrel (June 1979 U.S. dollars) as baseline world oil price and as floor price throughout the period.

Nuclear Delay Case

I. Coal Use, Production, and Trade	1977	1985		1990		2000		1977-2000 Avg. annual growth—%/yr.	
		A	B	A	B	A	B	A	B
Coal use in major markets (mtce)									
Metallurgical	11.1	11.0	11.0	11.5	11.5	12.0	12.0	0.3	0.3
Electric	1.8	10.0	10.0	9.3	18.8	25.5	48.0	-	-
Industry	0.2	1.0	1.5	2.0	2.0	2.5	3.0	-	-
Synthetic Fuels	-	-	-	-	-	19.0	21.5	-	-
Residential/Commercial	0.4	0.3	0.4	0.2	0.2	-	-	-	-
Total coal use	13.5	22.3	22.9	23.0	32.5	59.0	84.5	6.6	8.3
Distribution of coal use by market sector (%)									
Metallurgical	82.2	49.3	48.0	50.0	35.4	20.4	14.2	—	—
Electric	13.3	44.9	43.7	40.4	57.8	43.2	56.8	—	—
Industry	1.5	4.5	6.6	8.7	6.2	4.2	3.6	—	—
Synthetic Fuels	-	-	-	-	-	32.2	25.4	—	—
Residential/Commercial	3.0	1.3	1.7	0.9	0.6	-	-	—	—
Total coal use	100%	100%	100%	100%	100%	100%	100%	—	—
Coal consumption/imports (mtce) **Consumption**									
Metallurgical	11.1	11.0	11.0	11.5	11.5	12.0	12.0	0.3	0.3
Steam	2.4	11.3	11.9	11.5	21.0	47.0	72.5	-	-
Total coal consumption	13.5	22.3	22.9	23.0	32.5	59.0	84.5	6.5	8.3
Imports									
Metallurgical	11.1	11.0	11.0	11.5	11.5	12.0	12.0	0.3	0.3
Steam	2.0	10.3	10.9	10.5	20.0	44.0	69.5	-	-
Total coal imports	13.1	21.3	21.9	22.0	31.5	56.0	81.5	6.5	8.3
Coal production/exports (mtce) **Production**									
Metallurgical									
Steam	0.4	1.0	1.0	1.0	1.0	3.0	3.0	9.1	9.1
Total coal production	0.4	1.0	1.0	1.0	1.0	3.0	3.0	9.1	9.1
Exports									
Metallurgical									
Steam									
Total coal export									

Nuclear Delay Case

II. Coal's Role in Total Energy System	1977	1985		1990		2000		1977-2000 Avg. annual growth–%/yr.	
		A	B	A	B	A	B	A	B
Total Primary Energy Use (mtce)									
Oil, Domestic	1.6	3.6	3.6	4.3	4.3	5.5	5.5	1.8	1.8
Oil, Imported	135.5	158.1	155.5	160.2	148.7	156.5	145.5	0.3	0.3
Gas, Domestic	14.3	14.0	14.0	14.0	14.0	14.0	14.0	–	–
Gas, Imported	16.7	30.5	30.5	49.0	49.0	63.0	63.0	5.9	5.9
Nuclear	1.0	2.5	2.5	9.5	9.5	36.5	24.5	–	–
Hydro, Solar, Other	18.1	21.0	21.0	26.0	26.0	35.0	39.0	2.9	3.4
Coal, Domestic	0.4	1.0	1.0	1.0	1.0	3.0	3.0	9.1	9.1
Coal, Imported	13.1	21.3	21.9	22.0	31.5	28.5	57.5	3.4	6.6
Total energy use	200.7	252.0	250.0	286.0	284.0	342.0	352.0	2.3	2.4
Coal penetration (%)	6.7	8.8	9.2	8.0	11.4	9.2	17.2	—	—
Total primary energy (mtce) input to electricity									
Oil and Gas	31.5	44.5	44.5	46.2	44.7	33.5	34.0	0.3	0.3
Hydro, Solar, Other	18.1	19.0	19.0	20.0	20.0	21.0	22.0	0.6	0.8
Nuclear	1.0	2.5	2.5	9.5	9.5	36.5	24.5	–	–
Coal	1.8	10.0	10.0	9.3	18.8	17.0	37.5	–	–
Total energy input	52.4	76.0	76.0	85.0	93.0	108.0	118.0	3.2	3.6
Coal penetration (%)	3.4	13.1	13.1	10.9	20.2	15.7	31.8	—	—
Total electric capacity (GWe)									
Oil and Gas	18.3	30.2	30.2	32.3	32.3	28.0	28.0	2.8	1.8
Hydro, Solar, Other	14.4	16.5	16.5	17.5	17.5	18.0	20.0	0.9	1.4
Nuclear	0.5	1.5	1.5	5.5	5.5	21.0	14.0	–	–
Coal	2.4	6.6	6.6	6.0	11.7	10,8	23.0	6.7	–
Total capacity	35.6	54.8	54.8	61.3	67.0	77.8	85.0	3.4	3.8
Coal Penetration (%)	6.7	12.0	12.0	9.8	17.5	13.9	27.0	—	—
Peak load	28.3	45.7	45.7	51.0	55.8	64.8	71.0	3.7	4.1
Peak reserve margin (%)	20.5	20.0	20.0	20.0	20.0	20.0	20.0	—	—
Total oil imports (mbd)	1.89	2.21	2.17	2.24	2.08	2.19	2.04	0.6	0.3
Total oil consumption (mbd)									
Transportation	0.61	0.69	0.69	0.71	0.67	0.91	0.87	1.7	1.5
Residential/Commercial	0.45	0.45	0.44	0.44	0.38	0.37	0.29	-0.8	-1.9
Industry—Boilers	0.33	0.39	0.36	0.37	0.32	0.26	0.20	-1.0	-2.1
Industry—Other	0.13	0.17	0.18	0.23	0.24	0.32	0.35	4.0	4.4
Electric utilities	0.40	0.56	0.56	0.55	0.53	0.40	0.40	–	–
Total oil consumption	1.92	2.26	2.23	2.30	2.14	2.26	2.11	0.7	0.4
World oil price assumed for national coal analysis (1979 U.S. dollars/barrel)	$20*					25	40		
Economic growth assumed for national coal analysis (GNP, billion 1978 dollars)	223.8	287.9	287.9	330.5	341.2	423.0	472.1	2.8	3.3

* Uses current price of $20/barrel (June 1979 U.S. dollars) as baseline world oil price and as floor price throughout the period.

CHAPTER 11

JAPAN

FOREWORD

This report was prepared by Japan's World Coal Study Associates, with guidance provided by the following Japanese WOCOL Participants:

Mr. H. Inaba	Vice-Chairman Committee for Energy Policy Promotion
Dr. S. Okita	Chairman Japan Economic Research Center
Mr. T. Ikuta	President Institute of Energy Economics
Mr. S. Takagaki	Director of Research Affairs Institute of Energy Economics

The Committee for Energy Policy Promotion (Japan) organized the Japan National Committee for WOCOL headed by Mr. Inaba in order to make a contribution to the World Coal Study. Under the Japan National Committee for WOCOL, the Working Group, headed by Mr. Takagaki, has prepared the Japanese national report.

The following are the members of the National Committee:

Ariyoshi, Shingo	Chairman Japan Coal Association
Ejiri, Koichiro	Executive Managing Director Mitsui & Co., Ltd.
Idemitsu, Shosuke	President Japan Coal Liquefaction Development Co., Ltd.
Ikuta, Toyoaki	
Inaba, Hidezo (Chairman)	
Morozumi, Yoshihiko	President Electric Power Development Co., Ltd.

271

Ohgi, Ken-ichi   Vice-Chairman
The Federation of Electric Power Companies

Okita, Saburo

Sakisaka, Masao   Chairman
The Institute of Energy Economics

Senga, Tetsuya   Managing Director
Federation of Economics Organizations

Tajima, Toshihiro   Managing Director
The Industrial Bank of Japan, Ltd.

Takahara, Tomo-o   Managing Director
C. Itoh & Co., Ltd.

The Members of the Working Group are listed as follows:

Aoki, Yuzuru   Deputy Manager, Research Division
The Federation of Electric Power Companies

Enamido, Yasushi   Chief of Research Department
Japan Coal Association

Fujiwara, Katsuhiro   Assistant Director, Science and Economics
Federation of Economics Organizations

Ichikawa, Seiko   General Manager, First Overseas Coal Department
Mitsui & Co., Ltd.

Ikeda, Sada-aki   Managing Director
Japan Coal Liquefaction Development Co., Ltd.

Kawai, Satoshi   Assistant Director
Department of Fuel
Tokyo Electric Power Co., Inc.

Kimura, Tohru   Chief Economist
The Institute of Energy Economics

Kinoshita, Akira   Assistant Director
Department of General Planning
Electric Power Development Co., Ltd.

Kobayashi, Seiji   Manager
Thermal Coal Section
C. Itoh & Co., Ltd.

Matsui, Ken-ichi   Chief Economist
The Institute of Energy Economics

Murota, Yasuhiro   Associate Professor
Saitama University

Sato, Takao   Manager
Research Division
The Committee for Energy Policy Promotion

Takagaki, Setsuo
(Chairman)

INTRODUCTION

With scarce energy resources, the energy policy for Japan to pursue in se-curing an energy supply on a stable basis in the future is mainly composed of the development of substitute energy sources to replace oil and the promotion of an energy-saving program in both industrial and residential sectors.

Two principal types of energy capable of replacing oil, which is already in short supply, are considered to be nuclear energy and coal. The use of coal, which is currently being reevaluated worldwide, may enable Japan to rebuild her vulnerable energy supply structure, given her own natural and economic con-ditions from the viewpoint of the procurement and consumption of coal, through the consolidation of concrete measures for enlarged coal use.

Coal has fallen behind in competition with oil with regard to economic efficiency and convenience of handling and has been unable to compete in the world energy market for many years. In order to build a new coal (especially steam coal) distribution market in the world, many problems must be solved in connection with the improvement of an inadequate infrastructure and the devel-opment of application technology based on the principle of free trade involving economic and technological cooperation with developing countries. Therefore, a huge investment and a considerable lead time will be required before an effective market can be established through mutual cooperation between governments and private enterprises of coal-producing and consuming countries.

APPROACH FOR THE NATIONAL WOCOL ANALYSIS

THE OVERALL FRAMEWORK

The following framework has been prepared to provide an estimate of the demand for coal during the period 1977 through 2000.

	1977	1985 Low Coal Case	1985 High Coal Case	1990 Low Coal Case	1990 High Coal Case	2000 Low Coal Case	2000 High Coal Case	1977-2000 (%/yr) Low Coal Case	1977-2000 (%/yr) High Coal Case
GNP in 1978 Prices (billion US dollars)	912	1,258	1,307	1,538	1,636	2,298	2,566		
GNP Growth Rate (avg. annual %/yr)		5.0	5.5	4.0	4.5	3.5	4.0	4.1	4.6
Primary Energy Consumption (mtce)	534	704	722	808	843	1,034	1,111		
Increased Rate of Energy Consumption (avg. annual %/yr)		3.5	3.9	2.8	3.2	2.5	2.8	2.9	3.2
Production of Crude Steel (million tons)	101	130	135	135	140	140	150	1.4	1.7

SELECTION OF VARIABLES FOR HIGH COAL AND LOW COAL CASES

1. It is expected that Japan's economic growth rate will be 4.1% in the Low Coal Case and 4.6% in the High Coal Case.

2. In this estimate, a forecast of world oil prices is not explicitly included in the variables.

3. The growth per annum of energy consumption will be 2.9% in the Low Coal Case and 3.2% in the High Coal Case.

4. The elasticity of the rate of energy consumption increase to economic growth rate will be 0.7, which is considerably lower than for the last 10 years (0.82). This means that the efficiency of energy use in Japan will be further improved from today's level, which is already higher than other countries.

5. Nuclear power capacity in Japan will increase from 8 GWe in 1977 to 94 GWe in 2000 in the Low Coal Case and 100 GWe in the High Coal Case.

ANALYTICAL METHODS

CONSUMPTION

Consumption of metallurgical coal will increase in proportion to the increase in crude steel production.

The consumption of steam coal for power generation is based on the assumption that nuclear power, LNG and coal will replace a certain amount of oil for power generation. In this event, the capacity of nuclear power and LNG will be estimated prior to the estimation of that for coal-fired plants.

The consumption of industrial steam coal will increase, especially in the cement and paper/pulp industries.

The volume of liquefied coal will be around 0.5% of the total primary energy consumption in 1990, and around 2.5% in the year 2000 in the High Coal Case. In the Low Coal Case, coal liquefaction is not expected.

PRODUCTION

Domestic coal production will remain unchanged until the year 2000.

COAL CONSUMPTION

POTENTIAL COAL MARKETS

METALLURGICAL

The consumption of metallurgical coal in Japan will increase as the production of crude steel increases, from 101 million tons in 1977 to 140 million tons in 2000 in Low Coal Case and to 150 million tons in High Coal Case.

The consumption of coal per ton of crude steel will decrease from now on, while the amount of oil injection will decrease with oil prices rising. As a result, the consumption of coal per ton of crude steel will remain on the same level.

Moreover, in the 1990's research and development of formed cokes will make it possible to use steam coal in the iron and steel industry.

ELECTRICITY

The consumption of electricty in Japan will increase 4.0-4.5% per annum from 1977 to the year 2000. The elasticity of the increase rate for electricity consumption to economic growth will be considerably lower than that for the last 10 years, which was 1.15%.

Oil-fired power plants, which accounted for two-thirds of all power-generating capacity in 1977, will have their share reduced to 42-43% in 1985, 22-24% in 1990 and 11-12% in the year 2000. It is assumed that oil-fired power plants will not be built after completion of those plants which are now under construction.

Electric power companies in Japan expect to construct and operate nuclear power plants as their base-load generating capacity. It is assumed that nuclear power capacity will increase from 8 GWe in 1977 to 28-30 GWe in 1985, 50-53 GWe in 1990 and 94-100 GWe in the year 2000. Liquefied natural gas (LNG) will also increase as power generation fuel, especially for coping with environmental measures.

Coal use for power generation will increase from only 6 mtce in 1977 to 57-72 mtce in the year 2000. The increase rate for coal utilization will be higher in the late 1980's and 1990's as the conversion from oil to substitute fuels, including coal, will be accelerated.

Coal penetration for power generation will increase from 4% in 1977 to 15-17% in the year 2000. (See Tables 11-1 and 11-2.)

INDUSTRIAL STEAM COAL

The consumption of steam coal in manufacturing industries will not increase so much up to 1985 and will increase by about 200 thousand tons annually from 1985 to 1990 in the Low Coal Case. In the High Coal Case, however, its consumption will increase to 5 mtce in 1985 and 7 mtce in 1990.

Recently, there have been many plans for implementing conversion from oil to coal, in Japan's industry. Coal utilization in the cement industry, in particular, shows a rapid increase, starting from 260 thousand tons in 1977 and 420 thousand tons in 1978. About half of the cement manufacturing factories shown in Figure 11-1 are reported to have converted their fuels from oil to coal, or have decided to convert to coal. According to an estimate, coal utilization in the cement industry will increase to 2.7 mtce in 1980 compared to 1.3 mtce in 1979. Our estimates for 1985 and 1990 might be a little conservative.

According to a recent study, coal can supply as much as 70% of all heat used in the cement industry and 40% in the paper/pulp industry. We estimate that about 50% of all heat used in these industries will be supplied by coal in the year 2000 in the High Coal Case. In the Low Coal Case, the consumption will increase about 200 thousand tons annually from 1990 to the year 2000.

COAL LIQUEFACTION

Under the government's "Sun Shine Project" started in 1974, three processes such as coal hydrogenation, solvent-treated liquefaction, and solvolysis liquefaction have been developed. In addition to those projects, Japan is involved in two international joint projects for coal liquefaction. These are SRC II and EDS, which were originally developed by Gulf and Exxon respectively. All three of the domestic processes are still in the initial stage of R & D.

According to the government's recent forecast of energy supply and demand, three domestic projects may supply 15 million Kl (oil equivalent), or 20 mtce in 1990, and 28 million Kl (oil equivalent), or 37 mtce in 1995. Considering the present R & D stages for the processes mentioned above, a large volume of coal liquefaction is unlikely to be realized before 1990 or 1995. In the High Coal Case of our forecast, liquefied coal will attain 5 mtce of product in 1990 and 31 mtce in the year 2000. Although no firm decisions have been made, it is assumed that some plants will be built in foreign countries. In the Low Coal Case, any liquefaction of coal is not expected to be commercialized in either 1990 or the year 2000.

275

Table 11-1. Total Electricity Balance

WOCOL

Country: Japan

Units: GWe capacity

Power Plant Type	1977	1985 Low Coal	1985 High Coal	1990 Low Coal	1990 High Coal	1995 Low Coal	1995 High Coal	2000 Low Coal	2000 High Coal
Nuclear	8	28	30	50	53			94	100
Hydro/Pumped Storage	25	33	35	37	42			51	62
Gas Turbines/Combined Cycle									
Geothermal/Solar/Other		--	--	--	1			1	3
Fossil Steam									
Oil Steam	61	63	63	55	55			50	50
Gas Steam	11	32	32	40	42			44	46
Coal Steam	4	9	10	20	21			41	52
Total Electric Capacity	109	165	170	202	214			281	313
Coal Penetration (%)	4	5	6	10	10			15	17

-- Negligible

Table 11-2. Total Electricity Balance

WOCOL

Country: Japan

Units: mtce/yr. fuel input

Power Plant Type	1977	1985 Low Coal	1985 High Coal	1990 Low Coal	1990 High Coal	1995 Low Coal	1995 High Coal	2000 Low Coal	2000 High Coal
Nuclear	11	50	54	92	98			188	199
Hydro/Pumped Storage	25	26	27	27	30			28	36
Gas Turbines/Combined Cycle									
Geothermal/Solar/Other		1	1	1	2			2	8
Fossil Steam									
Oil Steam	100	95	95	63	63			43	43
Gas Steam	12	40	44	60	60			65	67
Coal Steam	6	13	14	30	37			57	72
Total Primary Fuel Input	154	225	235	273	290			383	425
Coal Penetration (%)	4	6	6	11	13			15	17

COAL OIL MIXTURE (COM)

TRENDS IN PRACTICAL USE OF COM

The Ministry of International Trade and Industry (MITI), which is a government division responsible for the execution of industrial policy of the nation, is searching for ways to attain conversion from petroleum fuel to other alternative energy sources in the 1980's. COM firing is a technology which can be taken up as one of the effective means to be materialized within a short-term period. MITI

276

is concretely planning to include in its budget funds to subsidize or support various demonstration tests required for commercialization of COM technology. Among these projects are included demonstration tests to be carried out by the Electric Power Development Company (EPDC) for power utility application and relevant tests for blast furnace applications. There are also projects covering cement kilns and small-sized industrial boilers.

In view of the recent severe crude oil supply situation, various kinds of industries are also showing an increased interest in COM technology and are beginning studies based upon their respective needs. As summarized, the power utility industries are primarily interested in converting existing heavy oil-burning boilers for COM firing, steel industries are interested in converting heavy oil-firing blast furnaces for COM firing, cement makers are interested in application of COM in their kilns, and other industries are interested in using COM in small-sized boilers and other possible applications.

Figure 11-1   Location of Cement Manufacturing Factories

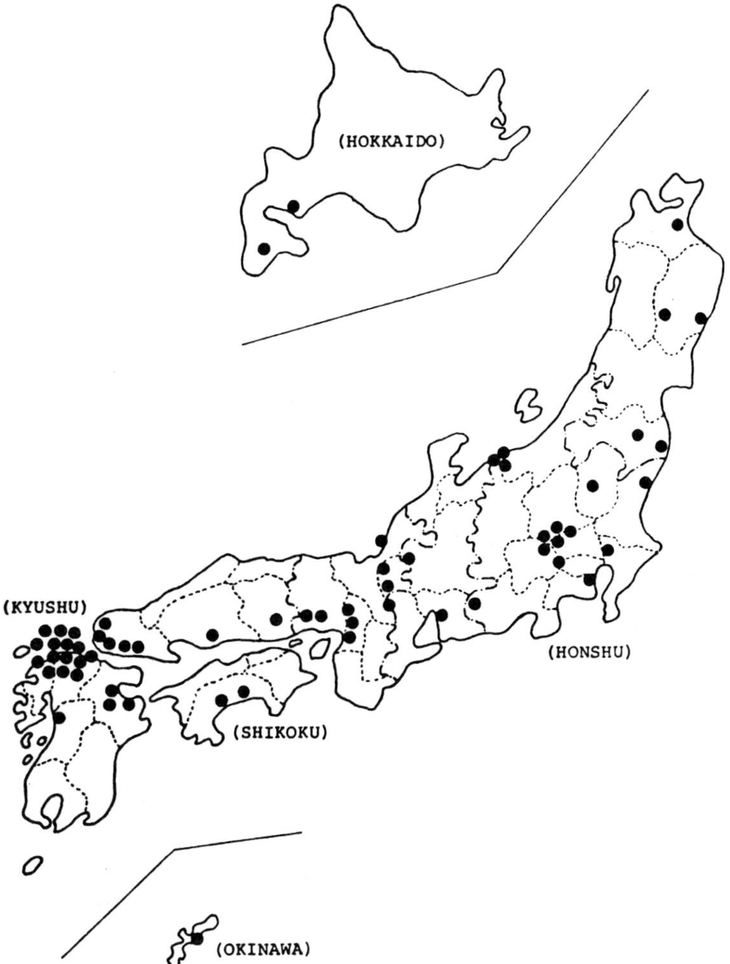

277

(1) Status of Fine COM

The EPDC pilot plant tests started with the construction of test facilities in 1977 and the actual tests were carried out between March 1978 and March 1979. The pilot plant was constructed at the site of the Research Laboratory of Mitsubishi Heavy Industry in Nagasaki. COM production capacity was one ton per hour.

This pilot plant showed satisfactory results in testing performance for preparation, storage, transportation by pipeline, ocean transportation, combustion and control.

Satisfactory data on wet mill operational know-how, use of very small amounts of additives and a uniform dispersion method were obtained. Compared with #6 oil, COM has a higher viscosity and a lower heat transfer coefficient. The test results showed that the storage tank should be designed differently from the conventional one, with regard to heating, agitation and discharge. The use of conventional type pumps such as centrifugal pumps, screw pumps, etc., is possible, but the head and capacity should be increased in view of the high viscosity of COM. Data on erosion is not yet completed but we believe that no problems will occur. Sufficient data on pump and piping design were obtained. The results of tests indicate that ocean transportation of COM requires a different tanker design from the conventional one. Combustion characteristics of COM were determined by means of experiments carried out using a test furance and a wear-resistant burner tip was developed. The development of basic measurement instruments, such as flow meter, pressure gauges, etc., was completed. The development of instrumentation for COM quality control is a study to be undertaken in the future. The present tests for 1980 are aimed at clarification of the mechanism of COM stabilization by means of additives, establishment of a COM quality control method and determination of the characteristics of COM obtained by mixing various types of coal and oil. The types of oil used for production of COM are Middle East crude oil, Minas oil from Indonesia, China oil and Alaskan oil. The types of coal are Australian bituminous coal, South African bituminous coal, Chinese bituminous coal, Australian brown coal and Alaskan subbituminous coal.

(2) State of the Art—Coarse COM

The pilot plant tests were carried out at the Takehara Power Station of the Electric Power Development Company, and at the site of the Research Laboratory of Mitsui Shipbuilding Co., located near Tokyo, during Mach 1978 to September 1979. Data on discharging characteristics from storage tank, deoiling characteristics, piping characteristics, etc., were obtained. At the same time, a trial design for a 1,000-megawatt unit was completed and feasibility studies were undertaken. Presently, studies on the demonstration tests are under way.

(3) R & D in the Steel Industry

In the experiments carried out by Sumitomo Metal during 1978 and 1979 at the Hazaki Research Center located in the Kashima Industrial Area are included tests on characteristics of COM transportation by a piping loop and COM injection experiments, with a 45-meter capacity furnace installed at the bottom of a blast furnace (COM injecting quantity, 300 Kg/h). COM injecting experiments with an actual blast furnace will commence from 1980.

FUTURE TRENDS IN PRACTICAL USE

Comparative features related to evaluation of #6 oil, Fine COM, Coarse COM and coal are summarized in Table 11-3.

As can be seen in the Table, handling of Coarse COM in case of its unloading is possible with conventional slurry pipeline technology. The form of supply and consumption of Coarse COM as fuel is almost identical to that of coal firing. In view of these factors, Coarse COM technology seems to be unsuited for fuel conversion in existing facilities and application to small-sized boilers is most appropriate for application in newly constructed power stations. We believe that through further improvements, Coarse COM technology will be commercialized but it will be no earlier than 1985. This relatively long lead time does not mean that technological development is behind schedule, but that a long lead time is required for such procedures as environmental impact assessment, in the case of new power station construction here in Japan.

Commercialization of Fine COM will be oriented mainly to fuel conversion for existing heavy oil-burning facilities and will comprise not only boilers for power generation but also those for general industrial use.

Commercialization of Fine COM will depend upon construction of supply center and distribution systems for Fine COM and modification of existing facilities, in addition to the Fine COM technology developed by the EPDC to date.

Table 11-3. Evaluation of Various Fuels (Heavy, Crude, Fine COM, Coarse COM, Coal)

Major Item	Item Minor Item	Heavy Crude	Fine COM	Coarse COM	Coal	Remarks
Alternate fuel	Coal/Heavy Oil, Crude Oil Ratio (Caloric ratio)	0/100 Construction of new facilities is not permitted (in principle)	40/60	90/10	95/5	In case of power plants
	IEA evaluation		?	?		
Fuel supply	Fuel supply	Refinery	Oil COM produc-Coal tion plant	Coal Mine	Coal Mine	
	Rigidity of supply	Small	Medium	Small	Small	Large for LNG
Location	Offshore unloading of fuel	Possible	Possible	Possible	Bad	
	Ash disposal site capacity	0	40	90	95	
	General location conditions	Easy	Easy	Medium	Difficult	
Atmospheric pollution	Dust, Sox, NOx	Small	Medium	Large	Large	
Area of application	Steelmaking and other industries	Possible	Possible	Bad	Bad	Blast furnace, cement kiln, small-sized industrial boilers Severe restrictions in case of Japan
	Utilization of existing heavy oil burning power plants	—	Possible	Bad	Bad	
Natural resources not utilized presently	Expansion of natural resources being unused presently, e.g., brown coal, etc.	—	Possible	Bad	Bad	
Economy		Medium	Medium	Large	Large	Depends upon future price trends
General evaluation		Not permitted by the IEA	Goes to the oil side, but restrictions are not severe	Located close to coal, with expansion of conditions	Severe restrictions	

The basic COM supply system in Japan is shown in Figure 11-2.

In the case of conversion from #6 oil used at existing facilities to Fine COM, moorage of large-sized ships is not possible in view of the restrictions imposed by existing fuel-receiving facilities. Thus, it will be necessary to transport Fine COM from a COM supply center constructed in the country to the various consumption sites by means of small ships. A conceptual diagram for this case is shown in Figure 11-2. Since construction of many COM preparation centers in the country is impossible, the most economic solution seems to construct a COM center in the vicinity of the coal center.

Figure 11-2. Basic COM Supply System Cases

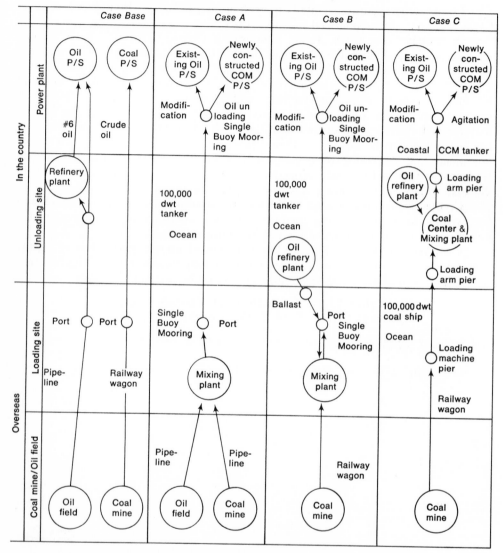

FINE COM DEMONSTRATION TEST PLAN

There are various problems to be solved prior to commercialization of Fine COM. Planning of demonstration tests aimed at solving these problems is presently under way. The fundamental plan for these tests is summarized in Table 11-4.

(1) Demonstration test using a 250-megawatt coal-burning boiler

In view of the correlation to the total schedule, the Fine COM to be used in this demonstration test will be produced at the power plant site. The tests can be roughly classified into two parts. In the first part, combustion of 50% of #6 oil and 50% of Fine COM will be carried out. These tests will be done for a short duration and are intended to verify Fine COM burning characteristics, ash distribution, etc. The results obtained will be utilized in design modification of a boiler originally designed for firing heavy oil only.

In the second part of the tests, two Fine COM burners with approximately 10 t/h capacity will be operated continuously for approximately one year, in order to demonstrate that controlled combustion of COM for a long period is possible. These tests will be performed in the second half of 1980 through early 1981.

(2) Demonstration tests with a 350-megawatt boiler designed for firing heavy oil only

The results obtained from the tests described above will be utilized in the modification of a 350-MW oil-fired unit, in order to perform the Fine COM demonstration tests. In this case, the Fine COM to be burned will be supplied from a Fine COM Preparation Center installed in an appropriate location and transported by ship.

In this test, experiments on the combustion characteristics of low-ash, low-sulfur COM, medium-ash, medium-sulfur COM and high-ash, high-sulfur COM will be carried out with reference to COM input limit allowing combustion without ash trouble and derating, COM characteristics without derating, etc. These tests will extend over a period of two years, from 1983 through 1984.

We are confident that the data obtained from the COM demonstration tests described above will provide useful information on Fine COM conversion, not only for Japan, but for countries throughout the world.

Table 11-4. Basic Plan of Fine COM Demonstration Test

	Facility	Outline of Test	Schedule						
			79	80	81	82	83	84	85
Demonstration with boiler designed for coal firing	250-MW Coal-fired boiler Evaporation rate 810 t/h	(1) Short-term test ½ Load test (2) Long-term test with 2 burners Endurance test	Design		Construction, erection		Test		
Demonstration with boiler designed for heavy oil firing	350-MW Heavy oil-fired boiler Evaporation rate 1,115 t/h	(1) Testing up to maximum COM mixture ratio (2) Construction of COM preparation center	Design			Construction, erection		Test	

COAL RESOURCES

Theoretical recoverable reserves in Japan are 20.3 billion tons and actual recoverable reserves are 3.2 billion tons. By region, the largest coal resources are in the Ishikari coalfield in Hokkaido, with an output achieved at 32% of total resources, followed by the Chikuho, Kushiro, and Miike coalfields and those in western Kyushu. With regard to coal quality, bituminous coal suitable for coking is more abundant in the Ishikari and Miike coalfields and those in western Kyushu. On the other hand, other coalfields produce bituminous or subbituminous coals to be used as steam coal.

PRODUCTION

Japanese coal production has been decreasing since 1961 when it reached a maximum of 55 million tons. This trend has been accelerating since 1967, when it dropped below the 50-million-ton level for the first time (47 million tons). In recent years, it has been at the 18-million-ton level, of which 9 million tons were metallurgical coal.

Judging from economic and other considerations, it will not be easy to maintain the present level of production. The government, however, has adopted a policy of maintaining domestic coal production.

Figure 11-3 Coalfields in Japan

NATIONAL COAL SUPPLY/DEMAND INTEGRATION

Consumption of metallurgical coal in Japan will increase from 69 mtce in 1977 to 86-92 mtce in the year 2000. Consumption of steam coal will increase from 10 mtce in 1977 to 64-84 mtce in the year 2000, which means an average growth rate of 8.1-9.7% per annum. Total consumption of coal will reach 150-207 mtce in the year 2000, of which 132-189 mtce will be imported. In the High Coal Case, coal consumption figures include coal for synthetic fuels, which are 7 mtce in 1990 and 48 mtce in the year 2000 (Tables 11-5 and 11-6).

As a result of expanded coal utilization, coal penetration in the total primary energy supply will increase from 15% in 1977 to 19% in the High Coal Case in the year 2000. Imported oil will increase from 398 mtce, or 5.3 mbd in 1977 to 471-476 mtce, or 6.0-6.1 mbd in 1985, and 483-490 mtce or 6.2-6.3 mbd in 1990. These figures are compared with the 1985 target figure for oil importation decided at the Tokyo summit meeting. However, oil imports in the year 2000 will increase to 7.2 mbd in the Low Coal Case and 6.9 mbd in the High Coal Case without any additional special measures for cutting oil imports (Table 11-7).

Table 11-5. Coal Use in Final Demand Sectors

WOCOL

Country: Japan

Units: mtce

Coal Market Sector	1977	1985 Low Coal	1985 High Coal	1990 Low Coal	1990 High Coal	1995 Low Coal	1995 High Coal	2000 Low Coal	2000 High Coal
Electric	6	13	13	30	37			57	72
Industry	4	4	5	5	7			7	12
Metallurgical	69	80	84	84	86			86	92
Synthetic Fuels	–	–	–	–	7 (5)			–	48 (31)
Residential/Commercial	–	–	–	–	–			–	–
Total Coal Use	79	97	102	119	137 (135)			150	224 (207)
Total Primary Energy Use	534	704	722	803	843			1034	(1111)
Coal Penetration (%)									
Total Energy	15	14	14	15	16			15	19
Electricity	4	6	6	11	13			15	17
Industry	0.4	0.5	0.6	0.6	0.9			0.6	1.1

Note: Figures in parentheses are product quantities from synfuel plants.

Table 11-6. Coal Supply/Demand Integration Summary

WOCOL

Country: Japan

Units: mtce

	1977	1985 Low Coal	1985 High Coal	1990 Low Coal	1990 High Coal	1995 Low Coal	1995 High Coal	2000 Low Coal	2000 High Coal
Coal Consumption	79	97	102	119	135*			150	207*
Potential Coal Production	17	18	18	18	18			18	18
Potential Coal Exports	–	–	–	–	–			–	–
Required Coal Imports	62	79	84	101	117*			132	189*

* Including liquefied coal for synthetic fuel which is 5 mtce in 1990 and 31 mtce in the year 2000.

283

Table 11-7. Total Primary Energy Consumption

WOCOL

Country: Japan

Units: mtce

Energy Source	1977	1985 Low Coal	1985 High Coal	1990 Low Coal	1990 High Coal	1995 Low Coal	1995 High Coal	2000 Low Coal	2000 High Coal
Domestic Oil —Conventional	5	11	11	12	13			19	19
—Unconventional	-	-	-	-	-			-	-
Imported Oil	398	471	476	483	490			566	542
Oil Subtotal	403	482	487	495	503			585	561
Domestic Gas —Conventional *	-	-	-	-	-			-	-
—Unconventional	-	-	-	-	-			-	-
Imported Gas	15	48	51	73	74			80	83
Gas Subtotal	15	48	51	73	74			80	83
Hydro/Geo/Solar	26	27	28	29	33			31	61
Nuclear	11	50	54	92	98			188	199
Domestic Coal	17	18	18	18	18			18	18
Imported Coal	62	79	84	101	117**			132	189**
Coal Subtotal	79	97	102	119	135			150	207
Total Primary Energy Use	534	704	722	808	843			1034	1111
Coal Penetration (%)	15	14	14	15	16			15	19

 * Included in domestic oil.
** Including liquefied coal, 5 mtce in 1990 and 31 mtce in the year 2000.

COAL TRANSPORTATION

DEMAND BY AREA AND TYPE

About four-fifths of the total demand for coal is directed to the Kanto, Kinki, Chugoku and Kyushu areas where the major steelworks are located, since coal demand for the iron and steel industry is more than 80% of total demand in Japan. The consumption of steam coal was 8.5 million tons in 1977, of which 6.3 million tons were allocated to power generation. Coal for power generation has been mainly consumed in the two major producing areas, Hokkaido and Kyushu.

COAL SUPPLY AND SOURCE

With 90% of metallurgical coal imported from Australia, the United States, Canada, the Soviet Union and the Republic of South Africa, coal imports amounted to 54.2 million tons of the total consumption of 60.5 million tons in 1977. Domestic metallurgical coal is supplied almost equally by Hokkaido and Kyushu.

The volume of imported steam coal is small, amounting to about 2 million tons, or 20% of the total supply. The domestic supply sources are Hokkaido, Kyushu, and, with lesser amounts, the Main Island of Japan.

PRESENT TRANSPORTATION SYSTEM

Imported metallurgical coal is chiefly transported from abroad by coal carriers (50,000-60,000 dwt) or other carriers which are unloaded at special ports built for steel companies. Imported steam coal for power plants is also unloaded at these special ports by smaller-sized carriers. However, trucks or trains convey domestic steam coal to power stations which are located near coal mines.

FUTURE TRANSPORTATION SYSTEMS

A. SHIPS REQUIRED (SEE TABLE 11-8)

The number of ships required by the year 2000 will be as follows;

	Case A	Case B
65,350 dwt vessel	103	139
111,230 dwt vessel	59	79
Total	162	218

Table 11-8. Number of Vessels Required for Steam Coal Imports (6,200 kcal/kg) (1,000 tons)

	1977		1990 LOW COAL CASE		1990 HIGH COAL CASE		2000 LOW COAL CASE		2000 HIGH COAL CASE	
	Tons demanded	Numbers of vessels needed (By A & B)	Tons demanded	Numbers of vessels needed (By A & B)	Tons demanded	Numbers of vessels needed (By A & B)	Tons demanded	Numbers of vessels needed (By A & B)	Tons demanded	Numbers of vessels needed (By A & B)
Australia	677	A: 2 B: 1	10,161	A: 18 B: 10	11,290	A: 20 B: 11	14,677	A: 26 B: 14	21,452	A: 38 B: 20
Canada (W. Coast)	—	—	1,129	A: 2 B: 2	1,129	A: 2 B: 2	4,516	A: 8 B: 5	6,774	A: 12 B: 7
India	—	—	—	—	—	—	1,129	A: 2 B: 1	1,129	A: 2 B: 1
Indonesia	—	—	—	—	—	—	2,258	A: 3 B: 2	4,516	A: 6 B: 3
China	226	A: 1 B: 1	2,258	A: 2 B: 1	2,258	A: 2 B: 1	5,645	A: 4 B: 3	7,903	A: 6 B: 4
South Africa	226	A: 1 B: 1	2,258	A: 6 B: 3	2,258	A: 6 B: 3	4,516	A: 12 B: 7	6,774	A: 17 B: 10
USA (W. Coast)	—	—	10,161	A: 19 B: 11	18,065	A: 34 B: 19	24,839	A: 46 B: 26	30,484	A: 56 B: 32
USSR	339	A: 1 B: 1	1,129	A: 1 B: 1	1,129	A: 1 B: 1	2,258	A: 2 B: 1	3,387	A: 2 B: 2
Total	1,468	A: 5 B: 4	27,096	A: 48 B: 28	36,129	A: 65 B: 37	59,838	A: 103 B: 59	82,419	A: 139 B: 79

(Remarks) Type of Vessel: A 65,350 dwt
B 111,230 dwt

B. PORT DESCRIPTION (SEE TABLE 11-9)

In line with an increase in imported steam coal, the required storage area will be 428 ha by the year 2000. By that time, three sites for 100 ha coal centers and two sites for 40 ha mini-coal centers are projected to be completed.

These coal centers will handle about 40 million tons of steam coal. Also, 33 million tons of imported steam coal will be handled by specialized port systems, mainly for power stations and by established coal stockyards.

C. COAL CENTER SYSTEM (SEE TABLE 11-10)

Concerning receiving systems, a specialized port system and a coal center system are being considered in order to expand coal imports in the future. The scale of demand and location will determine which system has the highest feasibility.

There is a strong possibility that the specialized port system will be chosen mainly for importation of steam coal for power stations. On the other hand, for several years the Ministry of International Trade and Industry has been studying a coal center system which may also be implemented for the importation of steam coal for power stations. MITI also has an idea to set up at least two coal centers,

Table 11-9. Importing Country Port Descriptions

Projected Coal Imports Million Metric Tons	Units	Current Met 60	Steam 2	1985 Met 76	Steam 7	1990 Met 79	Steam 33	2000 Met 85	Steam 73
Receiving port characteristics:									
Maximum draft	meters	8.5-24	7.0	8.5-24	12	12-24	12	12-24	21
Discharging rate	t/hr	98,200	1,450	98,200	3,500	98,200	10,000	98,200	28,000
Annual capacity	mt/yr	200.0	3.0	200.0	7.0	200.0	33	200.0	73
Storage capacity	mt	8 Turnover 8.0	0.6	9 Turnover 9.5	0.75	9 Turnover 9.9	3.7	10.6	107 / 3.7 / 7 (6 Turnover)
Storage area	ha		3.2		24		48	428	100 × 3 / 40 × 2
Other internal transportation infrastructure requirements:									
Rail		—	—	—	—	—	—	—	—
Barge		—	—	—	—	—	—	—	15000 × 2 × 9 set (90 Turnover)
Coastal vessels		—	—	—	—	—	—	—	5000 × 70 (50 Turnover)
Truck		—	—	—	—	—	—	—	—
Other		—	—	—	—	—	—	—	—

one in the Eastern District of Japan, and the other in the Western District of Japan; these coal center systems are now at the stage of feasibility study or planning.

In the current industrial market, the cement-producing industry feels an urgent need to convert high-priced heavy fuel oil into steam coal, and is seeking suitable transshipment receiving terminals. Most cement producers are planning to utilize such transshipment facilities.

As far as we can appraise the comparison of transportation cost of coal between the specialized port systems and the coal center systems through the prefeasibility study reports by the Japanese Government, the transportation cost of imported coal by the coal center system is much lower than the transportation cost of the specialized port system (see Table 11-10). However, it is thought that the power stations tend to prefer the specialized port systems to the coal center systems, because the coal-hauling tonnages are very large in the case of power stations and therefore are likely to avoid the complexities of secondary transportation (barges, mainly) of small lots of coal. The industrial users of coal have quite different needs from the power stations, because they use less imported coal than the power stations and can get much lower transportation costs for transshipment in the coal centers; in other words, a great reduction in seaborne transportation costs with bigger vessels. Consequently, it is expected that power stations tend to prefer the specialized port systems, while the industrial users of coal prefer the coal center systems, based on an appraisal of a comparison of the transportation costs for these two systems and the complexity or ease of transportation.

D. TRANSPORTATION TECHNOLOGY REQUIRED

Especially in the case of the transportation of lignite coal, technology is required for preventing spontaneous combustion. We can cite slurry transportation in the form of coal-oil mixtures or coal-water mixtures as examples of combustion control technology.

A group of companies are promoting COM R & D by receiving a substantial amount of government assistance. Now, COM-using technology is approaching

Table 11-10. Comparison of Transportation Costs for Coal Between the Coal Center System and Receiving Terminal System for Coal-Fired Power Generation Plants

[Case A] Coal Center System (Transshipment Terminal System)

	Coal Center (Transshipment Terminal)	Power Generation Plant
A.	7.5 million tons/year	2.5 million tons/year × 3 sites
B.	—	1 GWe x 3 sites
C.	2 berths for 100,000 dwt ship (Water depth —18 m) 2 berths for 100,000 dwt ship (Water depth —7.5 m)	3 sites capable of unloading 10,000 dwt ship (Water depth —7.5 m)

		Amount (million dollars)		Amount (million dollars)	Total Amount (million dollars)
1. Construction of piers Piers Connecting bridge	$62,000/m × 340 m × 2 berths for 100,000 dwt ship $16,900/m × 275 m	47 (42) (5)		47 (42) (5)	47 (42) (5)
2. Construction of quay	$29,000 × 180 m × 2 berths for 10,000 dwt ship	10	$25,000/m × 180 m × 3 sites (One berth for 10,000 dwt ship)	14	24
3. Construction of breakwater	—		$25,000 m × 500 m × 3 sites	38	38
4. Unloading facilities	One complete set of facilities	73	$7,500,000 × one set × 3 sites	23	96
5. Coal yard Land acquisition Reclamation Superstructure	$25/m² × 400,000 m² $100 m² × 400,000 m²	50 (10) (40)	$100/m² × 20,000 m² × 3 sites $51/m² × 20,000 m² × 3 sites	9 (6) (3)	59 (10) (6) (43)
6. Dredging	$10/m³ × 800,000 m³	8	$3.5/m³ × 1,000,000 m³ × 3 sites	11	19
7. Others		12		4	16
Total Investment (1-7)		200		99	299

Transportation Cost ($/t)				
(1) Repayment for total investment (interest, depreciation, etc.)	$5.3		$2.6	$7.9
(2) Primary transportation cost	$12.0		—	$12.0
(3) Secondary transportation cost	—		$2.1	$2.1
Total ((1) + (2) + (3))	$17.3		$4.7	$22.0

Note: A. Coal-hauling tonnages.
B. Electric power generation capacity.
C. Receiving facilities.

Table 11-10. Comparison of Transportation Costs for Coal (Con't)

[Case B] Receiving Terminal System

Coal-hauling tonnages	2.5 million tons/year × 3 sites
Electric power generation capacity	1 GWe × 3 sites
Receiving facilities	1 berth for 60,000 dwt ship × 3 sites (Water depth —15 m)

		Amounts (million dollars)

1. Construction of piers
    Piers
    Connecting bridge
	$50,000/m × 300 × 3 sites for
	60,000 dwt ship
		45
		(45)
		(—)

2. Construction of quay	—	—
3. Construction of breakwater	$75,000/m × 1,500 m × 3 sites	338
4. Unloading facilities	$25,000,000 × One set × 3 sites	75

5. Coal yard
    Land acquisition
    Reclamation
    Superstructure
	—
	$1,000/m² × 150,000 m² × 3 sites
	$51/m² × 150,000 m² × 3 sites
		68
		—
		(45)
		(23)

6. Dredging	$3.5/m² × 5,000,000 m³ × 3 sites	52
7. Others		21
Total Investment (1-7)		599

Transportation Cost ($/t)

(1) Repayment for total investment (Interests, depreciation, etc.)	$15.8
(2) Primary transportation cost	$15.5
(3) Secondary transportation cost	—
Total ((1) + (2) + (3))	$31.3
Comparison (A — B)	—$9.3

Note: (1) exchange rate $1 = 230 yen
      (2) 1979 prices
Source: Ministry of International Trade and Industry

the demonstration test stage for combustion by a newly constructed boiler for a coal-fired power station, and injection tests into large blast furnaces by at least three major steelmakers.

Because of highly increased fuel oil prices, many Japanese shipbuilders have begun designing coal-fired ships. In effect, it is reported that a few Japanese shipbuilders have already obtained some orders for building coal-fired ships from foreign shipowners.

ENVIRONMENTAL, HEALTH & SAFETY CONSIDERATIONS

CURRENT PRACTICE

Increased coal consumption is likely to cause environmental pollution by SO_2, NO_x, particulates, and ashes. Therefore, the elimination or suitable treatment of these pollutants is required.

In Japan, the regulations for environmental protection are as follows: (1) Environmental quality standards are established in order to maintain public health and preserve the life environment based on the Basic Law for Environmental Pollution Control (1967). (2) In order that these environmental quality standards are met, emission standards are established based upon various kinds of legislation to regulate the emission of environmental pollution. (3) Almost all local governments have independently enacted pollution prevention ordinances. This independence in forming ordinances by each local government is based on the concept that local differences in environmental problems do not make a uniformly applied standard throughout the nation by the central government sufficient to maintain the health of each local community and preserve their environments. (4) Local governments reach agreements on pollution prevention with enterprises operating locally which are likely to cause environmental pollution. In these agreements, measures to be taken are specified in detail for classified pollution sources (see Table 11-11).

Table 11-11. Environmental Control Standards and Limitations Which Impact on Coal Utilization

	Ambient Standards	Emission Limitations	
	Annual Mean Max. once per year	Major Metropolitan Areas	Rural
SO_2	0.04 ppm	Approx. 200 ppm*	Approx. 950 ppm**
ESP		0.2 g/Nm³	0.4 g/Nm³
		(at 5,000 kcal/kg)	
NO_x	0.04–0.06 ppm	Old 480 ppm New 400 ppm	

```
 * Stack 120 m
** Stack 200 m
```

FUTURE ENVIRONMENTAL HEALTH & SAFETY STANDARDS

The present situation for the environmental quality control and emission and efficiency standards mentioned above are shown in the Table 11-11 (for electric power). Although it is very difficult to estimate changes in these standards in the future, it can be said that these standards will be maintained as they are for the time being. However, since the regulations actually imposed on enterprises are based on pollution prevention agreements made with local governments, regulations in actual practice are more severe than legislated standards.

INDICATIVE COST ESTIMATES FOR CONTROL MEASURES

The cost incurred in complying with the present environmental regulations are shown in the Table 11-12 (the figures in the Table include costs resulting from local agreements on pollution prevention mentioned above). As shown in the Table, the cost of antipollution measures for particulate elimination, desulfurization, denitrification, ash treatment and wastewater treatment is approximately 20% of total electric power generation cost. Additional electric power transmission costs are incurred, however, since power plant sites must be located further away from markets and users in order to cope with environmental problems (see Tables 11-12 and 11-13).

EVOLUTION OF KEY ENVIRONMENTAL ISSUES

First, plant sites which meet environmental regulations are increasingly difficult to find. As a result, there is a tendency for construction works to be sited in remote and unpopulated areas. Secondly, possible increases in generation costs caused by higher pollution-prevention costs may prevent the utilization of coal as a fuel. Thirdly, the period from planning to completion is extended because of the time required for negotiations between enterprises and local governments.

Ash treatment, especially in Japan, is an important and urgent problem. A coal-fired plant of 1 GWe produces 320,000 tons of ash per year. In the normal serviceable life of the plant (15 years), total ash produced will amount to as much as 4.8 million tons. Although a part of the ash may be recovered for effective use, about half must be disposed of in ocean reclamation sites. Shore protection work for ash disposal sites increases the construction cost of power plants. Furthermore, it's more difficult to find marine areas for reclaimed sites. Lastly, even when a suitable area can be found, there is a problem that a sufficient reclamation period may not be available.

Table 11-12. Indicative Cost Estimates for Specific Environmental Measures
(average costs during serviceable period)

	Discount Rate: 8%		Discount Rate: 10%		Comments
	mills/kWh	$/ton	mills/kWh	$/ton	
1. Particulate Control ESP	0.52	1.34	0.57	1.62	
2. Control of SO$_2$					
a) Limestone FGD	5.7	11.95	6.13	14.16	
b) Dry FGD	5.7	11.95	6.13	14.16	
3. Ash Disposal	1.1	3.34	1.35	3.92	conventional
4. Control of NO$_x$					
a) Combustion techniques	0.22	0.63	0.26	0.76	
b) Other hardware	4.04	3.90	4.22	4.68	
5. Wastewater Treatment	0.22	0.70	0.30	0.95	including hazardous material treatment
6. Other Existing or Possible Future Control					
a) Fine particulates	1.61	4.47	1.83	5.39	
b) Storage	—	0.04	0.02	0.05	
c) Noise	0.04	1.39	0.04	0.17	
d) Closed coal storage	0.91	2.46	1.00	2.97	

Note: at 6,500 kcal/kg

Table 11-13. Initial Capital Cost for Environmental Equipment

	$/KW
ESP	17.3
FGD	116.0
Ash Disposal	63.6
NOx Control	
Combustion	8.0
Hardware	38.3
Wastewater	10.1
Fine Particulate	57.6
Storage	0.5
Noise	1.7
Closed Storage	31.7

Note: These costs include allocated cost for reclamation and indirect costs during construction period.

COAL CHAINS AND FINANCING

COAL CHAIN

As shown in the Figure 11-4, 2,178 million US dollars of capital costs will be required for a typical coal chain for power plants in Japan. Power plants including coal yard, power equipments, environmental equipments and ash-disposal facilities will account for around 60% of total capital costs.

Also shown is a model coal chain for coal & COM center (Figure 11-5). 230 million US dollars will be required for coal center (10mt/yr) and 130 million US dollars for COM plant. In this model chain, three-fourths of the coal will be transshipped to conventional users.

FINANCING

Cumulative coal-related capital expenditures in Japan (1977-2000) amount to about 43 to 60 billion dollars, as shown in Table 11-14. The share of investment for the construction of power-related capital expenditures is 57% of coal-related capital expenditures. However, the share of these capital expenditures is only 7.4% of total energy-related capital expenditures. This is caused by the following:

- The strong promotions of nuclear power station construction for which the power generation cost is lowest.
- The considerable amount of investment in other alternative energy sources such as LNG, gasohol, geothermal and solar energy.
- The great amount of investment in electricity-related facilities such as distribution facilities for electricity, and expenses for the development of power station sites.

The share for coal-related capital expenditures in the cumulative GNP at 1979 prices is about 0.2% and that for total energy-related capital expenditures in the cumulative GNP is about 2%. It seems that these figures are very small and we do not have any serious problem in financing capital expenditures for the development of energy. However, these figures don't include any capital which will be required to develop coalfields and build other infrastructures in foreign countries. And, based on the assumption that 33% (the share of Gross Fixed Investment) will

Figure 11-4. Illustrative Implementation Requirements for a Typical Coal Chain*

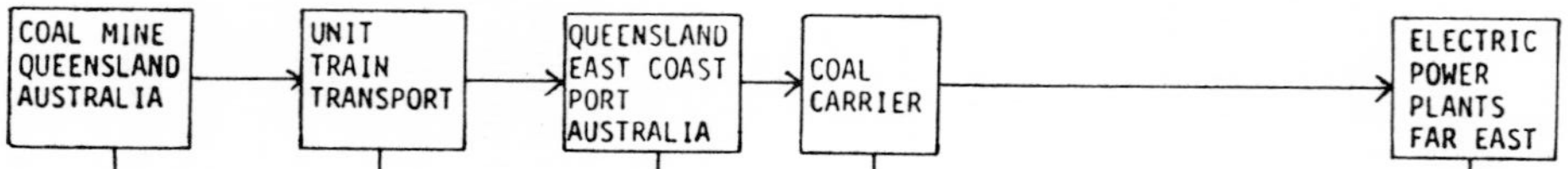

Flow diagram: COAL MINE QUEENSLAND AUSTRALIA → UNIT TRAIN TRANSPORT → QUEENSLAND EAST COAST PORT AUSTRALIA → COAL CARRIER → ELECTRIC POWER PLANTS FAR EAST

	MINES	TRAINS	PORT	SHIPS	PORT	COAL YARD	POWER EQUIPMENTS	ENVIRON-MENTAL EQUIPMENTS	ASH DISPOSAL FACILITIES	TOTAL
CAPACITY	5 Mtce/yr 6 Mt/yr	Same	Same	Same	Same	0.9Mt (45 days)	2000MW		9.9Mt ash	5 Mtce/yr 6 Mt/yr
FACILITIES	5 Mtce/yr 1 mine	120 cars @70t (net) 298 trips/yr, 200km 2.5 Mtpy per train 2.4 trains	20 Mt/yr 0.3 ports	100,000 DWT 11.6 trips 1,160,000 ton 4.3 ships		31 ha	1000MW 2 units	ESP, FGD NOx	110 ha	
LEAD TIMES**	3 years	3 years	4 years	1 year			5 years			
COSTS total capital***	$110 million	$180 million	$50 million	$150 million	$359 million	$842 million		$364 million	$123 million	$2,178 million

* All figures are "guesstimates" and listed for illustrative purposes only
** Lead times for actual projects execution after all permits granted
*** January 1978 dollars, included interest during construction at exchange rate of ¥230 per dollar.

292

Figure 11-5. Illustrative Implementation Requirements for a Model Coal Chain from Mine to Coal & COM Center

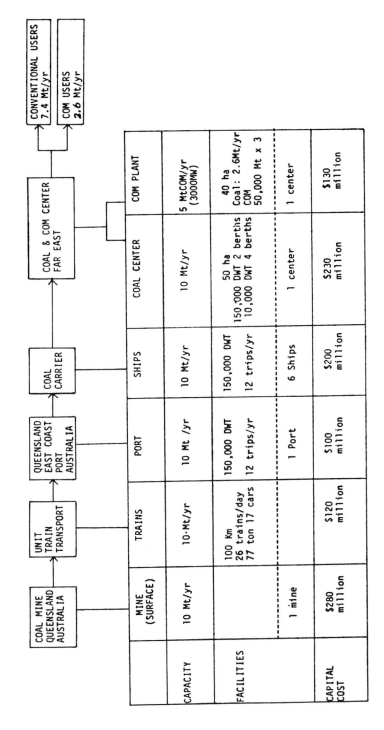

	MINE (SURFACE)	TRAINS	PORT	SHIPS	COAL CENTER	COM PLANT
CAPACITY	10 Mt/yr	10·Mt/yr	10 Mt /yr	10 Mt/yr	10 Mt/yr	5 MtCOM/yr (3000MW)
FACILITIES		100 Km 26 trains/day 77 ton 17 cars	150,000 DWT 12 trips/yr	150,000 DWT 12 trips/yr	50 ha 150,000 DWT 2 berths 10,000 DWT 4 berths	40 ha Coal: 2.6Mt/yr COM 50,000 Mt x 3
	1 mine		1 Port	6 Ships	1 center	1 center
CAPITAL COST	$280 million	$120 million	$100 million	$200 million	$230 million	$130 million

Flow chart (top): COAL MINE QUEENSLAND AUSTRALIA → UNIT TRAIN TRANSPORT → QUEENSLAND EAST COAST PORT AUSTRALIA → COAL CARRIER → COAL & COM CENTER FAR EAST → CONVENTIONAL USERS 7.4 Mt/yr; COM USERS 2.6 Mt/yr be maintained by the year 2000, the percentage of energy-related capital expenditures in cumulative Gross Fixed Investment will be 5.9-6.4% in which coal-related capital expenditures will only be 0.3-0.5%. In addition, supposing that Japan's future economic growth slows down henceforth, and the share of Gross Fixed Investment declines further, the percentage of energy-related capital expenditures in Gross Fixed Investment will be higher than approximately 6%. This fact indicates that the Japanese economy will have a considerably increased burden in financing the energy-related capital expenditures for breaking through economic growth limitations caused by energy constraints.

Table 11-14. Capital Expenditures (1977-2000)

	High Coal Case	Low Coal Case
Coal	59.8	43.0
(Production)	(12.0)	(12.0)
(Transportation)	(5.9)	(4.4)
(Power Plant)	(34.1)	(26.6)
(Liquefaction)	(7.8)	(—)
Other Power Plant	177.6	149.3
Other Electricity	319.9	277.8
Other Energies	255.9	255.1
TOTAL	813.2	725.2
GNP	38,215	37,080

Note: (1) 1979 US$, Billion
(2) $ = ¥230

Because of these situations, the Committee for Energy Policy Promotion made the following proposals on financing the required expenditures:

- Financing in the private sector which will provide most of the monetary requirements.
  - (a) To maintain the appropriate relationship between cost and price through the free market mechanism.
  - (b) To introduce more preferential fiscal measures for energy industries such as a more liberalized depreciation system; for example, an accelerated depreciation in the electric power industry, in order to expand retained earnings and improve the financial structure of the energy industries.
  - (c) To diversify financial sources through the introduction of measures such as subsidies to the interests of government's loans or private borrowings and the system of accounting the purchase of government's bonds for energy development as an expense account, in order to smoothly meet increased investment requirements.
  - (d) To apply preferential measures such as the liberalization of restrictions to excessive lending by private banks and the expansion of limits on bond issues to energy industries.
- To secure financial sources for energy development in the public sector, based on the following principles:
  - (a) Principle of preferred allocation for energy-related budgets.
  - (b) Fundamental amending of energy-related taxes.

It is noted that public financing will play a greater role in such fields as the promotion of R & D for nuclear energy, the setting up of infrastructures for the expanded use of coal and LNG, the exploration and development of crude oil, the expansion of oil stocks, and R & D for new energy.

- To establish the pivotal organization for the administration of R & D projects and the efficient utilization of public financial sources, in order to promote energy-related projects by considering international technical cooperations. The new organization should function as an effective intermediary between the public sector and the private sector.

On Dec. 29, 1979, the Cabinet of the Japanese Government decided the following policy:

- Establishment of the New Energy Development Authority on Oct. 1, 1980.
- The capital for the new organization is 600 million yen (2.6 million dollars, $1 = ¥230) and the scale of budgeted undertakings for the 1980 fiscal year is 36.5 billion yen (159 million dollars, $1 = ¥230). Also, 87 persons will be engaged in affairs related to the development of alternative energy.
- The principal undertakings are as follows:
    (a) To provide loans or loan guarantees for the exploration and the development of coal in foreign countries.
    (b) To carry out research or studies and provide loan guarantees for promoting the development of geothermal units.
    (c) To implement large-scale technological R & D for coal, geothermal and solar energy sources.

OBSTACLES AND CONSTRAINTS TO EXPANDED COAL USE

DISCUSSION OF KEY OBSTACLES AND CONSTRAINTS

In trying to expand the use of coal, Japan will first run into the problem of securing a supply of imported coal. Japan has to face this problem because, as has already been noted, there seems to be little room for increased production of coal in Japan.

The second problem is an environmental one. As has been noted earlier in this report, compliance with environmental regulations greatly increases the cost of coal-power generation and the need to dispose of ash from burnt coal makes the selection of suitable sites for coal-burning power plants a difficult task.

SUGGESTED ACTIONS AT LOCAL, REGIONAL, NATIONAL AND INTERNATIONAL LEVELS

The following are suggested actions at the national level:

- It is necessary to clarify the position of coal utilization, especially the use of steam coal, in a total energy policy. In this positioning, a renewed study is required to determine the role of domestic coal.

- It is essential to develop technologies for environmental preservation, coal utilization and disposal of coal ash for useful purposes.
- It is necessary to give tax, financial and other incentives to encourage the use of coal.
- Environmental controls must be defined with greater clarity, and the procedural matters eased in applying for approval of construction of coal-fired power plants.
- A well-coordinated coal transportation system must be set up, including the so-called coal center.
- It is necessary to evaluate the corollary economic effect of the expanded use of coal, such as land reclamation, by using coal ash as landfill.

Suggested actions at the international level are as follows:

- The principle of free trade must be upheld. The governments of exporting countries must refrain from interfering in the process of setting export prices or controlling export volumes.
- The exporting countries are required to build inland transportation systems and an adequate infrastructure for export, including the port facilities for export shipment.
- A way must be found to facilitate equity capital participation in coal resources development projects in the exporting countries.
- It is necessary to encourage establishment of multilateral or international joint development systems aimed at developing coal resources of the exporting countries.
- Possibilities must be studied of concluding technical and economic cooperation agreements with the coal-exporting countries for developing the exporting countries' coal resources in the form of regional and joint ventures.
- For efficiently increasing the import of coal, it is necessary to develop a mutual coal accommodation system to be set up on a regional basis.
- It is desirable to establish an international cooperation system for developing technologies in all phases of coal utilization from resources development, production, transportation and consumption.

Summary Worksheet

I. Coal Use, Production, and Trade	1977	1985		1990		2000		1977-2000 Avg. annual growth—%/yr.	
		A	B	A	B	A	B	A	B
Coal use in major markets (mtce)									
Metallurgical	69	80	84	84	86	86	92	1.0	1.3
Electric	6	13	13	30	37	57	72	10.3	11.4
Industry	4	4	5	5	7	7	12	2.5	4.9
Synthetic Fuels	–	–	–	–	7	–	48	...	...
Residential/Commercial	–	–	–	–	–	–	–	...	...
Total coal use	79	97	102	119	137	150	224	2.8	4.6
Distribution of coal use by market sector (%)									
Metallurgical	87	82	82	71	63	57	41	—	—
Electric	8	13	13	25	27	38	32	—	—
Industry	5	5	5	4	5	5	5	—	—
Synthetic Fuels	–	–	–	–	5	–	22	—	—
Residential/Commercial	–	–	–	–	–	–	–	—	—
Total coal use	100%	100%	100%	100%	100%	100%	100%	—	—
Coal consumption/imports (mtce) **Consumption**									
Metallurgical	69	80	84	84	86	86	92	1.0	1.3
Steam	10	17	18	35	44	64	84	8.1	9.7
Total coal consumption	79	97	102	119	130	150	176	2.8	4.6
Imports									
Metallurgical	60	73	76	77	79	79	85	1.2	1.5
Steam	2	6	7	24	33	53	73	15.3	16.9
Total coal imports	62	79	84	101	112	132	158	3.3	4.2
Coal production/exports (mtce) **Production**									
Metallurgical	8	7	7	7	7	7	7	...	...
Steam	9	11	11	11	11	11	11	...	...
Total coal production	17	18	18	18	18	18	18	...	...
Exports									
Metallurgical	–	–	–	–	–	–	–		
Steam	–	–	–	–	–	–	–		
Total coal export	–	–	–	–	–	–	–		

Note: Figures for "Total coal consumption" and "Total coal imports" exclude coal feed-stock for synthetic liquid fuels imported into Japan. These estimates are included in "Synthetic Fuels" in "Coal use in major markets."

297

Summary Worksheet

II. Coal's Role in Total Energy System	1977	1985 A	1985 B	1990 A	1990 B	2000 A	2000 B	1977-2000 Avg. annual growth–%/yr. A	1977-2000 Avg. annual growth–%/yr. B
Total Primary Energy Use (mtce)									
Oil, Domestic (incl. Gas)	5	11	11	12	13	19	19	6.0	6.0
Oil, Imported	398	471	476	483	490	566	542	1.5	1.3
Gas, Domestic									
Gas, Imported	15	48	51	73	74	80	83	7.5	7.7
Nuclear	11	50	54	92	98	188	199	13.1	13.4
Hydro, Solar, Other	26	27	28	29	33	31	61	0.8	3.8
Coal, Domestic	17	18	18	18	18	18	18	--	--
Coal, Imported	62	79	84	101	117**	132	189**	3.2	5.0
Total energy use	534	704	722	808	843	1,034	1,111	2.9	3.2
Coal penetration (%)	15	14	14	15	16	15	19	—	—
Total primary energy (mtce) input to electricity									
Oil and Gas	112	135	139	123	123	108	110	--	--
Hydro, Solar, Other	25	27	28	28	32	30	4	0.8	2.5
Nuclear	11	50	54	92	98	188	199	13.1	13.4
Coal	6	13	14	30	37	57	72	9.8	10.8
Total energy input	154	225	235	273	290	383	425	4.0	4.5
Coal penetration (%)	4	6	6	11	13	15	17	—	—
Total electric capacity (GWe)									
Oil and Gas	72	95	95	95	97	94	96	1.2	1.3
Hydro, Solar, Other	25	33	35	37	43	52	65	3.2	4.2
Nuclear	8	28	30	50	53	94	100	11.3	11.6
Coal	4	9	10	20	21	41	52	10.6	11.8
Total capacity	109	165	170	202	214	281	313	4.2	4.7
Coal Penetration (%)	4	5	6	10	10	15	17	—	—
Peak load	88	136	141	166	176	233	259	4.2	4.8
Peak reserve margin (%)	24	21	21	22	22	21	21	—	—
Total oil imports (mbd)	5.3	6.0	6.1	6.2	6.3	7.2	6.9	1.5	1.3
Total oil consumption (mbd)									
Transportation	1.1	1.5	1.6	1.6	1.8	1.9	1.9	2.4	2.4
Residential/Commercial	0.6	1.0	1.0	1.3	1.3	1.6	1.5	4.4	4.1
Industry—Boilers) Industry—Other	1.5	2.5	2.5	2.6	2.8	3.2	3.2	3.3	3.3
Electric utilities	1.3	1.1	1.2	0.8	0.7	0.8	0.6	-2.1	-3.3
Total oil consumption	5.3	6.1	6.3	6.3	6.5	7.5	7.2	1.6	1.3
World oil price assumed for national coal analysis (1979 U.S. dollars/barrel)	$20*								
Economic growth assumed for national coal analysis (GNP, billion 1978 dollars)	912	1,258	1,307	1,538	1,636	2,298	2,566	4.1	4.6

* Uses current price of $20/barrel (June 1979 U.S. dollars) as baseline world oil price and as floor price throughout the period.

** Including liquefied coal (5 and 31 mtce respectively).

HYPOTHETICAL COAL TRADE FLOWS

WOCOL   Country: <u>Japan</u>

Units: <u>mtce</u>

Trade Flows (indicated importer preferences)		1977	1990		2000	
			Low Coal	High Coal	Low Coal	High Coal
Australia	—Steam	0.6	9	13[3]	13	34
	—Metallurgical	28	30	32	32	33
Canada	—Steam	-	1	1	4	8[2]
	—Metallurgical	11	15	15	15	17
Germany, Federal Republic of	—Steam	-	-	-	-	-
	—Metallurgical	-	-	-	-	-
United Kingdom	—Steam	-	-	-	-	-
	—Metallurgical	-	-	-	-	-
United States	—Steam	-	9	21[4]	22	56[28]
	—Metallurgical	14	20	20	20	22
(Subtotal, OECD)	—Steam	(0.6)	(19)	(35)	(39)	(97)
	—Metallurgical	(53)	(65)	(67)	(67)	(72)
China, People's Republic of	—Steam	0.2	2	2	5	10[3]
	—Metallurgical	-	5	5	5	6
Colombia	—Steam	-	-	-	-	-
	—Metallurgical	-	-	-	-	-
India	—Steam	-	-	-	1	1
	—Metallurgical	-	-	-	-	-
Indonesia	—Steam	-	-	-	2	4
	—Metallurgical	-	-	-	-	-
Poland	—Steam	-	-	-	-	-
	—Metallurgical	1	1	1	1	1
South Africa, Republic of	—Steam	0.2	2	2	4	6
	—Metallurgical	2	2	2	2	2
USSR	—Steam	0.3	1	1	2	3
	—Metallurgical	4	4	4	4	4
Other Countries	—Steam	0.8	-	-	-	-
	—Metallurgical	-	-	-	-	-
(Subtotal, Non-OECD)	—Steam	(1.5)	(5)	(5)	(14)	(24)
	—Metallurgical	(7)	(12)	(12)	(12)	(13)
Total Required Imports	—Steam	2	24	40	53	121
	—Metallurgical	60	77	79	79	85
	—Total Coal	62	101	112	132	206

[ ] ... coal for liquefaction

CHAPTER 12

THE NETHERLANDS

PREFACE

A strongly growing role of coal in the Netherlands' energy supply system is to be expected. Because national experience with respect to coal utilization has dwindled over the past decades, the possible ways and problems of large-scale reintroduction have to be analyzed carefully in view of present and future socio-economic and environmental demands. The Netherlands Energy Research Foundation ECN being assigned a major role in the national analysis and R&D programs, R. Bosma and R. van der Wart of ECN were invited to act as Associates to the Netherlands' Participant, Mr. A.A.T. van Rhijn.

A working party on Seaport Facilities was set up to describe the distribution function of the Dutch seaports with respect to coal trade, with the participation of A.G. Beelaerts van Blokland (Shell), D. Hoogendoorn (Steenkolen Handelsvereniging, SHV), H. Molenaar (Municipal Port Management Rotterdam) and J. Lagendijk (Frans Swarttouw). This working party has drawn up the section on Coal Transportation. Further, the section on Implementing Actions Required for the Total Coal System contains a contribution of G. Taks (Netherlands Energy Development Company, NEOM) with the cooperation of Gasunie, on medium Btu gasification for gas utility purposes. This data reflects the findings at the time of analysis (early 1979).

INTRODUCTION

During the past decades the Netherlands' energy situation has been dominated by two factors. First, the discovery and exploitation of domestic natural gas resources entailed the replacement of coal as a main constituent of the fuel mix (50% coal and 50% oil in 1960). Low energy prices caused a complete phasing out of domestic coal production from a level of 13 million tons in 1961, and coal use declined to a few percent of total energy demand. Secondly, the exploitation of the natural gas resource changed the energy import/export ratio up to the point of the Netherlands becoming a net energy exporting country in 1974. This situation will prevail for a short period: in the early 1980's imports will once again exceed exports.

Future developments will be dominated again by natural gas exploitation policy. Gas consumption is being phased out of large boilers in the electricity production and industrial sectors, while expiring gas export contracts will not be renewed. As a result, production will decline substantially within the next two decades, the reserves and facilities serving as a strategic long-term back-up system. To this end, pipeline gas and LNG will also be imported from several sources.

Although the rational use of energy will be strongly stimulated and the growth rate of energy demand appears to have decreased permanently compared with the numbers of the 1960's and early 1970's, a growing energy supply gap is expected. Since the further development of nuclear capacity will be limited, being subject to a forthcoming nuclear debate, this supply gap has to be filled by increasing oil imports and the reintroduction of coal use on a nationally unprecedented scale.

Because it cannot be produced in the shorter term from the domestic resources for economic and technical reasons, all coal must be imported. Therefore attention must be given to the receiving end, i.e., the capacity of the Dutch seaports which also have an important international distribution function. On the user's end, the present lack of coal utilization know-how and the environmental burden to the densely populated country may present severe constraints to the large-scale substitution of natural gas and oil by coal.

APPROACH FOR THE NATIONAL WOCOL ANALYSIS

THE OVERALL FRAMEWORK

Earlier projections regarding national energy demand as given in WAES had to be revised downward because of recent socio-economic development in the Netherlands and related changes of GNP growth and energy demand assumptions. The Netherlands' government was preparing White Papers on energy, coal and electricity for publication in 1979/80, based on the requirements set by socio-economic policy. It was judged realistic to follow the same basic assumptions in the national WOCOL analysis, to arrive at the most useful conclusions and recommendations in the national framework.

The main elements dominating the framework for the development of coal demand are:

- Continuing growth of total energy demand, notwithstanding strong efforts in the field of energy conservation.
- A decrease of the natural gas component, increasing the supply gap.
- Continuing growth of electricity production, with limited coal demand growth in the short term because of existing surplus oil-fired capacity and stretching of natural gas available for this sector by temporarily increased substitution by oil. This sector merits special attention because it is the largest potential coal consumer in the next decades. The role of nuclear power is treated as the most important variable.
- A possible contribution of solar, wind and geothermal energy, not expected to exceed 1 or 2% of total energy demand in the year 2000.
- The supply gap has to be filled to a large extent by increasing oil imports. This trend can only be influenced effectively by the accelerated introduction of coal use in the electricity production and industrial steam sectors.

Through 1985 coal demand is determined by already planned additions of coal-based power plants and a possible switch to coal in industry. During 1985-2000, coal demand growth remains dependent on these two sectors, coal gasification and coal-fired district heating having less impact in this time frame.

CASE VARIABLES

Economic growth at a rate of 3.0% of GNP per year is judged a prerequisite to achieve the goals of socio-economic policy, in particular a lowering of the unemployment level. This growth rate is moderate compared to that of the past decades, but will be the maximum achievable in the decades to come. Therefore, a lower variant is also considered, assuming a GNP rate of 2.5% per year until 1985 and of 2.0% per year during 1985-2000.

The overall average growth of *energy demand* is projected at 2.9% per year in the high growth case and at 2.0% per year in the lower case. The average elasticity would thus decrease from more than 1.0% to 0.9% or 0.8% in the year 2000.

World oil prices will be very important in the setting of energy prices in general. Further increases will stimulate energy conservation measures and make available additional conventional and new energy sources. It is tentatively assumed that oil prices could about double in real terms until 2000, from their 1978 level. The scenarios adopted in this report are essentially normative, so the effects of this increase and of the lower one as indicated in Table 12-1 have not been considered in

Table 12-1. Coal's Role in the Netherlands' Energy System

	1977	1985 A	1985 B	1990 A	1990 B	2000 A	2000 B	1977-2000 Avg. annual growth—%/yr. A	B
Total Primary Energy Use (mtce)									
Oil, Domestic	2.3	2.9	2.9	2.9	2.9	2.2	2.2	—	—
Oil, Imported	33.4	49.0	56.4	52.4	61.8	58.9	80.3	2.5	3.8
Gas, Domestic	46.6	38.8	38.8	38.1	38.2	32.8	32.8	—	—
Gas, Imported	—	9.2	9.2	10.1	10.1	10.8	10.8	—	—
Nuclear	1.4	1.4	1.4	1.4	1.4	8.0	1.4	7.9	—
Hydro, Solar, Other	—	0.3	0.3	0.3	0.3	2.5	2.5	—	—
Coal, Domestic	—	—	—	—	—	—	—	—	—
Coal, Imported	4.5	10.4	10.4	13.1	16.6	22.8	38.2	7.3	9.7
Total energy use	88.2	112.0	119.4	118.3	131.3	138.0	168.2	2.0	2.85
Coal penetration (%)	5.1	9.3	8.7	11.1	12.6	16.5	22.7	—	—
Total primary energy (mtce) input to electricity									
Oil and Gas	14.4	16.1	17.2	15.7	16.3	3.9	4.3	—	—
Hydro, Solar, Other	—	—	—	—	—	1.4	1.4	—	—
Nuclear	1.4	1.4	1.4	1.4	1.4	8.0	1.4		
Coal	1.4	3.9	3.9	6.0	8.6	13.7	25.9	10.4	13.5
Total energy input	17.2	21.4	22.5	23.1	26.3	27.0	33.0	2.0	2.9
Coal penetration (%)	8	18	17	26	33	51	78	—	
Total electric capacity (GWe)									
Oil and Gas	13.3	12.8	12.8	13.0	12.0	8.0	6.0	—	—
Hydro, Solar, Other	—	—	—	—	—	( )	( )	—	—
Nuclear	0.5	0.5	0.5	0.5	0.5	5.0	0.5	10.5	—
Coal	0.7	2.2	2.2	4.0	5.5	8.5	16.5	11.3	14.6
Total capacity	14.5	15.5	15.5	17.5	18.0	21.5	23.0	1.7	2.0
Coal Penetration (%)	5	15	15	25	30	40	70	—	—
Peak load	8.7	11.3	11.3	12.8	13.1	15.7	16.8	2.6	2.9
Peak reserve margin (%)	65	27	27	27	27	27	27	—	—
Total oil consumption (mbd)									
Transportation	0.2	0.2	0.2	0.2	0.2	0.2	0.3	—	—
Residential/Commercial	—	—	—	—	—	—	—	—	—
Industry—Boilers		0.1	0.1	0.1	0.1	0.1	0.1	—	—
Industry—Other	0.1	0.2	0.2	0.3	0.4	0.5	0.7	—	—
Electric utilities	0.1	0.1	0.1	0.1	0.1	—	—	—	—
Total oil consumption	0.4	0.6	0.8	0.7	0.8	0.8	1.1	3.1	4.5
World oil price assumed for national coal analysis (1979 U.S. dollars/barrel)	$20*					30	25	1.8	1.0
Economic growth assumed for national coal analysis (GNP, billion 1978 dollars)	120	146	152	161	187	198	237	2.2	3.0

* Uses current price of $20/barrel (June 1979 U.S. dollars) as baseline world oil price and as floor price throughout the period.

detail. It is possible that the higher rate of increase will entail additional energy conservation measures resulting in a lowering of total energy demand by 10% by the year 2000 and nuclear expansion, resulting in a lower use of coal.

The growth of *electricity demand* in this report is assumed to average 2.9% per year in the high economic growth case and 2.0% per year in the low case during the period under consideration.

Nuclear penetration in the power production sector is specifically treated as a predominant variable in coal demand projections. In accordance with internationally agreed policy, power plant additions must be coal-fired or nuclear. Utilities will prefer to aim at a significant diversification with respect to primary energy input which might be achieved if base-load additions from 1990 to 2000 were 50% nuclear and 50% coal; this development leads to the Low Coal Demand Case for this sector. A negative government decision on nuclear additions would mean that all base-load additions should be coal-fired stations; this would lead to the High Coal Demand Case for this sector.

Coal penetration rates in the different final demand sectors are assumed to be influenced primarily by the sector development itself and to a smaller degree by the additional positive or negative effects—e.g., on availability of capital—of economic growth.

SELECTION OF VARIABLES FOR WOCOL HIGH COAL AND LOW COAL CASES

The projections of coal demand for WOCOL High Coal Case (B) and WOCOL Low Coal Case (A) are based on:

- the two different assumptions mentioned with respect to GNP growth with related high- and low-energy demand and electricity production;
- the two different assumptions mentioned regarding the use of nuclear energy in the power production sector resulting in a High and a Low Coal Demand Case in this sector.

A combination of these assumptions results in four coal demand cases, of which the highest and lowest are chosen (see Table 12-1 and Figure 12-1):

WOCOL High Coal Case thus representing the combined effects of high energy demand growth and no nuclear additions.

WOCOL Low Coal Case resulting from the lower energy demand growth projection combined with the assumption that 50% of base-load additions after 1990 would be nuclear.

COAL CONSUMPTION

POTENTIAL COAL MARKETS

The following markets are considered with regard to future coal demand (see Table 12-2):

METALLURGICAL INDUSTRY

Nearly 70% of current coal consumption in the Netherlands is taken up by the iron and steel industry: 3.0 mtce of metallurgical coal. The growth of metallurgical coal demand will depend on the international iron and steel market and on national

Table 12-2. Coal Use, Production, and Trade in the Netherlands

	1977	1985 A	1985 B	1990 A	1990 B	2000 A	2000 B	1977-2000 Avg. annual growth—%/yr. A	1977-2000 Avg. annual growth—%/yr. B
Coal use in major markets (mtce)									
Metallurgical	3.0	3.4	3.4	3.3	3.6	2.9	4.0	—	—
Electric	1.1	3.9	3.9	6.0	8.6	13.7	25.9	10.4	13.5
Industry	0.3	2.2	2.2	2.3	2.9	3.0	4.0	10.5	11.9
Synthetic Fuels	—	—	—	—	—	1.3	2.4	—	—
Residential/Commercial	0.1	—	—	0.6	0.6	1.0	1.0	—	—
Total coal use	4.5	10.4	10.4	13.1	16.6	22.8	38.2	7.3	9.7
Distribution of coal use by market sector (%)									
Metallurgical	66.7	35.8	35.8	27.0	22.9	13.2	10.7	—	—
Electric	24.4	41.0	41.0	49.1	54.8	62.6	69.4	—	—
Industry	6.7	23.2	23.2	18.9	18.5	13.7	10.7	—	—
Synthetic Fuels	—	—	—	—	—	5.9	6.5	—	—
Residential/Commercial	2.2	—	—	5.0	3.8	4.6	2.7	—	—
Total coal use	100%	100%	100%	100%	100%	100%	100%	—	—
Coal consumption/imports (mtce)									
Consumption									
Metallurgical	3.0	3.4	3.4	3.3	3.6	2.9	4.0	—	1.3
Steam	1.5	7.0	7.0	9.8	13.0	19.9	34.2	10.4	14.5
Total coal consumption	4.5	10.4	10.4	13.1	16.6	22.8	38.2	7.3	9.7
Imports									
Metallurgical	3.0	3.4	3.4	3.3	3.6	2.9	4.0	—	1.3
Steam	1.5	7.0	7.0	9.8	13.0	19.9	34.2	10.4	14.5
Total coal imports	4.5	10.4	10.4	13.1	16.6	22.8	38.2	7.3	9.7

economic growth. It is assumed that consumption in this sector will increase to a maximum of 4.0 mtce in the year 2000 in the High Coal Case. In the Low Coal Case this consumption would be limited to 2.9 mtce.

ELECTRICITY PRODUCTION

The power production sector potentially offers the most significant growth market for coal as a substitute of oil and gas. All new base-load capacity will be fitted for dual firing (coal and oil) with the prime objective to use coal, or will be nuclear after 1990. The supply of natural gas is being phased out; however, a total amount of about 100 billion cubic meters still remains available to this sector for the next decades. For the near term, there are severe limitations to the development of this coal market. The predominant factors in this respect are:

• *Electricity demand*

Power consumption is recently growing at a much lower rate than in the past decades. The utilities' 1979 estimate for the period 1977-1987 is based on an average per annum maximum load growth of 3.5% compared to 6.6% over the past 11 years. In this report a 2.9% per-year average growth during 1977-2000 is assumed for the High Coal Case, resulting in an increase of electricity demand from 50 TWh in 1977 to 96 TWh in the year 2000. In the Low Coal

Figure 12-1. Total Energy Demand for the Netherlands (mtce)

WOCOL High Coal Case: High Coal Demand Case based on high energy demand growth and no nuclear capacity additions

WOCOL Low Coal Case: Low Coal Demand Case based on lower energy demand growth and nuclear capacity expansion

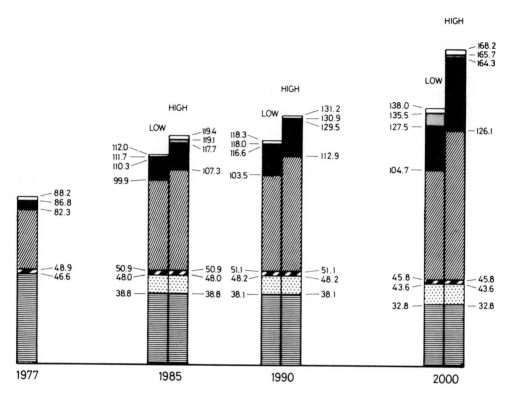

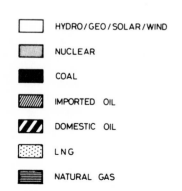

HYDRO / GEO / SOLAR / WIND

NUCLEAR

COAL

IMPORTED OIL

DOMESTIC OIL

LNG

NATURAL GAS

Case, consumption in the year 2000 is projected at 79 TWh, with an average growth rate of 2.0% during 1977-2000. In the year 2000 the share of electricity in total energy demand thus appears to be 19.6% on the basis of primary energy input for both cases.

• *Capacity growth*

The need for new base-load production capacity (which will be coal-fired or nuclear) is strongly influenced by the increase of surplus capacity related to the break in the consumption growth trend. This surplus at present is 2,700 MW of a total installed capacity of 14,700 MW, taking into account a 27% reserve normally adopted by the utilities.

Coal-firing will be primarily considered for large units. A trend toward installing more small units for combined power and heat production results from energy conservation policy, offering a submarket for coal that is much smaller in volume.

Against this background the capacity additions through the year 2000 have been estimated for the High Coal Case and the Low Coal Case. It appears that new base load capacity (coal-fired or nuclear) is to be expected only after 1985 and could not have a major impact on coal demand before 1990. This is illustrated by the age profile of existing capacity as given in Table 12-3.

Table 12-3. Power Production Capacity Structure and Age Profile (as of December 31, 1977)

Plant type	Existing capacity (MWe) December 31, 1977	Capacity under construction (MWe) December 31, 1977	Dates of existing capacity (MWe) installation		
			1970-1977	1960-1969	1950-1959
FOSSIL STEAM					
coal	389.8				389.8
oil	820.7[1]			523.1[1]	297.6
natural gas	1,809.1		1,219.6		589.5
coal/oil	469.8	596 + 627		469.8	
oil/natural gas	8,813.7	320 (oil *and* gas) +506 +633	5,143.1	3,275.9	394.7
oil/coal/ blast furnace gas/ natural gas	252			252	
oil/blast furnace	340.4			340.4	
blast furnace/ natural gas	449.2		449.2		
coal/natural gas	328.7			223.1	105.6
nuclear	495.3		443.2	52.1	
gas turbines/ combined cycle	591.5	93	430.9	160.6	
Total	14,760.2	2,775	7,686.0	5,297.0	1,777.2

[1] Of which 2 x 17 MWe incinerator plant
(Source: N.V. KEMA)

• *The choice between coal and nuclear*

New nuclear capacity is not to be expected before the early 1990's, taking into account the time needed for procedures to reach a decision on nuclear expansion and for planning and building nuclear installations. Because the outcome of the nuclear debate to be organized in the Netherlands is uncertain, the possible range of the nuclear share in base-load additions after 1990 has been taken as 0-50%.

These considerations lead to coal demand projections for the electricity production sector as indicated in Figures 12-2a and 12-2b: an increase from 1.1 mtce in 1977 to 25.9 mtce in 2000 in the High Coal Case or 13.7 mtce in the Low Coal Case (68% or 60% of total national coal demand in the year 2000, respectively).

Figure 12-2a. Electricity Consumption and Primary Fuel Input in the Netherlands in the WOCOL High Coal Case

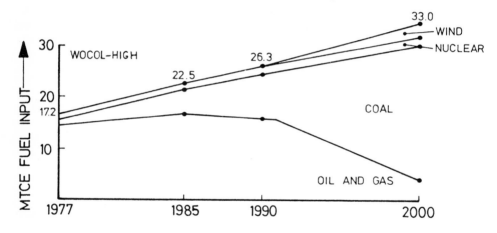

Figure 12-2b. Electricity Consumption and Primary Fuel Input in the Netherlands in the WOCOL Low Coal Case

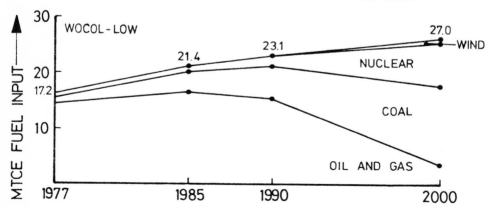

INDUSTRIAL USE OF STEAM COAL

Beginning in the early 1960's, many Dutch industries have generally invested in the replacement of coal- and oil-fired boilers by gas-fired systems. In view of the current economic situation, there is not much incentive to change back to coal even in cases where existing installations have been depreciated. Investments will be higher and exploitation and maintenance more complicated than in the alternative case of gas- or oil-fired systems.

The phasing out of natural gas supplies to big consumers will make the first opening for increased coal use in this sector. The rate of penetration will be strongly dependent on the combined effects of coal-to-oil price differences and public measures to stimulate the use of coal-fired systems in the sector as a whole.

The possible role of coal as a raw material for the chemical industry has not been considered in this framework. The possible shorter-term impact of developments in this field calls for further study.

Relating industrial development and connected energy demand growth to economic growth, it is estimated that coal demand in this sector could increase from 0.3 mtce in 1977 to 4.0 mtce for the High Coal Case or 3.0 mtce for the Low Coal Case in the year 2000.

RESIDENTIAL AND COMMERCIAL (COMBINED POWER
AND HEAT PRODUCTION FOR DISTRICT HEATING)

Capacity additions for combined power and heat production in district-heating systems will be integrated in the electric utilities' power supply system. Their coal consumption has, however, not been included in the coal demand projections for the electricity production sector, judging that the application for district heating is the predominant feature. Coal demand in the Residential and Commercial sector has thus been estimated on the basis of a recent study on developments regarding district heating; no other significant use of coal has been assumed for this sector. Coal consumption in this market could grow to 1.0 mtce in the year 2000 for both the High Coal and the Low Coal Case.

COAL CONVERSION

In the preceding sections the substitution of oil and gas by coal is considered by way of direct firing. In view of the long lead times for commercial introduction of the technologies considered, the alternative use of coal conversion products will not significantly change the coal consumption figures projected up till the year 2000. A considerable additional impact on national coal demand could only be assumed if gasification and liquefaction products could commercially take an extra share in the consumption of:

- oil and gas in the industrial sector; and
- natural gas in different sectors by mixing of coal gas and natural gas.

Only the latter option has been considered seriously in the Netherlands as a possible contribution to energy supply, before the year 2000. This special case is described on page 318 of this chapter. Here it is assumed that all applications of coal conversion could result in an additional coal demand in the year 2000 of 2.4 mtce for the High Coal Case or 1.3 mtce for the Low Coal Case (6.3% or 5.7% of total coal demand).

PROJECTIONS OF COAL CONSUMPTION FOR WOCOL HIGH COAL AND LOW COAL CASES

The development of coal demand as described by sector for a High Coal Case and a Low Coal Case results in the total coal consumption numbers given in Table 12-2. An increase is indicated from 4.5 mtce in 1977 to 38.2 mtce in 2000 for the High Coal Case or 22.8 mtce for the Low Coal Case. This increase is strongly dominated by the developments mentioned in the section on electricity production.

The share of coal in the Netherlands' energy supply system would increase from 5% in 1977 to more than 20% in the High Coal Demand Case or more than 15% in the Low Coal Case.

It should be pointed out that these numbers refer to the share in total national fuels consumption, including the use for non-energy purposes.

IMPLICATIONS FOR REQUIRED OIL IMPORTS

In most countries coal usage will be destined to substitute oil with the short-term goal to limit the growth of oil imports. From the projected development of energy supply in the Netherlands a different picture appears to emerge. Oil imports are assumed to increase by a factor of 2.4 in the High Coal Case or 1.8 in the Low Coal Case. This is caused by two factors reflecting the predominance of concern for longer-term effects over that for the problems connected with a stronger dependency on oil imports in the shorter term:

- The desirability of stretching the domestic natural gas resource.
- The structure of the electricity production capacity which necessitates a temporary switch to oil in existing dual-firing (gas/oil) plants to stretch the natural gas still available for this sector and to spread the increase of air pollution more evenly over a longer period of time.

If oil availability and/or oil price developments would threaten the implementation of current national objectives, these developments would at the same time offer additional incentives for a stronger switch to coal, as indicated in the next paragraph. Natural gas supply policy objectives imply that domestic gas can also be used in the shorter term as a temporary solution to the development of a real emergency.

REDUCTION OF OIL

In the case of a worldwide 20% reduction of oil available by the year 2000, as adopted for evaluation in WOCOL, the following effects may be considered assuming a relatively smooth development without major crisis situations:

- The reduction with accompanying rise of price will affect world trade, national economic growth and national energy demand in a negative way. This effect has not been analyzed quantitatively.
- The widening of the supply gap resulting from reduced oil availability will be limited by a strengthening of incentives to reduce specific energy demands by faster introduction of energy conservation technology and of more stringent energy conservation measures.
- The developments considered would offer additional incentives for a stronger switch to coal in the industrial steam coal sector and the power production sector.

It is tentatively concluded that a 20% reduction in oil consumption would result in a decrease of total energy consumption in the low growth scenario from 138.0 mtce to 131.9 mtce in the year 2000. Coal consumption in that case would rise to 28.9 mtce in the year 2000, assuming that the situation would call for a nuclear program as described for the lower coal demand scenario.

The 20% oil reduction band shown in Figure 12-3 would thus be absorbed for about equal parts by increased energy conservation on the one hand and increased coal consumption on the other.

Figure 12-3.

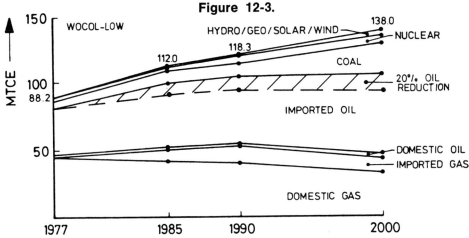

The 20% reduction of oil consumption indicated as band in the WOCOL Low Coal Case projection; it is assumed that the reduction will be absorbed in about equal parts by a lowering of total energy demand and by an increase of coal use.

It should be stressed that the assumed increase of coal consumption would call for additional policy measures influencing decision-making on fuel choice in the sectors under consideration. In particular, the accelerated replacement of oil- and gas-fired power plants by coal-fired installations would involve important financial burdens, in view of the age profile and surplus capacity in the existing power production structure.

COAL PRODUCTION

The situation with regard to potential coal production in the Netherlands is characterized by the existence of ample geological resources that are not economically recoverable.

RESOURCES

Recent estimates by the Netherlands' Geological Survey, based on existing data from deep drillings, indicate a resource base of 100 billion tons of hard coal. This estimate relates to coal seams more than 0.8 metres thick and to a depth of 1,500 metres.

Some 2% of this resource base, i.e., 2 billion tons, is situated in fields that have been considered for exploitation by conventional deep mining. Because production costs are too high for economic exploitation of any of the fields, the reserves are nil at the moment. Under the present circumstances this situation is not expected to change drastically in the near term, the price of imported coal being one half to one third of the estimated costs of production.

PRODUCTION

Until 1950 indigenous coal provided more than 70% of national coal consumption and about 50% of total energy demand, at a production level of some 12 million tons per year. Production reached a maximum of 13 million tons in 1961 but declined sharply after 1965 as a consequence of the development of world energy prices and low-cost domestic natural gas supply.

Coal mining was stopped in 1974, while coal consumption dropped to less than 5% of total energy demand. In view of the potential significance of the resource base, the economics of renewed exploitation is repeatedly under review, and advanced or completely new recovery techniques are now being given close attention as a long-term option.

NATIONAL COAL SUPPLY/DEMAND INTEGRATION

Domestic production lacking completely, national coal demand will have to be satisfied by imports in its entirety in the time frame under consideration.

This situation necessitates special attention with regard to security of supply. In this respect, measures to be considered relate to diversification regarding geographic origin of supplies, long-term supply contracts, participation in overseas production ventures and stock-building within the country.

COAL TRANSPORTATION

Seaport facilities in the Netherlands merit special attention because the combined inland transport capacity of waterways and railroads appears to be adequate in the time frame considered.

It is of international interest that the Dutch ports will continue their present international coal distribution function. A major role is envisaged in this respect for the Rotterdam area, in view of the expected use of large bulk carriers. The following therefore converges in a study on the facilities in this area. Other Dutch ports will, however, handle an important part of national coal imports, mainly serving individual consumers like power plants, steels works and, eventually, gasification plants.

MARITIME TRANSPORTATION

The position of the Netherlands will be specifically affected by factors relating to the economics of scale in overseas transportation. Maritime transport costs currently represent 30-35% of the CIF costs of coal imported into the Netherlands, warranting special attention to any possible savings on these costs as a contribution to more extensive coal usage. The predominant factor influencing maritime costs is the vessel size, with larger economies of scale being attained on longer routes, although it should be kept in mind that smaller carriers will more easily be able to find other commodity cargo as backhaul freight.

Nevertheless, it is generally assumed that it will be the terminal facilities which will determine the maximum vessel size to be used. The IEA Steam Coal study arrives at a maximum of 200,000 dwt on this basis, and for the South Africa-Europe trip calculates a saving of 20% ($1.60/ton) on transport costs when the ship size increases from 100,000 to 200,000 dwt. From Australia to Northwestern Europe, an increase from 75,000 to 150,000 dwt would result in a saving of 28% ($3.70/ton).

Only by making major investments in large-sized export and import terminals will it be possible to take full advantage of these economics. As only a limited number of large import terminals can be supported by the market, these should be well equipped for inland distribution and transshipment by sea.

THE INTERNATIONAL DISTRIBUTION FUNCTION OF THE DUTCH PORTS

During the past decade the Dutch ports have been of great and growing importance to all West European countries for the distribution of bulk commodities. The main reasons are their favorable geographic position, their modern equipment and their ample depth of water. These factors result in lower freight costs, sometimes up to $5-10/ton, comparing vessels of 80,000 dwt and over with smaller types of ships. Next, the large number of vessels arriving at the Dutch ports—more than 35,000 per annum—plays a role. Rotterdam is in an especially good position as a distribution center, because a large number of arriving ships, having a capacity between 2,000 and 30,000 dwt, are interested in return cargoes to the surrounding countries. The same applies to the inland craft arriving from Germany, France, Belgium, etc.

In the early 1950's more than 7 million tons of imported coal were already distributed yearly from the Netherlands to the UK and Baltic ports. Since 1976 more than 300 million tons/year of iron ore, grain, oil and large numbers of containers, arriving in vessels of 70,000-300,000 dwt, are being distributed by means of coaster, barge and railroad to various final destinations in Western Europe. The distribution function for these commodities is created by the same factors which will apply to coal. The flows of coal to and from the Dutch ports had a volume of 13.8 million tons in 1977. Of this amount, 65% had its origin and final destination outside the Netherlands, national coal demand being less than 5 million tons.

Four future freight flows of coal to the Dutch seaports are expected:

- Seaborne imports into the Netherlands. These will eventually form the largest flow, all coal for domestic consumption being imported in the next decades. Following the WOCOL Low Coal Case: 27 million (physical) tons in the year 2000.
- Seaborne transit to West Germany and France by inland vessels and rail. These will be largely influenced by the transport facilities on the continental side. Taking account of the excellent connections by railroad and inland waterways—especially push-barges remaining the most suitable means of inland transport of coal—it is expected that some 40% of West German imports and about 10% of French imports will be discharged in Dutch seaports. Following the WOCOL Low Coal Case: 10 million tons in the year 2000.
- Seaborne transit to Scandinavia and the UK by seagoing vessels. These transshipment flows through Dutch seaports are expected to account for about 10% of total coal imports of these countries. Following the WOCOL Low Coal Case: about 3 million tons in the year 2000.

- Transit traffic by inland vessels from West Germany through Dutch seaports to overseas destinations. The future development of this flow may show a growth dependent on German exports and their destination. Following the WOCOL Low Coal Case: about 5 million tons in the year 2000.

Most of these flows must be seen against the background of increasing quantities of coal arriving from distant countries with deep-water harbors, allowing to take full advantage of lower transport costs resulting from the use of large bulk carriers.

DUTCH SEAPORTS

Since 1970 investments have been made at a high rate for improvement of infrastructure, equipment and depth of water. Combined with the very large storage capacities, this enables the Dutch ports to act as a turntable in Western Europe and to guarantee a quick turnaround at attractive prices. There are six seaports with coal-handling terminals: Rotterdam, Amsterdam, IJmuiden, Delfzijl, Vlaardingen and Terneuzen. Dordrecht is the major inland port. In 1977 the seaborne imports of these ports totaled 8.7 million tons; seaborne exports amounted to 5.1 million tons.

In Rotterdam three terminals are accessible for discharge of coal from large bulk carriers: the Waalhaven terminal gives access to vessels drawing up to 11.3 metres and has an annual capacity of 6 million tons, the Botlek terminal accommodates vessels up to a 13.1-metre draft with a capacity of 18 million tons, while the Maasvlakte terminal handles carriers up to a draft of 19.8 metres with an annual capacity of 12 million tons. Besides coal, the latter two terminals also handle other bulk cargoes, mainly iron ores. The annual capacities mentioned refer to all bulk cargoes, totaling 42 million tons for the whole Rotterdam area; some 20% of this capacity is used for coal handling at present.

In the Amsterdam port area vessels up to a draft of 13.7 metres can be discharged at the Westhaven terminal. The annual capacity is 12 million tons of coal. This capacity could be doubled if access for vessels over 16 metres draft and improvements of waterways for inland barge traffic is provided. The other seaports can accommodate ships of 13.7 metres maximum draft (IJmuiden) or less (Delfzijl, Terneuzen and Vlaardingen).

Dutch terminals have a combined annual coal throughput capacity of 30.6 million tons, with a possible increase to 68.5 million tons in the year 1990 (see Table 12-4). Plans for the future center on a new terminal on the Maasvlakte where coal will be handled exclusively. This terminal will have an eventual throughput capacity of 25 million tons/year, 20 million imports and 5 million exports. It will be served by ocean vessels of up to 250,000 dwt, by inland motor- and push-barges and by rail. The terminal will handle import coal on a worldwide basis, serving a range of clients. It will have three berths for large seagoing vessels, equipped with four unloaders with a total average unloading capacity of 6,000 tons/hour and one loader with an average capacity of 3,000 tons/hour. The total storage capacity will be 3.5 million tons. The start of this new terminal has been planned for 1982, with an initial capacity of approximately half the final one.

CONCLUDING REMARKS

The combined coal-handling capacities of the Dutch seaports will be adequate to accommodate the projected imports for national coal demand well beyond the

Table 12-4. Current, Planned and Potential Port Characteristics (Amsterdam, Delfzyl, Dordrecht, Rotterdam, Terneuzen, IJmuiden)

		Current		1985		1990		2000	
PROJECTED COAL IMPORTS									
Low Coal Case		*Met*	*Steam*	*Met*	*Steam*	*Met*	*Steam*	*Met*	*Steam*
(MILLION METRIC TONS)		3.5	1.7	4.0	8.2	4.0	11.3	4.0	22.6
Characteristics:									
Maximum Draft	(meters)	19.8		22		22		22	
Total Discharging Rate	(metric tons/hr)	18,400		21,300		24,800		29,800	
Total Annual Capacity	(metric tons/yr)	30.6 mln		42.1 mln		64.0 mln		76.0 mln	
Total Storage Capacity	(metric tons)	7.85 mln		7.95 mln		13.45 mln		13.45 mln	
Total Storage Area	(square meters)	1.17 mln		1.20 mln		2.10 mln		2.10 mln	
Other Transportation Infrastructure Requirements:									
Total Rail Loading t/h		6,525		6,525		6,775		6,900	
Total Inland Barge Loading t/h		15,520		16,950		18,450		19,450	
Total Coastal Vessel Loading t/h		8,840		10,065		17,565		17,690	
Truck t/h		900		900		900		900	

year 2000. The distribution function of these ports for other countries being taken as a starting point of major importance, the projected flows will meet no technical constraints either, at least up till the year 1990 and possibly till the end of the century.

The same applies to transportation capacities if some improvements regarding inland navigation—already under consideration—are realized. It may be possible, however, to develop larger-scale railroad transportation of coal as a security alternative to inland water transport in the shorter term and as an indispensable supplement in the longer term.

It is obvious that environmental demands will arise with respect to the handling of such large quantities of coal. It is assumed that it will be possible to meet the standards, especially with regard to the spreading of dust, without the need for completely new approaches.

Assuming that coal trade will not be replaced at a high rate by imports of coal conversion products during many decades, several longer-term developments should be studied in time with regard to their consequences for harbor development, given the long lead-times and large investments involved:

- The possibilities of large-scale central preparation of coal and its distribution as ready-to-use boiler feed to individual consumers are currently being studied under a government contract. The results of this study could lead to the use of port facilities for such schemes.
- Another current study is concerned with the relations between size and draft of coal carriers on the one hand and terminal and water depth requirements on the other. This study could result in recommendations on vessel design, terminal layout and provision of deeper entrance channels in the longer term.
- The disposal of residues from coal use is considered a specific problem in the Netherlands. Current studies on this national problem will give due account to transportation aspects.

- Other developments which might have a large impact with regard to available acreage in the port areas are: strategic stock-building requirements, siting of gasification and liquefaction plants, and the use of coal as a chemical feedstock linking coal terminals to industrial complexes like the present combination of oil terminals, refineries and chemical plant.

ENVIRONMENTAL, HEALTH AND SAFETY CONSIDERATIONS

CURRENT PRACTICES

Although the energy demand density is high in the Netherlands as a consequence of high population density and per capita use of energy, the present level of atmospheric pollution is relatively low. This is due to the favorable composition of the actual mix of fuel supply: 53% very clean natural gas, 41% oil and 5% coal (both with a limit to their sulphur content) and 1% nuclear energy.

The current national standards relate to immission levels as well as to the sulphur content of fuels. A decree on sulphur content of fuels sets an upper limit of 2.5% S in oil and 1.5% S in coal. With respect to immission levels the ambient quality standard is set at a limit of 75 micrograms of SO_2 per m³ at a particulate concentration of 30 micrograms per m³ as median value, or 250 micrograms of SO_2 per m³ at a particulate concentration of 120 micrograms per m³ as 98 percentile. In the SO_2 White Paper of October 1979 it is proposed to adopt a 95 percentile value of 200 micrograms of SO_2 per m³.

In heavily industrialized areas additional emergency level measures are in force, such as obligatory switching to low-sulphur fuel oil under adverse weather conditions.

The control of pollution and noise levels, as well as safety regulations in the direct surroundings of installations handling coal, are based on municipal regulations in the framework of the Nuisance Act.

POSSIBLE FUTURE STANDARDS

On the national level, the expansion of the use of coal and oil over that of clean natural gas must be expected to entail more stringent measures to control air pollution. These will possibly pertain to a further decrease in fuel sulphur content permitted (2% S in oil, 1.2% S in coal) and adaptations of SO_2-emission standards to comply with an endeavor to limit total SO_2-emissions to a level of 500,000 tons per year. This will certainly lead to the application of coal utilization or flue gas desulfurization (FGD) technology that is completely new to the Netherlands.

The role of nitrogen oxides will be given more attention and standards may be expected that could also have a direct impact on coal utilization technology.

Additional local requirements for the technology to be applied will depend on the size and number of installations on the one hand and the environmental demands of their surroundings on the other hand.

INDICATIVE COST ESTIMATES FOR CONTROL MEASURES

Experience in the field of the control measures to be considered is lacking in the Netherlands. Currently, substantial efforts are being made to acquire the knowledge necessary to evaluate results from other countries and their applicability under national circumstances.

The technologies involved show costs in a range which is dependent on regionally determined factors. Taking account of the high population density, intensive use of land and labor costs in the Netherlands, it must be expected that the price of control measures will be on the higher side of available cost estimate ranges.

In utility studies on FGD application it is concluded that electricity production cost would be 15-20% higher than without desulfurization.

EVALUATION OF KEY ENVIRONMENTAL ISSUES

The most important issues may be divided into national and international ones. Since the Netherlands is geographically and economically strongly dependent on its suroundings, one of these issues may be regarded as a particular national problem: the disposal of solid residues. Other problems will be influenced to a large extent by international relationships. On the other end of the range of issues at hand is atmospheric CO_2-buildup as a purely worldwide problem.

The increasing content of CO_2 in the earth's atmosphere and its possible influence on world climate has been documented elsewhere, as well as in the framework of WOCOL. This problem is not specific to coal use; but any limitation to fossil fuel use, set by the buildup of atmospheric CO_2, could have a considerable impact on coal demand. A better knowledge of the extent of this buildup and its effects is urgently needed.

In a densely populated, industrialized country like the Netherlands, all forms of environmental pollution will tend to set limits to the use of coal. The application of technology to avoid pollution will bring economic penalties, and possibly extra requirements for already scarce land. Solutions to environmental problems will bear a strong relationship with industrial production policies. Generally, there is some flexibility in letting prevail either environmental or economic factors, or in shifting the problem, e.g., from air pollution to soil and water pollution (desulfurization and fly ash removal resulting in solid waste). This flexibility seems not to be great in the Dutch case:

- The environmental constraints will be greatest in regions where internationally competitive industrial production may least carry the burden of additional investment in "environmental" technology.

- As air pollutants over the Netherlands are also "imported" from neighboring countries, the possibilities to influence air pollution by national management are limited. Environmental policy and coal utilization technology in other countries may thus have a serious impact on coal use and its technology in the Netherlands. Because other countries will encounter the same problems to some degree, this issue should be considered an important subject for international study, to be given continued attention in the framework of organizations like OECD.

- Land, whether required for coal handling in users' centers or for the disposal of waste, is scarce.

- Because coal will be imported from different sources, technology choice will be influenced by the need to cope with coals of different qualities.

The dominating national issue may be found in the availability of ways and means for waste disposal (including site availability) and the economics thereof.

A strong effort may be directed to the use of waste in road building or as a raw material for industry. The extent to which such uses are possible and will be bound to specifications that might be difficult to meet by users of coal of different quality, is unknown. It may be necessary to work the ashes into an insoluble form to make large-scale disposal possible.

IMPLEMENTING ACTIONS REQUIRED FOR THE TOTAL COAL SYSTEM

Apart from the utilities' schedule for building coal-fired power plants, the projected expansion of coal consumption in all other sectors has to be implemented following decisions of a presently largely unknown scope. The definition of objectives and the choice between technological options have not advanced beyond the stage of preparatory studies on the merits of individual technologies or individual sectors of application. Integral studies are now under way; at this stage no more than rough outlines can be given. An exception is the following case study on coal conversion for utility purposes, which appears to be an example of an imaginative new approach to the application of coal.

COAL CONVERSION FOR UTILITY PURPOSES

The discovery of the Groningen gas field initiated a drastic change in the energy policy of the Netherlands. All domestic appliances were converted from coke-oven or town-gas quality to Groningen-gas quality or were replaced. Most industries also switched to the readily available clean fuel. Though the nitrogen content of the gas is high, the quantity was so large that Groningen gas became the standard gaseous fuel. A large amount of gas was also exported and there was no thought of the need to produce a synthetic gas from coal again.

The energy situation has, however, changed completely, nuclear energy not developing as expected and 1973 bringing the oil crisis. The gas resources seem sufficient for the years to come: in effect new sources were discovered so that reserves hardly decreased. Gas supply policy changed, however, exports continuing in accordance with contractual obligations with imports of gas from Norway and of LNG from other sources building up. Most of the new indigenous sources and all imports have a higher heating value than the nitrogen-rich Groningen gas. The difference is such that these gases can only be mixed in a restricted ratio in order to stay within the limits of safe operation of domestic appliances. For the big industrial users the higher heating value is no problem and the gas can be delivered to them as such.

In the present situation the Netherlands will dispose of:

- a large reserve of Groningen gas
- own resources of high calorific gas (h.c. gas)
- imported gas (Norwegian and LNG)

The Groningen field is the only large quantity resource under domestic control, so that it can serve for a long period as a constant quality buffer in domestic gas supply. To keep this proposition up there is an interest to use the h.c. gas preferentially. This will bring the need, within a couple of years, to dilute this h.c. gas to Groningen equivalent with, for example, nitrogen or air. By doing so, the possibilities of use are widened, but at a cost penalty and without adding any heating value. If a low or medium Btu gas from coal would be used instead, the same result would be obtained with the additional advantage of adding heating value. The amount of Groningen gas available is thus increased, and at the same time the coal gas is given the value of natural gas without having to convert it to SNG. The savings with respect to air- or nitrogen-dilution can be subtracted from the production costs of the coal gas. Thus for the amount of h.c. gas needing quality adjustment a medium Btu gas can be produced from coal at reduced costs, the product gas having the commercial value of Groningen gas.

The coal gas production costs have been evaluated assuming medium Btu gas production in an (oxygen) gasification unit using 500,000 and 1,000,000 tons of coal per year. The gas produced is sufficient for the dilution of 4 and 8 billion Nm^3* of h.c. gas respectively. For both cases NEOM calculated the cost price of an amount of coal gas, equivalent with 1 Nm^3 of Groningen gas (GGE), assuming a project life of 20 years, a realistic 4% interest and no profit.

Production costs, then, are 0.25-0.27 Dutch guilders/Nm^3 GGE (4.2-4.5 US dollars/million Btu). Subtracting the costs required for air- and nitrogen-dilution, the ultimate price is about 0.22 guilders. The medium Btu coal gas, to be valued as Groningen natural gas, would thus have production costs which are about two-thirds of those estimated for SNG.

Postponing the decision to start with coal gasification will force the production of an equivalent amount of SNG in the more distant future or to alternatively convert domestic appliances at an earlier stage. A quick start will further help to build up know-how gradually and will smooth the changeover from natural gas to coal-derived fuel which has to occur sometime. A disadvantage is the lack of cheap indigenous coal reserves. In the cost figures mentioned above, about 0.15 guilders/Nm^3 GGE has to be paid for imported coal (assuming a coal price of 100 guilders/ton with a heating value of 29.33 giga joules).

Due to the special case described, the financial barriers to the introduction of coal gasification can be partially overcome in the Netherlands. Due to the lack of cheap coal reserves, the rate at which this advantage can be materialized will depend on what good housekeeping allows to spend now in order to save in the future.

COAL-FIRED POWER PLANTS

By far the largest part of coal consumed in this sector will be directly fired in 600 MWe base-load units. Environmental requirements to limit future SO_2 emissions could lead to the installation of FGD installations, but integrated gasification plants will probably be a more attractive future alternative in view of overall costs and taking into account the waste problems and land use. A less significant part of coal consumption is assumed to be used in small- to medium-capacity industrial combined power and heat plants, probably equipped with fluidized bed boilers as the best solution to comply with environmental standards, two-stage firing being a possible alternative.

For the WOCOL High Coal Case, this would mean the building of 15-20 coal-based units and about 20-30 smaller combined plants up till the year 2000. For the WOCOL Low Coal Case, these numbers would be 8-12 and 15-20 respectively.

---

* N means normal and refers to a standard condition of the flue gas. Nm^3 therefore means normal cubic meter.

COAL-FIRED INDUSTRIAL BOILERS AND DISTRICT HEATING

If it is assumed that the average capacity of industrial boilers consuming the projected amounts of coal for the sector will be 50 MW thermal, the number to be installed up till the year 2000 would be 100 for the High Coal Case or 75 for the Low Coal Case. These installations would probably be of the fluidized bed type to cope with SO_2-emission standards, two-stage firing with desulfurization preceding the final burning step being a possible alternative. The same applies to combined power and heat plant in district heating systems, in numbers of 20-30 for both the WOCOL High Coal Case and Low Coal Case, up till the year 2000.

In general, the economics of industrial coal use is expected to be favorable compared to oil for firing medium- to large-sized boilers. The position will be dependent to a large extent on the cost sensitivity of the industrial products in the frame of international competition.

A special feature for the larger number of small capacity systems is, however, that their exploitation will meet relatively big problems in industrialized and populated areas. These relate to acreage available for storage of coal, limestone (for FBC systems) and waste, and nuisance with respect to spreading of dusts and to noise, e.g., from transportation and local coal preparation. Most of these problems could be mitigated by building up a "clean" system for the supply of ready-to-use boiler feed to individual consumers from a large capacity central preparation plant where coal is powder-milled, or sized and mixed with limestone as FBC-boiler feed. A feasibility study on this concept is currently carried out in the Netherlands under a government contract.

TRANSPORTATION OF COAL AND WASTES

Most of the transportation requirements will be related to the supply of power plants, in easy reach for barge transport, with a possibility of waste shipment on the return trip if disposal sites and/or users for the waste are suitably situated.

Smaller coal consumers may also be served by inland water transport and otherwise by rail or road transport. In the case of central preparation of the boiler feed, a system of dust-tight transport units like containers or tank-lorries could be envisaged. In this case, waste shipment would certainly be part of the same system.

A general conclusion is that existing transportation and other infrastructure facilities will be adequate for a relatively long period, e.g., taking into account the present surplus of waterway and railroad transport capacities. In the longer term no fundamental obstacles are to be foreseen either, in view of the relatively short lead times for expansion.

TOTAL COAL SYSTEM

Coal supply and utilization systems studies are at an early stage in the Netherlands, and practical experience is limited to the operation of a few small-sized installations. A more detailed description of a future large-scale coal consumption technology and its infrastructure requirements is urgently needed to identify timely policy measures, including stimulation of R & D necessary to cope with obstacles and constraints.

A useful tool for systematic study is the description of coal "chains," an example of which is given in Figure 12-4. From such chains, drawn up for different supply sources and user's markets, the critical steps regarding investment and

Figure 12-4. Illustrative Implementation Requirements for a Coal Chain Australia-Netherlands*

	Coal Mine NS Wales Australia	Unit Train Transport	NS Wales Port Australia	Coal Carrier	Rotterdam Port Netherlands	Barge Transport Nijmegen	Power Plants Netherlands	Total System
	Mines	*Trains*	*Ports*	*Ships*	*Port*	*Barges*	*Power Plants*	*Total System*
Coal Flows	5 mtce/yr 5.6 mt	5.6 mt	5.6 mt	5.6 mt	5.6 mt	5.6 mt	5.6 mt	5 mtce/yr 5.6 mt/yr
Facilities	7.5 mt raw coal 3.75 mt saleable 1.5 mines	80 km 42 cars 72 t(net)/car 3.8 trains	30 mt/yr 0.2 ports	110,000 dwt 13 ships	25 mt/yr 0.25 terminal	2.8 pusher tugs 28 barges	600 MWe 4.6 plants (2,700 MWe)	
Lead Times†	3 years	3 years	2.5 years	3/4 years each	2.5 years	3/4 years each pusher tug	5 years each	5 years
Cost Total Capital††	360 M US$	40 M US$	80 M US$	350 M US$		34 M US$	2,300 M US$	3,164 M US$
Labor Required Total Construction Annual Operating				6,330 manyear 970 my/year	500 manyear 75 my/year	n.a. 100 my/year	6,900 manyear 700 my/year	

* All figures are estimates and listed for illustrative purposes only.
† Lead times for actual project execution after all permits granted.
†† 1979 US$, includes escalation and interest during construction.

321

labor costs as well as their influence on incremental coal costs can be identified. They should be detailed and extended for studies on the national level, e.g., for comparison of different strategies with regard to inland transport, conversion technology and disposal or use of wastes.

However, also from the broad approach visualized in Figure 12-4, several conclusions may be drawn. The lead times at the user's end, for instance, seem to be sufficiently long to ensure that all preceding steps in the chain may be implemented before starting operation of large coal-consuming units. Because the lead times listed do not account for possible time-lags involved with granting of permits, it will, however, be necessary that consideration of eventual constraints in other steps of the chain be drawn into the planning of user's facilities. The investment costs of power plants (and other large units for coal conversion) may be about 75%, and annual operating costs nearly 50%, of those for the whole chain. This should lead to maximization of conversion efficiency as the prime objective, if necessary at a higher cost in terms of investment or efficiency losses in other steps of the chain.

Labor requirements appear to be concentrated in shipbuilding next to power plant construction, drawing attention to the fact that coal chain studies will not only reveal the need to prepare for constraints, but also for possible opportunities, e.g., new developments in shipbuilding. Environmental aspects may be quantified likewise for different steps of the coal chain and different strategies compared with a view of optimization in terms of minimizing negative effects and costs to accomplish this.

OBSTACLES AND CONSTRAINTS TO EXPANDED COAL USE

KEY OBSTACLES AND CONSTRAINTS

The predominant problem areas are related to economic, physical and environmental aspects. Coal availability and price levels, as well as air and water pollution are more or less international issues. The disposal of large amounts of solid waste may add a severe national problem in the way of soil and water pollution as well as disposal licensing.

AVAILABILITY, ECONOMICS AND COAL DEMAND

The availability of coal, its price and its quality will be key factors in the development of coal use. For reasons of security of supply, coal should be imported from different sources and hence may have very different qualities. This would call for long-term contracting and for tailoring of markets by way of using technology accepting a wide range of coals. Coal price levels will not only be of direct influence on the development of demand, but also on the technology to be applied. More expensive high-efficiency systems may be sooner economically acceptable in the case of higher coal prices. On the other hand, higher energy price levels may have a negative effect on national economy, which in turn will influence energy demand growth in general and coal demand markets in particular. Especially in the sectors where smaller capacity units demand relatively high investments if coal-equipped, a slower economic growth may impede the expansion of coal use.

The national economic situation and coal price levels will thus combine as possible constraints to the expansion of coal demand, affecting:

- industrial growth, also to be related to competition on the international markets in which national energy price levels play an important role;
- energy demand growth in general, also of major importance for the largest coal market, i.e., the electricity production sector;
- financial margins available for higher investments in coal utilization equipment, compared with that for the use of other fuels; and
- financial margins available for higher investments related to environmental requirements, in particular when coal is considered as a substitute for natural gas.

PHYSICAL PLANNING AND TRANSPORT

Coal-handling capacity of seaport terminals, including sites for central storage and transshipment and capacity of inland transport ways are not considered to pose major problems in the time frame 1977-2000. The same applies to siting and coal supply of large-scale coal consumers such as power plants and gasification plants.

Constraints may be found in the availability of suitable coal and waste storage sites at individual points of use in industry and district heating systems.

Severe problems and possibly the major obstacle to expanded coal use in the Netherlands may be expected in the field of availability of sites for waste disposal, to be related to environmental factors.

ENVIRONMENTAL AND SOCIETAL FACTORS

The combined impact of the economic, social and environmental situation in the Netherlands appears to give little room for a flexible approach. A better knowledge of all aspects of a strongly expanding coal use is needed to choose the expectedly narrow pathways through all constraints.

Public acceptance may be the key obstacle in which many of the constraints considered will converge. In a situation where the national choice is between coal and nuclear, the issue is to avoid a resistance to coal use similar to that with respect to nuclear energy. The problem is that much less is known about the effects, global and national, of a very large-scale use of coal than in the case of nuclear power generation. The lesson learned from the nuclear debate is that a quantitative evaluation of all positive and negative aspects is urgently needed and results should be made available to the public as early and as clearly as possible.

RECOMMENDATIONS

On the international level further agreements should be developed, building on those currently reached in the IEA framework, relating to:

- Efforts to establish coal trading levels and distribution patterns
- Co-operative coal exploration and production ventures
- Joint studies and R & D in the field of:

 —Atmospheric CO_2 levels and their possible impact on world climate
 —Levels of other air pollutants, their migration patterns and their toxic effects
 —New technology to avoid environmental pollution
 —Coal availability related to coal quality, and possible distribution patterns related to economics and just distribution over different countries

—New technology to increase the efficiency of coal use and to accept a wide range of coal qualities.

On the national level, measures should be taken to secure supply and early introduction of coal as a substitute for oil as well as natural gas, in a way that is acceptable from an economic, social and environmental viewpoint. These measures should stimulate:

- Conclusion of long-term coal supply contracts
- Private and public participation in overseas coal production
- Early demonstration of available new technology for environmentally acceptable use of coal
- Accelerated introduction of demonstrated coal utilization technology in the electricity production sector
- Accelerated introduction of coal-fired boilers in industry and district heating schemes
- Coal use in general, by public intervention in waste disposal operations, including waste utilization and preparation
- Development of coal technology know-how in national industry to avoid the loss of markets following switches to coal use in demand sectors
- Public acceptance, by supplying suitable information on the need for expanded coal use and on its effects with respect to economic, social and environmental factors
- Studies and technological R & D in the field of:

  —the possible sources of imports and the expected quality of coal from these sources,

  —the possible future exploitation of domestic coal resources,

  —the possible development of national coal markets,

  —the infrastructure required to meet national and international demands for coal supply and national needs for shipment, use and disposal of waste,

  —the environmental effects, on national and regional levels, of a strongly expanding use of coal, in particular those of wastes from different utilization technologies,

  —coal utilization technology to meet energy, environmental and industrial policy demands, and

  —public acceptance issues.

Early and effective action will be needed to achieve the levels of coal use projected. The recent developments in the international oil market make it desirable to aim at still higher penetration rates of coal, which calls for even stronger efforts of all national public and private parties involved in its implementation.

Summary Worksheet

I. Coal Use, Production, and Trade	1977	1985		1990		2000		1977-2000 Avg. annual growth—%/yr.	
		A	B	A	B	A	B	A	B
Coal use in major markets (mtce)									
Metallurgical	3.0	3.4	3.4	3.3	3.6	2.9	4.0	–	–
Electric	1.1	3.9	3.9	6.0	8.6	13.7	25.9	10.4	13.5
Industry	0.3	2.2	2.2	2.3	2.9	3.0	4.0	10.5	11.9
Synthetic Fuels	–	–	–	–	–	1.3	2.4	–	–
Residential/Commercial	0.1	–	–	0.6	0.6	1.0	1.0	–	–
Total coal use	4.5	10.4	10.4	13.1	16.6	22.8	38.2	7.3	9.7
Distribution of coal use by market sector (%)									
Metallurgical	66.7	32.7	32.7	25.2	21.7	12.7	10.5	—	—
Electric	24.4	37.5	37.5	45.8	51.8	60.1	67.8	—	—
Industry	6.7	21.2	21.2	17.6	17.5	13.2	10.5	—	—
Synthetic Fuels	–	–	–	–	–	5.7	6.3	—	—
Residential/Commercial	2.2	–	–	4.6	3.6	4.4	2.6	—	—
Total coal use	100%	100%	100%	100%	100%	100%	100%	—	—
Coal consumption/imports (mtce) Consumption									
Metallurgical	3.0	3.4	3.4	3.3	3.6	2.9	4.0	–	1.3
Steam	1.5	7.0	7.0	9.8	13.0	19.9	34.2	10.4	14.5
Total coal consumption	4.5	10.4	10.4	13.1	16.6	22.8	38.2	7.3	9.7
Imports									
Metallurgical	3.0	3.4	3.4	3.3	3.6	2.9	4.0	–	1.3
Steam	1.5	7.0	7.0	9.8	13.0	19.9	34.2	10.4	14.5
Total coal imports	4.5	10.4	10.4	13.1	16.6	22.8	38.2	7.3	9.7
Coal production/exports (mtce) Production									
Metallurgical									
Steam									
Total coal production									
Exports									
Metallurgical									
Steam									
Total coal export									

Summary Worksheet

II. Coal's Role in Total Energy System	1977	1985		1990		2000		1977-2000 Avg. annual growth–%/yr.	
		A	B	A	B	A	B	A	B
Total Primary Energy Use (mtce)									
Oil, Domestic	2.3	2.9	2.9	2.9	2.9	2.2	2.2	--	--
Oil, Imported	33.4	49.0	56.4	52.4	61.8	58.9	80.3	2.5	3.8
Gas, Domestic	46.6	38.8	38.8	38.1	38.2	32.8	32.8	--	--
Gas, Imported	--	9.2	9.2	10.1	10.1	10.8	10.8	--	--
Nuclear	1.4	1.4	1.4	1.4	1.4	8.0	1.4	7.9	--
Hydro, Solar, Other	--	0.3	0.3	0.3	0.3	2.5	2.5	--	--
Coal, Domestic	--	--	--	--	--	--	--	--	--
Coal, Imported	4.5	10.4	10.4	13.1	16.6	22.8	38.2	7.3	9.7
Total energy use	88.2	112.0	119.4	118.3	131.3	138.0	168.2	2.0	2.85
Coal penetration (%)	5.1	9.3	8.7	11.1	12.6	16.5	22.7	—	—
Total primary energy (mtce) input to electricity									
Oil and Gas	14.4	16.1	17.2	15.7	16.3	3.9	4.3	--	--
Hydro, Solar, Other	--	--	--	--	--	1.4	1.4	--	--
Nuclear	1.4	1.4	1.4	1.4	1.4	8.0	1.4		
Coal	1.4	3.9	3.9	6.0	8.6	13.7	25.9	10.4	13.5
Total energy input	17.2	21.4	22.5	23.1	26.3	27.0	33.0	2.0	2.9
Coal penetration (%)	8	18	17	26	33	51	78	—	—
Total electric capacity (GWe)									
Oil and Gas	13.3	12.8	12.8	13.0	12.0	8.0	6.0	--	--
Hydro, Solar, Other	--	--	--	--	--	( )	( )	--	--
Nuclear	0.5	0.5	0.5	0.5	0.5	8.0	0.5	10.5	--
Coal	0.7	2.2	2.2	4.0	5.5	8.5	16.5	11.3	14.6
Total capacity	14.5	15.5	15.5	17.5	18.0	21.5	23.0	1.7	2.0
Coal Penetration (%)	5	15	15	25	30	40	70	—	—
Peak load	8.7	11.3	11.3	12.8	13.1	15.7	16.8	2.6	2.9
Peak reserve margin (%)	65	27	27	27	27	27	27	—	—
Total oil imports (mbd)									
Total oil consumption (mbd)									
Transportation	0.2	0.2	0.2	0.2	0.2	0.2	0.3	--	--
Residential/Commercial		--	--	--	--	--	--	--	--
Industry—Boilers		0.1	0.1	0.1	0.1	0.1	0.1	--	--
Industry—Other	0.1	0.2	0.2	0.3	0.4	0.5	0.7	--	--
Electric utilities	0.1	0.1	0.1	0.1	0.1	--	--	--	--
Total oil consumption	0.4	0.6	0.8	0.7	0.8	0.8	1.1	3.1	4.5
World oil price assumed for national coal analysis (1979 U.S. dollars/barrel)	$20*					30	25	1.8	1.0
Economic growth assumed for national coal analysis (GNP, billion 1978 dollars)	120	146	152	161	187	198	237	2.2	3.0

* Uses current price of $20/barrel (June 1979 U.S. dollars) as baseline world oil price and as floor price throughout the period.

326

CHAPTER 13

POLAND

PRELIMINARY REMARKS

This report has been written to meet the stipulations of the WOCOL Conferences held in Aspen—USA, in 1978 and in St. Paul de Vance—France, in 1979.

The presented data deal mostly with the problems of coal reserves and the expected development of hard-coal and brown-coal (lignite) production in the light of the expected general demand for fuels and primary energy in the national economy. The data contained in the report are not to be considered as a strict interpretation of the country's national economy requirements. They simply provide guidelines to what may be expected in the future production of hard and brown coal and how this relates to the WOCOL study.

INTRODUCTION

In Poland's energy balance, coal has been up to now, and will be in the future, the basic energy source.

This results both from the economic and historic development of the coal industry, and from the reserves of coal in Poland. On the other side, the insignificant reserves of crude oil and natural gas were decisive in the evolution of the country's energy balance, which relies to the highest possible extent on coal and in the share of coal exports in the country's foreign trade.

The domestic direct demand for energy in Poland was (in mtce/year*) as follows:

Fuels	1970	1975
1. Primary fuels total:	37.08	40.28
thereof i/a: coal	30.25	30.50
crude oil	0.02	0.01
natural gas	4.67	8.25
2. Energy and secondary fuels total:	54.22	71.62
thereof i/a: coke and semicoke	10.88	12.26
liquid fuels of crude oil	8.00	13.61
synthetic gas	4.67	5.08
electric energy	6.68	9.91
centrally produced heat	20.25	26.21
3. Grand total	91.30	111.90

* According to Prof. dr. K. Kopecki—Prognosis on Poland's demand for electric energy till 2000 and conditions for its meeting, Przegląd Elektrotechniczny—July 1977.

327

Within the general demand for fuels and primary energy, a high production of hard coal and brown coal is expected. This will take place by extension of existing mines and by construction of new mines, along with the development of the necessary social and technical infrastructure. The availability of Polish coal for export up to 1995 is expected to be at the level of around 40 mt/year; thereafter at about 50 mt/year. In Poland, all hard-coal production comes from underground mining, and all brown-coal production comes from open pits.

APPROACH FOR THE NATIONAL WOCOL ANALYSIS

The forecast was based on an analysis of macroeconomic interdependencies based on the assumption that the development of the fuel and energy development is a function, and a condition, for the socioeconomic development of the country.

The alternatives of a High Coal Case development were considered within the range of 5.0-5.3% yearly growth of gross national income, which was also defined as the "desirable development" and the alternative within the range of 4.0-3.5%. The development of coal production presented in this report to the High Coal Case alternative, assuming that by 2000 the production of hard coal may reach 300 mt and out of that, about 50 mt will be destined for export.

The average yearly growth of demand for electric energy for the years 1968-1975 was 7.2%.

The expected development of electricity production in Poland would be as follows*:

Year	Yearly Production (bln kWh/y (10^9))	Installed Power (GWe)
1975	97.2	20.1
1985	188-191	40.9
1990	261-268	57.0
1995	362-376	80.0
2000	492-515	110.0

COAL CONSUMPTION

The domestic coal consumption is expected to grow as follows:

hard coal —from 116.6 mtce in 1977
to 191.2 mtce in 2000
brown coal—from 10.8 mtce in 1977
to 71.4 mtce in 2000
total —from 127.4 mtce in 1977
to 262.6 mtce in 2000

The biggest individual customer for hard coal in Poland remains electricity production, which in 1977 consumed 27.1% of production, i.e., 31.6 mtce; its anticipated consumption in 2000 will be 24.2%, i.e., 46.2 mtce. The distribution of hard-coal consumption is given in Tables 13-1 and 13-2. For the future,

* According to Prof. dr. K. Kopecki—as before.

Table 13-1. Domestic Hard Coal Consumption

	1977			1985			1990			2000		
	mln tce	%	mln ton	mln tce	%	mln ton	mln tce	%	mln ton	mln tce	%	mln ton
Energy generation	31.6	27.1	47.4	43.4	28.6	65.8	46.2	27.3	70.0	46.2	24.2	70.0
Other branches of industry	56.7	48.6	69.2	72.7	47.9	88.7	94.3	56.0	115.0	117.2	61.3	143.0
Transport	4.2	3.6	5.1	3.0	2.0	4.0	1.2	0.7	2.0	0.8	0.4	1.0
Individual household supply	24.1	20.7	26.9	32.4	21.5	36.0	27.0	16.0	30.0	27.0	14.1	30.0
Total domestic coal consumption	116.6	100.0	148.6	151.5	100.0	194.5	168.7	100.0	217.0	191.2	100.0	244.0
Domestic demand for fuels and prime energy	162.0			230.0			280.0			400		

Table 13-2. Domestic Brown Coal Consumption

	1977			1985			1990			2000		
	mln tce	%	mln ton	mln tce	%	mln ton	mln tce	%	mln ton	mln tce	%	mln ton
Energy generation	10.5	97.4	40.2	22.7	95.6	79.4	37.5	93.9	131.4	64.6	90.4	226.0
Other branches of industry	—	—	—	0.9	3.6	3.1	2.5	6.1	8.6	6.8	9.6	24.0
Transport	—	—	—	—	—	—	—	—	—	—	—	—
Individual household supply	0.3	2.6	0.6	0.2	0.8	0.5	—	—	—	—	—	—
Total domestic coal consumption	10.8	100.0	40.8	23.8	100.0	83.0	40.0	100.0	140.0	71.4	100.0	250.0
Domestic demand for fuels and prime energy	162.0			230.0			280.0			400.0		

FORESEEN REQUIREMENT OF FUEL AND PRIMARY ENERGY FOR POLAND

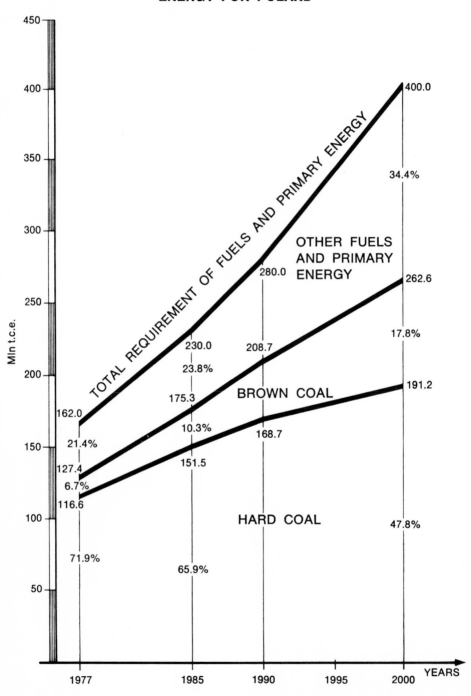

despite the rapidly growing production of coal, the fuel supply will not come up to more rapidly growing demand, thus making necessary a continuous growth of imports of crude oil and natural gas as well as nuclear fuel.

COAL RESERVES AND THE PRESENT AND ANTICIPATED COAL PRODUCTION

A SHORT DESCRIPTION OF COAL REGIONS

In Poland there are several rich hard-coal and brown-coal regions and basins (see Figure 13-1). The location of these coals has a dominant influence on the rate and distribution of energy consumption in Poland.

Figure 13-1. Coalfields—Hard and Brown Coal

CHARACTERISTICS OF BASINS WITH HARD COAL

Hard coals occur in 3 basins:

1. Upper-Silesian Coal Basin (5,500 km^2 area)
2. Lower-Silesian Coal Basin (530 km^2 area)
3. Lublin Coal Basin (about 5,000 km^2 area)

331

Upper-Silesian Coal Basin (Figure 13-2)

The Upper-Silesian Coal Basin contains about 94 percent of all documented reserves of hard coal.

Figure 13-2. Upper Silesia Coalfield—Geological Map of Carboniferous Strata

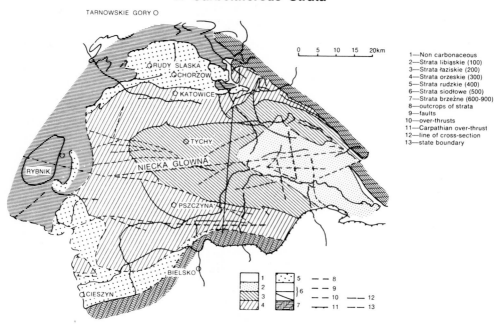

1—Non carbonaceous
2—Strata libiąskie (100)
3—Strata łaziskie (200)
4—Strata orzeskie (300)
5—Strata rudzkie (400)
6—Strata siodłowe (500)
7—Strata brzeżne (600-900)
8—outcrops of strata
9—faults
10—over-thrusts
11—Carpathian over-thrust
12—line of cross-section
13—state boundary

The productive Silesian Carbon Stratum is underlaid with the nonproductive lower Dinant Carbon stratum. The thickness of the coal-bearing stratum grows from 2,400 m in the east to 6,000 m in the western part of the basin.

The stratigraphic division of the carbon strata was settled during the Herlen Congress in 1935 with the division into groups and strata (according to T. Bocheński and St. Doktorowicz-Hrebnicki) being as follows:

Groups	Strata	Coal seams numeration
Synclinal	Libiąźskie	100
	Łaziskie	200
	Orzeskie	300
	Rudzkie	400
Anticlinal	Siodłowe	500
Edging	Porębskie	600
	Jaklowickie	700
	Gruszowskie	800
	Pietrzkowskie	900

332

About 400 coal seams and coal interlayers do occur in the carboniferous strata, about 100 of them being of industrial value. Classification of coals, according to Polish Standard Specification PN-68/6-97002, covers 10 types of coal (from 31 to 42, i.e., from the steam coal to anthracite).

The average thickness of coal seams is approximately:

in edging strata	0.65-0.95 m
in anticlinal strata	4.0-15.0 m
in synclinal strata	1.5-2.4 m

The seams dip from 0 to 90°, but in most of the basin are about 20°. Because of the accompanying rocks surrounding the seams of siodłowe and porębskie strata, rock bursts occur at greater depth. Moreover, in coal seams, especially those in the southwestern portion, gas hazards (CH_4) occur.

The water content of coal deposits is quite varied—from 1 to 20 cu.m/min of water inflow. The geothermal gradient in this basin ranges from 22 to 33 m/1°C. Tectonic and sedimentation disturbances add to the difficulties of exploitation.

Productive carbon formations are covered with overlying strata of varying thickness, from a few metres to 1,000 metres. The overlying strata are formed from the products of Perm, Trias and Cretacieous Tertiary and Quaternary.

Figure 13-3. Simplified Geological Sketch Map of the Central Sudetic Synclinorium

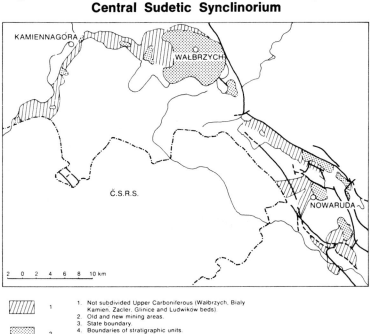

2 0 2 4 6 8 10 km

1 — 1. Not subdivided Upper Carboniferous (Wałbrzych, Biały Kamien, Zacler, Glinice and Ludwikow beds).
2 — 2. Old and new mining areas.
3 — 3. State boundary.
4 — 4. Boundaries of stratigraphic units.
5 — 5. Faults.

Lower-Silesian Coal Basin (Figure 13-3)

In the Lower-Silesian Coal Basin, thin coal seams occur (0.4-1.0 m) in the wałbrzyskie and zaclerskie stratas which are being mined in the vicinity of the towns Wałbrzych and Nowa Ruda. These strata include the Namur and the Westfalian stages. Exploitation is rendered difficult by numerous faults and intrusions of igneous rocks and by gas outbursts (CO_2 and CH_4). Those seams contain coking coals (of the type 34 to 42) and their carbonification grows with depth. The dip of the seams is steep (40 to 50°). Water inflow does not create any serious difficulties.

Figure 13-4. Extent of the Coal-Bearing Formation in the Lublin Coal Basin

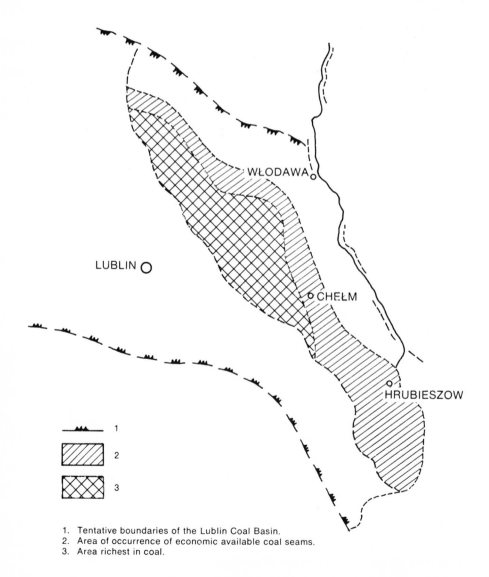

1. Tentative boundaries of the Lublin Coal Basin.
2. Area of occurrence of economic available coal seams.
3. Area richest in coal.

Lublin Coal Basin (Figure 13-4)

In the newly surveyed Lublin Coal Basin, the lubelskie strata (of group 300) are below the overburden of Quaternary, Cretaceous and Jurassic strata. About 22 coal seams occur in those strata, over 15 of them being of industrial value. The thickness of coal seams ranges from 0.7 to 3.6 m.

The tectonics of the deposit are not yet well known, but the occurrence is almost a horizontal one (from 0-12°, in average 3-5°). In the central area of the basin, of about 140 sq. km, some new mines are under design and construction.

Balance Sheet of Industrial Reserves of Hard Coal in Poland According to Coal Basins (bln t-10⁹)

Coal Basin	Coal Quality	Documented Reserves to Categories			Prospective Reserves to 1,500 m Depth	Total Documented and Prospective Reserves
		A,B,C₁	C₂	Total		
Upper-Silesian	total	18.0	34.0	52.0	59.0	111.0
	steam	13.5	24.0	37.5		
	coking	4.5	10.0	14.5		
Lower-Silesian	total					
	coking	0.2	0.3	0.5	0.4	0.9
Lublin	total	1.0	5.0	6.0	75.6	81.6
	steam	0.6	4.5	5.1		
	coking	0.4	0.5	0.9		
Grand total	total	19.2	39.3	58.5	135.0	193.5
	steam	14.1	28.5	42.6		
	coking	5.1	10.8	15.9		

The Polish classification of reserves A,B,C_1,C_2 roughly corresponds to the USA classification as follows:

Polish Classification	USA Classification
$A + B$	measured
C_1	indicated
C_2	
D_1	inferred

In the total amount of documented reserves, coals of types 31, 32 and 33 (steam coals) make up about 75%. These coals have advantageous characteristics for electricity generation. The advantageous properties are:

- an average high calorific value (from 10,100 to 28,500 kJ/kg),
- low ash content,
- good milling properties, and
- low-sulphur content of about 1 percent.

The anticipated program of documenting new reserves includes the work to be done to secure the appropriate production level for 50-60 years.

Brown-coal deposits (Figure 13-1)

The occurrence of brown-coal deposits in Poland is mainly in the Tertiary formation in which nine coal-bearing strata do occur. Of dominant importance are the coals of Miocene age and among them the central-Polish group of seams of upper Miocene (Konin, Adamów) and the Scienowskie group of seams of middle Miocene (Turów, Legnica, Bełchatów).

As of January 1, 1978, the industrial reserves amount to 8.8 billion tons—documented, and 7.6 billion tons—expected in the D_1 category. The expected reserves are characterized by their relatively advantageous geologic and mining factors (ratio N:W) but they occur at considerable depths (average 200 m).

The assumed growth of production will be achieved partly from the existing mines, Turów, Konin and Adamów, but mainly by construction of new big mines.

PRODUCTION OF HARD COAL AND BROWN COAL

HARD COAL

A very intensive growth of hard-coal production is being anticipated, by the extension of existing mines as well by the construction of new ones. This refers both to steam coal and coking coal. The anticipated production is expected to be —in mt:

Year	1977	1985	1990	2000
Total production	186.1	232-235.0	250-260.0	280-300.0
Thereof steam coal	159.2	198.0	211.0	243.0

The anticipated consumption is expected to be—in mt:

Year	1977	1985	1990	2000
mt	148.6	194.5	217.0	244.0

BROWN COAL

Development of brown-coal production will be done mainly in connection with the development of new mining areas. The anticipated production of brown coal in mt will be:

Year	1977	1985	1990	2000
mt	40.8	80-90.0	140.0	250.0

The coal will be solely for internal consumption inside the country primarily for the generation of electric energy, and, after 1985, also for conversion.

Table 13-3. Hard Coal Production from Underground Mines

	1985	1990	1995	2000	2005	2010
Total reserves*/ Bln metric tons/10⁹/	193.0			193.0		
Reserves economically mineable**/ Bln metric tons/10⁹/	58.5			74.0		
Potential production size per costs of 1978 Bln metric tons	232.0 235.0	250-260.0		280-300.0	300.0	300.0

* Refers to geologic reserves to the depth of 1500 m per estimates of 1977.
** According to Polish nomenclature the industrial reserves are calculated to the depth of 1000 m.

Table 13-4. Brown Coal Production from Opencast Mines

	1985	1990	2000	2005	2010
Total reserves Bln metric tons/10⁹/	16.4	16.4	16.4	16.4	16.4
Reserves economically mineable*/ Bln metric tons /10⁹/	8.8	8.8	8.8	8.8	8.8
Expected yearly size of production per costs of 1978**/ Bln metric tons	80.0-90.0	140.0	250.0		

* Industrial reserves /documented/ per situation of 1977.
** Data refer to the High Coal Case alternative.

DOMESTIC COAL SUPPLIES

Rich and relatively easily mined deposits close to the big consumption centers make coal the most important fuel in the Polish national economy. This is very significant in the energy national balance, not only now and in the past, but also for the future, as mentioned in the preceding section.

It is anticipated that by 1990 the model of consumption of hard coal in Poland will be as follows (at coal consumption 168.7 mtce as 100%):

(a) input for energy convertion processes:

—power plants, power and thermal plants as well as thermal plants	66.0%
—coking plants	18.1%
—gas generation, low-temperature carbonization plants, etc.	3.0%
	87.1%
(b) input for coal liquefaction and gasification	1.8%
(c) direct consumption of coal	11.1%
	100.0%

Domestic supplies of hard coal for the years 1990-2000 will come mainly from the Upper-Silesian Coal Basin. They will comprise about 90% of the total production of the mines of Upper-Silesian Basin (besides the now-commenced construction of new mines in Lublin Coal Basin). Only by about 2000 can a greater growth of coal production from the LCB be anticipated. This is mainly because of the possibility of a quick development of geological research and investment in construction of mines, accompanied by a parallel development of the necessary infrastructure, for this new coal basin. The anticipated growth of hard-coal production will require a constant extension of many existing mines with rich reserves, as well as the construction of further new mines in the Upper-Silesian Basin.

Both the extensions and the construction of new mines will occur in more and more difficult geologic and mining conditions (increasing depth, rock bursts, temperature, water influx, etc.) which will result in a growth of capital outlay and running costs.

The suggested development of hard-coal production up to 300 mt in 2000 is in line with present perceptions of the possible production potential, bearing in mind all the technoeconomic aspects and consequences.

COAL TRANSPORTATION

The basic mode of coal transportation from the various coal regions to domestic users and to export markets is the railway system. At present, about 75% of the extracted coal is conveyed by railway. It represents about 30% of the total freight handled within the country.

Apart from the above, the following transport methods are also used:

- trucks for carrying smaller quantities to the users situated close to the coal regions,
- waterway routes (Odra river and Wisła river systems) in barges to users located along these rivers and to the Baltic port complexes: Gdańsk-Gdynia, and Szczecin-Świnoujście,

338

- belt conveyors, when suitable conditions exist to convey coal from mines to electric plants or large thermal plants or from mines to river harbors. In the case of shorter distances, particularly within the Upper-Silesian Coal Basin, narrow-gauge railway transport is used.

Broad trends in coal transportation from the particular coal basins are shown in Figure 13-5.

The distance of railway transport from the coal basins to domestic users and to ports for the export varies from 70 km to 600 km.

The brown coal, on the whole, is used in an integrated system: mine and an electric plant or briquetting plant. Thus, this coal is not, as a rule, sent to consumers by railway.

As further increases in hard-coal output, as well as the economic growth of the country, are planned, the present transport equipment for the coal transportation is insufficient.

Coal-loading capacities in the Świnoujście port and Gdańsk-Gdynia ports amount currently to about 25 mt/year and will have to be augmented to about 30-35 mt/year. The following facilities for transport of coal from the Upper-Silesian Basin are planned:

- development of a railway circle line, bypassing the concentration of industrial structures and residential sections in the coal basin. A number of central coal-storage piles will be sited beside this railway line which will be equipped with loading facilities for the unit coal trains that carry coal to big users, within the country, and for the export markets,

- development of new railway lines to connect the Upper-Silesian Coal Basin with the Baltic ports; development of railway lines to connect the coal mines of the Lublin Coal Basin with the entire railway network of the country.

As far as truck transport is concerned, a development of several truck bases and loading points, as well as an improvement of existing roads and the construction of new roads, is planned. To extend coal transport from the Upper-Silesian Coal Basin by waterway, the development and modernization of the river harbors on the Odra and Wisła rivers is planned. Moreover, extension of nonconventional transport modes such as belt-conveyor-systems ways and slurry pipelines is being considered.

Linkage of several selected collieries to adjacent electric plants, to central coal preparation plants and to the river harbors by belt conveyor is being planned. The above-mentioned plans for coal transportation by nonconventional means (i.e., belt-conveyor highways and pipes) are currently being reviewed in order to ascertain their technical and economic efficiency.

ENVIRONMENTAL PROTECTION IN COAL MINING

To neutralize negative effects on the environment, the Polish coal-mining industry carries out a broad range of activity directed toward protection of mine surfaces and surface structures, water courses and the atmosphere. This activity also includes noise suppression.

Table 13-5. Handling Capacities of Polish Ports

Particulars	Świnoujście (Swinoport II)	Port Północny	Szczecin	Gdynia	Gdańsk Old Port
Max. draught of ships	40 feet fresh water	49 feet brackish water	35-36 feet fresh water	33 feet brackish water	33 feet fresh water
Ship length LOA max.	220 m	280 m	180 m	no limits	230 m
Loading possibilities	up to 65 thous. tons	up to 100 thous. tons	up to 14 thous. tons	up to 24 thous. tons	up to 25 thous. tons
Loading facilities	automated equipment, bucket wheels	belt-conveyor automated self-loading equipment, wagon tippler	cranes, gantry cranes, automated belt-conveyor line	gantry cranes	gantry cranes
Handling capacities	2,000 t/h	4,000 t/h	700 t/h	6,400 t/d	6,400 t/d
Storage possibilities (thous. tons)	200	500	250	80	50

Note: Present capacities allow for loading and sea-dispatch of about 25 mt of coal per year. There are possibilities of raising the loading capacities to 30 mt.

Figure 13-5. Main coal routes.

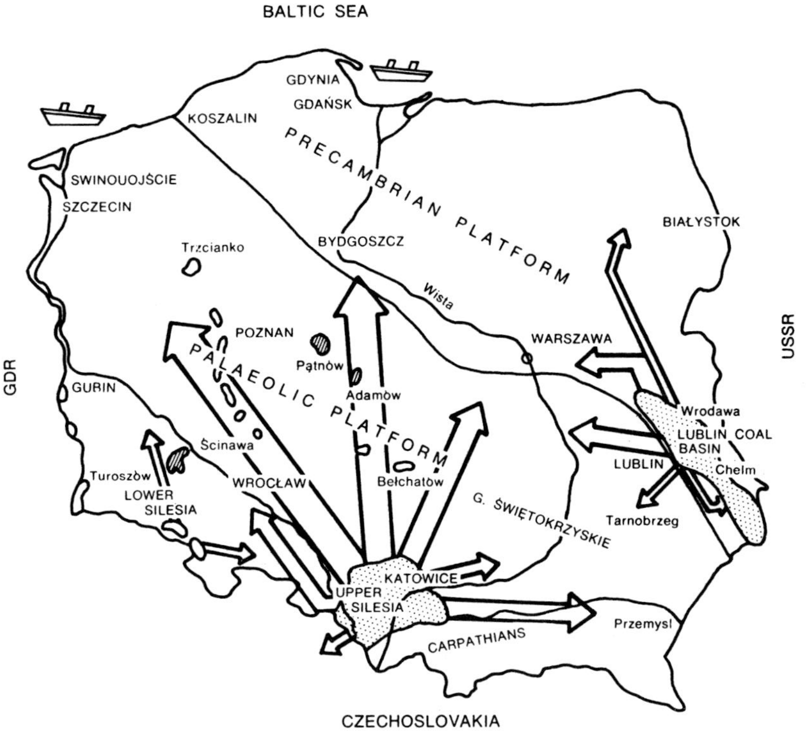

BALTIC SEA

GDYNIA
GDAŃSK
KOSZALIN
PRECAMBRIAN PLATFORM
SWINOUOJŚCIE
SZCZECIN
BIAŁYSTOK
Trzcianko
BYDGOSZCZ
Wisła
POZNAN
WARSZAWA
GDR
GURIN
PAŁAEOLIC PLATFORM
Pątnów
Adamów
Wrodawa
LUBLIN COAL BASIN
USSR
Scinawa
LUBLIN
Chelm
Turoszów
LOWER SILESIA
WROCŁAW
Bełchatow
G. SWIĘTOKRZYSKIE
Tarnobrzeg
KATOWICE
UPPER SILESIA
CARPATHIANS
Przemysl
CZECHOSLOVAKIA

PROTECTION OF SURFACE AND SURFACE STRUCTURES

To ascertain whether areas under which mining is to be carried out are suitable to be developed, the environmental effects of mining on the surface are in Poland classified into following categories:

Category of the Ground	Particulars	Anticipated Deformation		
		Inclinations T max mm/m	Deformations E max mm/m	Radius of Curvature N min Km
I	No protection of surface structures is needed (but small damage may take place, e.g., harmless scratching of walls)	≤2.5	≤1.5	>20
II	Areas where partial protection of all structures would be uneconomical (negligible damage can be easily repaired)	≤5	≤3	>12
III	Areas where partial protection of structures is necessary	≤10	≤6	>6
IV	Areas where major protection of structures is necessary	≤15	≤9	>4
V	Areas unsuitable for surface building development	>15	>9	<4

341

The classification makes it possible to work out a number of methods to protect the existing structures and those under construction. These methods vary according to the type of the structures (buildings, roads, water projects).

MINING DIRT AND WASTE DISPOSAL

Mines are now obliged to stop piling wastes above ground level. Several years' efforts in this field has resulted in the fact that, at present, scarcely 6% of the waste derived from current coal production is piled above ground level; the remaining 94% is disposed of in the following way:

- 12% of waste is left below ground in the workings,
- 15% is used for hydraulic stowing,
- 6% for packing (dry stowing),
- 41% for levelling of surface areas and for sublevel piling,
- 6% dispatched to the central stockpiles,
- 1% for production of the building material, and
- 2-3% for other purposes.

LAND RECLAMATION

Broad action is being taken to restore the land in former mining areas. In the present five-year period, reclamation and development of about 3,000 hectares annually is planned.

PROTECTION OF NATURAL RESOURCES

The planned economy of Poland controls, by appropriate regulations and standards, the siting of plants and other industrial facilities in such a way that compact forest areas and arable soils of higher categories (as well as nature reserves) are to be excluded from industrial development.

PROTECTION OF WATERS

Surface-water protection is carried out to save water both in the domestic and the industrial sector. In the coal-mining sector there are standards issued by the Ministry of Mining to regulate water demand for mines and other establishments within the mining sector.

These standards are as follows:

- drinking water consumption amounts to 197 l/t of coal output,
- industrial water consumption amounts to 766 l/t of coal output.

To protect surface waters against excessive salinity caused by salty underground waters, two methods have been developed: the hydrotechnic method used currently, and the utilization method which is now at the stage of research and demonstration; this method may be used for waters containing more than 70 G/l Na Cl.

The hydrotechnic method consists of carrying off the brine which, after processing in settling tanks, is directed to the main drains and afterward to a storage reservoir. From the reservoir, salty waters are drained to a river in such a way that the tolerable concentration of ions Cl^- and SO_4^{2-} in the river are not exceeded. According to the Polish standards promulgated by the Polish Government, inland surface waters are grouped in three classes of cleanness, where the chloride and sulphate content should not exceed following figures.

			Purity Class	
Pollutant	Concentration Unit	I	II	III
chlorides	mg Cl/cu.dm.	250	300 and below	400
sulphates	mg SO₄/cu.dm.	150	200 and below	250

The utilization method consists of:

- selecting out of the total volume of waters pumped in mines that having the highest degree of mineralization. From these waters, fresh water and table salt are produced by means of thermal treatment and the use of vacuum evaporators.

To protect surface waters against pollution by industrial and communal effluents, a large program is being implemented in the Polish Mining Industry to develop sewage treatment plants. The program is adjusted to the needs of development of the Polish Mining Industry and to the environmental requirements, according to the following table:

Sl No.	Type of the Purification Plant	Basic Year 1970	Number of Plants to Be Constructed in the Year			
			1975	1980	1985	1990
1.	Purif. plants for washery and flotation effluents	89	11	13	16	19
2.	For underground water and hydraulic waste water	57	19	38	28	24
3.	For effluents from water treatment and boiler and cooling-tower sludges, and other industrial effluents	44	10	7	23	23
4.	For communal effluents and waste waters	111	21	19	13	17
	Total	301	61	77	80	83

According to the Polish Standards based on the above-mentioned regulation, the permissible pollution of the sewage drained to the sewage system, which is State property, is as follows:

Sl No.	Particulars	Concentration Unit	Admissible Concentration
1.	5-day biochemic need of the oxygen (BZT₅)	mg O₂/dm³	700 and below
2.	Chemical need of the oxygen by the bichromate method (ChZT)	mg O₂/dm³	1,000 and below
3.	Chlorides (Cl⁻)	mg Cl/dm³	400 and below
4.	Sulphates (SO₄²⁻)	mg SO₄/dm³	300 and below
5.	Soluble substances	mg/dm³	1,000 and below

Sl No.	Particulars	Concentration Unit	Admissible Concentration
6.	Suspension (in general)	mg/dm^3	330 and below
7.	Temperature	°C	35 and below
8.	Value pH	pH	6.5-9
9.	Ammonia nitrogen	$mg\ ^NNH_3/dm^3$	6 and below
10.	Iron—total	$mg\ Fe/dm^3$	10 and below
11.	Phenol volatile	mg/dm^3	40 and below
12.	Detergents	mg/dm^3	10 and below
13.	Substances extrainhibiting by the petroleum benzine	mg/dm^3	50 and below

In the coal-mining industry, regulations and guidelines have been prepared for the design, construction and operation of water reservoirs and industrial settling ponds in areas involved in deep mining and opencast mining.

Implementation of these regulations and guidelines results in the suppression of water hazards arising from the above-mentioned structures, either by their modernization, reconstruction, repair or in extreme cases, demolition.

PROTECTION OF THE ATMOSPHERIC AIR

The problem of protection of the atmospheric air against pollution is controlled in Poland by regulations and guidelines applicable in the following areas:

- areas which are particularly protected, i.e., health resorts, national parks and nature reserves. Tolerable concentrations of particular components on these areas are as follows:

Sl No.	Pollutant	Instantaneous Concentration 20 min.D_{20} $mg/cu.m$	Average Daily Concentration $D_{24}\ mg/cu.m$
1.	Sulphur dioxide	0.25	0.075
2.	Sulphuric acid	0.15	0.05
3.	Nitric oxides (N_2O_5)	0.15	0.05
4.	Hydrogen sulphide	0.008	0.008
5.	Carbon monoxide	3.0	0.5
6.	Gasoline	2.5	0.75
7.	Nontoxic dust, with particles below 20 um	0.2	0.075

- the other areas protected are included in the remaining regions of the country, with the exception of areas occupied by industrial plants or other sources of pollution or protected zones. Tolerable concentrations of components within these areas are:

344

Sl No.	Pollutant	Instantaneous Concentration 20 min.D_{20} mg/cu.m	Average Daily Concentration D_{24} mg/cu.m
1.	Sulphur dioxide	0.90	0.35
2.	Sulphuric acid	0.30	0.10
3.	Nitric oxides (N_2O_5)	0.60	0.20
4.	Hydrogen sulphide	0.06	0.02
5.	Carbon disulphide	0.045	0.015
6.	Nontoxic dust, with particles below 20 um	0.60	0.20

The permissible dustfall on the earth surface must not exceed—for areas particularly protected—40 t/sq.km/year, maximum per month 6.5 t/sq.km/year, and for protected areas—250 t/sq.km/year on average.

Moreover, to protect the environment against pollution by dusts and gases, industrial plants have been grouped in five classes according to their environmental noxiousness. For each class standard, widths of zones have been established:

Plant Class	Zone Width m
I	1,000
II	500
III	300
IV	100
V	50

In this classification, the deep-coal mines have been included in Class III for which the protective zone width is 300 m, whereas opencast lignite mines belong to Class II, where the zone width is 500 m.

Furthermore, the principles of development of areas belonging to the protected zones have been worked out. These recommend the cultivation of adequate plants, afforestation, and the planting of trees. Location in the areas of residential buildings, colleges, hospitals, creches, nursery schools and other buildings and structures designed for continuous occupation by people, and not directly linked to the production or services of a plant, is forbidden. Each plan referring to a protected zone must be approved by the organ responsible for the atmospheric cleanness and by the State Sanitary Inspection.

PROTECTION AGAINST NOISE

In order to reduce the intensity of noises produced by industrial plants, chiefly technical means are used, such as noise suppressors, insulators and acoustic baffles, as well as adequate planting of greens in the protective zones.

On the boundary of the indicated protected zone, admissible noise intensity, according to the Polish standards, is:

- for human settlements: $35 + 5 = 40$ dB/A/
- for recreation and leisure areas: $30 + 5 = 35$ dB/A/.

IMPLEMENTING ACTIONS REQUIRED FOR THE DEVELOPMENT OF COAL PRODUCTION

The continued high share of hard and brown coal in meeting the national demand for fuel and primary energy until 2000 is justified in the forecast by a high degree of utilization of coal deposits and a concentration on coal production. Those are two very essential factors indicating the necessity of continuation, i.e., of the following actions:

- improvement and intensification of geological R & D, especially from the point of view of decreasing its expense and duration,
- technological improvements in mining construction aimed at shortening the time for extensions and new mines construction, through new solutions and highly efficient technical and technological means,
- further development of specialized planning and design offices, and of mining contracting enterprises,
- further rationalization of mining machinery and equipment under production, and research in new and unconventional technologies for coal mining and separation under more difficult geologic-mining conditions,
- preparing new mining crews with adequate qualifications for future changes in staff structure,
- further development of technical infrastructures needed for the production of mining machinery and equipment and for specialized electricity generation and mining electronics plants,
- further development of the social infrastructure which is the basic background necessary for the development of mines and mining regions in all coal basins,
- advance actions on the development of transport facilities for land and for water transportation of coal, having in view a lot of individual discharge points, and also conducting further research into improvements in the environmental impact caused by mining exploitation.

A separate specialized development program is being followed in the field of utilization of coal, and is connected with research on coal gasification and liquefaction.

The research work is led in Poland by scientific research centers, by planning and design offices in the mining industry, and by university centers and research institutes of the Polish Academy of Science in accordance with long-term programs directed to meet the requirements of the industry.

Table 13-6. Activities on Environmental Protection

Hazards Affecting Elements	Deformation and Degradation	Industrial and Communal Effluents	Underground Waters	Dusts, Gases, Flue Gases	Wastes	Noise and Vibration
	reclamation and development of the overflow land without outflow	mechanical treatment	mechanical purification	dedusting	utilization	protective zones
	regulation of surface flows	mechanical and biological treatment	retention utilization	desulphurization	reclamation	
Biosphere	reclamation of post-industrial waste lands	protective zones		protection zones	protection against effects on surface and underground waters	
	land melioration and phytometry			change of cultivation pattern	protection zones	
	change of the cultivation pattern					
Earth Surfaces and Surface Structures	civil engineering protection	protective zones		protective zones	utilization	noise suppression
	protective pillars				reclamation	vibration damping
	substitute structures				protection zones	

Figure 13-6. Environmental Hazards Caused by Mine Operations

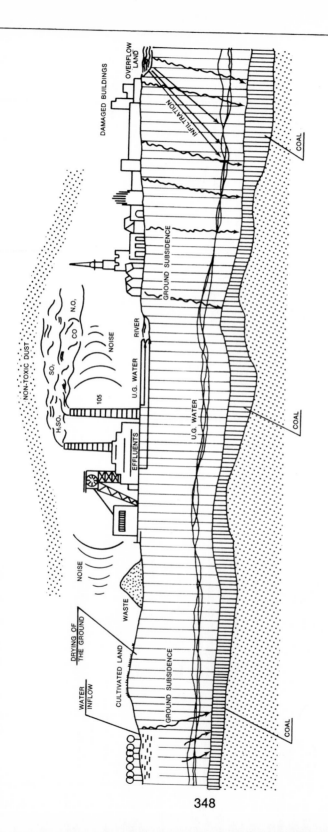

Figure 13-7. Environmental Protection Included in the Activity of a Mine

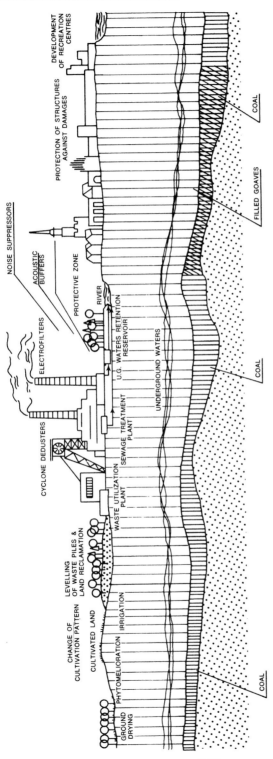

CHAPTER 14

SWEDEN

INTRODUCTION

This report has been developed by Kurt Lekås and Håkan Neuman, Loussavaara-Kiirunavaara AB (LKAB), under the chairmanship of Arne S. Lundberg, The Royal Swedish Academy of Engineering Sciences (IVA). Essential contributions have also been made by Roy Carlson, The Swedish State Power Board, and Göran Sondén, LKAB.

THE SWEDISH SITUATION

Swedish coal deposits are small and of poor quality. The technically recoverable reserves have been estimated to be 30 million tons with an energy value of 540 PJ. From 1940 to 1945, an average of half a million tons a year was mined. Today there is no coal production in Sweden except small quantities obtained from clay production for the ceramics industry. From this very limited resource it is anticipated that coal production will increase during the next few years.

During the first 50 years of this century coal and coke dominated the supply of energy in Sweden, accounting for more than fifty percent. Since the 1950's, coal has been almost entirely replaced by oil products.

During the 1970's the Swedish imports of coal and coke have been between 2-3 million tons a year, used primarily within the iron and steel industry and, to some extent, in the cement industry. During the last ten years (except in 1974) very small volumes of steam coal have been used for heating and power production.

The utilization of steam coal in Sweden could reduce the use of primarily heavy fuel oils. This means that coal would be used for district heating, in industry, and in thermal power plants for the combined generation of electric energy and heat. Coal could also be used in conventional thermal power plants. The possibility of replacing fuel oils by coal, and, to some extent, by domestic fuels as peat and biomass by the end of the 1980's, is considered to be rather good.

In March 1979 the Swedish government sent a bill to Parliament concerning future energy policy. Among other actions, the bill established short-term goals of reducing dependency on oil by increasing coal usage. It was estimated that the Swedish consumption of coal by the end of the 1980's could amount to between 6-9 million tons. The increase from today's level of about 2 million tons will mainly be made up of steam coal.

There are two main problems in foreseeing the consumption of coal in Sweden for the years 1990 or 2000—even with wide margins. First is the almost total uncertainty concerning future environmental restrictions, a question which is dealt with in more detail later in this report. Second, the greatest uncertainty is created by the parliamentary decision to subject Swedish nuclear future to a referendum in March of 1980. The opponents of nuclear power have formulated their alternative: six reactors may operate, for the time being, but are to be shut down by 1990 at the very latest. The adherents of nuclear power have formulated two rather similar alternatives based on a nuclear program, with 12 reactors in operation by 1990.

If the antinuclear side wins the referendum, it will be necessary to immediately start building new conventional power plants based on imported fuels. The government's policy is that no more oil-fired power plants will be permitted; the main target of the Swedish energy policy is to reduce the country's extreme dependence on imported oil. To substitute for the 12 reactors (which will be necessary by 1990) with coal-fired plants may not be possible. In any case, a "no" in the referendum will cause a forced expansion of coal-based power production. It will also cause strong conservation activities and the development of domestic energy sources. The figures presented in this report reflect the two main alternatives which are the basis for the WOCOL cases. The alternatives give a rather good picture of the possible steam-coal use in the Swedish energy system during the next ten to twenty years.

APPROACH FOR THE NATIONAL WOCOL ANALYSIS

THE OVERALL FRAMEWORK

Because of the inadequate recent Swedish experience in coal use, the possible methods and problems of large-scale coal reintroduction have to be analyzed carefully. This analysis must cover the coal flow from the mine to the disposal of waste materials. The work on this analysis was at an early stage when WOCOL started. Due to a strong negative attitude toward coal in Sweden, it has not been included on a large scale in energy forecasts during the last decade. In 1977 the State Power Board, Sydkraft AB and LKAB, began a joint coal investigation—Coal 90 —in order to clarify the conditions for increased future coal use in Sweden.

Arne S. Lundberg was invited to be the Swedish participant in WOCOL, with Kurt Lekås and Håkan Neuman as his associates. The staff of the Coal 90 has been the Swedish WOCOL team.

The information used in this national report comes from official material and from Coal 90. Since June 1979 the WOCOL team has received material from various Swedish studies. The WOCOL team has taken part in several investigations studying the consequences of a "no" to nuclear power in Sweden. Other than energy conservation, coal is now considered as the main alternative to nuclear power.

SELECTION OF VARIABLES FOR HIGH COAL AND LOW COAL CASES

Economic growth of GNP at 3.1% a year from 1979 to 1985, 2.7% from 1986 to 1990, and of 2.5% thereafter is judged to achieve the goals of Swedish economic policy. The average total economic growth from 1977 to 2000 is therefore expected to be 2.6%. This growth rate is moderate compared to that of the past 2-3 decades but will probably be the maximum achievable in the next 10-20 years. The influence on economic growth from higher-than-anticipated oil prices has not been taken into consideration.

Depending on Sweden's economic growth, it is anticipated that the growth of the total primary energy use will be 1.3% on average for the period to the year 2000 if there are at least 12 nuclear reactors in operation. The forecast reflects economic growth and strengthening the program for energy conservation. If the Swedish reactors have to be shut down, the growth of the total primary energy use will be limited to 1.0% a year, which in turn means that a very tough conservation program has to be implemented. This development is also reflected in the ratio between the growth of total primary energy use and the growth of GNP. The ratio is, in the Low Coal Case, 0.5, and in the High Coal Case, about 0.4.

World oil prices will be very important in the setting of energy prices in general. Further increases will stimulate energy conservation measures and make available additional conventional and new energy sources. It is assumed that the oil price in the two cases will increase in real terms from $20 in 1979, compounded at 3.5% a year to 1990, and then at 2.0% after 1990. It is assumed that oil prices will primarily influence coal consumption in two main areas in Sweden: industrial use, and municipal use for district heating or for combined generation of electricity and heat. Oil prices are not expected to directly influence the consumption of coal in thermal power plants; the main influence here will come from attitudes toward nuclear power.

The primary target of the Swedish energy policy is to reduce the extreme dependence on imported oil. All official and unofficial energy forecasts reflect this. Therefore, no special calculations have been made for an oil limitation case.

ANALYTICAL METHODS FOR THE NATIONAL ANALYSIS

The projections of *coal consumption* are based on the following assumptions.

Among industries using metallurgical coal it has been estimated that existing steel plants will be utilized up to their full capacity and with future increased production. This increase in the demand for coke can take the form of either increased imports of metallurgical coal or increased imports of coke.

The expected increase in the use of steam coal in industry will primarily take place in industries with big boilers, such as the pulp and paper and cement. We expect this increase in consumption will accelerate early in the 1980's.

We assume new district heating plants, especially in and near big cities, will be constructed to burn coal. The potential for coal use in these plants may be higher than estimated. In some places thermal power plants are planned for combined generation of electric energy and heat. This will especially be the case during the 1980's if the nuclear reactors are to be shut down. We also assume that some plants which are now oil-fired will be converted to coal-fired ones.

In the Low Coal Case we estimate that the production of electricity will grow at 2.7% a year from 1977 to 2000. In the High Coal Case the figure is 1.7% a year. In both cases we assume that coal-fired thermal power plants are going to be built during the 1990's. For the 1980's such plants will probably be built only if the reactors are shut down, i.e., the High Coal Case.

The supply of oil to Sweden today is based largely on the spot market. This is a subject of gravest concern in Sweden. Therefore, it is assumed that when some oil is replaced by coal there will be a strong interest in increasing the security of supply. This can be handled either by long-term contracts or by financial involvement in foreign coal deposits. Because of different lead times for production as opposed to consumption, the *integration of coal supply and demand* will be of the utmost importance.

COAL CONSUMPTION

LEAD TIMES AND MARKET DYNAMICS

Forecasts for demand and supply of oil and coal are usually presented in curves, without attempting to show short-time variations. Such variations are usually regarded as being caused by business cycles of short duration. However, studies of the iron ore market have shown that there may be longer periods of market imbalance caused by different lead times for investments in mining and steel-producing industries.

It has been shown that the lead time for an underground mine can be up to 15 years. In Australia it can take eight to ten years, in the case of open-pit mines. It should be noted that Australia is a country where land both for mining and railways is easily available. (Lead time as used here means the time from the moment a decision is taken to open a mine to the moment the mine is working at full speed.) The decision to open a mine will come only when very clear demand indications or sales contracts exist. Even before a decision can be made many preparatory studies for new coal-fired plants will have been made without much publicity, and then it will take as long as 5 years for engineering and construction. If the lead times for mining are longer than for a lot of consuming installations, the supply of coal to the world market will be insufficient during a certain period.

Other factors may contribute to this type of market dynamics. In Sweden there exist a few oil-fired power plants and other industrial installations where coal once was used. In some cases, old boilers for coal may still be used for oil. In other cases, new boilers and arrangements for the handling of coal must be installed, if the necessary space is available. In such cases the time for conversion from oil to coal can be three years.

The conclusion is that there may be a risk of oil shortages, causing a faster increase in the consumption of coal than of production capacity.

POTENTIAL COAL MARKET

The future consumers of coal in Sweden can be divided into three different categories. The first is very large consumers using more than 500,000 tons a year. These consumers are mainly power companies and the steel industry.

Deliveries of coal to this category of consumer are supposed to take place at the customer's own port and/or storage facility. The need for coal in this consuming sector during the 1980's is, to a great extent, dependent on how and whether nuclear power will be utilized in the future.

The second category of consumers use between 50,000 and 500,000 tons a year. Most of the coal in this sector will be used for district heating, in plants for combined production of electricity and heat, and in some industries like cement. The distribution to these customers will take place partly directly to their own ports and/or storage facilities and partly via transshipment. This sector is probably the one that will expand fastest during the 1980's.

Small towns, industries, and hospitals are examples of customers of the third category. Deliveries of coal will take place either to their own storage areas or from a regional or transshipment storage area if on-site storage space is not available. These coal consumers are probably those who could most rapidly convert present oil-fired plants to coal-fired ones.

The conclusion to be drawn is that Swedish consumption of steam coal will increase rather slowly in the beginning of the 1980's, even if a lot of new coal-fired capacity is installed. From the middle of the decade the consumption will increase rapidly because a few big coal-using plants will come on stream.

THE FUTURE COAL CONSUMPTION

The Swedish production of electricity is presently about 90 TWh, of which about two-thirds is hydro, one-fourth is nuclear and one-tenth is produced in thermal (mainly combined) power plants. The capacity of thermal power plants that can possibly use coal, is 380 MW. These plants are rather small and old. If nuclear power is not going to be phased out, it is anticipated that there will be at least an installed coal-fired capacity of 1,300 MW by 1990. These will be combined plants for production of electricity and heat. If nuclear power is phased out, there will be an installed coal-fired capacity in 1990 of about 6,500 MW, of which 3,600 MW will be in thermal power plants. For the period thereafter, in both cases there will be a sharp increase in coal-fired production capacity from thermal power plants.

About 20% of the total heat needed for residential purposes today is produced in district heating plants with an installed capacity of 13,000 MW thermal. In the year 1990, the capacity is estimated to be 21,000 MW thermal, or about 45% of the total need. For the period from 1990 to 2000 the increase will be rather modest. Even if this development represents a large potential for the installation of coal-fired capacity, we estimate that the use of coal in this sector will be limited because of high investment costs, environmental, and distribution constraints.

The current consumption of heavy fuel oils in Swedish industry is 6 million tons. We estimate that a lot of new industrial coal-fired capacity will be installed in this sector when old oil-fired plants need to be refurbished. Crucial to this development will be the economics of using coal instead of oil, environmental restrictions, the possibilities of storing coal at plant sites, and the security of supply. As has been indicated, the potential for coal use is very big but very difficult to predict accurately.

If the nuclear plants are going to be phased out by about 1990, there will be an immediate need to build new electric-production capacity. Coal will be the main alternative to oil. Estimates by an official government committee show that if we start now, there can theoretically be about 4,200 MW of new installed coal-fired capacity in thermal power plants by 1990 and 5,400 MW in the years that follow.

There will also be a need to convert oil-fired combined plants to coal-fired ones; and there will be a need to halt the increment in the electric consumption and to strengthen the energy conservation program. On the whole, this will lead to an increase in consumption of fuels for direct use. Estimates show that the physical and technical limits of steam-coal use in the Swedish energy system in 1990 can be at least 17 million tons or more. As has been indicated in the High Coal Case, most of the coal is to be used in the electric sector.

THE PENETRATION OF THE ENERGY SYSTEM

It is quite obvious that coal will penetrate the Swedish energy system at a rather high speed under certain conditions. Excluding the question of nuclear power, the crucial point about further development will be how fast the energy system can be transformed from a heavy dependence on oil into a system based on a variety of energy sources. The future possibilities of using coal can be divided into three different categories: the use of coal in new installations; the possibilities of substituting oil in existing plants; and, in the High Coal Case, the question is also how to substitute nuclear power.

Excluding the electric sector, it has been estimated that coal in both cases will be used as a fuel for about 10% of the total primary energy consumption in 1985, 15% in 1990, and 20-25% in 2000. This means that coal will constitute roughly 50% of the total increase in energy consumption through 2000. The industrial sector will be penetrated fastest, and by 1985 coal could amount to about 15% of industry's total energy supply. The increase will then probably slow down and the percentage of coal will be about 20% in 1990 and 25% in 2000. The development of the residential and commercial sector will go slower during the 1980's but will increase substantially during the 1990's. From a penetration rate of about 5% in 1985, we estimate that coal will be used for 10-15% in 1990 and 25% in 2000.

In the High Coal Case, existing nuclear power plants will be replaced by coal-fired ones. It cannot be said that this has been proved possible because of the problems of lead times in the energy sector and siting of new coal-fired power plants. Excluding the problems of substitutions for the six nuclear reactors now in operation, about 60% of the new electric production capacity will be coal-fired during the 1980's in the High Coal Case. In the Low Coal Case, the corresponding figure will be about 10% because further nuclear capacity will come on stream. In both cases, about 85-90% of the new electric production capacity during the 1990's will probably be coal-fired if no new nuclear capacity is built.

COAL SUPPLY AND TRANSPORT

The Swedish coal import is expected to increase rapidly by the end of the 80's and in the beginning of the 90's. To create security in the coal-supply pattern, the risk has to be spread over several different coal-producing countries combined with a policy of storing coal in Sweden. Some increased security of supply and flexibility can also be gained by Swedish involvement in foreign coal-mining projects. It is possible, therefore, to create conditions for an expansion of coal production and delivery to Sweden if there is a disturbance in the international energy market.

For Sweden the most important coal-exporting countries through the beginning of the 90's are the present coal producers. Australia, Canada, Eastern Europe (Poland and the Soviet Union), and probably Colombia form the natural base of the Swedish coal supply. The USA will probably also be an exporter of steam coal to Sweden. However, US energy policy is uncertain and there are also uncertainties concerning their capability and willingness to increase the future steam-coal export.

In the 1990's countries like China and some of the developing countries are expected to become important coal exporters. It is likely that Sweden will receive some coal from these countries.

Today's Swedish coal import is almost solely metallurgical coal. The deliveries take place mainly through the ports of Oxelösund (max. 70,000 dwt) and Luleå (max. 60,000 dwt), where facilities adjacent and connected to the steelworks handle the coal. The lack of steam-coal consumption for the last 2-3 decades has led to a discontinuation of earlier existing infrastructures for the distribution of steam coal. Thus Sweden has neither any specific infrastructure nor any practical experience in handling steam coal.

To be able to reintroduce the use of steam coal to Sweden, it will be necessary to find simple logistical solutions. In the introductory stage, it might be advantageous to use existing ports through which metallurgical coal is imported—preferably Oxelösund for distribution in eastern Sweden. Oxelösund, located on the east coast, has a port which is able to handle vessels up to 70,000 dwt and has additional storage space for steam coal. Further, it is located close to large-population areas which are easily accessible by railway. With Oxelösund as a steam-coal terminal center on the Swedish east coast, an infrastructure for distribution of steam coal to the final consumers could gradually be built up. Oxelösund can be expanded to handle vessels up to 100,000 dwt.

On the Swedish west coast, the coal will initially be imported through either continental terminals or directly to small domestic ports which can be gradually enlarged. On the west coast, Gothenburg or Landskrona could be the location for a future port for incoming overseas coal on a large scale. Both these ports could handle vessels of 150,000-200,000 dwt.

When the Swedish utilities will build new coal-fired power plants on the coast, most of the coal will be shipped directly to the plants where ports with direct offloading facilities will have to be built.

The relatively small steam-coal consumption during the 1980's will not give the economic incentives needed to build a new, large coal terminal. The feasibility of such a terminal will be achieved only when Swedish coal imports have reached considerable size—perhaps not until the 1990's. Building a terminal for Swedish coal imports, however, is not just a question limited to Sweden. From our point of view, a project of this size must be of inter-Scandinavian interest and be done in cooperation with Denmark and Finland. Because all three countries expect to import coal from overseas suppliers, large vessels must be used to keep the sea transportation costs to a competitive level. Therefore, a large terminal on the Swedish west coast or in Denmark for storage and transshipment to smaller ports in Sweden, Finland and Denmark is of mutual interest. The Swedish location for such a terminal could be either Gothenburg or Landskrona.

STRUCTURE OF THE SWEDISH COAL INDUSTRY

There is no coal production in Sweden, but some small quantities are obtained from clay production in the ceramics industry. The coal produced in this way is used for local consumption. This production is expected to increase slightly.

There are some Swedish companies that trade coal, but these companies are very small. Whatever the result is of the referendum, coal consumption in Sweden will increase. Therefore, there are negotiations between several companies representing the mining industry, the metallurgical industry, the power industry and the local authorities on future cooperation in purchasing coal. This cooperation addresses the security of supply, long-term contracts, and joint ventures in coal mines abroad.

ENVIRONMENTAL, HEALTH & SAFETY CONSIDERATIONS

The last large coal-fired power plant in Sweden was built in the mid-1950's. Since then, all fossil-fuel-fired power plants constructed have been exclusively oil-fired. The result of this development is that there are poor traditions in Sweden for burning coal, poor infrastructure when importing and transporting coal into the country, and a strong public belief that coal is very dirty and impacts the environment adversely.

Because of the public's attitude toward coal, attention has to be paid to the quality of the coal imported. Of special interest is the content of trace elements, sulphur, nitrogen, and ash. To fulfill the environmental impact requirements caused by burning coal, a lot of consideration has to be given to the design of power and other plants. These requirements will become stronger with the passing of time; we will have to look to the problems to be solved in the 1980's with techniques we master today. For plants commissioned in the late 1990's, we may be able to use techniques which are currently under development.

The techniques we know, or which we can acquire within a short time, are summed up as follows.

Particulate cleaning of exhaust gases is well developed by several methods, of which electrostatic precipitators today are considered the best. Mass collecting efficiencies of 99.5% are common. However, demands have been put forward that mercury and cadmium also should be collected. At prevailing temperatures all the mercury and part of the cadmium seem to be gasified and not collectible in electrostatic precipitators. To catch mercury, attention must be put on dust-filter bags. Measurements have been made, and more will be made, to evaluate the possibility of collecting mercury in bag filters. Indications received so far show a 60% collecting efficiency in the gaseous phase, and more than 98% in the particulate phase. The mass collecting efficiency of a bag filter used to be 99.8%. With the help of the precipitators mentioned, it seems possible to meet the requirements on limitation of the outlet of the trace elements.

Getting rid of sulphur dioxide (SO_2) in the exhaust gases is a major consideration of the Swedish Environmental Protection Agency. There are two principle ways to reduce the SO_2 impact: one consists of cleaning the gases after combustion; the second is to eliminate sulphur from the coal prior to combustion. Another solution might possibly be the addition of lime to acidic land areas and lakes to buffer the emissions of SO_2.

Several methods have been developed in laboratories, pilot plants and even full-scale plants to clean the exhaust gases up to now. However, such plants are not commercially available, as the availability is still too low to be considered justified by a utility. Further, there is a large problem how to deposit the gypsum and calcium sulphite sludge. As yet, there is no good method to make use of the sludge. Great efforts in research and development are being made all over the world on scrubbing techniques which may solve today's problems.

Physical deep-cleaning of coal prior to combustion reduces the pyrite and ash content. Sulphur (S) in coal consists of organic sulphur, pyrite and sulphate. (Sulphate can be neglected.) By eliminating the pyrite, the S-content can be reduced by some 30-70% for many coals. In general, it seems that when the S-content is in the range of 0.6-0.7% and lower, there is a very low pyrite content. The technology of physical methods for separating pyrite from coal is known and can be applied in Swedish plants in the 1980's. However, there are limitations as to what is possible in such plants, depending on the pyrite content and what pyrite structure in the coal is. At present, the best way to meet the requirements on SO_2 discharge seems to be to import coal with a low S-content.

Reducing the content of nitrogen oxides (NO_x) in exhaust gases is another important task. The formation of NO_x is caused by several things, of which the most important are nitrogen content of the coal and excess air at combustion. Many methods are under development to reduce the formation of NO_x. The most promising of these seems to be the development of a new burner where the NO_x formation is cut down to a level of 20-25% of what can be expected today. Methods available today to lower formation of NO_x include combustion of coal in two steps, lower excess air, low preheating of the combustion air, and recirculation of the combustion gases. These methods combined may cut down the NO_x formation by 40-50%.

To make use of the ash is a very important problem which has to be solved. Today at least 25 different applications are known. These applications are now under study, with special emphasis on our climate and economics. The possibility of finding uses for the ash is good.

Dust and noise when transporting and storing coal is considered an environmental impact. Sweden's climate rarely allows dust to become a problem. However, for safety the systems already developed in other countries will be adopted, such as water-sprinkling and coal-dust-evacuation plants. The noise level will be lowered by using the know-how and experience of other countries.

The conclusion is that it should be possible to meet the requirements of the 80's, limiting the environmental impact of burning coal through techniques known today and/or in combination with the import of low-sulphur coal.

To meet the demands on the environment in the 90's and the next century, much research and development has to be undertaken. Probably not only will the impact levels set today be lowered, but also new types of demands will occur about which we are ignorant today. One example of a new problem is polyaromatic organic matter (POM) which is already starting to worry the public.

Methods used today will, of course, be developed to their limits, but they may not be sufficient. Therefore, much attention and hope is on the techniques of fluidized bed combustion (FBC), liquefaction, gasification and chemical cleaning of coal. These methods are being studied, especially the FBC. Several testing plants for different FBC systems are already in operation in Sweden. Their sizes are still small and it will be at least 15 years before this technology is developed to the point that it can make a considerable contribution to our energy production. The techniques of liquefaction and gasification are being demonstrated by pilot plants now in operation. Many problems remain, both technically and economically. Chemical cleaning of coal is still on the benches in the laboratories.

One common problem with all these new technologies is that we do not know what their total impact on the environment will be. We might solve the problems of keeping below the limits set for impact on air and water, but what will the total impact be when disposing of the final residue?

Finally, it is obvious that clean coal always makes the lowest impact on the environment. Countries which have their own coal have to burn it even if the coal contains a great many impurities. Sweden's lack of its own coal may, therefore, not be a disadvantage; if the market permits, it can give us the opportunity to import the coal which impacts the least on our environment.

IMPLEMENTING ACTIONS REQUIRED FOR THE TOTAL COAL SYSTEM

For the next 20 years our estimates show that there is a good possibility of expanding coal use in Sweden, especially in the electric sector and in plants for combined generation of electricity and heat. The possibilities of substituting coal for oil in district heating and in the industry sector are also good.

Considering the lead times needed to have this development in place in the 80's, it is necessary to start the planning and designing now. We must also overcome the institutional problems as well as convincing the public of the necessity of these actions.

The critical question for the further development is the environmental restrictions which will be imposed on the plant owners. This will determine where the plants will be located, the economics of coal burning, and whether there have to be flue gas desulfurization (FGD) installations.

To avoid FGD installations, Sweden must have access to low-sulphur coal. It is estimated that this will be possible if the production capacity in the exporting countries is expanded, and if the nuclear programs in the industrialized countries go ahead as planned. To secure coal supplies for the long run, it will be necessary for Swedish coal users and importers to participate in coal projects abroad.

The existing ports in Sweden will be able to take care of the small volumes of steam coal to be imported during the beginnings of the 1980's. As imports grow it will be necessary at some time to build a new, large coal terminal. Such a terminal can be located either on the Swedish west coast or in Denmark. The infrastructure (handling and distribution for the inland market) has to be developed. In the 80's most of the coal will be consumed in plants located at the coasts, but later on relatively more of the coal will be consumed in the interior parts of Sweden. On the inland market coal will compete to some extent with peat, firewood and other domestic energy raw materials.

As we have pointed out, the environmental restrictions can limit the use of coal and affect the quality of the coal that is required. For bigger units such as power plants, this can lead to the installation of FGD installations. For smaller units such as industrial boilers, it may be necessary to utilize installations of the fluidized bed type.

The disposal of coal ash and sludge from the scrubbers pose environmental problems. The Swedish government has instructed the State Power Board to investigate these problems. This investigation will take three years.

The lack of steam-coal consumption for the past 2-3 decades has led to a discontinuation of the infrastructure for coal and of the knowledge about how to use coal. There is, therefore, a need for a systems analysis about introducing coal to the Swedish energy system. In the project Coal 90, related questions are dealt with. Additional analysis has been made available in some of the government reports published in the autumn of 1979.

OBSTACLES AND CONSTRAINTS TO EXPANDED COAL USE

Besides the economic aspects, the main limitation on expanded coal use in Sweden is the uncertainty related to future environmental restrictions and the public's attitude toward coal. Therefore, the authorities who develop guidelines in this field must clarify what environmental standards will be imposed on the utility owners as soon as possible. For several reasons it will be necessary to build up the coal consumption step by step. This will make it possible to alter the plants as changes in environmental demands occur.

Because Sweden has no coal of its own, securing the future supply of coal is vital to the reduction of the country's dependence on oil.

If these problems can be solved, and if the legal procedures related especially to the siting of power plants could be speeded up, it would then be possible to reintroduce coal to the Swedish energy system at a rather high speed.

Summary Worksheet

I. Coal Use, Production, and Trade	1977	1985		1990		2000		1977-2000 Avg. annual growth—%/yr.	
		A	B	A	B	A	B	A	B
Coal use in major markets (mtce)									
Metallurgical	1.8	2.2	2.2	2.4	2.4	2.8	2.8	1.9	1.9
Electric	0	0.4	0.7	0.8	6.3	6.7	15.2	20.7[1]	22.8[1]
Industry	0.3	1.8	1.8	2.8	2.8	3.3	3.3	11.0	11.0
Synthetic Fuels	–	–	–	–	–	0.7	0.7	–[1]	–[1]
Residential/Commercial	0	0.7	0.7	1.5	2.4	3.6	3.9	7.4	8.1
Total coal use	2.1	5.1	5.4	7.5	13.9	17.1	25.9	9.6	11.5
Distribution of coal use by market sector (%)									
Metallurgical	86	43	41	32	17	17	11	—	—
Electric	0	8	13	11	46	39	58	—	—
Industry	14	35	33	37	20	19	13	—	—
Synthetic Fuels	–	–	–	–	–	4	3	—	—
Residential/Commercial	0	14	13	20	17	21	15	—	—
Total coal use	100%	100%	100%	100%	100%	100%	100%	—	—
Coal consumption/imports (mtce) Consumption									
Metallurgical	1.8	2.2	2.2	2.4	2.4	2.8	2.8	1.9	1.9
Steam	0.3	2.9	3.2	5.1	11.5	14.3	23.1	18.3	20.8
Total coal consumption	2.1	5.1	5.4	7.5	13.9	17.1	25.9	9.6	11.5
Imports									
Metallurgical	1.8	2.2	2.2	2.4	2.4	2.8	2.8	1.9	1.9
Steam	0.3	2.9	3.2	5.1	11.5	14.3	23.1	18.3	20.8
Total coal imports	2.1	5.1	5.4	7.5	13.9	17.1	25.9	9.6	11.5
Coal production/exports (mtce) Production									
Metallurgical									
Steam									
Total coal production									
Exports									
Metallurgical									
Steam									
Total coal export									

(1) From 1985.

Summary Worksheet

II. Coal's Role in Total Energy System	1977	1985		1990		2000		1977-2000 Avg. annual growth-%/yr.	
		A	B	A	B	A	B	A	B
Total Primary Energy Use (mtce)									
Oil, Domestic	0	--	--	--	--	--	--		
Oil, Imported	39	33	38	28	31	22	25	-2.5	-1.9
Gas, Domestic	--	--	--	--	--	--	--		
Gas, Imported	--	--	--	--	--	--	--		
Nuclear	6	14	6	18	1	18	--	4.9	--
Hydro, Solar, Other	20	26	26	29	30	34	34	2.3	2.3
Coal, Domestic	0	0	0	0	0	0	0		
Coal, Imported	2	5	5	7	14	17	26	9.6	11.5
Total energy use	67	78	75	82	76	91	85	1.3	1.0
Coal penetration (%)	3	6	7	9	19	19	30	—	—
Total primary energy (mtce) input to electricity									
Oil and Gas	4	1	4	1	4	1	1	-5.9	-5.9
Hydro, Solar, Other	16	20	20	21	21	22	22	1.4	1.4
Nuclear	6	14	6	18	1	18	--	4.9	--
Coal	0	0	1	1	6	7	15	13.9[1]	19.8[1]
Total energy input	26	35	31	41	32	48	38	2.7	1.7
Coal penetration (%)	0	1	2	2	20	14	39	—	—
Total electric capacity (GWe)									
Oil and Gas	7.9	7.4	7.5	6.0	6.6	3.7	4.7	-3.2	-2.2
Hydro, Solar, Other	13.1	16.2	16.2	16.9	17.1	17.8	18.2	1.3	1.4
Nuclear	3.8	8.4	3.1	9.5	--	9.5	--	4.1	--
Coal	0	0.6	0.9	1.3	6.5	8.2	11.6	19.0[1]	18.6[1]
Total capacity	24.8	32.6	27.7	33.7	30.2	39.2	34.5	2.0	1.0
Coal Penetration (%)	0	2	3	4	22	21	34	—	—
Peak load	5.2	9.7	7.6	7.6	8.9	8.0	8.7	1.9	2.3
Peak reserve margin (%)	21	30	27	23	29	20	25	—	—
Total oil imports (mbd)	0.55	0.52	0.60	0.44	0.49	0.36	0.39	-2.5	-1.9
Total oil consumption (mbd)									
Transportation	0.16	0.18	0.18	0.18	0.18	0.17	0.17	0.3	0.3
Residential/Commercial	0.20	0.17	0.19	0.12	0.13	0.05	0.08	-5.9	-3.9
Industry—Boilers	0.11	0.12	0.13	0.09	0.09	0.09	0.09	-0.9	-0.9
Industry—Other	0.03	0.04	0.04	0.04	0.04	0.04	0.04	1.3	1.3
Electric utilities	0.05	0.01	0.06	0.01	0.05	0.01	0.01	-6.8	-6.8
Total oil consumption	0.55	0.52	0.60	0.44	0.49	0.36	0.39	-2.5	-1.9
World oil price assumed for national coal analysis (1979 U.S. dollars/barrel)	$20*	24	24	28	28	34	34	2.6	2.6
Economic growth assumed for national coal analysis (GNP, billion 1978 dollars)	78	97	97	111	111	142	142	2.6	2.6

* Uses current price of $20/barrel (June 1979 U.S. dollars) as baseline world oil price and as floor price throughout the period.

(1) From 1985.

HYPOTHETICAL COAL TRADE FLOWS

WOCOL   Country: Sweden

Units: mtce

Trade Flows (indicated importer preferences)		1977	1990		2000	
			Low Coal	High Coal	Low Coal	High Coal
Australia	—Steam		1.8	4.0	4.0	6.7
	—Metallurgical		0.2	0.2	0.2	0.2
Canada	—Steam		0.8	1.5	3.0	4.7
	—Metallurgical		0.3	0.3	0.3	0.3
Germany, Federal Republic of	—Steam	} 0.4	-	-	-	-
	—Metallurgical		0.3	0.3	0.3	0.3
United Kingdom	—Steam		-	-	0.3	0.3
	—Metallurgical		0.2	0.2	0.2	0.2
United States	—Steam	} 0.3	0.3	1.0	1.5	2.4
	—Metallurgical		0.4	0.4	0.6	0.6
(Subtotal, OECD)	—Steam	( )	(2.9)	(6.5)	(8.8)	(14.1)
	—Metallurgical	( )	(1.4)	(1.4)	(1.6)	(1.6)
China, People's Republic of	—Steam				-	1.0
	—Metallurgical				-	-
Colombia	—Steam		0.7	1.0	1.5	2.0
	—Metallurgical		-	-	-	-
India	—Steam					
	—Metallurgical					
Indonesia	—Steam					
	—Metallurgical					
Poland	—Steam	} 0.3	1.5	3.5	3.5	5.5
	—Metallurgical		0.4	0.4	0.5	0.5
South Africa, Republic of	—Steam					
	—Metallurgical					
USSR	—Steam	} 0.6	-	0.5	0.5	0.5
	—Metallurgical		0.6	0.6	0.7	0.7
Other Countries	—Steam					
	—Metallurgical					
(Subtotal, Non-OECD)	—Steam	( )	(2.2)	(5.0)	(5.5)	(9.0)
	—Metallurgical	( )	(1.0)	(1.0)	(1.2)	(1.2)
Total Required Imports	—Steam	[1] 0.3	5.1	11.5	14.3	23.1
	—Metallurgical	1.8	2.4	2.4	2.8	2.8
	—Total Coal	2.1	7.5	13.9	17.1	25.9

[1] Including others 0.5 mtce

COAL USE IN FINAL DEMAND SECTORS

WOCOL

Country: Sweden

Units: mtce

Coal Market Sector	1977	1985		1990		1995		2000	
		Low Coal	High Coal	Low Coal	High Coal	Low Coal	High Coal	Low Coal	High Coal
Electric	0	0.4	0.7	0.8	6.3			6.7	15.2
Industry	0.3	1.8	1.8	2.8	2.8			3.3	3.3
Metallurgical	1.8	2.2	2.2	2.4	2.4			2.8	2.8
Synthetic Fuels	–	–	–	–	–			0.7	0.7
Residential/Commercial	0	0.7	0.7	1.5	2.4			3.6	3.9
Total Coal Use	2.1	5.1	5.4	7.5	13.9			17.1	25.9
Total Primary Energy Use	67	78	75	82	76			91	85
Coal Penetration (%)									
Total Energy	3	6	7	9	19			19	30
Electricity	0	1	2	2	20			14	39
Industry[1]	9	17	18	22	22			23	24

1 Including metallurgical coal

TOTAL ELECTRICITY BALANCE

Country: Sweden

Units: mtce/yr. fuel input

WOCOL

Power Plant Type	1977	1985 Low Coal	1985 High Coal	1990 Low Coal	1990 High Coal	1995 Low Coal	1995 High Coal	2000 Low Coal	2000 High Coal
Nuclear	6	14	6	18	1			18	–
Hydro/Pumped Storage	16	20	20	20	20			20	20
Gas Turbines/Combined Cycle	0	–	–	–	–			–	–
Geothermal/Solar/Other	0	0	0	1	1			2	2
Fossil Steam									
Oil Steam	4	1	4	1	4			1	1
Gas Steam	–	–	–	–	–			–	–
Coal Steam	0	0	1	1	6			7	15
Total Primary Fuel Input	26	35	31	41	32			48	38
Coal Penetration (%)	0	1	2	2	20			14	39

TOTAL PRIMARY ENERGY CONSUMPTION

WOCOL Country: Sweden
Units: mtce

Energy Source	1977	1985 Low Coal	1985 High Coal	1990 Low Coal	1990 High Coal	1995 Low Coal	1995 High Coal	2000 Low Coal	2000 High Coal
Domestic Oil —Conventional	0	–	–	–	–			–	–
—Unconventional									
Imported Oil	39	33	38	28	31			22	25
Oil Subtotal	39	33	38	28	31			22	25
Domestic Gas —Conventional									
—Unconventional									
Imported Gas									
Gas Subtotal									
Hydro/Geo/Solar	20	26	26	29	30			34	34
Nuclear	6	14	6	18	1			18	–
Domestic Coal	0	0	0	0	0			0	0
Imported Coal	2	5	5	7	14			17	26
Coal Subtotal	2	5	5	7	14			17	26
Total Primary Energy Use	67	78	75	82	76			91	85
Coal Penetration (%)	3	6	7	9	19			19	30

TOTAL ELECTRICITY BALANCE

WOCOL

Country: Sweden

Units: GWe capacity

Power Plant Type	1977	1985 Low Coal	1985 High Coal	1990 Low Coal	1990 High Coal	1995 Low Coal	1995 High Coal	2000 Low Coal	2000 High Coal
Nuclear	3.8	8.4	3.1	9.5	–			9.5	–
Hydro/Pumped Storage	13.1	15.9	15.9	16.2	16.2			16.7	16.7
Gas Turbines/Combined Cycle	1.7	1.8	1.8	1.8	1.8			1.8	1.8
Geothermal/Solar/Other	0	0.4	0.4	0.8	1.0			1.2	1.6
Fossil Steam									
Oil Steam	6.2	5.5	5.6	4.1	4.7			1.8	2.8
Gas Steam	–	–	–	–	–			–	–
Coal Steam	(0.4)	0.6	0.9	1.3	6.5			8.2	11.6
Total Electric Capacity	24.8	32.6	27.7	33.7	30.2			39.2	34.5
Coal Penetration (%)	(2)	2	3	4	22			21	34

CHAPTER 15

UNITED KINGDOM

SUMMARY AND CONCLUSIONS

The UK, in common with the rest of the world, is faced with the prospect of seeking to maintain economic growth against a background of increasingly limited oil supplies. Unlike many other countries, the UK is fortunate in having oil and gas reserves which will give self-sufficiency in energy for a limited period, but during the Nineties indigenous production of oil and gas based on present reserve estimates will decline and the UK will have to adjust to importing oil again. This additional burden on the balance of payments will place considerable strain on the already weak UK economy.

Against this background successive UK Governments have adopted a strategy based on the complementary development of conservation, coal and nuclear. Through its ownership and part ownership of a large proportion of the energy sector in the UK, its role as regulator, its determination of the tax regime, and as final arbiter of the national interest, the UK Government plays a central role in determining the direction and outcome of UK energy policy. The projections included in the UK National Report for use in the WOCOL study are therefore based on the pursuance of the Government's chosen strategy.

If increasing demands of oil for transport fuels, chemical feedstocks and other premium uses are to be met, and at the same time the total demand for oil is to be kept constant or reduced, the nonpremium uses of oil, mainly fuel oil used for bulk heat production, must be minimised. Coal is best able to contribute to this through increased direct combustion in large-scale applications. Coal will therefore meet the lion's share of the fossil-fuel burn in power stations and will play an increasingly important role in the industrial market. Existing coal-fired power stations will need to be refurbished and supplemented by some new stations in order to maintain sufficient coal-burning capacity. Increasing coal demand in industry will depend on decisions by many individual firms. This process of change may be too slow, requiring some additional encouragement. Coal conversion plants are unlikely to play an important commercial role this century, but, given the long lead times, there should be an early commitment to demonstration plants for future use.

With a large resource base of coal, the UK is well placed to expand coal production. Only a small proportion of UK coal is minable by opencast methods and therefore an expansion of deep-mined capacity is called for. Two decades of declining demand for coal from the mid-fifties to the early Seventies led to an industry starved of investment and badly in need of new capacity. After the oil crisis in 1973-74, Plan for Coal was launched to achieve higher capacity

369

and productivity through a programme of exploration, investment, and R & D. The investment programme has now built up to over 0.5 billion pounds per year and it is essential that this momentum is maintained, that new capacity is brought in to replace exhausted capacity and that production is built up to meet the challenge of a growing demand. This requires continuity of government policy and the avoidance of planning delays.

All this must be carried out in an environmentally responsible manner, the impacts of coal being weighed against those of other fuels and the cost of controlling the impacts being set against the benefits achieved. In the past, improved environmental standards have been achieved by introducing the best practical technology as it becomes available and a continuation of this approach is envisaged.

As far as coal trade is concerned, the UK is largely self-contained, a few million tonnes being both imported and exported each year. Broadly, this position is likely to continue and the UK is unlikely to be an important element in the international market. However, if either home demand fell short of the projections for a period or if slippage delayed the buildup of production, trade could become important.

By international standards, UK coal is transported only very short distances, mainly by rail, and there should be no difficulty in expanding the existing rail network to meet the growing demand. Existing ports are sufficient to handle the coastal trade and some increase in international trade. Steam-coal imports are, at present, transhipped via Rotterdam and if trade does develop, additional port facilities or coastal power stations capable of taking larger ships could be developed.

The UK Participants believe that the developments for coal outlined in this report provide an opportunity that will be extremely demanding, both for the producers and users of coal. The postwar period of confident economic growth is now over and we face a period of uncertainty, unsatisfied ambitions, shocks to the system, and increasing social, economic and political tensions. Against such a background it is difficult to act with confidence, to identify and commit resources to a particular direction. We are, however, convinced that the case for developing the production and use of coal in the UK is compelling. It is only by each country committing itself to reducing the world demand for oil by using it efficiently, and by developing vigorously those alternatives that each country has available, that the global problem of limited oil availability can be met.

ORGANISATION OF THE WOCOL STUDY

INTRODUCTION

The World Coal Study is an international project involving about seventy-five individuals from sixteen major potential coal importing or exporting countries. Its objective is to examine the future needs for coal in the total energy system and to assess the prospects for expanding world coal production, utilisation, and trade to meet these needs. The study includes (a) the identification of likely constraints to increased coal production and use; and (b) development of desirable policies to lessen constraints and uncertainties and to reduce lead times in order to meet future needs for coal.

OBJECTIVES

A purpose of the World Coal Study is to highlight the period of transition when coal must begin to replace oil and gas and the quantities of coal that are likely to be required. To replace one million barrels of oil per day (approximates 50 million tons of oil per year) will require about 80 million metric tons of coal per year for direct consumption, and even larger quantities, if coal is converted to synthetic fuels. Placing coal in its proper economic perspective during this transition period will be an important aspect of the study. A result of this study should be better preparedness to meet the increased demand for coal. By engaging the cooperative efforts of leading persons from government, industry and academia —acting as individuals—from the principal coal-using and producing countries to carry out the study, the prospects for influencing policy and action will be greatly enhanced.

ORGANISATION

These considerations have led to the formation of a World Coal Study under the leadership of Professor Carroll L. Wilson of the Massachusetts Institute of Technology (MIT). The organisation includes:

The Participants: 35 key industrial, governmental and academic people from sixteen countries who have experience in the coal and energy field, who provide the overall study direction.

The Associates: provided by most Participants, who take part in the work program needed as the basis for the findings and conclusions of the study.

The Project Director: who provides executive leadership for all parts of the project.

The Project Staff: at the MIT School of Engineering for project coordination.

THE UK NATIONAL TEAM

In the study participants and associates act as individuals and this report should not be taken as representing the views of any public or private organisation with which they may be associated. As with the study as a 'whole', no single member of the UK national team had either the time or expertise to judge every topic covered; in particular the section on production relies on the specialist knowledge of the NCB members. The report has sought the consensus of the majority, and it is accepted that each member does not necessarily subscribe to all of the statements in the report. Nevertheless, all members of the UK National team agree on the general analysis and main findings of this report.

The members of the UK national team are:

PARTICIPANT

Robert Belgrave
Director, BP Trading Co. Ltd.
Policy Adviser to the Board
British Petroleum Company
London

ASSOCIATES

Bill Limond
Ken McKinlay

PARTICIPANT	ASSOCIATES
Sir Derek Ezra Chairman National Coal Board London	Richard Ormerod Michael Parker
Professor Sir William Hawthorne Chairman, Advisory Council on Energy Conservation Master, Churchill College Cambridge	
Sir Ronald McIntosh Executive Director S.G. Warburg & Co. Ltd., London Former Director General of National Economic Development Office	Peter Horrobin
Frank Pecchioli Managing Director, Shell Coal International Ltd. London	Brian Elms

ENERGY AND COAL DEMAND

INTRODUCTION

The UK energy situation is characterised by:

- A slowly growing economy, and hence, demand for energy
- Indigenous reserves of oil, gas and coal
- A slowly growing nuclear contribution
- A large integrated electricity network
- Short distances between production and markets of coal
- Heavy involvement of government through ownership of the coal, gas, electricity industries and part-ownership of oil.

Within this context the UK coal industry, which has seen the decline of the Sixties levelled off in the Seventies, is projected to grow through to 2000 to help meet a growing demand for energy as indigenous supplies of oil and gas diminish and imports are increasingly difficult to obtain.

The UK faces wide choices as to the timing and extent of the development of its indigenous resources as discussed in the 1978 Government consultative Green Paper on Energy Policy (1). The UK has to be considered within the context of world energy developments and, in particular, within the context of IEA and EEC commitments. Despite the present availability of indigenous oil and gas, the long-term emphasis in the UK is directed toward complementary development of conservation, coal and nuclear. All three will need to be pursued vigorously for the UK to adjust to the decreasing availability of both indigenous and world supplies of oil and gas by the turn of the century.

372

The coal industry has the demanding task of reversing a long period of decline and lack of investment. Plan for Coal (2), an investment programme agreed upon between the National Coal Board, the government and the mining industry unions, seeks to provide replacement and new capacity, together with the necessary exploration and R & D. programmes. Launched in 1974, and initially covering the period to 1985, some projects are already completed and the first results from the programme are now beginning to be seen. The outcome of this programme, extended to 2000, will determine the size and contribution of the UK coal industry by the turn of the century.

THE UK ENERGY SITUATION

The two most significant features of the UK's national energy situation since 1970 have been the negligible growth in total demand and the progress toward net self-sufficiency in energy. As Table 15-1 shows, inland energy demand in 1975 and 1976 was significantly below, and demand in 1978 still had not reached, the peak level of 1973. This has been the result of

- Economic stagnation,
- Conservation induced by higher energy prices and other measures (particularly lower levels of activity),
- Recession in the steel industry, and
- Increasing use of natural gas.

Table 15-1. UK Primary Energy Consumption (mtce*)

Inland Primary Energy Consumption	Total	Coal	Oil	Natural Gas	Nuclear	Hydro
1970	334.9	156.9	147.9	17.9	9.6	2.6
1971	331.1	140.9	149.7	28.9	9.9	1.8
1972	336.6	122.8	160.1	40.9	10.8	2.0
1973	353.5	133.0	164.2	44.2	10.1	2.1
1974	337.5	117.9	152.5	52.9	12.1	2.1
1975	324.8	120.0	136.5	55.4	10.9	2.0
1976	329.8	122.0	134.2	58.8	12.9	1.9
1977	338.4	122.7	136.6	62.8	14.3	2.0
1978	338.6	119.7	139.1	64.3	13.4	2.1
1979		128.9				

* Note that mtce here refers to the UK definition of 1 mtce = .025 Quadrillion BTU

Some of these factors will have a continuing influence in the years to come and, therefore, the historic relationship between economic growth and energy demand can be expected to change. The extent of this change has been the subject of vigorous debate in the UK recently (3) and, although the question is by no means resolved, considerable reductions in energy demand forecasts have resulted.

Oil was first consumed in greater quantities than coal in the UK as recently as 1971, though by 1973 oil's contribution was significantly higher. The oil crisis of 1973-74 caused a drop in oil consumption and since then demand has risen only gradually. Production of North Sea oil is now rising to the level of UK demand but oil is still both imported and exported in large quantities in order to make the best use of the North Sea oil's high quality and the existing refinery pattern, both in the UK and on the Continent. It is important to note that the growing production of North Sea oil has no direct effect on the consumption of oil as it is sold at world prices. The level of reserves and depletion policy for oil, however, do have indirect effects on energy demand through the stimulus given to the economy via the balance of payments, government income and employment benefits.

UK North Sea gas production, on the other hand, has a very direct effect on the consumption of gas and hence competing fuels because all the gas is consumed in the UK. All natural gas in UK waters must be landed in the UK and the British Gas Corporation has the monopoly to buy all the gas landed for sale in the UK. This permits UK gas to be priced independently of world energy prices while supplies last. The changeover from town gas has been both rapid and total, resulting in a 260% increase in gas demand between 1970 and 1978 within a stagnant total energy demand.

Uncertainty surrounds the ultimate reserve levels of both North Sea oil and gas. The 1979 government estimates (4) give ultimately recoverable reserves as 2.4-4.4 btoe (3.4-6.3 btce) for oil and 35-80 tcf (0.8-2.2 btce) for natural gas. On present expectations of reserve and production levels it is likely that both oil and gas production will be declining before the end of the century.

Despite Britain's early lead in the development of civil nuclear power and the successful Magnox programme, the next phase of nuclear development based on Advanced Gas Reactors (AGR) has had problems and setbacks. Delays and cost escalations, resulting in a very slow growth in nuclear contribution, have led to uncertainty as to the future course of nuclear policy. Some of the uncertainty has been resolved with the recent government announcement of future ordering intentions. Nevertheless, the ultimate size of the nuclear programme, the reactor choice, the ability of the nuclear industry to mount a substantial programme in the face of opposition to nuclear power, recent performance and organisational problems remain unresolved. This study assumes that substantial nuclear development will be achieved, the upper limit being set by the maximum of 40 GW estimated by the Department of Energy.

In 1978 domestic energy production was able to supply about three-quarters of inland energy demand. As Table 15-2 shows, after oil the greatest level of imports occurred in gas, mainly from the Norwegian sector of the North Sea. However, total indigenous energy production could rise over approximately the next 10 years so that the UK can expect to be self-sufficient for a period. In the light of the uncertainties surrounding future world supplies of energy, self-sufficiency, or at least minimising the levels of imports, will be a continuing goal.

Table 15-2.   UK Dependency on Energy Imports 1978

	Total Consumption mtce	Net Imports mtce	% of Product Total Consumption
Coal	120	1	less than 1%
Oil	139	70	50%
Natural Gas	64	7	11%
Total (including primary electricity)	339	78	23%

* Net imports = total imports minus exports

374

Political factors also influence UK energy production. For example, UK indigenous production is an important element within the EEC and IEA and production may be affected by subsidies to encourage conversion to coal and intra-community trade, as well as commitments by the government to reduce imports of oil. The coal, gas and electricity industries in the UK are fully nationalised and the government, through the British National Oil Corporation and its shareholding in BP, has interests in oil. These industries account for a substantial proportion of the country's GNP, employment and capital investment. So far as the wholly government-owned corporations are concerned, considerations other than those of energy policy may be imposed by government in order to achieve wider economic and social goals such as:

- Enhanced economic growth
- Reduced unemployment
- Control of inflation
- Control of the money supply
- Regional development
- Environmental protection.

These general policy objectives translate into specific goals via investment criteria, pricing policies, cash limits, grants and profit objectives and impact on the ability to restructure and expand via control of investment and planning enquiries into new facilities.

THE ROLE OF COAL

In meeting over one-third of the country's inland primary energy demand, coal supplies a variety of markets. Coal is at its most competitive against oil in the iron and steel industries where coking coal has valuable qualities over and above its heat content. Beyond the applications where coal is used for its chemical and physical, as well as its combustion properties, coal is most competitive in bulk combustion applications where advantage can be taken of the size of application. Thus the power-station market for coal has continued expanding through the period of overall market decline and now accounts for some two-thirds of total UK coal consumption. It is in bulk steam raising in power stations and large industrial boilers that coal can most economically replace heavy fuel oil. Such a development will be greatly assisted by the development of the Industrial Fluidised Bed that is at the front of a vigorous coal utilisation R & D programme designed to improve combustion and conversion technology. In the longer term, the development of liquefaction and gasification technology may provide further opportunities for coal use.

The development of the production of coal in the UK is the responsibility of the National Coal Board (NCB). The NCB is the largest single coal undertaking in the Western World, producing some 120 million tonnes, employing over a quarter of a million people and operating 220 deep-mined pits as well as opencast sites. The NCB is wholly government-owned, created by nationalisation in 1947. The Board is responsible for the running of the industry and is accountable to the Secretary of State for Energy and, ultimately, Parliament. In recent years considerable use has been made of Tripartite Meetings between management, unions and government to agree to industry objectives and strategy. Such meetings have endorsed the investment programme, 'Plan for Coal', and the report by the Tripartite Research and Development Working Party entitled 'Coal Technology:

Future developments in Conversion, Utilisation and Unconventional Mining in the United Kingdom'. (5)

The task of expanding production after the rundown of investment in the Sixties is a demanding one. The objective of the coal industry is to expand production in an economic and environmentally responsible manner. An extensive exploration programme is showing that the coal is available and investment is now running at about 1 billion dollars per year. In deep mining, lead times are long and only now are the first results of the investment programme starting to show through. The full impact will be apparent when the new pits, including the 10 million tonnes per annum Selby project, start to build up production during the Eighties. The targets set in the aftermath of the 1973-74 oil price increase were ambitious, but there is little doubt that a healthy expanding coal industry will be a valuable asset in the difficult years ahead as the world adjusts to limited availability of oil and gas.

OUTLINE OF THE WOCOL CASES

The UK, in line with other country teams, has considered two cases. The first case assumed that a high coal consumption arises from high economic growth, high oil prices and generally successful pursuit of expanded coal production. The low case, on the other hand assumes a more moderate increase in coal consumption resulting from lower economic growth, lower oil prices and lower production of coal. Both cases use 1977 as the base year and project forward to 2000.

HIGH COAL CASE

The High Coal Case implies an economic growth rate of 3% per annum. This rate is high for the UK in historical terms:

	1950-60	1960-70	1970-77
UK Economic Growth % per annum	2.5	2.8	1.4

However, such a growth rate would enable society's aspirations to be met while avoiding growing unemployment. The growth rate assumes a successful economic outcome based on North Sea oil partially lifting the balance of payments constraint. It also assumes that the world economy and international trade are buoyant.

The second key assumption was that the oil price would rise in line with the UK Department of Energy oil price projection. At the time of the analysis (early 1979) the world oil price stood at $14.5/barrel. Oil prices were held constant in dollar terms to 1982, increasing thereafter to a level of approximately $35/barrel (early 1979 US dollars).*

Both nuclear and coal expansion programmes are assumed to:

• Receive continuous government support
• Not suffer from planning delays
• Not be subjected to further environmental and safety legislation.

LOW COAL CASE

The Low Coal Case assumes less success in pursuing economic and energy goals against a background of more modest world economic growth and interna-

---

* Since this report was prepared the price of crude oil has risen to $30 per barrel (Jan. 1980 dollars).

tional trade. An economic growth rate of 2% per annum is assumed.

The oil price was assumed to rise rather more slowly staying constant at $14.5/barrel (early 1979 dollars) to 1985 rising to $25/barrel in 2000.

Both nuclear and coal are assumed to reach lower levels of production suffering particularly from planning and construction delays. However, higher levels of conservation are assumed than in the High Coal Case.

NORTH SEA OIL AND GAS

The production of North Sea oil is assumed to build up from the 1977 level of 0.9 million barrels/day to a plateau of 2.5 million barrels/day in 1985 and 1990, falling to 1.0 million barrels/day in 2000. This projection takes into account the Government's estimates of reserves.

Total remaining recoverable gas reserves of 70 trillion cubic feet are assumed and government policy to conserve gas reserves by limiting nonpremium use in the industrial market are taken to limit gas sales to 77 mtce** in 1985 and 1990. By 2000, gas production is assumed to have fallen to 63 mtce in the High Coal Case and 54 mtce in the Low Coal Case. With the reserves assumed, the fall thereafter would be rapid.

ENERGY DEMAND AND CONSERVATION

The impact of higher energy prices on conservation and hence energy demand, despite recent experience, remains uncertain. It is not clear to what degree economic growth and energy growth can be decoupled and therefore, consistent scenarios of economic growth-energy demand-conservation-energy prices are difficult to develop. The approaches to the problem can be broadly classified as *either* analysis of the overall economics (aggregated approach) *or* detailed analysis of requirements (disaggregated approach).

The approach taken in this analysis has been to adopt a moderately disaggregated sectoral approach using the NCB's Energy Model (7) checking for overall consistency using an energy-economy model (8). A summary of the overall economic and energy assumptions for the WOCOL High Coal and Low Coal Cases is given in Figures 15-1 and 15-2.

The sections that follow give the detailed analysis of coal demand, production and trade including the WOCOL concept of coal chains followed by sections on R & D and environmental issues. After the main assumptions of the two cases had been set and the analysis carried out, the impact of the supply shortage became apparent (9). It was decided therefore that a sensitivity analysis involving lower oil consumption should be carried out and this is reported in a later section.

In the section on comparisons with other studies, the results of the two cases are summarised and compared with other recent studies of the UK.

DEMAND FOR COAL

Demand projections for coal can be approached either by examining the overall UK demand for energy and then considering the role that coal might play within the overall total or by considering the detailed requirements in the home, on the road, and at the workplace in order to build up the demand for energy and

---

** Unless stated otherwise, mtce refers throughout to the adopted WOCOL definition of 0.0277 Quadrillion Btu's per tonne, 277 Therms per tonne or 7,000 kcal per kilogramme.

Figure 15-1.   Overall Assumptions for UK WOCOL Cases (2000)

Assumptions	WOCOL Low Coal Case	WOCOL High Coal Case
World Oil Price (early 1979 US $)	25 dollars/barrel	35 dollars/barrel
GNP Growth (1977-2000)	2% pa	3% pa
Primary Energy Use	358 mtce	448 mtce
Energy Coefficient	0.35	0.57
Electricity Generation (1977-2000)	2% pa	3% pa
Nuclear Power Capacity	26 GWe	40 GWe
UK Coal Production	133 mtce	162 mtce
Coal Imports/Exports	Net Zero	Net Imports of 17 mtce
North Sea Oil Production	Rising to a plateau of 2.5 mbbl/day in 1985 and 1990, falling to 1.0 mbbl/day in 2000.	
North Sea Gas Production	Rising to a plateau of 5,670 mcfd (76.7 mtce) in 1985 and 1990 falling to 4,670 mcfd (63.2 mtce) in High Coal Case and 4,000 mcfd (54.2 mtce) in Low Coal Case in 2000.	

coal. The UK WOCOL analysis has approached this question from both directions, arriving at a sectoral demand analysis which will be described in the sections that follow.

An important emphasis in the demand analysis is that coal demand is derived from the ownership and use of coal-burning equipment. This has the following implications:

- The analysis must start with the existing stock of coal-fired appliances.
- The change in this stock will be determined by the age profile, the lead times and the desire of the consumer to switch fuels.
- Coal use is derived from the projected appliance stock taking into account level of activity, efficiency and conservation.
- New technology can only be introduced as fast as the stock of appliances is renewed.

In 1977 the total consumption of coal broken down by market sector was as follows:

	m. tonnes	%
Power Stations	80	64
Industry	10	8
Coke Ovens	17	14
Domestic & Commercial	17	14
Total Coal Consumption	124	100

Each of these sectors, together with the possible future market for synthetic fuel production are discussed in the sections that follow.

POWER STATION DEMAND

When coal competes against other fuels, and in particular against oil, it suffers certain disadvantages. For a given output, coal-fired boilers tend to be larger than

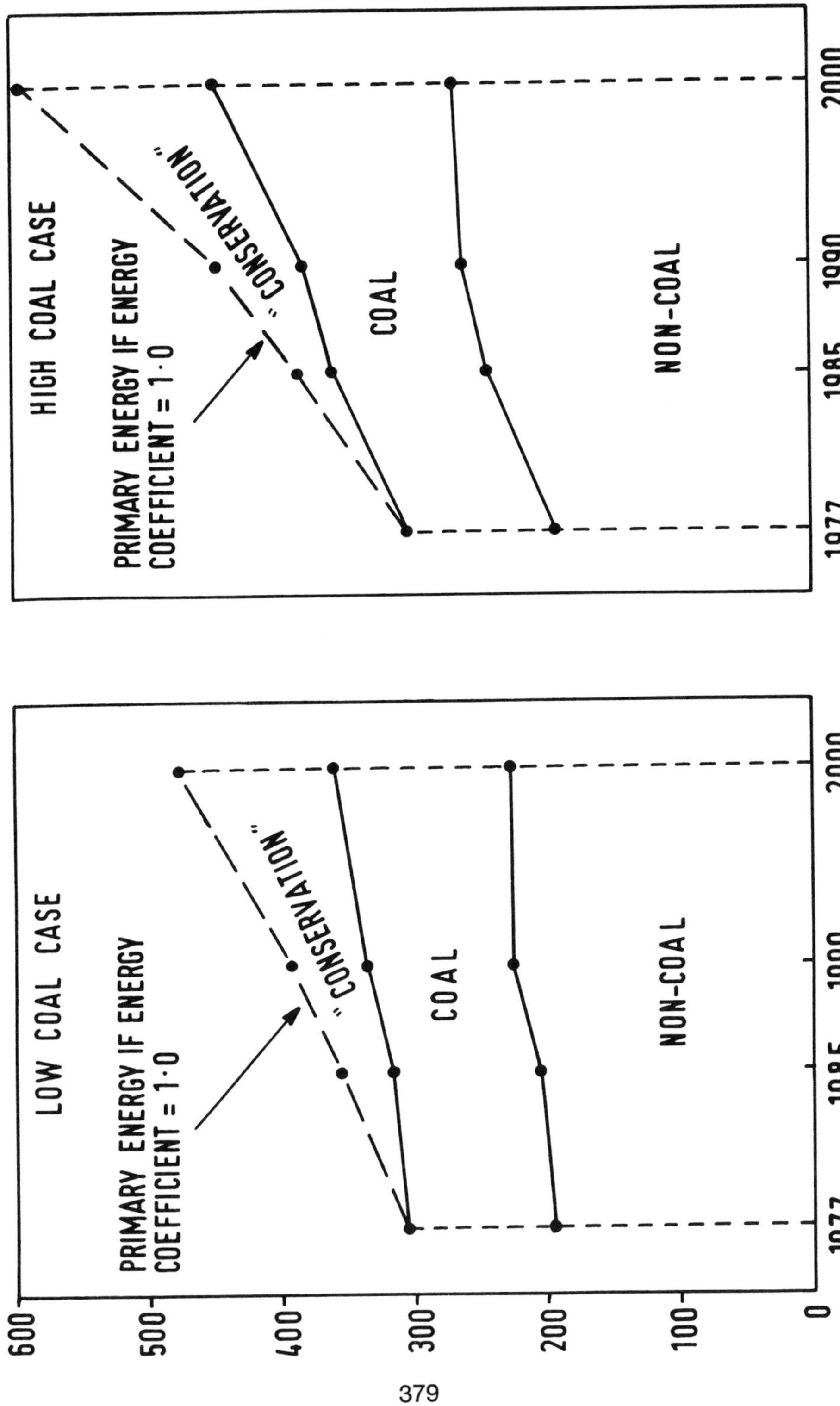

Figure 15-2. U.K. Total Energy Use (mtce)

the oil equivalent and require additional equipment to handle the fuel input and the ash output. Coal can therefore be considerably more capital-intensive than oil. In addition, the handling and stocking of the coal and the disposal of the by-products involve operating costs. These disadvantages are minimised with large-scale use where the equipment is being used intensively. Such a case is the use of coal in power stations and, while the demand for coal in the UK has declined, the demand for power-station coal has steadily increased:

Power Station Coal Demand	m. tonnes	% of total Inland Coal
1950	33	16
1960	51	26
1970/71	74	50
1977/78	78	65

The electricity-generating industry in the UK consists of four utilities which have capacity as follows:

		GWe
England and Wales	CEGB	56½
South of Scotland	SSEB	7½
North of Scotland	NSHB	1½
Northern Ireland	NIJEA	2

The NSHB has mostly hydroelectricity, the NIJEA has only oil-fired capacity and therefore we are concerned here with the CEGB and SSEB. England, Scotland and Wales are integrated with 9,160-circuit kilometres of 400 kv grid. Apart from a 186-MW link to France, the system is isolated from continental Europe.

In 1977 the UK capacity was fuelled as follows:

	GWE
Coal	41½
Oil	13
Nuclear	5½
Coal/Oil	2
Coal/Gas	1½
Hydro, Gas Turbines, etc.	4½

The small amount of dual-fired capacity operates today on coal.

Starting from today's existing capacity and power stations already under construction, the logic outlined in Figure 15-3 was followed to derive the future demand for power-station coal.

Electricity generation in the UK in the Fifties and Sixties increased at about 7% per annum, as shown in Figure 15-4. This growth was assisted in the late Sixties by the rapid growth in the sales of off-peak electricity which are now declining, as shown in Figure 15-5. The decline in overall growth rate has left the generating industry with considerable excess capacity. The result of these changes has been as follows:

Figure 15-3. Derived Demand for Coal in the Electricity Market

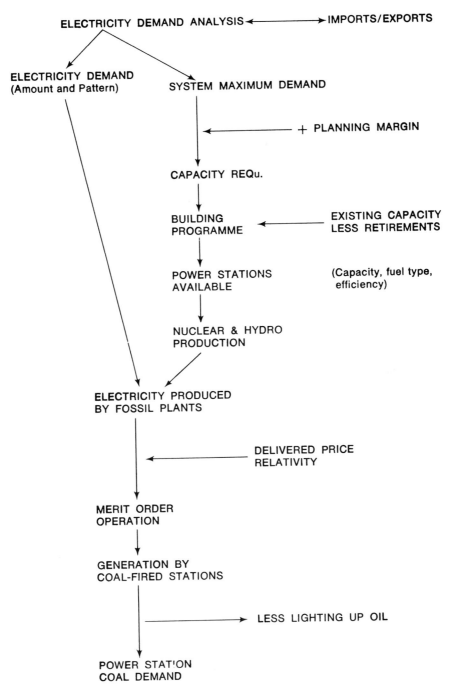

Great Britain (England, Scotland and Wales)

	1967	1977
Simultaneous Maximum Demand* (GW)	40	48½
Generation TWh	188	256
System Load Factor* %	50½	56½
Plant Load Factor* %	45½	41½

*For definitions of these terms, see the Digest of United Kingdom Energy Statistics 1979, HMSO.

It has been assumed that System Load Factor will further increase to 59½% in 2000 and that the demand for electricity will grow at 2% in the Low Coal Case and 3% in the High Coal Case, resulting in a growth in SMD (Simultaneous Maximum Demand) as follows:

UK (GB & NI)		1977	1985	1900	2000
SMD	High	50	62	71	93
	Low	50	57	62	75

The planning margin, recently increased to 28%, is assumed to remain constant but due to slippage in the building programme lower margins are achieved.

Figure 15-4. U.K. Electricity Generated

Source: Energy Trends.

Figure 15-5.   Off-Peak Sales of Electricity

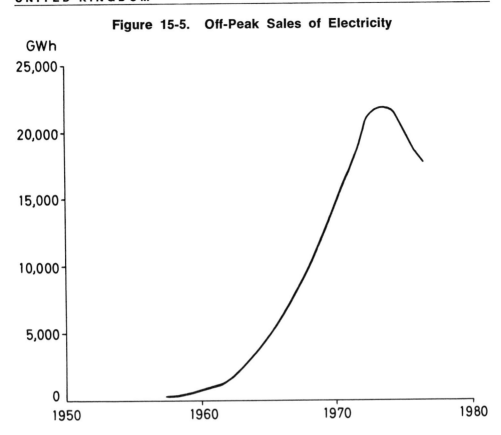

Source: Handbook of Electricity Supply Statistics 1977.

A key assumption is the level of nuclear capacity that will be built by 2000. Despite Britain's early start in the civil nuclear field and the success of the Magnox reactors, the UK nuclear industry has been slow to expand. The AGR programme has had technical problems and construction delays. The nuclear construction industry meanwhile has failed to win further orders at home or abroad. It has been assumed, therefore, for this study that between 26 Gwe (Low Coal Case) and 40 GWe (High Coal Case) of nuclear will be available in 2000. Though the CEGB maintain that higher levels could be achieved, the 40 GWe is based on the Department of Energy's estimate of the maximum possible by 2000 (10).

The resulting generating capacity after allowance for slippage was therefore projected as follows:

$$GWe$$

	Actual 1977 m	1985		1900		2000	
		Low Coal Case	High Coal Case	Low Coal Case	High Coal Case	Low Coal Case	High Coal Case
Coal-Fired	45	44	44	44	45	44	55
Nuclear	5	10	10	14	17	26	40
Total	67	77	78	80	87	90	115

Figure 15-6 shows the profile of UK capacity if stations are retired after 30 years and no new stations are ordered over that indicated. Thus, a substantial programme of new and refurbished capacity needs to be launched to meet the SMD plus planning margin targets in 2000. The capacity in 1990, on the other hand, is very largely determined already. Typical lead times (see Figure 15-7) mean that plants not already approved stand little chance of being commissioned by 1990.

Finally, based on the efficiencies of the stations, the delivered fuel prices and the demand variation through time, the operation of the UK generating system was simulated using the NCB Energy Model (11) to give fuel requirements shown in the WOCOL Summary Worksheet at the end of the report. This shows that power-station-coal demand in the Low Coal Case builds up to 85 million tonnes (69 mtce) in 1990 but remains constant to 2000 in the Low Coal Case as nuclear increasingly meets the base load demand, while in the High Coal Case demand builds up to 95 million tonnes (77 mtce) in 2000.

Figure 15-6. U.K. Generating Capacity

Based on :- 1. Existing Capacity retired after 30 years

2. Capacity under construction

3. Two additional AGR's approved

4. One PWR

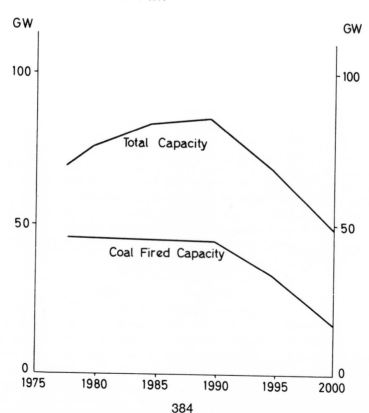

Figure 15-7. Power Station Lead Times

Station	Fuel	Spec. Cap. GWe	Net Cap. GWe	Start On-Site	Commissioning Complete
GRAIN	OIL	3.3	3.3	1971	1981
INCE B	OIL	1.0	1.0	1972	1982
LITTLEBROOK D	OIL	2.0	2.0	1974	1983
DUNGENESS B	NUC	1.3	1.2	1966	1981
HARTLEPOOL	NUC	1.3	1.2	1968	1982
HEYSHAM	NUC	1.3	1.2	1970	1982
HINKLEY PT B	NUC	0.7	0.6	1967	1978
DRAX B	COAL	2.0	2.0	1978	1986
DINORWIC	PUMPED STORAGE	1.5	1.5	1974	1983

INDUSTRIAL DEMAND

In the UK coal has very largely been replaced in the industrial market by oil, and more recently, gas. The industrial market is very diverse and the requirements vary considerably from one industrial sector to another and from one factory to another. A number of industries have applications where one particular fuel has advantages such as convenience, cleanliness or ease of control. Coal, for instance is the favoured fuel for cement production. However, coal is largely used in the 'nonpremium' or bulk heat uses, which are predominantly bulk steam raising for heat and process uses.

The demand for bulk heat is derived, as indicated in Figure 15-8, by deducting the 'premium' uses from the projected sectional energy demands. As in the power-station market, the starting point is the existing boiler stock and the age of plant. This information is only now becoming available in detail via a research project conducted by the Science Policy Research Unit at Sussex University (12) which shows, for instance, that coal boilers are considerably older than oil and gas boilers (see Figure 15-9).

The decision to replace an existing boiler and the choice of fuel for new capacity will depend on the costs as perceived by the consumer. These in turn depend on such factors as the size of the demand to be met, the temperature of the heat required and the proximity to a coalfield. Coal may suffer in competition with oil on three counts:

- Lower efficiency of combustion.
- Higher capital costs.
- Higher maintenance and operating costs.

These disadvantages are particularly acute for small-scale uses but in the larger applications fuel costs dominate and coal can expect to make early gains in the market.

Extensive research and development is now being undertaken in the UK to reduce all the present disadvantages of coal. Fluidised beds with automated materials handling now being tested in the field, indicate a potential for higher efficiency, lower capital costs and lower operating costs. The combination of this new technology, the substantial price advantage coal could have over oil together with the reducing availability of natural gas for industry suggests that the industrial use of coal could expand rapidly.

385

Figure 15-8. Derived Demand for Coal in the Industrial Sectors (other than Iron and Steel)

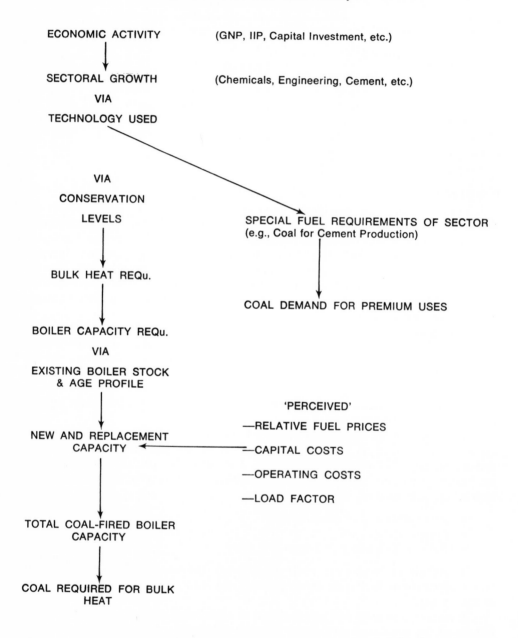

ECONOMIC ACTIVITY   (GNP, IIP, Capital Investment, etc.)

SECTORAL GROWTH   (Chemicals, Engineering, Cement, etc.)

VIA

TECHNOLOGY USED

VIA

CONSERVATION

LEVELS   SPECIAL FUEL REQUIREMENTS OF SECTOR
(e.g., Coal for Cement Production)

BULK HEAT REQu.

COAL DEMAND FOR PREMIUM USES

BOILER CAPACITY REQu.

VIA

EXISTING BOILER STOCK
& AGE PROFILE

'PERCEIVED'

—RELATIVE FUEL PRICES

NEW AND REPLACEMENT
CAPACITY   —CAPITAL COSTS

—OPERATING COSTS

—LOAD FACTOR

TOTAL COAL-FIRED BOILER
CAPACITY

COAL REQUIRED FOR BULK
HEAT

Notes: 1. Bulk heat can be split between process and space heating or between low- and
high-temperature applications.
2. Cogeneration can supply both 'premium' electricity and steam for bulk heat.

Figure 15-9. Distribution of Boilers by Age
Source: Boiler Study by SPRU Sussex University

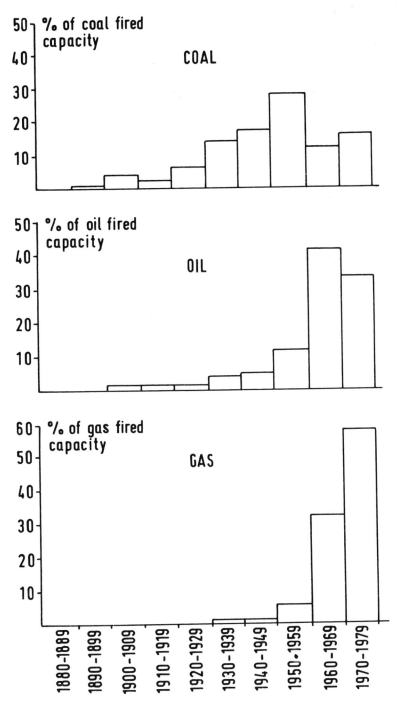

The demand for industrial coal is projected to increase from 10m. tonnes (9.4 mtce) in 1977 to 30m. tonnes (28.2 mtce) in the Low Coal Case and 50m. tonnes (47.1 mtce) in the High Coal Case in the year 2000.

COKE OVEN DEMAND

'British Steel Corporation: the Road to Viability', the British Government's statement of the future of the industry, published in March 1978, placed the difficulties being encountered by the industry in their international context. 'The examination of world demand in the short and longer term and of developments in world production confirm (the White Paper said) that the pattern of trade in steel has been changing and will continue to change to the disadvantage of traditional suppliers.'

The deepest steel recession for forty years has led to efforts to protect the home industry from low-priced foreign competition in every major steel-making country (13). Demand for steel has traditionally been cyclical; however, the unprecedented rise in the cost of oil in 1973 and 1974 and the widespread recession it engendered may well have stalled this cycle of demand, precluding any return to earlier growth rates for the short (and quite possibly into the medium) term.

The excess capacity in the world adds to the problems in the UK, particularly of the British Steel Corporation. Although BSC produce about 85% of the UK's crude steel, they are faced with serious financial problems and also have substantial surplus capacity.

In Britain (as in other developed economies) there has been a progressive shift away from heavy industry to lighter industry and services. This trend of deindustrialisation has resulted in a decline in the use of steel relative to economic growth. The steel intensity (the ratio of steel consumption to GDP) has declined from 0.63 in 1957 to 0.43 in 1977 and is projected to decline to 0.35 in the year 2000. Allied to broad assumptions about GDP, future levels of UK steel consumption and production can be estimated to be about 25 million tonnes in the year 2000.

The repercussions on energy demand in general, and on solid fuel sales in particular, of such steel levels will depend on the relative share of the different production processes. Open Hearth capacity is steadily being phased out so that by 1985 the last plants should be closed and taken out of operation. The two most important parameters for determining coking coal demand will be the amount of Electric Arc capacity and the efficiency of the steel-making process as reflected in the coke rate (see Figure 15-10)

Allowing for an increasing share of electric arc production and a falling coke rate, together with the demand for Foundry, Domestic and Industrial coke, the demand for coking coal is projected as follows:

	m. tonnes	mtce
1985	16.5	17.0
1990	19.0	19.5
2000	17.5	18.0

DOMESTIC/COMMERCIAL COAL DEMAND

As with the other markets the demand for coal depends on the stock of coal-burning appliances. There have been two phases in the decline of coal in the

Figure 15-10. Derived Demand for Coking Coal

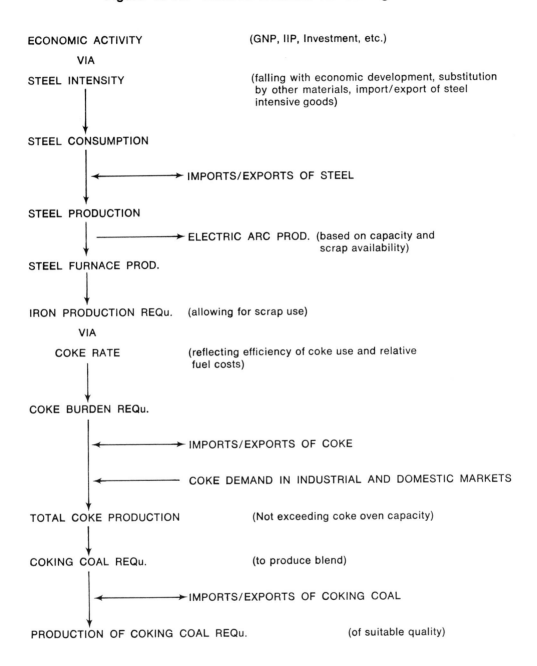

ECONOMIC ACTIVITY   (GNP, IIP, Investment, etc.)

     VIA

STEEL INTENSITY   (falling with economic development, substitution
                              by other materials, import/export of steel
                              intensive goods)

STEEL CONSUMPTION

           IMPORTS/EXPORTS OF STEEL

STEEL PRODUCTION

           ELECTRIC ARC PROD. (based on capacity and
                                  scrap availability)

STEEL FURNACE PROD.

IRON PRODUCTION REQu.   (allowing for scrap use)

     VIA

     COKE RATE   (reflecting efficiency of coke use and relative
                       fuel costs)

COKE BURDEN REQu.

           IMPORTS/EXPORTS OF COKE

           COKE DEMAND IN INDUSTRIAL AND DOMESTIC MARKETS

TOTAL COKE PRODUCTION   (Not exceeding coke oven capacity)

COKING COAL REQu.   (to produce blend)

           IMPORTS/EXPORTS OF COKING COAL

PRODUCTION OF COKING COAL REQu.   (of suitable quality)

Note: Factors above generally change slowly through time depending on existing capacity, new investment, closures, technical change and relative prices.

domestic market. During the Fifties and Sixties slum clearance changed the housing stock and the introduction of smokeless zones meant that consumers had to choose whether to switch to oil, gas and electricity or whether they would turn to the newly developed smokeless briquettes manufactured from coal. More recently, the spread of the natural gas network and the rapid growth in central heating have been the main factors in the market. In the future, levels of insulation, whether houses have chimneys or not, and the existence of the gas grid will all have an important bearing on the market.

Although there are still some areas in the UK without mains gas supply, cheap natural gas has achieved a very high level of penetration, reaching 47% in 1978. Small-scale users place a high premium on ease of use and the attraction of networked fuels, such as gas and electricity, which present no ordering, storage or handling problems, is very great. Gas also has the advantage that it can be stored relatively easily to meet the widely fluctuating demands in this market. Gas is therefore well placed to hold its dominance of this market, provided sufficient supplies are available.

When natural gas supplies from the North Sea start to dwindle, there are several possibilities:

- Increased imports from Norway
- Increased direct burning of coal
- SNG manufactured from coal
- Imports of LNG
- Increased use of off-peak electricity
- Combined heat and power schemes
- District heating schemes based on coal
- Heat pumps based on electricity or natural gas

Contributions can be expected from all of these sources and the relative economics and attractiveness to consumers are not easy to predict. SNG, in particular, would seem a promising long-term option and is receiving substantial R & D effort.

It is particularly difficult to evaluate the role that direct burning will play in domestic heating in the future. There are now available highly efficient appliances which can burn ordinary house coal without production of smoke, known in the UK as 'smoke-eaters'. The consumer will be influenced by cost, convenience and, unlike other markets for coal, by fashion.

The UK has a large number of small, relatively old and inefficient power stations which are due for replacement. These are mainly located in urban areas and are therefore potential sites for combined heat and power schemes. The energy efficiency of providing both electricity and heat would be substantially improved by such schemes.

In the commercial market boilers with higher efficiency and lower capital costs can be expected to increase coal competitiveness. More important for this market are advances in improving the operational amenity of coal through improved methods of coal and ash handling in association with increased automation. This is a subject of current R & D but it will be some time before the market is affected.

This study projects the demand in the domestic and commercial market to fall from 17 million tonnes (17.5 mtce) in 1977 to 10 million tonnes (10.3 mtce) in 1985, picking up thereafter to between 15 and 20 million tonnes (15.4 and 20.6 mtce) in 2000.

SYNTHETIC FUELS

Whatever cost advantage coal attains over oil and gas, its future direct use must remain restricted to applications where its impurity (e.g., sulphur, sodium and chlorine, etc.), inflexibility and/or variable fuel quality are not prohibitively disadvantageous. The significant number of uses to which oil and gas are put that fall outside this category will, therefore, remain closed to coal as coal, however attractively it is priced. The demand for the premium derivatives of oil and gas such as transport fuels, lubricants and chemical products, already high, is likely to increase, demonstrating the potential need for technological advances beyond coal combustion and into the field of coal conversion into gaseous and liquid fuels toward the end of the century.

SNG can be regarded as a future attractive option for coal in that one of the reasons that natural gas consumption was able to expand so rapidly in the early Seventies was because much of an existing transmission network could be used— in a similar way this would also be suitable for SNG.

In recognising the potential importance of liquifying coal, the NCB is at present researching into conversion techniques including the supercritical gas extraction process which 'creams' or 'skims' lower molecular weight constituents from the coal, leaving the remainder for fuel uses or for coal conversion feedstock.

One factor that must be taken into account is the enhanced security gained by using indigenous coal supplies to reduce oil imports.

Given the need to develop techniques and the considerable cost advantage of coal over oil and gas that is required to make conversion economically viable, although important as a sign of things to come, this market is not seen as a major market for coal before the end of the century. 15m. tonnes (13.2 mtce) is included in the High Coal Case and 5m. tonnes (4.4 mtce) in the Low Coal Case for the production of SNG to replace the reducing supplies of North Sea gas in 2000.

COAL WITHIN THE TOTAL DEMAND FOR ENERGY

Putting the sectoral analyses together, the projections contained in the two attached Summary WOCOL Worksheets on coal use and total energy consumption are obtained. As mentioned earlier, the projections were also approached from the top down to make sure that the analysis made sense as a whole.

Starting from primary energy rising at 0.7% per annum in the Low Coal Case and 1.7% per annum in the High Coal Case, we can follow through the implications for coal as shown in Table 15-3. Deducting the estimates for natural gas and nuclear and hydro in 2000 from the primary energy estimates, we arrive at the energy to be met by coal and oil. Premium uses of oil are estimated to be approximately half of current use and this is projected forward to increase in line with primary energy demand. Premium uses of coal, mainly for metallurgical purposes, are projected forward using the results of the sectoral analysis. Thus, we arrive at the coal and oil that compete to supply the remaining bulk heat market. Noting that in 1977, at an oil price of $12.5/bbl (1977 US dollars), coal had 59% of this market it can be seen that the WOCOL Low Coal Case projects coal having 72% of this market against an oil price of $22 and the WOCOL High Coal

Case projects coal obtaining 82% against an oil price of $30 in 2000. Thus a progressive penetration of coal is projected.

Table 15-3. UK Demand for Coal in 2000 (mtce)

	Actual 1977	2000 WOCOL Low Coal Case	WOCOL High Coal Case
Total Primary Energy	303	358	448
Natural Gas	56	54	63
Nuclear & Hydro	14	54	81
Coal/Oil	233	250	304
'Premium' Oil (50%)	62	73	91
'Premium' Coal	20	20	25
Coal/Oil Bulk Heat	151	157	188
Coal Bulk Heat	89	113	154
TOTAL COAL	109	133	179
Oil Price 1977 US $ per bbl	12½	22	30
Coal % of Coal/Oil Bulk Heat	59	72	82

Note: 1. "Non-energy" uses are excluded
2. 277 Therms/tce

PRODUCTION OF COAL

PRODUCTION OF COAL BY THE NCB

Production of Coal in the UK is the responsibility of the NCB and therefore this section has been produced for the study by the NCB members of the team. Some 220 collieries produce 105½ million tonnes and 60 opencast sites produce 13½ million tonnes which, with the coal produced at the small licensed mines and coal recovered from tips and slurry, gives a total of 120 million tonnes for 1978-79. A statistical summary of the NCB from 1950 to 1978-79 is given in Table 15-4.

OBJECTIVE OF NCB

The NCB's general strategy is directed to the implementation of Plan for Coal as endorsed in 1974 and 1977 by the Coal Industry Tripartite Group—involving Government, the mining unions and the Board. This strategy provides for a capital investment programme to generate about 40 million tonnes of capacity at new and existing collieries by the mid-1980's and to increase opencast output to 15 million tonnes. Plan for Coal covers the period to the mid-1980's. But, because of the long lead times on new capacity, the Board are already having to look to the longer term. The Board's Plan 2000 envisages the need to establish about 4 million tonnes a year of new and replacement capacity in the latter part of the century.

Because of the long lead times involved in investment in the mining industry, the NCB are already making investment decisions within the framework of Plan 2000. Virtually the whole Plan for Coal investment programme, covering some 40 million tonnes of capacity, has now been initiated (subject in certain cases to

Table 15-4. Statistical Summary 1950 to 1978/9

	1950	1955	1960	1965/6	1970/1	1975/6	1976/7	1977/8	1978/9
NCB production, m tonnes									
Deep mines and tip coal	205.5	211.1	186.7	176.9	135.4	114.4	108.4	106.2	105.4
Opencast	12.4	11.6	7.7	6.9	8.0	10.4	11.4	13.6	13.5
Licensed mines, etc.	1.6	2.4	2.3	1.9	1.2	1.0	1.0	1.1	1.0
Total	219.6	225.2	196.7	185.7	144.7	125.8	120.8	120.9	119.9
Imports, m tonnes	—	11.3	—	—	1.2	4.8	2.4	2.7	2.1
Inland consumption, m tonnes									
Power stations	33.5	43.6	51.9	69.9	74.7	75.8	78.9	78.9	83.3
Coke ovens	22.9	27.5	29.0	26.0	25.1	18.5	19.6	16.3	14.6
Other markets	149.5	147.6	119.0	88.1	50.9	27.9	26.1	26.4	24.5
Total	205.9	218.7	199.9	184.0	150.7	122.2	124.6	121.6	122.4
Exports, m tonnes	17.2	14.1	5.6	3.7	3.0	1.4	1.4	1.8	2.1
Stocks at end year, m tonnes									
NCB stocks	1.7	2.2	29.7	18.8	6.3	11.0	9.6	10.3	14.3
Consumers' stocks	12.6	12.7	10.0	10.9	11.7	18.9	18.5	19.5	14.7
Total	14.3	14.9	39.6	29.7	18.0	29.9	28.1	29.8	29.0
Number of collieries at end year	901	850	698	483	292	241	233	231	223
Output per man-year, tonnes	298	302	310	387	470	462	447	441	443
Output per manshift, tonnes									
Face	3.24	3.34	4.04	5.57	7.30	7.89	7.75	7.91	8.53
Overall	1.23	1.25	1.42	1.83	2.24	2.28	2.21	2.19	2.24
Mechanised output, %	3.8	11.1	37.5	80.7	92.2	93.6	93.8	93.6	93.5
Average manpower, thousands	690.8	698.7	602.1	455.7	287.2	247.1	242.0	240.5	234.9
Absence, %	12.0	12.5	14.7	18.0	19.2	16.7	17.3	17.6	17.1
Average weekly earnings, £	8.73	12.46	14.70	19.14	27.07	74.00	76.10	84.10	101.76
Safety									
Casualties per 100,000 manshifts	139.8	127.0	143.7	210.3	135.8	105.3	100.0	97.9	94.6
Number of fatal accidents	476	408	316	217	92	59	38	48	72
Number of serious reportable accidents	1,982	1,850	1,553	1,156	599	538	515	520	473

planning permission), and further major investments will need to be started in the next few years, particularly new mines, which will not become effective until after 1985. Without such continuing investment in new capacity, potential deep-mined output would fall progressively from the mid-1980's.

PLAN FOR COAL AND PLAN 2000

Plan for Coal, prepared just before the 1973-74 oil crisis, was drawn up to halt the decline of the UK coal industry and to prepare for expansion once again. The elements of the plan were as follows:

- An extensive *exploration* programme,
- *Investment* in new and replacement capacity,
- An expanded *R & D* programme, and
- Increased *opencast* output.

Since the plan was adopted in 1974 considerable progress has been made. The R & D programme is described in a later section of this report. Progress with the other elements, the thinking behind the plan, and projections forward to 2000 are discussed in the sections that follow.

EXPLORATION AND RESERVES

The major exploration programme launched with Plan for Coal has been outstandingly successful. In addition to proving new areas of coal at existing long-life collieries, it has identified new mine sites, representing total operating reserves of about 2 billion tonnes. The expansion in the NCB's geological effort can be seen by contrasting the 153 boreholes and 440 km of seismic survey completed in 1978-79 with the 1972-73 total of only 45 boreholes and 32 km of seismic survey. The NCB's Plan 2000 envisages the development of additional and replacement deep-mined capacity at an average rate of 4 million tonnes each year over the period 1985-2000, mostly from new mines. A National Exploration Unit has been formed to prove the necessary reserves. More than half the deep-drilling effort during 1978-79 was devoted to the identification of further new mine sites.

On the basis of geological evidence accumulated over many years, reasonably reliable estimates can be made of the total coal originally in place in the UK defined as the coal in seams over 60cm. thick and less than 1,200m. deep. After allowing for the coal which has already been worked to date (around 25 bn tonnes), *the total coal now in place is estimated at 190 bn tonnes*. Further exploration is unlikely to significantly increase this total. However, if new technology and economics allowed the extraction of coal at depths greater than 1,200m. or under the North Sea, then this total could be greatly increased.

That proportion of the coal in place which could be recovered using established technology is termed recoverable reserves. On the basis of existing technology, *recoverable reserves are put at 45 bn tonnes*, sufficient for over 300 years at current rates of production. Recoverable reserves are less than the total coal in place because:

(a) under any system of mining, some coal is inevitably left behind, because of the need to leave shaft pillars, areas of disturbed ground, etc. Further, the coal in place includes some coal previously accessed, but subsequently abandoned, which would now present formidable recovery problems;

(b) longwall mechanised mining (which accounts for the greater part of current deep-mined production) requires a certain selectivity in the coal to be worked in order to obtain optimum production;

(c) a proportion of the coal in place will be in seams of unacceptable quality in relation to current utilisation techniques.

Operating reserves represent that proportion of recoverable reserves which have been fully proved in respect of thickness, quality and mining conditions, and which are either accessible to existing mines (collieries and opencast sites) or have been proved sufficiently to identify new collieries or opencast sites. The operating reserves at existing mines are currently put at some 4½ bn tonnes and a further 2½ bn tonnes have been identified for new mines. In total, the operating reserves are equivalent to some 50 years' life at present rates of output, although they are unevenly distributed among the existing mines.

Operating reserves are, of course, diminished by the actual production of coal. However, as an offsetting process, there will be a progressive upgrading of recoverable reserves into operating reserves by means of:

(a) technical improvements designed to increase the proportion of accessible coal extracted—e.g., recovery of coal currently left to form a roof;

(b) major investment to gain access to new operating reserves;

(c) continuing detailed exploration to identify further opportunities to develop new capacity, or new seams within existing collieries.

The speed of this process will be conditioned by the costs of coal production and the increase in the value of coal relative to the prices of other forms of energy, particularly oil. In their Plan 2000, the NCB have set out their strategy for developing some 4m. tonnes a year of additional/replacement capacity in the period 1985 to 2000. To take account of the coal to be worked and to give the projects concerned a life of 50 years will involve exploration to establish further potential operating reserves of around 3 bn tonnes. Implementation of Plan 2000 will, therefore, involve the upgrading into operating reserves of only a small proportion of the ultimately recoverable reserves of 45 bn tonnes (which in turn could also be increased as exploration confirms the presence of speculative coalfields).

In presenting their Plan 2000, the NCB have pointed out that the geological evidence does not support the view that all the best coal has been worked, or that the remaining recoverable reserves will be less productive; on the contrary, the geological evidence points to very substantial recoverable reserves of thickness and low geological disturbance comparable to those currently encountered in the productive Midlands and Yorkshire coalfields. The working depth of these new reserves, although of course greater than typical with nineteenth-century sinkings, will be no more than experienced in some of the most productive of existing collieries. Although detailed exploration will be necessary to determine the best sites for individual new mines, it is possible to make these broad judgments since our general knowledge of coal measures has shown that, although individual seams may vary considerably, the rate at which the total thickness of coal in workable seams changes is normally very slow across a coalfield. These characteristics enable broad generalisations to be made on the basis of a few boreholes, but without obviating the need for detailed exploration to determine the precise location of viable mining prospects.

Figure 15-11. Age Distribution of Existing Collieries

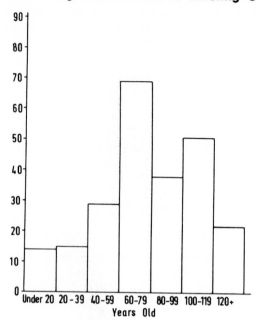

The wide variation of coal 'reserves' quoted in the past has been a source of some confusion. The reason for these wide variations has been the radical changes in prospects for the industry. The increase in quoted coal reserves in the late 19th century and first half of the 20th century is readily understood as a consequence of the development of the coal industry, at a time when there was no feasible substitute for coal as a source of bulk energy supply. In the national assessment in 1942, coal reserves were designated at 40 bn tonnes. However, during the 1960's, under the influence of increasing availability of oil at falling 'real' prices, UK energy policy assumed that there would be no case for new capacity for the foreseeable future. Furthermore, the imperative of obtaining the highest productivity to contain competition with oil, reduced the percentage of reserves extracted. Thus, reserves by the early 1970's were assessed as those accessible to existing collieries (i.e., the operating reserves of some 4 bn tonnes). However, the events of 1973-74 are now seen to have been a turning point in world energy developments so that it is now once again meaningful to talk in terms of the recoverable reserves of 45 bn tonnes as consistent with plans for the long-term expansion of UK coal.

On these bases, the position on UK coal reserves at present may be summarised as follows:

Total coal in place (over 60 cm thick and under 1200 metres deep)	190 bn tonnes
Of which recoverable reserves	45 bn tonnes
Of which	
(a) operating reserves at existing mines	4½ bn tonnes
(b) operating reserves at identified new mines	2½ bn tonnes

THE INVESTMENT PROGRAMME

As outlined above, the question is not one of the physical availability of UK coal but of economics. Here we have to remember that the UK coal industry is a mature extractive industry with the average age of pits being around 80 years. The NCB currently obtain only about 13% of national output from pits sunk since the Second World War and more than half of pits currently operating were sunk before the First World War, as shown in Figure 15-11. This ageing profile of the industry was exacerbated by a very rapid rundown of major project expenditures during the 1960's, when oil was cheap.

Figure 15-12 shows the capital expenditure of the NCB split between major projects and other investment, all expressed in constant prices. The other capital expenditure throughout the period was maintained at a high level. Indeed, per unit of output, it increased, reflecting increased face mechanisation. However, the major projects, which give access to new reserves and provide the basic facilities for production, fell to virtually nothing in the early 1970's. This was an insupportable position for an extractive industry and made Plan for Coal a necessity.

Figure 15-12.   NCB Capital Expenditure at 1978/79 Prices

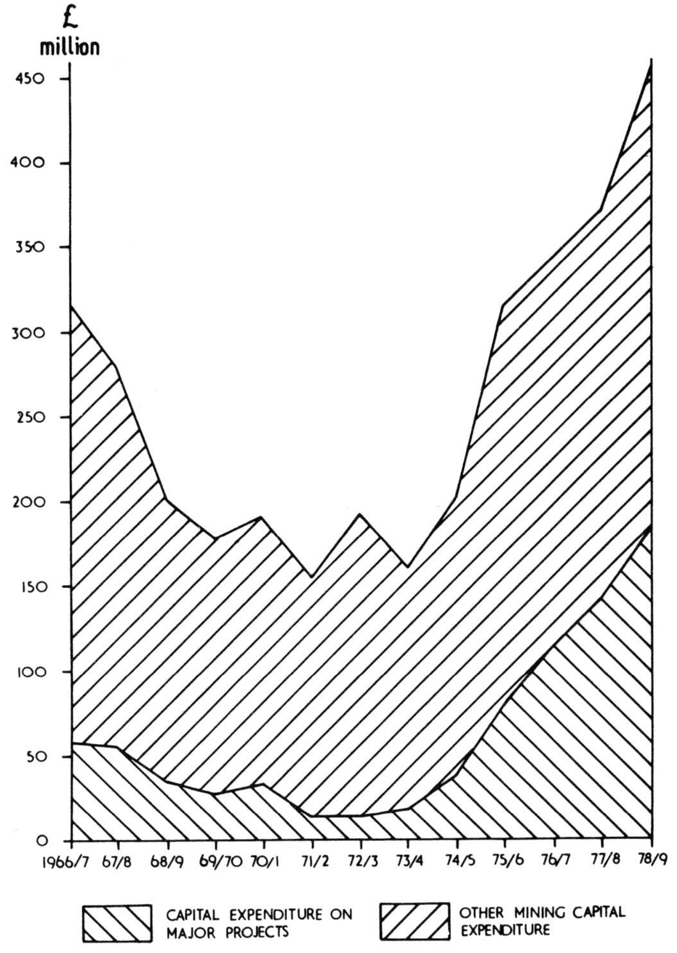

CAPITAL EXPENDITURE ON MAJOR PROJECTS

OTHER MINING CAPITAL EXPENDITURE

Since the oil crisis and the adoption of Plan for Coal in 1974, there has been a tenfold increase in expenditure on major projects and a trebling of overall capital expenditure in real terms, although it will be some time before the full benefits can be realised. This question of lead times can be best illustrated by examining the Board's previous capital expenditure programme in the 1950's. If the major capital expenditure at constant prices is plotted against the output of continuing pits, as shown in Figure 15-13, there is a strong correlation. Although capital expenditure is not the only determinant of output, it is an essential precondition for it. The most important point to note is that there is a gap of up to a decade between the two trends so that the industry is now seen to be significantly influenced by the underinvestment of the late 1960's. Furthermore, it will take some time for the benefits of the present Plan for Coal to show through as increased output.

Figure 15-13. Capital vs. Output (Three-Year Moving Averages)

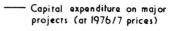

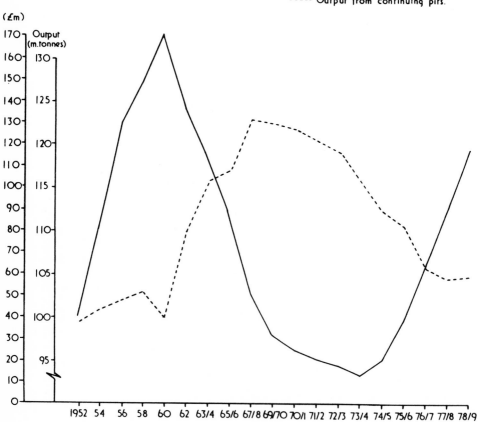

By the end of March 1979, the number of projects approved by the NCB since the inception of Plan for Coal was 123, four new mines and 119 projects at existing collieries.

Plan for Coal—major projects approved by end March 1979
(Projects costing over £1 million)

	New mines	Existing mines
No. of collieries	4	87
No. of projects	4	119
Output 1978-79, million tonnes	1	65
Projected output without projects, million tonnes	—	61
Planned output on completion of projects, million tonnes	11	83
OMS* 1978-79, tonnes	4.80	2.44
Planned OMS* on completion, tonnes	10.55	3.19

* Output per Manshift.

The schemes already approved are designed to provide 33 million tonnes of incremental capacity, 11 million tonnes at new mines and 22 million tonnes at existing mines. The NCB have also made planning applications for the three new mines at Asfordby, Hose and Saltby, that make up the North East Leicestershire Project and for a fourth at Park in Staffordshire. These projects have a planned output of 9 million tonnes, so that the NCB have now initiated schemes to provide all the 42 million tonnes of new and replacement capacity envisaged in Plan for Coal.

If investment were to stop at Plan for Coal, the industry's productive potential would once again begin to decline, both in terms of bulk output and efficiency, as Figure 15-14 shows. For this reason further new capacity will be needed, and because the opportunity for such development at existing collieries will necessarily become more limited, in future an increasing proportion will have to come from new mines. In view of the long lead times involved both in reaching the stage of capital expenditure and in obtaining the benefits from such expenditure, an early start will have to be made with the new capacity envisaged in Plan 2000.

A programme of 4m. tonnes a year of new capacity will involve the mobilisation of considerable quantities of men and machinery, both within the mining industry itself and within the mining supplies and construction industries. Following on, as it does, from Plan for Coal, Plan 2000 should not suffer from bottlenecks through lack of, for instance, shaft-sinking capacity, mining machinery supply and availability of skilled staff. The buildup of manpower at greenfield sites is one problem that will require special attention involving the phasing of the buildup with the exhaustion of existing pits. The success of the programme of new capacity will also require the avoidance of unduly protracted planning procedures. The major North East Leicestershire development was extensively explored by 1975, but the Public Inquiry did not begin until 1979 and final authorisation has not yet been obtained.

Figure 15-14. Total Projected Deep-Mined Capacity to 2000

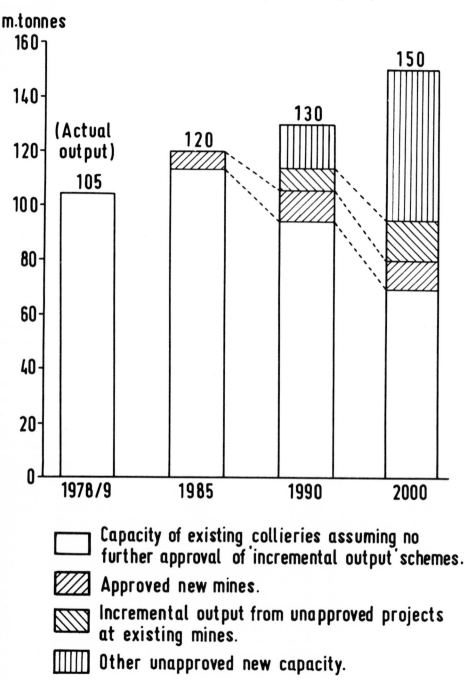

Capacity of existing collieries assuming no further approval of incremental output schemes.

Approved new mines.

Incremental output from unapproved projects at existing mines.

Other unapproved new capacity.

OPENCAST

Opencast production, in particular, is vulnerable to delays in obtaining authorisation. More applications are now going to Public Inquiry, and six Inquiries took place in 1978-79. In the UK, opencast sites tend to be relatively small, of limited life, and are often situated near populated areas. A continuing programme of sites (and therefore of Public Inquiries) is required merely to maintain production.

The NCB recognises that opencast mining can have a detrimental effect on the environment in the short term. However, they ensure that site contractors use the most efficient procedures to reduce the nuisance from noise, dust and blasting to a minimum. Wherever derelict land is included in opencast sites, the subsequent restoration produces an improvement in the environment. However, increasing output levels now and in the future mean that a larger proportion of sites involves agricultural land. The NCB's methods of restoring land after working have long been highly regarded and efforts are being made to raise standards further. For example, research projects are in progress to study:

- the effectiveness of organic farming compared with other methods of restoring opencast sites to good agricultural land;
- wildlife before, during and after a site is worked; and
- drainage characteristics of land before and after opencast operations.

Opencast production, today at some 14 million tonnes per year, is projected to increase to 15 million tonnes by 1985 and at least maintained at that level thereafter.

PRODUCTIVITY

Many factors contribute to the productivity achieved at any time and the effect of any particular factor is often difficult to unravel. The increase in productivity in the Sixties is usually associated with the mechanisation of the coal-winning process, but a number of other factors went hand in hand with this technical change. A large amount of capital was spent on major projects during the Fifties and early Sixties which, if considered to act cumulatively with a 5- to 10-year lag, provided a powerful stimulus to productivity increases. Similarly closures, the increase in pit size and the concentration of production in the best regions and thickest seams can all be shown to coincide with increased productivity. We have therefore to be satisfied with a composite statement as follows:

The major factors leading to improved productivity between 1950 and 1975 were changes in technology at the coal face, increasing output at the better pits following capital expenditure, and rundown of the least efficient units.

In the future, geological conditions are not expected to deteriorate and, indeed, our knowledge of them is expected to be greater with improved exploration techniques and seismic methods. Working depths will tend to increase, and faces at existing collieries to move further from the shaft, but the average seam thickness will be about the same as today. Increasing depth has little effect on productivity and increasing distance from the shaft can be offset by extending and speeding up manriding systems. As more new capacity is introduced, the trend to greater distances from the shaft will be reversed.

The effect of new mining equipment at the R & D stage is difficult to predict, but is likely to be less dramatic than in the Sixties. However, the combination of more reliable and robust equipment, automatic monitoring and computer control providing better management information may have a dramatic effect on delays, the main operating constraint on productivity. The proper integration of the mining system, the spread of best practice and the standardisation of equipment should all contribute to higher productivity. This process of getting the best out of existing mining systems will be aided by an incentive scheme. A guide to the potential performance of existing mining systems is given by the performance of the best collieries. In 1977-78, the 10 pits with the highest productivity produced 8m. tonnes at an output per manshift (OMS) of 4.47 tonnes (twice the industry average).

As discussed above, capital expenditure plays a vital role in achieving higher productivity. Productivity today is still suffering from the lack of investment in the 1960's, but currently total capital expenditure is at a rate of over ½ billion per annum, and this rate will continue into the future. A delay of between 5 and 10 years can be expected between increasing capital expenditure and increased output and improved productivity can be expected rather earlier.

The potential for further substantial increases in productivity can be illustrated by the performance of the best faces compared with the average as follows:

1977-78	*Average Output Per Machine Shift (Tonnes)*
Best 25 Retreat Faces	840
Best 25 Advance Faces	714
Industry Average	306

In addition, new mines will operate at substantially higher productivities (say three times the present industry average), so that the progressive restructuring of the industry, as new capacity replaces old, together with technological advance, should mean that industry productivity could be doubled by the end of the century.

SUPPLY/DEMAND INTEGRATION

COAL CHAIN

As discussed in the section on railways and ports, most British coal is consumed within a short distance of the point of production. This factor, allied to the already highly developed state of the transport network, results in the UK coal chain being somewhat less complex than those for other countries.

A further British specific factor is that all the organisations involved in the coal chain illustrated (Midland deepmine via merry-go-round train to Midland power station) are public corporations. The National Coal Board, British Rail and the various electricity corporations (in the case of the Midlands the Central Electricity Generating Board) have access to public funds in order to implement national policy in their respective spheres. They have a responsibility to meet the government's financial targets and to act with reference to the public interest.

ADMINISTRATIVE AND TECHNICAL LEAD TIMES

COAL MINE

A lead time of 7 years represents an example of an actual new colliery project on a greenfield site in the Midlands. The lead time is taken as the time between formal approval of the project by the NCB and the first tonne of production coal being produced (although a further period elapsed before full production levels were reached).

New mines, however, now have to go through an increasingly prolonged consultation procedure with local authorities and the general public. As mentioned elsewhere, the tendency is for new mine projects to be bigger (2 mtce per annum, at least) than existing collieries and this trend will act to increase lead times. To take account of these factors a period of 8 years was chosen for the coal chain example. These periods, from approval to production, take as a starting point an existing knowledge of the geological conditions and that various technical and layout decisions have already been taken. To illustrate the time that can be involved, the Public Inquiry for the North East Leicestershire development did not begin until 1979, having been extensively explored by 1975, while full production from Selby is not expected until 1987-88, planning consent having been granted by the Secretary of State for the Environment in 1976.

RAIL

Lead times are not included for the rail links, as only very short spur lines connecting the loading facilities to a main line would have to be installed. Often (as in the case of Selby) the levelled beds of disused railway lines can be retracked and this further reduces the work necessary.

Further along the chain, at the power station, rail facilities can be brought up to the required standard within the general construction time of the project.

POWER STATION

In 1977 the Central Policy Review Staff considered the case for the early ordering of a new coal-fired station of the type used as an example in the coal chain. They estimated the construction time to be 6 years from ordering to the first set becoming operational. Recently, however, the electricity supply industry building programme has suffered significant slippages in construction time and this situation is often complicated by design changes having to be accommodated during construction. Here, too, the time taken by administration and consultation may be expected to increase in the future.

MANNING LEVELS, CAPITAL AND OPERATING COSTS

Increasing investment in mechanisation and automation will lead to improved levels of productivity at all stages of the coal chain. For example, the Central Policy Review Staff estimated that the newest coal-fired power stations required only a quarter of the men needed to run an old solid-fuel station.

Capital costs given include escalation during construction and interest. Operating costs exclude interest but are the sum of labour, energy and raw material costs.

403

Figure 15-15.   U.K. Illustrative Coal Chain
Midland Pit to Midland Power Station

	Deep Coal Mine English Midlands	"Merry-Go-Round" Train	Base Load Power Plant English Midlands	
	Mines	Trains	Power Plants	Total System
COAL FLOWS	5 mtce/yr 6.1 mt/yr	Same	Same	Same
FACILITIES Unit Size	2.2 mtce/yr 2.7 mt/yr	43 wagons each payload 32t	2 GW (4 × 500 MW sets) Pulverised Fuel	
# Required	2.3	18	1.1	
LEAD TIMES†	8 years		7 years	8 years
COSTS				
Total Capital††	$830m	$30m	$1,450m	–$2,310m
Annual Operating	$130m	$15m	$15m	$160m
LABOUR REQUIRED				
Annual Operating	5,150 man/yrs	200 man/yrs	715 man/yrs	6,065 man/yrs

† Lead Times for actual project execution after all permits granted.
†† January 1978 costs, includes escalation and interest during construction.

RAILWAYS AND PORTS

Nearly three-quarters of all coal produced in the UK is transported by rail, while a further sixth is transported by road. The breakdown in 1978 was as follows:

Inland Transport (m. tonnes)

Railways	
Main Line	84.4
Private Line	3.4
Road	19.6
Waterways	1.8
Other methods*	6.8
TOTAL DISPOSALS	116.0

* By conveyor, aerial ropeways, etc.

Included in the above is the coal transported to ports for shipment. In 1978 shipments were as follows:

Shipments (m. tonnes)

Coastwise	5.3
Overseas	2.3

By international standards the distance moved by coal in the UK from pithead to the point of consumption is, on the average, very short. See Figure 15-16. Turnaround times for trains are therefore of paramount importance. The most efficient means of rail transporting is via rapid loading bunkers and permanently coupled trains which continuously follow a looped route from colliery to power station. Termed "merry-go-round" trains (MGR) these typically have about forty wagons each of gross laden weight of 45 tonnes with a payload of 32 tonnes, and are usually fed by a rapid loading bunker with a capacity of about 3,000 tonnes. Such trains take about forty-five minutes to load and, therefore, have a turnaround time of under one hour. Similar lengths of time are involved at the power-station end.

Over the financial year 1978-79, 9,600 merry-go-round wagons moved 52m. tonnes of coal, 61% of the total railborne despatches. Ultimately, it is hoped to increase this figure to 75% and steady progress has been made since 1973 when a special programme to invest in merry-go-round facilities was instigated.

Coal Transported by MGR
(tonnes)

1973/4	15
1974/5	38
1975/6	42
1976/7	45
1977/8	46
1978/9	52

Although principally developed for the coal industry's main market, power stations, MGR links are also suitable for other large consumers. In 1977, for example, this system was extended to the new British Steel Corporation works at Scunthorpe. Such developments have presented both the need and the opportunity to modernise other aspects of coal transport, for example, bunkers—the expensive high-capacity MGR rail wagons must be kept constantly on the move and are, therefore, not available for short-term storage as were the old conventional type of railway truck.

Road despatch facilities have also been improved, although road haulage is only economic for smaller consumers. For industry the development of the coal tanker (which removes the need for bagging) allows coal to compete more equally with oil.

The UK has a large number of small ports that can handle coal in ships up to 10,000 tonnes. The main flows are from the North East to the Thameside power stations, from the North of England to Northern Ireland and imports transshipped via Rotterdam. In addition, much larger ships can be handled at Immingham for exporting coal and at Redcar, Port Talbot and Hunterston for imports of coking coal. Details of these ports are given in Table 15-5.

Table 15-5. UK Port Capacities

Name - Location	Imports(I) Exports(E) Steam(S) Met(M)	Max. Draft (meters)	Max. Ship (m.t.)	Loading Discharge Rate (t/day)	Annual Capacity (t year)	Storage Capacity (t)	Year
REDCAR	I/M	16½	140,000	15,000	10/12m*	Large*	1979
PORT TALBOT	I/M	14½	110,000	15,000	10/11m*	1.75m*	1979
HUNTERSTON	I/M	30	200,000	15,000	12m*	2.0m*	1979
HUNTERSTON	E/M	21	100,000	15,000	5m*	2.0m*	1979
IMMINGHAM	E/S	11½	30,000	10,000	2½ m	0.25m	1979

* These capacities are for both coal and iron ore in terms of tons of iron ore.

405

Figure 15-16. Location of Major Coal-Burning Power Stations

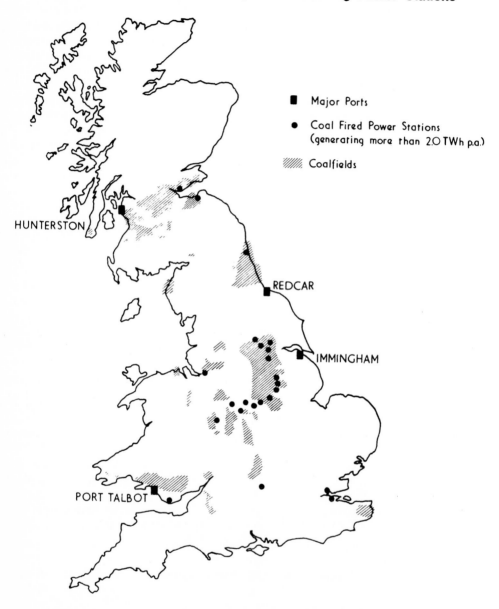

Increased use of the existing rail and port facilities should present no problems. The country has a well-developed rail network which, given adequate investment, should be able to handle greater tonnages. Indeed, the new development at Selby was able to take advantage of existing rail links which had fallen into disuse. Existing port facilities have the capacity for some increase in trade, but should substantially greater flows develop, new facilities could be developed as the need arises to take advantage of the economies associated with larger ships.

REDUCED AVAILABILITY OF OIL AND NUCLEAR ENERGY

The two WOCOL cases were defined and analysed in early 1979 before the full implications of the Iranian supply shortfall were known. When, at a meeting in June 1979, the demands for oil arising out of the WOCOL country team reports were compared with an updated, rather optimistic, projection of likely oil availability from OPEC countries, a 'gap' of some 8 mbbl per day by the year 2000 resulted. While the current WOCOL cases went further than most energy studies in greatly increasing coal production, consumption and trade, they simply didn't go far enough to meet the presumed shortfall in oil. The participants at the June 1979 meeting were concerned that on the one hand, the sorts of policy actions required to achieve the level of coal production, consumption and trade contained in both the WOCOL High Coal and Low Coal Cases were not yet evident in most countries, while on the other hand, the oil import requirements implicit in the WOCOL cases were unlikely to be met.

Each country team was, therefore, directed to consider a 'sensitivity analysis' which reduced the 2000 projection of oil consumption in its country by 20%, consistent with the belief that the non-Communist world cannot count on any greater oil availability than in 1978. It was further suggested that, if thought appropriate, country teams would consider the impact of a reduction in the availability of nuclear energy. This section considers these two possibilities.

IMPACT OF A 20% REDUCTION IN UK OIL CONSUMPTION IN 2000

The analysis was carried out by increasing the oil price separately in the two cases until the necessary 20% reduction in oil consumption was achieved. Two models were used to calculate the impact of increasing oil prices:

- A UK version of the ETA-MACRO (14) model developed by Professor Alan Manne of Stanford University which examined the impact on economic growth, energy consumption and displacement of oil by electricity.
- The NCB's Energy Model of the UK (15) which examined the displacement oil by coal in the electricity, industrial, domestic and commercial markets.

Despite the experience of the step in oil prices in 1973-74, it has not been possible to estimate with any precision the long-term elasticity of substitution between capital-labour and energy, which is the key parameter in the ETA-MACRO model. Three assumed values have been taken to cover the range of uncertainty. In interpreting the results it should be remembered that in both cases it is assumed that the contribution from natural gas is limited by reserves and depletion profile considerations and that nuclear is limited by the capacity of the nuclear construction industry and the lead times involved. Oil consumption, therefore, is reduced ultimately by a combination of reduced energy demand and displacement by coal. This may involve the intermediate step of displacing oil with electricity, and hence, coal.

Table 15-6 shows the following results of the 'Oil Limitation' analysis:

- The main contribution to reduced oil consumption will come through direct substitution of coal for oil in the Industrial, Domestic and Commercial Markets.
- Conservation could contribute as much as a third of the reduction required.

407

- The reduction would be accompanied by increasing the oil price to $30/bbl in the Low Coal Case and $43/bbl in the High Coal Case (early 1979 US dollars).

- Additional coal required would amount to about 20 mtce in the Low Coal Case and 15 mtce in the High Coal Case.

Table 15-6. "Oil Limitation" Analysis
(mtce = 250 therms/tonne)

	LOW COAL CASE			HIGH COAL CASE		
	A*	B*	C*	A*	B*	C*
	mtce	mtce	mtce	mtce	mtce	mtce
Oil Consumption reduced by:						
Reduced GDP	2½	1½	1½	3	2	1½
Reduced Energy per unit of GDP	—	3½	5	1½	6½	9½
Substitution by electricity	2½	2	1½	4½	4	2
Substitution by coal for electricity production	4	4	4	—	—	—
Sustitution by coal directly in the Industrial, Domestic & Commercial Markets	17	15	14	19	15½	15
Total Reduction in Oil Consumption (20% of Total Oil Consumption)	26	26	26	28	28	28
Increase in Oil Price %	25	21	20	29	24	23
Oil Price (Early 1979) US dollars	31	30	30	45	43	43
Increase in Coal Consumption, mtce	23½	20	17½	29	15½	13

* Elasticity of Substitution between Capital-Labour and Energy
  A = 0.25, B = 0.75, C = 1.01

IMPACT OF REDUCED NUCLEAR AVAILABILITY

In the case of a 30% reduction in the availability of nuclear energy in 2000, the result would be the increased construction of coal-fired power stations. This would mean an additional 8 GWe in the Low Coal Case, involving about 18 mtce of coal and 12 GWe in the High Coal Case, involving about 25 mtce of coal. These amounts are in addition to the coal required in the 'Oil Limitation' analysis above.

ADDITIONAL DEMAND FOR COAL

In both of the sensitivities considered above, it was assumed that additional quantities of coal would be available from either indigenous production or imports. In these circumstances, on the assumptions made, the demand for coal unsatisfied by its assumed indigenous production would be as follows:

	Low Coal Case	High Coal Case
'Oil limitation'	18	31
'Oil limitation and Nuclear Reduction'	36	56

To the extent that the above levels cannot be met by further indigenous production or increased imports, reduced economic growth would result.

IMPORT AND EXPORT POSSIBILITIES

As in in recent years the UK is expected to be neither a major net importer nor a major net exporter of coal during the first half of the period under consideration. There will, however, be exports and imports amounting to several million tonnes. By 2000 the estimates range from a net balance in the Low Coal Case to an import requirement of 17 mtce in the High Coal Case to supplement indigenous production and even higher quantities in the oil limitation and nuclear reduction cases. These estimates of net imports or exports are, of course, based on the demand and production projections contained in this report and are sensitive to relatively minor changes in assumptions. Significant imports would not displace indigenous production but would complement such production in the replacement of oil. Thus, to the extent that NCB production falls short of their production targets, or demand does not develop in the manner suggested, imports would be greater or less than indicated.

While substantial levels of imports by the year 2000 are therefore a possibility, these would probably require the siting of new coal-fired power-station capacity close to ports capable of taking large ships. At present, such ports are conveniently sited for blast furnaces rather than power stations. The UK ports that are able to handle coal are described in a previous section.

The availability of foreign coal to satisfy the projected level of imports is determined in the main report, when all the national import requirements and export availabilities are put together under various assumptions.

THE ENVIRONMENT AND R & D

ENVIRONMENTAL ISSUES

In common with all major industrial activities, coal production and utilisation have a considerable impact on the environment and society. This should, however, be seen in the context of the benefits which the coal industry contributes to the economy and compared with the environmental effects of alternative energy sources and with the consequences of a failure to meet the energy demand.

The general approach to environmental questions in the UK has been more cautious and specific than in the USA. For example, no general emission standards for SO_2 or NO_x have been set. However, ground-level concentrations of SO_2 have fallen significantly over recent years following the introduction of regulations to ensure adequate dispersal of combustion gases from power stations and industry (the 'tall stack' policy). City smogs have been virtually eliminated following the controls on smoke emission from domestic fires and industrial plant introduced by the Clean Air Acts of 1956 and 1968.

In addition to their research programmes on new technologies which can assist environmental control (e.g., fluidised-bed combustion and the production of clean fuels from coal), the NCB is involved in three major activities in this area:

The International Energy Agency

In February 1979, under the auspices of the IEA, the NCB organised a meeting on Environmental Projects on Coal Utilisation. Six European countries, Canada and the USA were represented. Outline proposals for collaborative work in four areas were discussed: an environmental task force (UK), atmospheric fluidised-bed combustion (Canada), disposal and use of coal ash (Sweden), practical methods of preventing atmospheric pollution (USA).

Commission on Energy and the Environment

A Government Commission has been set up to review and report on the impact of energy production and consumption on the environment. The Commission is reviewing coal first and is taking evidence from all interested parties, including the NCB, coal consumers and environmental groups. The study will consider coal production, preparation, transport and utilisation, and will include the environmental and societal impacts of these activities.

The Commission of the European Communities

The NCB is preparing a report to the Environmental and Consumer Protection Service of the Commission of the European Communities on the emission of air pollutants coming from the use of coal within the United Kingdom. Part I of the study (submitted to the Commission in August 1978) concentrates mainly on future emission levels of SO_2, NO_x and particulate matter. Part II of the study (in preparation) will examine the feasibility and economics of pollutant reduction during production and combustion processes, including fuel desulfurisation, flue-gas washing and fluidised-bed combustion.

SUMMARY OF NCB EVIDENCE SUBMITTED BY NCB TO THE COMMISSION

In their activities, the NCB have a firm commitment to protect, and improve the environment wherever possible. The NCB devote great attention and effort to offset any side effects from mining and using coal. The environmental issues in the coal industry are complex, and can involve a compromise with economic factors. This is not, however, unique to the coal industry; similar problems arise with every other source of energy or means of energy utilisation.

In common with all major industrial activities, coal production and utilisation have a considerable impact on the environment and society. This should, however, be seen in the context of the benefits which the coal industry contributes to the economy and compared with the environmental effects of alternative sources of energy and with the consequences of a failure to meet the energy needs of the nation.

The NCB appreciate the extent to which the coal industry changes the environment and have established elaborate consultative procedures to ensure that the views of those affected by mining operations and by coal utilisation are respected, as well, of course, as meeting the various statutory requirements placed on them.

The current issues of greatest concern occasioned by coal-mining operations appear to be subsidence, the disturbance of land by opencast mining and the disposal of colliery spoil. The NCB recognise these as problem areas and conduct their operations in such a way as to minimise the impact and, wherever possible, to turn the problems into opportunities for positive improvement.

By planning underground operations carefully, subsidence at the surface which follows the extraction of coal underground can normally be controlled within inches, where necessary. When damage to buildings or land does occur, the NCB aim to act quickly and fairly by carrying out repairs or providing compensation. Virtually all the claims that are made are settled locally in this way, but subsidence does cause very real problems for the people affected.

The disturbance of the land caused by opencast mining is temporary and, when mining operations are finished, care is taken to restore the land and return it to agricultural use. In some cases, the land is in better condition when restored than originally. Here again, the NCB recognise that opencast mining can cause problems for those living nearby.

Methods of disposal of colliery spoil other than placing it on tips nearby have been reviewed many times by the NCB. All the other methods (for example, underground stowing or transfer to distant sites where infill is needed) are either impractical or expensive or themselves cause further environmental questions.

It should not, however, be thought that NCB activities necessarily lead to a net reduction in land available for other purposes. In recent years considerably more land has been released by the NCB than has been acquired for new operations. Over the last ten years, for example, the land acquired for deep-mining operations totalled 3,096 hectares, whereas 8,543 hectares were released.

For the future, a change on the environment will come from establishing new deep mines in areas without a previous history of coal mining. For the local communities there are, of course, immediate benefits such as higher employment and prosperity, but there are also local concerns about the direct effects of mining activities (such as those discussed above), the integration of any incoming miners into local society, and the implications for the transport infrastructure (e.g., new railways and road use). The NCB make great efforts to select sites and methods of working, waste disposal and coal despatch to minimise dusturbance. Attention is also paid to the visual aspect of the colliery workings, with trees, banks, etc., being used for landscaping. In Yorkshire's Selby project, for example, 10 million tonnes of coal a year will be mined at five collieries in 25,000 hectares (100 square miles) of coalfield. However, the collieries will all be linked underground so that the entire output will be brought to the surface from two drifts at Gascoigne Wood, and the movement of coal can take place by railway with minimum disturbance to the locality. Very little minestone has to be brought to the surface and so pitheaps are avoided. Subsidence is designed to fit with a coherent solution to the neighbourhood's water drainage.

The environmental implications of coal mining are, of course, not confined to production of the coal. The way in which it is used is perhaps equally important.

The pattern of coal utilisation has changed considerably over recent years, and further changes are expected in the future, as illustrated in Table 15-7.

Table 15-7. Coal Consumption in the UK

	1955 million tonnes	1977 million tonnes	2000 forecast million tonnes
Power stations	44	80	85-95
Coke ovens	27	17	15-20
Industry	50	10	30-50
Domestic/commercial	50	17	15-20
Railways	12	—	—
Gas works	28	—	5-15
Total	211	124	150-200

References 16, 17 and 18

411

At present, nearly two-thirds of the coal produced by the UK is burned in power stations, reflecting a general trend toward coal utilisation in large central units rather than by small consumers who have more difficulty in overcoming environmental problems. This pattern is likely to persist with the continuing growth of the use of coal in the power-generation market and with a dramatic expansion of the larger-scale industrial market. In the longer term, probably early in the next century, the manufacture of substitute natural gas. (SNG) and liquid fuels from coal will play their part in supplying energy in the forms required for premium heating, transport, chemicals and other specialist users. The present indications are that these conversion processes are also likely to be most economic on a large scale. In many cases, the problems of controlling emissions to the environment from coal combustion and conversion processes are eased with centralised plant, and the new processes are being designed with environmental considerations in the forefront.

For domestic heating, the widespread use of solid smokeless fuels and the replacement of coal, for example by natural gas and electricity, have combined to reduce smoke emissions dramatically so that dense city smogs are now events of the past. In addition, the introduction of new domestic appliances such as the 'Smoke-Eaters' enables high-volatile, bituminous coals to be burned smokelessly and efficiently. Parallel advances in industrial appliance design and operation have reduced the emission of grit and dust in flue gases.

The combustion of coal results in the emission to the atmosphere of sulphur and nitrogen compounds and particulate material. The CEGB have undertaken detailed studies of atmospheric emissions from their plants (19) and have demonstrated that the use of tall stacks has resulted in a considerable reduction in ground-level atmospheric pollution from their stations. Similar benefits arising from the application of the tall-stack policy to industry can be inferred. Although many questions about the long-range transport of atmospheric pollutants remain to be answered, recent work (20) has led to international recognition that sulphur emissions arising from coal combustion in the UK have considerably less environmental significance than had previously been suggested. The NCB, in association with other bodies such as the CEGB, will ensure that the environmental disturbance continues to be minimised.

The carbonisation of coal to make coke for metallurgical use and for the manufacture of smokeless domestic fuel is associated with special environmental problems at coke ovens and briquetting plants. Many improvements have been made both to the traditional methods at existing plants and are designed into new plants.

The introduction, at about the end of the century, of new processes for the conversion of coal will require new types of environmental control, but these are not expected to present problems different in nature from those of current oil refinery, petrochemical plants, carbonisation and power-station activities.

What does perhaps tend to colour thinking about the environmental effects of coal (as opposed to other energy sources) is its long history in the UK and its close involvement in the dereliction associated with the industrial revolution. Coal mining, like other sources of energy, should surely be judged on its present environmental record and future plans.

PRINCIPAL LEGISLATION RELATING TO AIR POLLUTION IN THE UNITED KINGDOM

The control of atmospheric pollution in Great Britain is effected principally by the Alkali, etc., Works Regulation Act 1906 and the Clean Air Acts 1956 and 1968. The Public Health Act 1936, and the Control of Pollution and Health and Safety at Work, etc., Act 1974 also contain provisions dealing with the matter. There are similar provisions for Northern Ireland, but they are not all identical with those for Great Britain.

ALKALI, ETC., WORKS REGULATION ACT 1906

This Act applies to works in a large number of classes listed in a Schedule to the Act, including power stations, coke ovens, chemical process plants and cement works. Additions to the classes may be made by Regulations under the Health and Safety at Work, etc., Act 1974. Works to which the 1906 Act applies may not be carried on unless they are registered and the best practicable means are required to be used to prevent the escape of noxious or offensive gases from them into the atmosphere. Registration is for one year at a time and may be refused if the works do not comply with this requirement.

For the purposes of the 1906 Act, 'gases' includes smoke, grit and dust. A large number of particular gases is specified in a list in the Act as noxious or offensive. Some may contain liquid in the form of droplets. Additions to the list may be made by order of the Secretary of State.

CLEAN AIR ACTS 1956 AND 1968

The principal provisions of the Clean Air Acts 1956 and 1968 are those that:

(a) prohibit the emission of dark smoke,
(b) permit the establishment of smoke control areas in which the emission of any smoke is controlled,
(c) restrict the emission of grit and dust from chimneys,
(d) provide for the measurement of grit and dust from chimneys, and
(e) require chimneys serving furnaces to be of a height approved by the local authority.

Some of the provisions of the Acts apply only to furnaces used to burn:

(a) pulverized fuel, or
(b) any other solid matter at a rate of 100 lbs an hour or more, or
(c) any liquid or gas at a rate equivalent to $1\frac{1}{4}$ Btus an hour or more.

These furnaces are referred to in the following paragraphs as "large furnaces". The Acts do not apply to works that are subject to the 1906 Act unless, in an exceptional case, the Secretary of State provides for them to do so.

(a) Dark Smoke

The emission of dark smoke (as dark as, or darker than, Ringelman 2) from the chimneys of buildings, chimneys serving the furnaces of boilers and industrial plant on land but not in buildings, or otherwise from industrial or trade premises, is prohibited except in certain classes of case prescribed by Regulations. These provide for lighting-up, soot-blowing, breakdown, etc.

413

(b) Smoke Control Areas

A local authority may make a Smoke Control Order declaring the whole or part of their district to be a smoke control area and the Secretary of State may require them to make such an Order. The confirmation of the Secretary of State is required for any Order. The occupier of a building in such an area commits an offence if smoke is emitted from the chimney of the building unless the smoke is caused by the use of fuel declared by Regulations to be an authorised fuel. The Secretary of State may, however, exempt on such conditions as he may prescribe, fireplaces he is satisfied can be used for burning other fuels without producing any substantial quantity of smoke.

(c)(d) Grit and Dust

Large furnaces installed on or after 1st October, 1969, are required to be provided with plant approved by the local authority to arrest grit and dust unless an exemption is granted on the grounds that there will be no emission of grit and dust that will be prejudicial to health or a nuisance. The same applied to furnaces installed on or after 1st January, 1958, which burned pulverized fuel or, at the rate of one ton per hour or more, solid fuel in any other form, or solid waste.

The local authority may also require provision to be made for grit and dust from large furnaces to be measured, and for measurements to be taken and recorded, but if the furnace is used to burn solid matter at a rate less than 1 ton an hour, or gas or a liquid at a rate less than 28m Btus an hour, the occupier of the building may require the local authority to make the measurements and keep the records.

Regulations may prescribe limits on the rate of emission of grit and dust from the chimneys of furnaces other than those designed solely or mainly for domestic purposes and used for heating boilers with outputs of less than 55,000 Btus an hour. The Clean Air (Emission of Grit and Dust from Furnaces) Regulations 1971 and corresponding Regulations for Scotland have been made for this purpose in relation to certain classes of furnace.

(e) Chimney Heights

Since 1st January, 1957, if a new chimney is erected to serve a large furnace, or the combustion space of a large furnace is increased, or a new large furnace is installed to replace a furnace with a similar combustion space, the chimney serving the furnace must, subject to certain exemptions, be of a height approved by the local authority. The height may not be approved for these purposes unless the authority are satisfied that it will be sufficient to prevent, so far as is practicable, the smoke, grit, dust, gases or fumes from the chimney becoming prejudicial to health or a nuisance, having regard to:

(a) the purpose of the chimney,

(b) the position and descriptions of the buildings near it,

(c) the levels of the neighbouring ground, and

(d) any other matters requiring consideration in the circumstances.

Similar requirements have applied since 1st April, 1969 to the height of other chimneys serving buildings used as residences, shops or offices.

CONTROL OF POLLUTION ACT 1974

The Control of Pollution Act 1974 contains provisions

(a) to permit Regulations to impose requirements as to the composition of motor fuel and the sulphur content of oil fuel,

(b) to prohibit the burning of insulation from cables to recover metal from them except at works registered under the Alkali, etc., Works Regulation Act 1906, and

(c) to permit local authorities:

   (i) to undertake research relevant to the problem of air pollution,

   (ii) to publish the results, and

   (iii) to require the occupiers of premises other than private dwellings to provide information about the emission of pollutants into the air.

Under (a) above, the Oil Fuel (Sulphur Content of Gas Oil) Regulations 1976, which came into operation on the 29th December, 1976, prescribe 0.8% as the limit for gas oil until the 1st October, 1980, and 0.5% as the limit thereafter, but there are some exceptions, e.g., for power stations. Other Regulations have been made relating to motor fuel.

Under (b), the Control of Atmospheric Pollution (Research and Publicity) Regulations 1977 have been made to govern local authorities in the exercise of their powers. Local authorities using these powers must consult representatives of industry and persons conversant with problems of air pollution or having an interest in local amenity at least twice a year about the way in which they exercise their powers and the extent to which information collected should be made available to the public.

MISCELLANEOUS

Under the Public Health Act 1936, the local authority may take proceedings to abate statutory nuisances, and such proceedings may be taken in respect of smoke that is a nuisance to the inhabitants of the neighbourhood other than smoke from the chimney of a private dwelling or dark smoke of which the emission is otherwise prohibited.

The Health and Safety at Work, etc., Act 1974 requires employers and self-employed persons to carry on their undertakings in such a way as to ensure, so far as is reasonably practicable, that persons not in their employment who may be affected thereby are not exposed to other risks to their health and safety. This could apply to risks resulting from atmospheric pollution.

Apart from Acts of Parliament, the occupier of premises whose enjoyment of them is materially injured by smoke from other premises may have a right of action for Nuisance at Common Law and be able to obtain an injunction to restrain the nuisance or damages.

ASSUMPTIONS FOR THIS STUDY

This study assumes that in the UK, as in the past, environmental standards are progressively improved as and when new technologies are developed which can be cost-effectively introduced.

RESEARCH AND DEVELOPMENT

Research and development has a vital part to play in the future of the coal industry. This section describes the direction being taken by current R & D programmes in the fields of coal production and coal utilisation, indicating briefly the part each technology may play in meeting the UK's future energy needs and the present state of the technology. Mention is also made of R & D in related fields.

COAL PRODUCTION

The NCB's mining research programme aims to expand output and increase productivity through the development of new, more efficient and safer mining methods and technology. Expenditure on mining research amounted to £21.3 million in 1978-79, compared with £17.1 million in 1977-78.

The scope for improvements in overall productivity at deep mines could be a factor of two or more, mainly by designing new pits so as to take full advantage of existing mechanized mining techniques. There is more scope for containing the pithead cost of coal by improving daily output per face (DOF—a measure of the efficiency of use of capital) than by measures which increase directly output per manshift (OMS—a measure of the efficiency of use of manpower).

Most of the work of the Mining Research and Development Establishment (MRDE) at Bretby is concentrated on improving the reliability and performance of existing methods and on developing systems for remote or automatic control. Machinery is tested extensively in order to determine the scope for design improvements.

Important areas of work include:

- Systems have recently been developed to improve machine guidance along the coal face, and to achieve better integration of equipment on the face and the face-end. Face-monitoring systems are under development to analyse stoppages and breakdowns.
- The MINOS (Mine Operating System), developed at MRDE, is now being installed in many collieries. This system monitors and controls underground conveyors and bunkers, giving improved overall coal clearance and contributing to increased machine running time at the face.
- Production can obviously be increased if the time taken for men to travel to the face can be reduced. Good progress is being made with research into safe methods of raising man-riding speeds. Experiments have been carried out with free-steered diesel vehicles running on properly prepared roadway surfaces.
- Improvements in geological prediction lead to better colliery planning and extended face life. Seismic in-seam research recently passed an important stage when a seismic signal reflected from a known fault was processed by a computer to give a contour map of the fault.
- In order to improve the mining environment, MRDE are developing systems to reduce the amount of dirt produced underground and sent out of the pit. Projects contributing to this work include automatic steering of face machines using natural gamma radiation; design of roof supports to prevent loose material falling onto the face; and mechanical underground stowing of ripping debris. The quantity of dirt will be further reduced by using dirt-absorbing heading systems, thin seam in-seam miners, and by using cutting waste for pump packing.

416

- Technical support is being given to North East Area in the hydraulic transport of mine waste to the sea.
- Improved coal preparation systems which will treat fines more effectively and give better water clarification are also being developed.

Long-term mining research work includes studies of hydraulic mining, supportless longwall mining systems and telechirics—whereby underground equipment can be manipulated and controlled remotely from the surface. The feasibility and economics of in-situ coal gasification and other possible extraction techniques are being examined. In contrast with the evolution of current techniques, which characterises most of mining R & D, little is known about the broad range of remote-mining techniques. These have the potential for allowing the exploitation of deeper deposits, thereby making available to the UK substantial supplies of energy which would otherwise be inaccessible. The only one of these techniques to have been examined in any detail is underground coal gasification (UCG). This was the subject of a recent reappraisal by the NCB (Underground Gasification of Coal, 1976), where it was concluded that UCG was not competitive with existing mining methods; technical difficulties were also identified. However, these alternative technologies have the potential to be good insurance technologies for the UK.

The NCB is participating in programmes of international collaboration with member countries of the European Coal and Steel Community (ECSC), with the USA and the USSR. The UK is also involved in the IEA's collaborative coal projects based in London: a Technical Information Service, an Economic Assessment Service, a World Coal Reserves and Resources Data Bank, and a Mining Technology Clearing House which is primarily concerned with coal extraction.

Opencast mining, which currently contributes about 10% to the UK's output of coal, is a relatively inexpensive method of mining coal. Techniques are well established and reserves of opencast deposits are limited, so it is not an area which, in the UK, will benefit from further R & D.

COAL UTILIZATION

The Board's coal research policy is aimed at strengthening existing markets and developing new uses for coal. Expenditure amounted to £8.9 million in 1978-79 against £7.3 million in 1977-78. As in previous years the bulk of the research was financed by the Board and its subsidiaries, but with a substantial element of funding coming from the ECSC and contracts from the USA.

The work of the Coal Research Establishment (CRE) at Stoke Orchard, near Cheltenham, falls into two main categories:

- developing more efficient coal combustion equipment, and
- investigating processes for converting coal to liquids and gases.

Technologies for coal combustion, which reduce coal's inherent disadvantages compared with oil and gas, are important in maximising coal's share of the heat market as oil and gas become more expensive and difficult to obtain. They also encourage the use, in the long term, of a low-cost fuel in place of high-cost secondary fuels (SNG and electricity) and could therefore be important in decreasing long-term national energy costs, and can also help to minimise the environmental impact of burning coal at least additional cost.

Coal is likely to have greater market penetrations in medium- and large-scale applications (industrial, commercial and institutional markets) than in small-scale domestic use. Thus it is sensible for R & D programmes to concentrate on the former. Much of CRE's work is undertaken in collaboration with manufacturers of coal-using equipment.

- Extensive field testing and development has been done on new closed domestic appliances for burning house coals efficiently and a commercial launch is expected in 1980. Laboratory tests on modifications to conventional open fires with high output backboilers are also in progress and marked improvements in combustion efficiency and smoke reduction have been obtained. Moreover, a prototype freestanding, dryback room heater has been designed to meet the need for a cheap, easily run direct space heater.
- Particular efforts are being devoted to work on blending coals for good-quality blast-furnace coke, including coal previously considered unsuitable for this purpose. Special tests are being carried out at Lambton Coke Works to prepare suitable coke from British coals for the new BSC blast furnaces at Redcar.
- Research work for NCB (Coal Products) Ltd. includes support for the introduction of Multiplas (a multilayer roofing material) in the UK and the development of fireproofing products for the Scandinavian market.

The medium-term activities include:

- Fluidised combustion of coal has been successfully demonstrated in three prototype industrial boilers. Results from these units have been used as a basis for the shell boiler designs being developed commercially with several manufacturers. The design of the commercial fluid-bed, hot-gas furnace for direct drying of agricultural crops has been improved. Its use has been extended to other commercial applications requiring hot gases, such as market gardens.
- Efforts are being made to extend the range of coals that can be burned satisfactorily in commercial boilers and furnaces, and to provide fully automatic operation and control. Improved coal-handling techniques have also been tested on commercial sites. Prototype equipment for automatic de-ashing of an underfeed stoker and automatic ignition on a chain-grate stoker has been constructed. These developments are aimed at making conventional coal-burning equipment more efficient and easier to use. A new boiler house has been built at Stoke Orchard to accommodate the large combustion and test rigs necessary for this work.
- Construction work on the 80-MW, pressurised fluidised-bed pilot plant at Grimethorpe, near Barnsley, was approaching completion by the end of the year. This project is under the auspices of the International Energy Agency and is financed equally by the UK, USA and W. Germany; the Board's subsidiary NCB (IEA Services) Ltd is the operating company. Commissioning of the plant is now expected to begin in 1979-80.

Processes for converting coal to liquids and gases are long-term work. Several of the required conversion technologies required have already been operated commercially (though mostly on a small scale) and the main aim of current R & D programmes worldwide is to improve on these existing processes by reducing capital costs and increasing plant reliability. Increased flexibility in operation is also being sought by widening the range of acceptable coal types and sizes. Relevant areas of technology are:

- Coal to Substitute Natural Gas,
- Coal to Other Gases,
- Coal to Synthetic Liquid Fuels, and
- Coal to Chemicals.

CRE are mainly active in the second and third of these areas:

- In May 1978, on the recommendation of the Research and Development Working Party of the Coal Industry Tripartite Group, the Government agreed to provide funds for the construction of two 25-tonnes-per-day pilot plants for the liquefaction of coal, using liquid and gaseous solvents. Since then, work has concentrated on developing these processes and evaluating their economic and technical merits. The results show that both processes compare favourably with alternative methods of liquefaction, including pyrolysis. An agreement between the Department of Energy and the Board in February 1979 authorised funds for the design stage of these plants. The first-phase design study is in progress and the plants are planned to be ready for commissioning by mid-1982.
- A further recommendation of the Tripartite Committee led to a joint study with CEGB to decide how best to develop more efficient methods of producing electricity from coal. There is great interest in converting a proportion of the coal to a low-calorific-value gas for burning in a gas turbine as one stage of a combined cycle. There is a strong possibility that the fluidised-bed partial gasification process already under development at the CRE could be used for this process.

The Board are collaborating with British industry to explore possible overseas markets for these technologies. There are also exchanges of technical information with organisations in the USA, Canada, Australia and Europe.

The British Gas Corporation's Westfield Development Centre is engaged, partly under US funding, in R & D into the production of SNG from coal (and also from petroleum); the NCB's Leatherhead Laboratories are also carrying out work on high CV coal gasification under US funding.

The coal liquefaction processes being studied at CRE could be used to produce organic chemicals, either by refining to produce a feedstock, or by direct formation of chemicals by pyrolysis. These methods produce a range of products and their introduction may not, therefore, depend primarily upon the demands of the chemical industry. The UK chemical industry is carrying out research studies into the production of chemicals from coal-derived synthesis gas.

The CEGB have a wide-ranging research programme aimed at reducing furnace-wall corrosion in their boilers, which is it believed is associated, among other things, with the chlorine content of coal. As part of this programme, MRDE and NCB Scientific Control are working jointly with CEGB on the feasibility of leaching a part of the chlorine from the coal before it is used.

With the introduction of newer and larger plants, the BSC is including new laboratory test requirements in specifications for coke. Comprehensive testing is being carried out by NCB Scientific Control to find blends of coal which can consistently meet these requirements.

Shell Coal Research Activities in the UK

The handling of coal fines frequently presents problems. In many areas the losses at mines can be as high as 10-15%, and if coal slurry pipelines are to be used to move coal destined for distribution or export as opposed to direct use, some means of handling fines must be developed. Shell Research Ltd. have examined the use of binders to solve this problem and practical experience has been gained at a colliery in the UK. The next stage is the construction of a pilot plant to gain experience in continuous operation. In all such work considerable attention is paid to the safety aspects of the product.

In order to allow coal to be used in equipment designed to use fuel oil, 'Colloil' has been developed. This is a stable emulsion of finely ground coal and fuel oil which can be handled in a similar manner to heavy fuel oil. Trials have been carried out in conjunction with Babcock and Wilcox at their works boiler house in Scotland.

Colloil is possibly even more attractive as a replacement for fuel oil injection into blast furnaces where fuel oil was introduced to economise on coke use. In conjunction with British Steel, Shell Research have successfully evaluated Colloil's performance injected into a single tuyere of a blast furnace and plans are now in hand for a full-scale blast-furnace trial.

Experience gained in the oil and petrochemical industries has been beneficial in the improvement of coal analysis techniques and Shell Research have extended this work into coal-quality monitoring. The latter is considered to be a very important adjunct to the introduction, or reintroduction, of coal to replace oil or gas.

BP's Coal Research in the UK

BP's coal research in the UK involves developing improved methods for the borehole logging, preparation, transport and direct use of coal and studies for the future use of coal in conversion processes.

Improved methods of borehole logging are being developed. One advance already made is that by computer correlation with results from core samples, the density log has been developed so that it can give density, ash and a calorific value. Methods for the deashing, desulfurisation and drying of coal are being studied; these include both improvements to existing methods such as flotation and other more novel methods. BP is a participant in a BHRA project on pipelining of coarse coal slurries and also carries out work of its own on improving coal transportation, one of the developments being coal/oil dispersions which are described below.

A principal objective is research to increase the use of coal as a primary fuel. A detailed study of the technical and logistical problems in the switchover from oil to coal in industrial boilers is being carried out. A major effort is the development of coal/oil mixtures to be burned in existing oil-fired equipment. The potential areas of use are oil-fired power stations, oil-fired industrial boilers, marine steam turbines, direct-heat applications and for injection into blast furnaces. The cost of converting equipment originally designed for oil-firing to burn coal is excessively expensive, and there is, therefore, a need for an interim technology which allows the partial use of coal in this equipment. Considerable work on developing coal/

oil mixtures is being done by others, particularly in the US. This normally involves the mixing of pulverised coal with fuel oil, and normally the use of an additive to stabilize the mixture, but the resulting mixture shows instability above 60°C. BP has developed a method which involves a special grinding technique but does not require the use of an additive; the product would normally contain 40%-weight coal. This product, which BP calls a coal/oil dispersion, is considerably more stable than coal/oil mixtures prepared by the additive method, being completely stable at temperatures of at least 100°C. This greater stability will help overcome handling problems and enables it to be burned in equipment designed for oil-firing without the coal settling out as the dispersion is preheated prior to the burner. 10,000 UK gallons of dispersion were prepared and burned in a marine burner test rig; this involved handling the dispersion in normal equipment at three locations over a period of 6 weeks; no settling problems were encountered. Further burner trials are planned for the near future. A route for the large-scale (1 million tons/annum) production of the dispersions has been established. It is believed that these coal/oil dispersions can be commercially competitive with the burning of fuel oil. The technology should be available for use in the medium term.

BP are partners with the NCB in Combustion Systems Limited which licenses the basic technology of fluidised-bed combustion. BP are partners with Babcock and Wilcox in Fluidised Combustion Contractors Limited (FCCL) a company which has been set up to provide a complete design, contracting and engineering service for the installation of fluidised-bed combustion.

Technologies for the gasification and liquefaction of coal are studied and assessed. In the UK, BP's work has been on coal liquefaction. A route involving the solvent refining of coal and the hydrocracking of the coal solution produced has been studied. A 1,000-hour run on the hydrocracking of coal solution over a fixed bed of catalyst was successfully completed. BP's current involvement in this method is through collaboration with the NCB on their design studies for two 24 ton/day pilot plants to demonstrate the solvent extraction plus hydrocracking process and the supercritical extraction plus hydrocracking process. BP are also carrying out work on more novel methods of converting coal to liquid fuels and chemicals.

OTHER RESEARCH AFFECTING COAL

There is substantial research and development in other fields, notably electricity generation, electricity utilisation and energy conservation, which can also have an important role in determining the future of the coal industry. These technologies are however outside the scope of this chapter.

MEDICAL RESEARCH

The NCB has been engaged for more than 20 years in a major programme of field research on pneumoconiosis, now drawing to a close, and is attaching increasing importance to research into chronic bronchitis and emphysema among mine workers. Further details are given in the Board's Annual Report.

RESEARCH BY UNIVERSITIES IN THE UK

A number of Universities, particularly, those in the traditional coal mining areas, have active research programmes which cover the whole range of coal geology, science, mining engineering and use which are too numerous for description here.

COMPARISON WITH OTHER STUDIES

The results of the WOCOL analysis and the assumptions used have been compared with the following studies:

UK Department of Energy Consultation Green Paper (21),
Workshop on Alternative Energy Systems (WAES) (22),
IEA 'Steam Coal: Prospects to 2000' (23), and
IIED 'A Low Energy Strategy for the United Kingdom' (24).

The key assumptions and some of the numerical results are set out in Table 15-8. Each study was addressing a different problem and developed an analysis as appropriate; the Green Paper, for instance, examined energy policy options to support economic growth, while the IIED study illustrated the potential of conservation and low-energy policies. The results are not, therefore, simply comparable and to understand fully the differences reference should be made back to the studies listed above. In particular, each study attaches a different meaning to High Coal and Low Coal Cases, usually referring to the level of total energy demand, but in the case of the IEA Steam Coal study the two cases refer to high and low nuclear availability.

One of the problems with energy studies is the plethora of units used. At the same time, it is often difficult to find the relevant statistic in each study. A certain amount of interpretation and interpolation has therefore been necessary to derive Table 15-8 in common units. The differences in the assumptions are shown in Figure 15-17, and the resulting demands for coal are shown in Figure 15-18.

The studies, which have all been carried out over the last few years, illustrate the wide divergency of results that are possible when looking 20 years ahead. Consumption of coal ranges from 85 mtce (WAES Low Coal Case) to 180 mtce (WOCOL High Coal Case); while both are possible, the risks of planning for low levels of consumption, given the enormous pressure on the supply of energy indicated by the WOCOL study as a whole, would be unacceptably high.

UNITS IN THE TABLES

The summary in the tables is presented in mtce where 1 tce has a thermal value of 277 therms. This has been used throughout the WOCOL study. The thermal value of UK coal varies considerably from market to market. In particular, the estimated gross calorific value for coal delivered to power stations in the UK in 1978 was 224 therms per tonne. Thus 4 mtce delivered to power stations is equivalent to 5 million tonnes of coal.

Table 15-8. Summary of Comparison With Other Studies For Year 2000

	WOCOL Low Coal Case	WOCOL High Coal Case	GREEN PAPER (1) Low Coal Case	GREEN PAPER (1) High Coal Case	WAES (2) Low Coal Case	WAES (2) High Coal Case	IEA (3) Low Coal Case	IEA (3) High Coal Case	IIED (4) Low Coal Case	IIED (4) High Coal Case
OIL PRICE 1979 US $ BBL	$25.00	$35.00	$30.00		$14.95	$22.45	$21.00		NA	
GDP % GROWTH PA TO 2000	2%	3%	2%	3%	1.7%	3%	-1985 / 85-1990 / 90-2000	2.7% / 2.1% / 3%	-1990 / 90-2000	3% / 2.4%
PRIMARY ENERGY USE *mtce IN 2000	358	448	414	516	438	542	NA		294	323
GROWTH IN ELECTRICITY SALES % PA TO 2000	2%	3%	2%	3%	2.4%	3.7%	2.8%		0%	0.3%
NUCLEAR CAPACITY IN 2000	26GW	40GW	28GW	40GW	29GW	58GW	30GW	25GW	13GW	11GW
COAL PRODUCTION IN 2000 *mtce — DEEP	124	144	138 →							
COAL PRODUCTION IN 2000 *mtce — O. CAST	9	18	19 →							
COAL PRODUCTION IN 2000 *mtce — TOTAL	133	162	157 →		72	122	120		100	105

* (1 mtce = 0.0277 Quadrillion BTU)

423

Table 15-8. Summary of Comparison With Other Studies For Year 2000 (cont.)

	WOCOL Low Coal Case	WOCOL High Coal Case	GREEN PAPER (1) Low Coal Case	GREEN PAPER (1) High Coal Case	WAES (2) Low Coal Case	WAES (2) High Coal Case	IEA (3) Low Coal Case	IEA (3) High Coal Case	IIED (4) Low Coal Case	IIED (4) High Coal Case
Coal Markets										
Electricity	70	77		54	43	107	74	74	53	51
Industry	28	47		39	32	42	+ 22	+ 22	25	23
Iron and Steel	16	21		28			24	24	18	16
Syn. Fuel	4	13		28	4	10	(inc. +)	(inc. +)	—	—
Resid. and Comm.	15	21		8	6	6	(inc. +)	(inc. +)	9	9
Total	133	179	Total Includes 45 Policy Gap*	157	85	165	120	120	105	99
Coal Production	133	162		157	72	120	120	120	105	100
Net Imports	0	17		0	13	45	0	0	0	0
Energy Consumption					*Low Nuclear*					
Oil	116	124		124	213	262			117	142
Gas	54	63		47	51	56	NA	NA	46	52
Primary Elect.	54	81		79	52	59			26	30
Coal	133	179		153	126	165			105	99
Total	358	448		448	442	542	—	—	294	323
Coal (as %)	37%	40%		34%	29%	30%			36%	31%
Elect. Mix					*Low Nuclear*					
Coal	70	77		54	76	107	74	74	53	51
Oil	14	14	Policy Gap*	13	14	29	24	14	9	9
Gas	—	—		—	NA	—	—	—	—	—
Nuclear	54	81		79	50	57	50	60	30	24
Others				38*	1	1	1	1	3	2
Total	138	172		184	141	194	149	149	95	86

All Units = mtce = 0.0277 Quadrillion BTU (cf mtce in the UK = 0.025 Quadrillion Btu)

* In the Green Paper a "Policy Gap" of 45 mtce was left unallocated to any particular fuel.

Figure 15-17. Comparison of Basic Assumptions

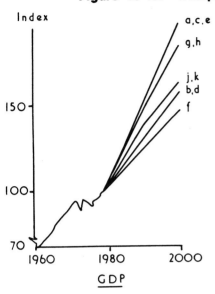

GDP

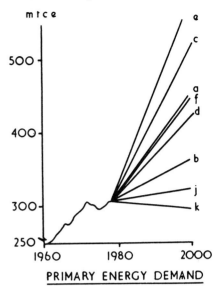

PRIMARY ENERGY DEMAND

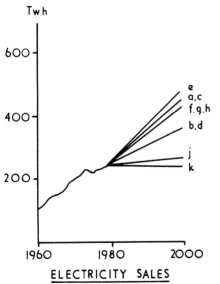

ELECTRICITY SALES

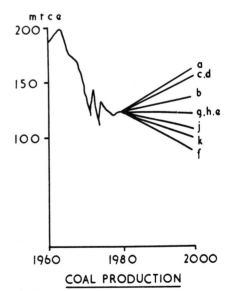

COAL PRODUCTION

	High	Low
WOCOL	a	b
GP	c	d
WAES	e	f
IEA	g	h
IIED	j	k

Figure 15-18. Comparison With Other Studies
Markets For Coal (High Cases Only)

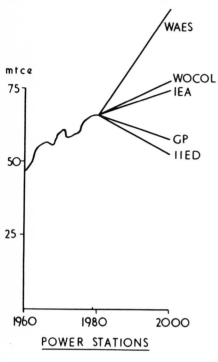

POWER STATIONS

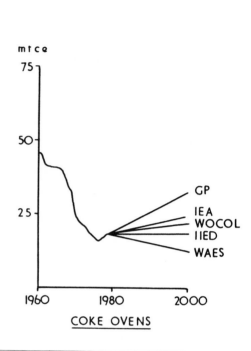

COKE OVENS

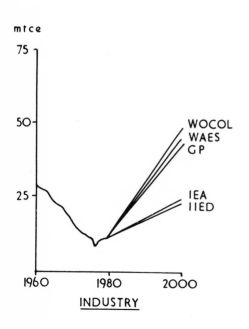

INDUSTRY

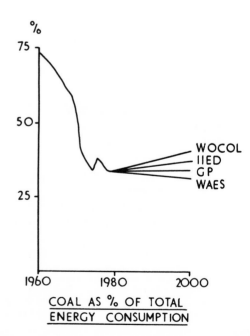

COAL AS % OF TOTAL
ENERGY CONSUMPTION

REFERENCES

(1) 'Energy Policy. A Consultative Document'. Presented to Parliament by the Secretary of State for Energy, February 1978. Cmnd. 7101 (Green Paper).

(2) 'Plan for Coal' NCB. Originally drawn up in 1973 and endorsed by the Coal Industry Examination in 1974. See also 'Coal for the Future: Progress with "Plan for Coal" and prospects to the year 2000', Department of Energy, Thames House South, Millbank, London SW1.

(3) See, for instance, 'A Low Energy Strategy for the United Kingdom', by Gerald Leach and others, the Institute for the Environment and Development, Science Reviews Ltd., 1979.

(4) 'Development of the Oil and Gas Resources of the United Kingdom 1979'. A report to Parliament by the Secretary of State for Energy, July 1979 (Brown Book).

(5) 'Coal Technology: Future developments in Conversion, Utilisation and Unconventional Mining in the United Kingdom', Department of Energy, Thames House South, Millbank, London, SW1.

(6) See Reference 4.

(7) 'The O.R. Contribution to Planning the Long Term Future of Coal in the UK', R.J. Ormerod and R.C. Tomlinson, the Institute of Management Sciences, Athens, 1977.

(8) 'Energy Demand Sensitivities', R.J. Ormerod and R.F. Kirkman, National Coal Board, March 1979.

(9) 'Oil Crisis . . . Again', BP Policy Paper, 1979.

(10) See Reference 1.

(11) 'The National Coal Board Model of the UK Energy Economy', Plackett, International Energy Symposium, Montreux, 1979.

(12) 'Survey of the Industrial Boiler Stock in the UK: A Progress Report', John Cheshire and Mike Robson, SPRU, University of Sussex, 1979.

(13) 'Impact of Rising Energy Prices on the Global Location of the Iron and Steel Industry', Ormerod, Hunt and Toft, NCB/GE, 1979.

(14), (15) See References 7 and 8.

(16) 'Digest of United Kingdom Energy Statistics 1978', Department of Energy, London, HMSO.

(17) 'Energy Conservation in the United Kingdom; Achievements, Aims and Options', National Economic Development Office, London, HMSO 1974.

(18) NCB Press Release, January 22, 1979. Statement by the Chairman, Sir Derek Ezra, to the Commission on Energy and the Environment.

(19) D.J. Moore and A.G. Robins, 'Experimental and Theoretical Investigations into Chimney Emissions', Proc. Inst. Mech. Engrs., Vol. 189, 4/75, 1977.

(20) 'Long-range Transport of Air Pollutants; Final Report of a Cooperative Technical Programme Prepared for the OECD by the Norwegian Institute for Air Research', OECD, Paris, 1977.

(21) See Reference 1.
(22) 'Supply-Demand Integrations to the Year 2000', WAES Technical Report, MIT Press, 1977.
(23) 'Steam Coal: Prospects to 2000', International Energy Agency, Paris, 1978.
(24) See Reference 3.

Summary Worksheet

I. Coal Use, Production, and Trade	1977	1985		1990		2000		1977-2000 Avg. annual growth—%/yr.	
		A	B	A	B	A	B	A	B
Coal use in major markets (mtce)									
Metallurgical	18	17	17	18	21	16	21	–	0.7
Electric	65	68	72	69	73	70	77	0.3	0.7
Industry	9	12	16	14	22	28	47	4.9	7.3
Synthetic Fuels	–	–	–	–	–	4	13	+	+
Residential/Commercial	17	10	10	10	12	15	21	–	0.9
Total coal use	109	107	115	111	128	133	179	0.6	2.2
Distribution of coal use by market sector (%)									
Metallurgical	16	15	15	17	17	12	12	—	—
Electric	59	64	62	62	57	53	43	—	—
Industry	9	11	14	12	17	21	26	—	—
Synthetic Fuels	–	–	–	–	–	3	7	—	—
Residential/Commercial	16	10	9	9	9	11	12	—	—
Total coal use	100%	100%	100%	100%	100%	100%	100%	—	—
Coal consumption/imports (mtce) **Consumption**									
Metallurgical	18	17	17	18	21	16	21	7	0.7
Steam	91	90	98	93	107	117	158	1.0	2.4
Total coal consumption	109	107	115	111	128	133	179	0.7	2.2
Imports									
Metallurgical	1	2	2	2	2	2	2	–	–
Steam	1	–	–	–	–	–	15	–	–
Total coal imports	2	2	2	2	2	2	17	–	–
Coal production/exports (mtce) **Production**									
Metallurgical	16	15	15	16	19	14	19	–	0.7
Steam	92	94	101	96	109	119	143	1.1	1.9
Total coal production	108	109	116	112	128	133	162	0.9	1.7
Exports									
Metallurgical	–	–	–	–	–	–	–	–	–
Steam	1	3	3	3	2	2	–	–	–
Total coal export	1	3	3	3	2	2	–	–	–

Summary Worksheet

II. Coal's Role in Total Energy System	1977	1985		1990		2000		1977-2000 Avg. annual growth-%/yr.	
		A	B	A	B	A	B	A	B
Total Primary Energy Use (mtce)									
Oil, Domestic Oil, Imported	123	103	139	116	144	116	124	--	--
Gas, Domestic Gas, Imported	56	77	77	77	77	54	63	--	--
Nuclear Hydro, Solar, Other	14	27	27	32	32	54	81	6.0	7.9
Coal, Domestic Coal, Imported	109	107	115	111	128	133	179	0.6	2.2
Total energy use	303	313	358	336	380	358	448	0.7	1.7
Coal penetration (%)	36	34	32	33	34	37	40	—	—
Total primary energy (mtce) input to electricity									
Oil and Gas	18	14	19	18	23	14	14	--	--
Hydro, Solar, Other Nuclear	14	27	27	32	32	54	81	6.0	7.9
Coal	65	68	72	69	73	70	77	0.3	0.7
Total energy input	97	109	118	118	127	138	172	1.6	2.5
Coal penetration (%)	67	62	61	58	57	51	45	—	—
Total electric capacity (GWe)									
Oil and Gas Hydro, Solar, Other	17	23	24	22	25	20	20	--	--
Nuclear	5	10	10	14	17	26	40	7.3	9.5
Coal	45	44	44	44	45	44	55	--	0.9
Total capacity	67	77	78	80	87	90	115	1.7	2.4
Coal Penetration (%)	67	57	56	55	52	49	48	—	—
Peak load	50	57	62	62	71	75	93	1.8	2.7
Peak reserve margin (%)	34	35	26	29	23	20	23	—	—
Total oil imports (mbd)**	0.9	(1.1)	(0.7)	(1.0)	(0.6)	0.5	0.6	--	--
Total oil consumption (mbd)									
Transportation									
Residential/Commercial									
Industry—Boilers									
Industry—Other									
Electric utilities									
Total oil consumption **	1.7	1.4	1.8	1.5	1.9	1.5	1.6	--	--
World oil price assumed for national coal analysis (1979 U.S. dollars/barrel)	14½	14½	18	18	23½	25½	35	2.5	3.9
Economic growth assumed for national coal analysis (GNP, billion 1978 dollars)	257	301	326	332	377	405	507	2.0	3.0

** Excluding Oil for Non-Energy Use and Bunkers.

CHAPTER 16

UNITED STATES

PREFACE

This report has been prepared for the World Coal Study (WOCOL), in accordance with the guidelines established by WOCOL. The report is the product of the collective work of the United States WOCOL team, which met together to review progress at five meetings of the U.S. team, in addition to the five full meetings of the entire worldwide membership of WOCOL.

The senior members of WOCOL from the United States, called Participants, included: Mr. Thornton F. Bradshaw, President, Atlantic Richfield Co.; Mr. Gordon R. Corey, Vice Chairman, Commonwealth Edison Co.; Mr. W. Kenneth Davis, Vice President, Bechtel Power Corp.; Mr. Pierre Gousseland, Chairman and Chief Executive Officer, AMAX, Inc.; Prof. Robert C. Seamans, Jr., Dean, School of Engineering, MIT and Former Administrator, Energy Research & Development Administration (ERDA); and Mr. Russell E. Train, President, World Wildlife Fund—U.S. and Former Administrator, Environmental Protection Agency (EPA).

The U.S. Associates, selected by Participants from their own organizations, formed the working group for the WOCOL studies: Dr. Arnold B. Baker, Atlantic Richfield Co.; Dr. Irving Leibson, Bechtel, Inc.; Mr. Robert L. Major, AMAX Coal Company; Mr. Joseph P. McCluskey, Commonwealth Edison Co.; Mr. F. Taylor Ostrander, AMAX, Inc.; and Dr. David Sternlight, Atlantic Richfield Co. In addition, formal liaison was established with the U.S. Department of Energy (DOE) and the Electric Power Research Institute (EPRI), which both provided Study members who served in the role of Associates without Participants: Mr. Michael Gaffen and Dr. John Stanley-Miller of DOE and Mr. René H. Malès of EPRI.

The MIT Secretariat of the World Coal Study took principal responsibility for preparing the U.S. report with technical and editorial assistance from the various U.S. team members.

The Introduction and Summary, the sections describing the analysis of U.S. coal supply and demand, and the section Capital Requirements for Coal Facilities were written by Dr. J. Michael Gallagher, WOCOL Technical Director at the MIT Secretariat. Suggestions from Mr. Robert Major in particular contributed significantly to the final draft. The description of domestic coal transportation systems was written by Mr. Michael Gaffen. The report on coal ports and transportation infrastructure necessary to support various levels of U.S. coal exports, which is summarized in the section on Coal Transportation and described in full in Appendix 1, was prepared for WOCOL by Dr. Martha Kohler of Bechtel, under the guidance of Bechtel's WOCOL members. The section on U.S. Environmental

431

Laws, Regulations and Standards Pertaining to Coal Production and Utilization was jointly drafted by Mr. Robert Greene, Mr. René Malès, and Mr. Joseph McCluskey.

Various drafts of each section of the report were reviewed by all Associates and some Participants. All Participants reviewed the Introduction and Summary which provides the summary and implications of the U.S. analysis as well as recommendations for action.

INTRODUCTION AND SUMMARY

The United States is one of the largest producers, consumers, and exporters of coal in the world. Government energy policy now assigns a major role for coal as a vital source of energy in the years ahead, both in direct use as a fuel for electric power stations and industries, and also increasingly as a source of synthetic liquid and gaseous fuels. Industry concurs in this policy.

In this report we have developed estimates of a plausible range of future requirements for U.S. coal production, use and export, under a wide variety of realistic assumptions. We have also explored the feasibility of producing and using the required amounts of coal, and considered transportation and port infrastructures, capital and labor resource requirements and environmental issues associated with the projected coal expansion.

We conclude that coal production in the United States will need to at least triple from 1977 levels to more than 2 billion short tons[1] annually by year 2000 to meet the projected expansion in domestic and export coal demand. During the period of study 1980-2000, it is likely that coal will have to supply about two-thirds of the total *increase* in U.S. energy needs. These conclusions appear to be valid even if U.S. energy demand grows very slowly, because substantial amounts of coal will be needed to offset probable future reductions in oil imports and to compensate for potential delays in the expansion of nuclear power. Domestic coal requirements would be even higher if the large improvements in U.S. energy use efficiency that are assumed in the U.S. WOCOL projections are not achieved.

Of fundamental importance are two WOCOL findings about world energy prospects which have broad implications for the United States:

- Maintaining a global balance in oil supply and demand throughout this century will require strong measures by the United States to reduce oil imports.
- There will be a growing demand for imported coal in many countries, requiring the expansion of exports from producing countries, especially Australia and the United States. By the 1990's, the U.S. appears likely to become the world's balancing supplier of steam coal.

The future availability of oil for import by the industrial nations of the OECD is projected by the WOCOL analysis to be limited to no more than the 1979 levels, and a gradual decline of 10-20% by the year 2000 appears more likely. It appears that the United States, which is currently the world's largest oil importer, would have to reduce its imports from about 8 mbd in 1979 to 5 mbd or less by year 2000 to adjust to this projected oil limitation. Increased supplies of coal for domestic use could provide a major part of the incremental energy needed to compensate for such a reduction in oil imports.

---

[1] A short ton, the unit commonly used in the United States, is 10 percent lighter by weight than a metric ton.

The WOCOL analysis also shows that imported coal will be needed by many countries to provide a large share of their increase in future energy needs, and to compensate for reduced oil imports, as well as for possible delays in their nuclear power expansion programs. WOCOL concluded that world steam coal trade will need to increase by 10-15 times over the next twenty years, and that such an expansion in coal trade would be possible only if the United States increased its coal exports very significantly. U.S. coal exports are projected to increase from the 1979 level of 59 million metric tons per year (roughly ⅔ metallurgical coal and ⅓ steam coal), to at least 125-200 million metric tons and perhaps to as much as 300-400 million metric tons by year 2000. The principal customers for these coal exports are likely to be France, Italy, other countries of Western Europe, Japan, and the newly industrializing countries in East Asia (especially South Korea and Taiwan).

The United States is the only nation identified by WOCOL which appears to be capable of exporting significantly more than 200 million tons of coal by year 2000. It has very large coal reserves adequate to support growing domestic needs as well as greatly expanded export levels, which would still represent less than 20 percent of domestic production. Under such conditions the United States could, by the 1990's, be providing additional exports as needed to balance the total world demand and supply of coal.

Coal exports of 300-400 million tons per year would be the energy equivalent of 4-5 million barrels a day of oil—i.e., equal to one-half 1979 U.S. oil imports, and greater than the 1979 oil exports of any OPEC nation except Saudi Arabia. Even at today's coal prices (about $35/metric ton F.O.B. port), such exports of coal would represent $10-15 billion annually in U.S. foreign exchange earnings— equal to the current earnings from grain exports. The projected increase in coal for domestic use would, in addition, allow large savings in U.S. international payments for oil imports, which amounted to $59 billion in 1979.

However, achieving such an expansion of coal for domestic and export use will not be without difficulties. Significant physical and institutional obstacles will have to be overcome; moreover, there is a general lack of awareness within the United States that there may be a demand for such expanded export levels. A recent government projection, for example, anticipated export requirements of only 100 million tons in the year 2000.[2]

The United States coal industry has also been skeptical that a large domestic or export market will develop, and many potential coal importers are not yet persuaded that the United States will make the commitments necessary to satisfy the projected increase in export demand. Clearly, however, this skepticism in both the United States and coal-importing countries is subject to change as coal markets and prices develop, and as commitments by coal importers and exporters are demonstrated.

A strong national commitment to coal in the United States, evidenced by realistic plans and programs, will be required in order to achieve the projected expansion of coal production, use and export. While this prospect has been viewed with some skepticism, the urgent need for such an American commitment has begun to be recognized. "The stakes are enormous in its doing so," according to Dr. Ulf Lantzke,[2a] Executive Director of the International Energy Agency, "not only for

---

[2] National Energy Plan II, U.S. Department of Energy (May 1979).
[2a] "Expanding World Use of Coal," *Foreign Affairs,* December 1979.

the sake of American interests but for the sake of the entire structure of cooperation among the industrialized nations, and ultimately for the future health of the world economy as a whole."

RECOMMENDATIONS FOR ACTION IN THE UNITED STATES

We believe that a broadly based national program of action is required to overcome the skepticism and demonstrate the necessary commitment to coal.

The lead time for individual coal projects is long, usually 5-10 years. Even more significant, the large-scale industrial developments necessary to realize the coal expansion projected by WOCOL consist of many interweaving coal "chains" that will take sustained effort over all of the next two decades to complete. They must be started now, even before all the uncertainties about coal supply and demand are resolved.

We believe that federal and state governments and public authorities have a major part to play and should give serious consideration to the 10 action recommendations of the U.S. team which follow:

1. Make all efforts to ensure that the American public hears, understands, and accepts the message on: (1) the urgency of the world's energy problem; (2) the essential role which coal must play in providing a major part of the future increase in energy needs; and (3) the importance to America of reducing oil imports and expanding coal exports, and, thereby, providing leadership in solving the world energy problem.

2. Permit the price of domestic fuels to rise to market levels to assure effective competition between the various energy sources and conservation, and to foster efficient energy consumption and production of the lowest-cost energy resources.

3. Stabilize the environmental standards for mining, transporting and using coal, and integrate them with an energy policy which encourages the expansion of coal, so that the necessary investment decisions in coal mines, transport and user facilities will be taken soon. While providing for appropriate review by interested parties, expedite the environmental decision process for siting new coal facilities, so that coal projects can be executed without delay.

4. Intensify research on the regional and atmospheric effects of fossil fuel use such as acid rain and CO_2 buildup, and support development of international guidelines regarding border transport of pollutants.

5. Encourage decisions to build new coal-using facilities, especially actions to replace oil-using equipment with coal equipment, and to provide alternative fuel substitutes for oil. Examples include:

   —Support the improvement of financial viability in the nation's electric utilities, which will be the largest users of coal throughout the century. Provide appropriate investment incentives to encourage utilities to make oil-saving investments, e.g., early downrating or retirement of oil-fired capacity, conversion to coal, or the use of coal-oil mixtures where feasible.

   —Encourage industries, through incentives, regulatory measures such as the 1978 Fuel Use Act, etc., to reduce oil use by building coal-using equipment.

—Provide incentives to establish a domestic synthetic fuels industry, based on coal, oil shale and other fuels.

6. Facilitate the federal, state, and local process for approving federal leasing of Western coal lands, where some 60% of the coal reserves are owned by the U.S. Government, so that delays are avoided in the expansion of Western coal production.

7. Support the expansion of the U.S. coal transportation capacity, including a combination of coal slurry pipelines and expanded rail and barge facilities, and ensure that the transportation system remains competitive and economically viable, in terms of freight rates, for domestic and export customers.

8. Facilitate the local, state and federal approval process for siting and building modern coal ports on the East, Gulf, and West Coasts, so that expanded U.S. coal exports are not delayed by inadequate port capacities or by over-complicated institutional processes.

9. Encourage developing countries, through U.S. support of multilateral activities of the World Bank, United Nations Development Program and other agencies, to consider coal as a viable and economic energy option for supporting their future economic growth while reducing their needs for imported oil. Support also the financing of their activities to develop domestic coal resources, as well as the infrastructure necessary to transport and use or export the coal.

10. Continue and strengthen discussion and coordinated action on coal use and trade with other countries through the International Energy Agency.

Coal can provide the principal part of the additional energy needs of the next two decades. But the public and private enterprises concerned must act cooperatively and promptly if this is to be achieved.

APPROACH USED FOR THE UNITED STATES WOCOL ANALYSIS

Future U.S. coal requirements will be affected by many factors, including the rate of economic, energy and electricity growth, the efficiency of energy use, availability and price of domestic and world oil supplies, nuclear penetration in the electric utility sector, and the supplies of other forms of energy. Coal demand will also be affected greatly by nonquantifiable factors such as public attitudes toward mining, transporting and using greatly expanded amounts of coal.

A wide array of projections of U.S. coal demand has been published in the last few years, with the extreme projections for the year 2000 ranging from as little as 1.2 billion short tons per year to as much as 4.5 billion short tons per year. These projections compare to actual production of 688 million short tons in 1977, 654 million short tons in 1978, and 770 million short tons in 1979.

REFERENCE "LOW COAL" AND "HIGH COAL" CASES

In accordance with the guidelines established for the WOCOL country studies, two reference estimates were initially developed by the U.S. team to illustrate a plausible range of future coal production, use and exports in the United States: Case A ("Low Coal" Case) and Case B ("High Coal" Case).

The coal demand estimates were developed by analysis of the specific markets for coal: electric power generation, metallurgical (coking coal), industrial, residential/commercial, and synthetic fuel feedstock. In addition to domestic uses, a range of estimates for future coal exports was also developed.

The WOCOL Low Coal and High Coal Cases were derived within the range of energy use projections developed by the U.S. Department of Energy (DOE) for the National Energy Plan (NEP-II) of May 1979. The cases examined in NEP-II provide a range of total primary energy use from about 100 quads[3] to 125 quads in the year 2000, which was considered acceptable by WOCOL for examining the critical issues regarding coal. This range is compatible with U.S. economic growth of about 2.5-3% per year if primary energy use grows roughly 50-70% as rapidly as GNP during the 1977-2000 period (i.e., E/GNP eleasticity range is 0.5-0.7), compared to an E/GNP elasticity over the 1960-1973 period of approximately 1.0. Clearly, a range of 100-125 quads in the year 2000 implies considerable success in improving the efficiency of energy use.

Case A (Low Coal Case) investigates coal requirements under the lower energy growth assumptions of 1.2% per year over the 1977-2000 period corresponding to primary energy use of 100 quads in the year 2000. The higher coal demand estimates of Case B (High Coal Case) are associated with the more rapid growth rates of 2.2% per year for primary energy use—125 quads energy use in the year 2000. Within the total energy use, the assumed growth rates for electricity generation were 2.5% per year (annual average for 1977-2000) in Case A and 4.1% per year in Case B—again the same range investigated in NEP-II.

Although the projections developed by WOCOL use the same range of total energy and electricity requirements as the DOE analysis prepared for NEP-II, different estimates of coal market requirements have been developed to reflect WOCOL's focus on coal, as well as the judgment of the U.S. WOCOL team. As an example, the DOE analysis projected that coal use in industry would grow rapidly from 60 mtce in 1977 to 100 mtce in 1985, and to a narrow range of 225-235 mtce in 2000. The WOCOL team's judgment was that a much slower growth is likely prior to 1985, and that a considerably wider range in the year 2000 would more accurately reflect the uncertainties in the growth of industrial coal use. Accordingly, the WOCOL projections show industry use growing only to 70-80 mtce by 1985, and to a range of 125-225 mtce in 2000. Another example is the NEP-II projection of U.S. coal exports of only 100 mtce in year 2000, under all scenarios, whereas WOCOL expects much greater export requirements under any conceivable set of assumptions.

Details of the WOCOL projections of coal demand in the various market sectors for the Low Coal and High Coal cases are provided in the section on Coal Demand and Appendix 3. Coal production requirements are described in the section on Coal Supply.

SENSITIVITY CASES—OIL LIMITATION AND NUCLEAR DELAYS

WOCOL review of all the country studies provided by teams participating in the World Coal Study led to two additional analyses: "Oil Limitation," and "Nuclear Delays." These "sensitivity" cases investigated the possible impacts on coal requirements over and above the reference Low Coal and High Coal projections, of (1) a limitation on the amount of oil available for import, and (2)

[3] The term "quads" is used in this report to refer to quadrillion (10^{15}) Btu.

delays in the projected expansion of nuclear power. The U.S. WOCOL analysis of these sensitivity cases is set forth in the section on Impact of Oil Import Limitations and Nuclear Energy Delays on Coal Demand.

TIME PERIOD FOR CONDUCTING THE ANALYSIS

The data collection and analysis for the WOCOL study of U.S. coal requirements began in October 1978 and was largely completed by October 1979. Most of the text of this report was completed by January 18, 1980. During the period of study the world price of oil increased from $13/barrel to an average of $30/barrel, and the developments in Iran and Afghanistan and the Three Mile Island nuclear accident have all had their impacts. While the full effects of these events remain to be seen, they are not expected to significantly alter the conclusions of this report. In fact, they are likely to reinforce the conclusion that a major expansion of United States coal production, use, and export is required to support even moderate economic growth.

COAL DEMAND IN MAJOR MARKETS— LOW COAL AND HIGH COAL CASES

WOCOL projections of coal use by market sector for the Low Coal and High Coal Cases are presented in this section. The following section describes the possible effects of limitations on world oil availability and delays in expansion of nuclear power on the coal demand projections. Supporting data are provided in Appendix 3.

The projections are generally expressed in *million metric tons of coal equivalent* (mtce). One mtce is equivalent to 27.78 trillion (10^{12}) Btu, 1.15 million short tons of Appalachian bituminous coal at 12,000 Btu/lb, or 1.6 million short tons of Western subbituminous coal at 8,500 Btu/lb).

ELECTRIC UTILITY SECTOR

Coal use by market is illustrated in Figure 16-1. In 1979, 78%[4] of U.S. domestic coal use was consumed by electric utilities in coal-fired power plants. The utility sector is expected to see significant growth in the next several years. The dominance of electric utilities as the driving market force for additional coal use is projected to continue through the 1980's and most of the 1990's. In developing a plausible range of estimated future coal use in the electric sector, several factors need to be considered, including current electric power capacity, future load growth, and future capacity mix, as well as plant capacity factors and thermal efficiencies.

CURRENT SITUATION AND LOAD GROWTH PROJECTIONS

After twenty years of electric load growth in the range of 7-8%/yr, there has been a significant reduction in the growth of total electrical output (kWh/yr) to an average of about 3.5%/yr since 1973. The annual figures for peak load growth in the 1974-1979 years are 1.3%, 2.1%, 4.0%, 6.5%, 3.3% and 0.6%.

---

[4] As a percentage of total tonnage consumed. Electric utility coal use was 476 million short tons (mst) in 1977, 480 mst in 1978, and 527 mst in 1979.

Figure 16-1. Coal Flow Diagram—1979 (Million Short Tons)

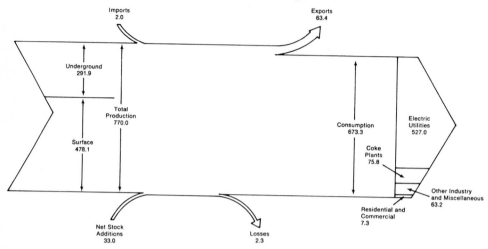

Source: U.S. Department of Energy.

Installed capacity grew more rapidly at an average 5.8%/yr over this period due to the completion of plants begun in the period of higher growth before 1974. Thus, for the total U.S. electric system, the gross peak reserve margin (i.e., excess of peak capacity over peak load) grew from 21% in 1973 to 38% in 1979. This national average, however, masks significant variations among regions; the U.S. electric system is highly fragmented and diverse both in number and size of firms as well as type of ownership (private, municipal, federal, etc.).

To derive the WOCOL coal-electric estimates, a range of assumptions about future electricity generation growth has been used.

- High Coal Case: 4.4%/yr for 1977-85, 4.0%/yr for 1985-2000.
- Low Coal Case: 3.4%/yr for 1977-85, 2.0%/yr for 1985-2000.

The WOCOL estimates cover approximately the same range used by DOE for NEP-II (May, 1979).[5]

Figure 16-2 shows projections of electrical peak load and capacity. Construction work in progress leads to projecting a relatively narrow band of uncertainty for installed peak capacity in 1985, from 680-711 GWe. Under these conditions, the reserve margin could decline somewhat to 25% by 1985 in the High Coal Case, but would still exceed 30% under the Low Coal Case conditions.[6]

After 1985, the two WOCOL projections portray very different futures of electric utility growth. The Low Coal Case assumes modest load growth which, coupled with the excess capacity situation in 1985, leads to the addition of 220 GWe of electric capacity in the 1985-2000 period. The High Coal Case assumes

[5] *Electrical World*, in its 30th Annual Electrical Industry Forecast, September 15, 1979, projects total electrical output to grow at 3.9%/yr from 1977-1985 and 3.8%/yr from 1985-1995, which also falls within the WOCOL range of assumptions.

[6] *Electrical World* (1979) projects a peak capacity of 702 GWe in 1985, with a peakload of 524 GWe and a derived gross peak margin of 34%. The *EW* projections also show a peak capacity of 785 GWe in 1990 and 950 GWe in 1995, with an average system-wide gross peak margin of 18% in 1995.

Figure 16-2. Electric Peak Load and Capacity (1977–2000)

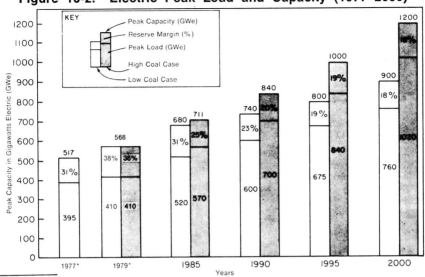

* Data for 1977 and 1979 (preliminary) taken from *Electrical World*, September 15, 1979.

robust growth in generation load after 1985, requiring the addition of nearly 500 GWe of new capacity in the 1985-2000 period. Additions during the past fifteen-year period, 1965-1980, totaled 360 GWe, halfway between the WOCOL projections for 1985-2000.

Replacement of old capacity would make the gross additions somewhat higher than these figures which refer to net additions. Appendix 2 presents an age profile of existing electric power capacity. About 20%, or 100 GWe, was installed before 1960, and a considerable part of this old capacity—perhaps 50-75 GWe—would probably have to be replaced by the year 2000.

ELECTRICITY CAPACITY MIX

Electric capacity mixes for the Low Coal and High Coal Cases are summarized in Figure 16-3, and detailed in Table 16-1. The coal-fired capacity is expected to grow from about 200 GWe in 1977 to 284-305 GWe in 1985. After 1985, the coal capacity is derived as a residual to meet total installed capacity projections, after subtracting the projected capacity of oil and gas, hydroelectric, geothermal, solar, and nuclear plants.

Coal capacity in year 2000 ranges from 465-625 GWe in the two cases as shown.

The capacity of oil and gas-fired power plants is expected to plateau following completion of plants now under construction and then to decline somewhat due to retirements.[7] Growth of hydro, geothermal, and solar capacity in the 1977-2000 period is expected to be quite limited.

[7] Total output from oil and gas-fired power plants is likely to decline faster than capacity as these plants are increasingly removed from baseload operation and used for peaking or cycling service. See the section on impacts of oil import limitations for a discussion of further reductions in oil use in the electric sector in response to a projected limitation on the availability of imported oil.

Figure 16-3. Electric Capacity Mix (1977–2000)

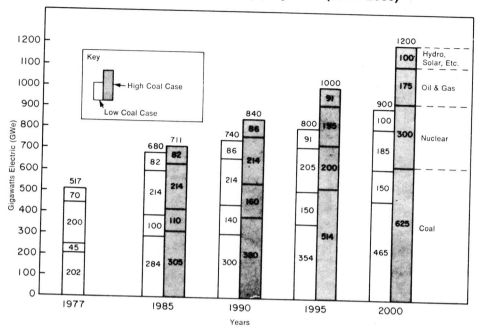

The major alternative to coal for new utility plants is nuclear power. In the Low Coal Case, in which electric load generation grows only at 2%/yr after 1985, the 100 GWe of nuclear power capacity now under construction is assumed to be completed and licensed to operate. New construction licenses are, however, assumed to be delayed until after 1990, which leads to an assumed nuclear capacity of 150 GWe by the early 1990's and the same capacity in the year 2000.

In the High Coal Case, with its higher electricity load growth assumption, the nuclear plants under construction are assumed to be completed by 1990, the 50 additional GWe of capacity which have already been ordered are assumed to receive construction licenses before 1985, and to be built by 1995, and about 20 GWe/yr of new nuclear orders are assumed to be placed by utilities after 1985. This case leads to a nuclear capacity of 200 GWe by 1995 and 300 GWe by year 2000.

The range of 150-300 GWe used in the WOCOL projections of year 2000 nuclear capacity is similar to the range of 150-250 GWe developed in the recent estimates by the DOE Energy Information Administration (EIA, October 1979). The corresponding EIA range for 1995 was 156-196 GWe, which compares with the WOCOL range of 150-200 GWe. Such projections pose fundamental questions about the future viability of the American nuclear energy industry, at least as it now exists. Even the higher nuclear levels projected represent considerable delays compared to previous expectations, and would use only two-thirds of the current capacity of the domestic nuclear steam supply system (NSSS) industry.

Table 16-1. Total Electric Capacity, 1977-2000

WOCOL   Units: GWe capacity

Power Plant Type	1977	1985 Low Coal	1985 High Coal	1990 Low Coal	1990 High Coal	1995 Low Coal	1995 High Coal	2000 Low Coal	2000 High Coal
Nuclear [+]	45	100	110	140	160	150	200	150	300
Hydro/Pumped Storage	69	80	80	83	83	85	85	88	88
Gas Turbines/Combined Cycle	45	55	55	60	60	70	70	80	80
Geothermal/Solar/Other	1	2	2	3	3	6	6	12	12
Fossil Steam									
Oil Steam [+]	98	114	114	114	114	110	110	95	85
Gas Steam	59	45	45	40	40	25	25	10	10
Coal Steam [*,+]	202	284	305	300	380	354	514	465	625
Total Electric Capacity	517	680	711	740	840	800	1000	900	1200
Coal Penetration (%)	39%	42%	43%	41%	45%	44%	51%	51%	51%

[+] See following section for a discussion of possible impacts of oil limitation and nuclear delays on these projections

[*] The coal capacity is derived as a residual to meet total peak capacity needs after subtracting the projected capacity of other sources.

REQUIREMENTS FOR NEW COAL-FIRED POWER PLANTS

Both the Low Coal and High Coal Cases lead to substantial requirements for new coal-fired generating capacity, as shown in Figures 16-4 and 16-5. Construction now underway involves the completion of about 10 GWe/yr for the 1977-85 period.

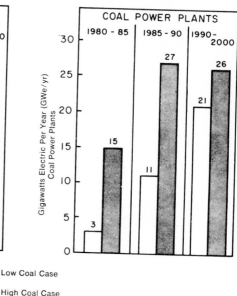

Figure 16-4.
Annual Net Additions to Capacity

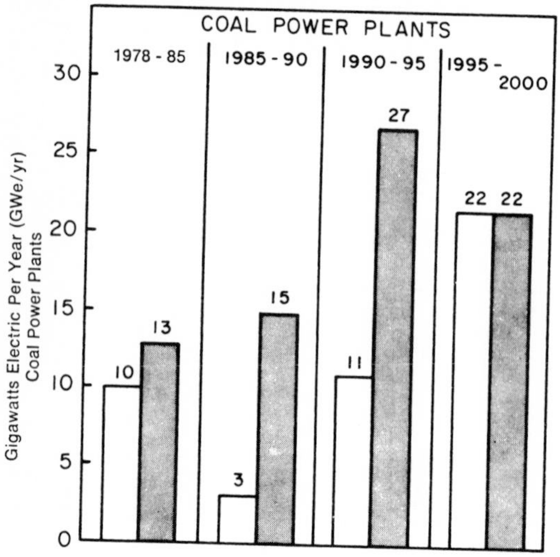

Figure 16-5.
Annual New Construction Starts

Key:
☐ Low Coal Case
▨ High Coal Case

The High Coal Case requires a slight increase over that level to 15 GWe/yr of new construction starts in the early 1980's, with activity doubling in the late 1980's (Fig. 16-5). In this case the electric utility market would provide a steady driving force for expansion of the domestic coal supply industry.

The Low Coal Case presents a somewhat different picture. Due to the combined effects of excess current capacity, construction in progress on coal and nuclear facilities, and the assumed low load growth, the Low Coal Case requires a very low rate of new construction starts in the early 1980's before a moderate rate returns later in the 1980's. The rate accelerates substantially in the 1990's however, even with the low load growth assumed in the Low Coal Case.

COAL REQUIREMENTS IN THE ELECTRIC SECTOR

Both the Low Coal and High Coal Cases require significant increases in coal use by the electric sector, ranging from a doubling to a tripling by the year 2000 from the 1977 level of just under 400 mtce/yr. Coal use in the electric sector grows by 3.4-5%/yr over the 1977-2000 period. Coal requirements as well as the complete primary energy fuel balances for the electric power sector are presented in Table 16-2.

442

Table 16-2. Total Electricity Consumption, 1977–2000

WOCOL Units: mtce/yr. fuel input

Power Plant Type	1977	1985 Low Coal	1985 High Coal	1990 Low Coal	1990 High Coal	1995 Low Coal	1995 High Coal	2000 Low Coal	2000 High Coal
Nuclear [+]	97	200	220	280	320	300	400	300	600
Hydro/Pumped Storage	86	108	108	114	114	122	122	138	138
Gas Turbines/Combined Cycle	11	16	16	20	20	22	22	25	25
Geothermal/Solar/Other	1	2	2	3	3	6	6	12	12
Fossil Steam									
Oil Steam [+]	130	166	166	170	170	160	150	140	100
Gas Steam	115	68	68	50	50	25	25	10	10
Coal Steam [+,*]	372	500	560	533	748	655	965	800	1170
Total Primary Fuel Input	809	1060	1140	1170	1425	1290	1690	1425	2055
Coal Penetration (%)	46%	47%	49%	46%	52%	51%	56%	55%	57%

[+] See following section for a discussion of the possible impacts of a limitation on world oil availability and delays in nuclear power expansion on these projections. In the case of oil steam electric requirements, the "oil limitation" projections are compatible with a U.S. Government proposal under consideration in 1980 designed to substantially reduce utility oil use by 1990.

[*] The coal-fired generation (and primary fuel requirement) is derived as a residual to meet total electricity generation needs, after substracting the projected contributions of other sources.

METALLURGICAL SECTOR

Use of coal to make coke for metallurgical purposes was the second largest U.S. consumer of coal in 1977, accounting for 77 mtce, or 15%, of total domestic coal use.[8] Metallurgical use had fluctuated between 83 and 96 mtce/year over the previous decade. Current projections show a modest growth in the consumption of metallurgical coal to 100-110 mtce/yr by the year 2000. This has been used as the WOCOL range.

Projecting future metallurgical coal use is difficult because of possible changes in the structure of the iron and steel industry, recent declines in coke oven capacity, and development of the technique of direct reduction of iron ore in making steel. In particular it is important to note that not all the demand for coke will necessarily be satisfied by domestic metallurgical coals and coke ovens. As the productive capacity of domestic ovens continues to decline, due to retirement of old ovens, some increase in coke imports may be required to meet the domestic demand.

A second factor is the question of technological improvement. Because of a wide variety of factors, the average coke rate (amount of coke required to produce a ton of pig iron) has declined over the years. If this trend continues and the rate of growth of raw steel demand remains low (½%/yr), and the use of electric furnaces and/or direct reduction increases, the demand for metallurgical coals in the United States could be somewhat less than indicated in the projections.

INDUSTRIAL/RETAIL SECTOR

The consumption of coal by the industrial/retail sector was 60 mtce in 1977, of which about 6 mtce is accounted for by retail trade (residential/commercial). Coal has nearly disappeared as a fuel for homes and commercial facilities over the last 30 years, declining steadily from nearly 100 mtce in 1947 (then about 50% of all energy used in the residential/commercial sector). No significant increase in coal use in the retail sector is currently expected by most analysts, although it can not be entirely ruled out.

The outlook for coal use by industry is quite different. While industrial coal use has declined over the past three decades, falling from about 240 mtce in 1947 to 53 mtce (60 million short tons[9]) in 1977, the industrial coal market is projected to reverse its decline in response to the rising price and decreasing availability of oil and gas. In addition, federal regulation in the form of the 1978 Fuel Use Act now allows government to mandate coal use in large industrial boilers by prohibiting oil or gas as the primary fuel.

Industrial energy use is concentrated in a few key industries and can be divided into three categories: boilers; process heat; and raw material feedstock. Table 16-3 shows the breakdown among these categories for oil and gas use in the major energy-consuming industries.

Chemicals, petroleum refining, and paper manufacture are expected to be major coal consuming industries because they use large boilers at high load factors, where the economics of coal are most attractive. In addition, direct use

---

[8] Metallurgical coal use was 77 million short tons in 1977, 71 mst in 1978, and 76 mst in 1979.

[9] Industrial coal use was 60 million short tons in 1977, 59 mst in 1978, and 63 mst in 1979.

of coal in the cement industry (Stone, Clay, & Glass Products in Table 16-3) is increasing significantly as many manufacturers are converting their kilns from oil and/or gas to coal.

Table 16-3. Oil and Gas Use in Manufacturing by Use Category, 1974 (mtce)

Industry	Boiler Fuel	Process Heat	Feed Stock	Other	Total Oil and Gas Use
Petroleum Refining	22.4	78.5	—	2.1	103
Primary Metals	10.7	39.0	3.6	7.1	60
Stone, Clay & Glass Products	0.3	27.7	—	—	28
Chemicals	40.2	18.0	81.0	8.9	148
Paper	24.9	5.3	—	4.6	35
Food	14.2	3.6	—	3.6	21
All Other Manufacturing	24.5	24.9	—	—	50
Total All Manufacturing[a]	137	197	85	26	445

[a] Totals are rounded.
Source: EEA, Inc., *Energy Consumption Data Base* (1977).

The major increases in industrial coal use are projected to occur after 1985. The following range of estimates for growth in industrial coal use has been used for WOCOL:

- Low Coal Case: 2%/yr in 1977-85, 4%/yr in 1985-2000.
- High Coal Case: 3.5%/yr in 1977-85, 7%/yr in 1985-2000.

These assumptions translate into a growth of industry/retail coal use from 60 mtce in 1977 to 70-80 mtce in 1985, and to 125-220 mtce in 2000.

Among the factors affecting future industrial coal use will be federal interpretation and enforcement of the Fuel Use Act and environmental controls specified in the revised New Source Performance Standards (NSPS) for industrial boilers, which EPA expects to propose in 1980. Other factors include:

- future availability and price of oil and natural gas;
- the level of investment tax credits for new coal-fired boilers; and
- the development of technology such as fluidized bed combustion and coal-oil mixtures to facilitate the burning of coal in small boilers.

The conversion of coal to low or medium-Btu gas may also have special attraction to some sectors of the industrial market.

COAL USE IN SYNTHETIC FUELS SECTOR

A major long-term potential coal market is conversion of coal into synthetic liquid and gaseous fuels in large-scale synfuel plants. This option could allow the continued use of existing oil and gas distribution/use systems and could be particularly important in meeting future needs for liquid motor fuels. Other sources of unconventional oil and gas will also be important in this regard, with most attention in the United States being given to heavy oil, oil shale, enhanced oil recovery, unconventional gas, and biomass conversion.

In the past, interest in building coal-based synfuel plants has been limited because such plants were not competitive with oil and gas available from conventional sources. However, interest has intensified recently in expediting the creation of a synthetic fuels industry, which could help to provide some insurance against rapidly rising world oil prices and uncertainties about future oil supplies.

At the time of this report, the United States Congress was in the final stages of discussion likely to result in 1980 legislation which may provide significant incentives for a new "synfuels" industry. The precise nature of the final legislation and its impact on the future development of coal-based synfuel plants remain uncertain. Many uncertainties also remain concerning the capital costs of synfuel plants, their coal conversion efficiencies and other factors.

For the purpose of projecting the demand for coal, the WOCOL team postulated initially a range of U.S. synfuel development programs for the Low Coal and High Coal Cases[10]:

- Low Coal Case: 50 mtce annual coal feedstock requirement by year 2000, roughly equivalent to 1 large-scale facility on-line by 1990, 4 facilities by 1995, and 10 facilities by 2000[11]
- High Coal Case: 200 mtce by year 2000, roughly equivalent to 1 large-scale facility on-line by year 1990, 10 facilities by 1995, and 40 facilities by 2000[11]

The Low Coal Case synthetic fuels program could be viewed as a significant demonstration program, but would have little effect on the overall U.S. energy supply/demand balance as it would produce only about 0.5 mbdoe (oil and gas) by the year 2000.

The High Coal Case synthetic fuels program would begin to have a significant effect on the U.S. energy balance in the 1990's, producing 1.75 mbdoe of oil and gas by year 2000. More importantly, a significant coal synfuels industry would be developed and in place by the end of the century which could, at the rate of building 10 facilities/yr, produce the energy equivalent of 4.1 mbdoe in 2005, and 6.6 mbdoe by 2010. Under such assumptions, the synthetic fuels sector would consume more coal in 2005 than now consumed by electric utilities. Moreover, another large contribution to a U.S. synfuels program could be provided by oil shale, which would add further to the production levels cited above.

The possibility of expedited synfuel programs, beyond the Low Coal and High Coal estimates used here, is discussed later in the context of possible responses to a limitation on world oil availability. These expanded synfuel programs are more in line with the objectives of the synfuel initiatives under discussion in the U.S. Congress in 1980.

---

[10] The WOCOL synfuel range for Low Coal and High Coal Cases was developed in early 1979 in line with the U.S. DOE projection of 150 mtce by year 2000 in the base case of NEP-II (May 1979). See the section on oil import limitations for discussion of increased synfuel levels projected under conditions of an "Oil Limitation."

[11] Number of facilities indicated assumes 50,000 bdoe synthetic oil or gas plant operating 330 days per year.

446

COAL EXPORT MARKET

Considerable expansion of the demand for coal exports from the United States appears likely in the 1980-2000 period. In fact, the levels of world coal imports projected by WOCOL to be required by year 2000 are not feasible without a major expansion of exports from coal producers, especially the United States, Australia, Canada, and the Republic of South Africa.

Projecting the future level of U.S. coal exports is difficult, because exports are determined not only by U.S. decisions and actions, but even more importantly by decisions in the major energy-using countries which do not have significant coal production potential. The major potential coal-importing countries identified by WOCOL include Japan, France, Italy, several other countries of Western Europe, South Korea, and Taiwan. The requirements of these countries for coal imports—total imports in general and requirements for U.S. coal in particular—will depend on energy and coal developments in each country as well as the quality, availability, price and reliability of coal supplies from the coal-exporting countries.

The U.S. WOCOL team initially assumed year 2000 U.S. export requirements of 125 mtce in the Low Coal Case, and 200 mtce in the High Coal Case, based on initial expectations of the likely growth of the demand for exports. However, the possibility of greatly expanded demand for U.S. exports, up to 350 mtce by year 2000, is discussed later, and these higher levels appear to be required if the WOCOL projections of world coal import requirements are to be satisfied.

TOTAL COAL REQUIREMENTS BY MARKET

Total requirements of U.S. coal for electric, metallurgical, industry/retail, synthetic fuel and export markets are projected to grow from 560 mtce in 1977 to 1,200 mtce in the year 2000 for the Low Coal Case and to 1,900 mtce (about 2,500 million short tons) for the High Coal Case, as detailed in Table 16-4. These two WOCOL cases present a picture of future U.S. coal use with a required doubling or tripling over current use by the year 2000. For comparison, projections of coal requirements are also provided from the NEP-II Base Case and an updated DOE projection, as well as recent studies by the U.S. Department of Commerce, the Energy Modeling Forum (EMF), and the International Agency (IEA).

Figure 16-6 shows the shares of the various coal markets in the total requirement. As can be seen, the electric utility sector remains the dominant factor in determining the scale of coal use throughout this century, although significant expansion of the industry, synthetic fuels and export markets are also projected.

A slightly different picture emerges if the *incremental* shares of the different coal markets are considered, that is, the share of the *growth* in coal requirements attributable to the five sectors. Figures 16-7 and 16-8 present these incremental market shares for the 1977-1985 period as contrasted to the 1990-2000 period for the two cases.

In the Low Coal Case, the utility share of incremental coal use declines from 80% in the 1977-1985 period to 66% in the 1990-2000 period, while the combined share of industry, synthetic fuels and export markets increases from 15% to about 30%. The High Coal Case indicates a somewhat greater decline

447

Table 16-4. Total Coal Requirements, 1977 and 2000 (mtce)

Coal Market Sector	Year 1977	YEAR 2000						
		WOCOL Low Coal (Case A)	High Coal (Case B)	U.S. DOE NEP-II Base Case 1979	1980[12] Update	Com- merce[13]	IEA[13]	EMF[13]
Electric	372	800	1,170	810	975	1,094	800	1,159
Metallurgical	77	100	110	100	100	105	92	105
Industry/Retail	60	125	220	230	225	137	} 160	458
Synthetic Fuels	0	50	200	150	275	72		108
Export	50	125	200	100	100	150	129	100
Total Coal Requirements	560	1,200	1,900	1,390	1,675	1,548	1,171	1,930

[12] Unpublished update of NEP-II projection by U.S. DOE/Policy and Evaluation in January 1980. The updated DOE projection of coal use in year 2000 is 20 percent higher than the NEP-II projection. The updated projection assumes higher world oil prices, lower economic growth, and lower nuclear capacity than NEP-II.

[13] Sources: U.S. Dept. of Commerce: *Forecast of Likely U.S. Energy Supply/Demand Balances for 1985 and 2000 and Implications for U.S. Energy Policy* (1977). Energy Modeling Forum: *Coal in Transition: 1980-2000,* Stanford University (September 1978). International Energy Agency: *Steam Coal Prospects to 2000* (December 1978).

Figure 16-6. Total Coal Requirements by Sector (1977–2000)

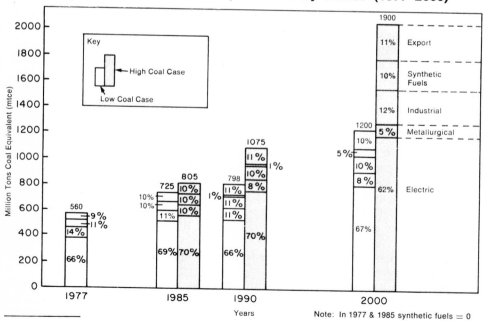

Note: In 1977 & 1985 synthetic fuels = 0

of the utility market share of incremental coal use from 78% in the near term to 50% in the 1990's, while the combined share of industry, synthetic fuels, and exports is projected to grow from 19% in 1977-1985 to 47% in 1990-2000.

In summary, both cases indicate a significant shift of coal from essentially a one-market fuel (electric utilities) today to a broad-based energy market in the 1990's, with substantial growth expected in the industry, synthetic fuels and export markets as well as the electric utility market. Such a multiple-market coal energy economy could provide a measure of continuity in coal demand patterns not available to the United States coal industry in the 1970s.

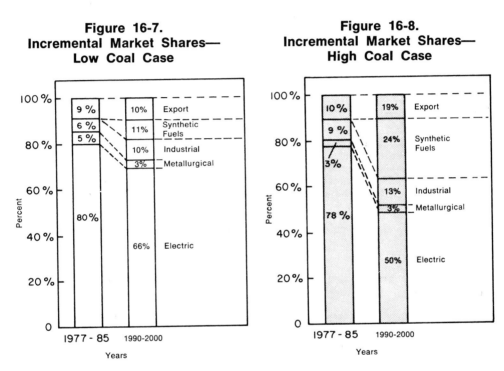

Figure 16-7.
Incremental Market Shares—
Low Coal Case

Figure 16-8.
Incremental Market Shares—
High Coal Case

IMPACTS OF OIL IMPORT LIMITATIONS AND NUCLEAR ENERGY DELAYS ON COAL DEMAND

The evolution of United States energy supply and demand patterns will not be independent of energy developments in the rest of the world. A special feature of the World Coal Study has been the assessment of the implications for individual WOCOL countries of (1) a limitation on the availability of world oil supplies, and (2) possible delays in several countries in the expansion of nuclear power programs.

ENERGY SUPPLY BALANCES FOR REFERENCE LOW COAL AND HIGH COAL CASES

The primary energy supply balances developed for the reference U.S. Low Coal and High Coal Cases are shown in Table 16-5, which also provides for comparison two of the DOE NEP-II case balances.

449

Table 16-5. Energy Supply Balances, 1977 and 2000 (quadrillion Btu)

Supply Source	1977	2000			
		WOCOL		DOE NEP-II	
		Low Coal (Case A)	High Coal (Case B)	Low Demand Case	Base Case*
Domestic Oil & NGL	20	18	18	21	21
Imported Oil	18	18	20	15	18
Natural Gas	20	17	17	18	20
Hydro, Solar, Geothermal**	2	9	7	7	8
Nuclear	3	8	17	13	16
Coal	14	30	47	28	36*
Total Primary Energy**	76	100	125	101	117*

* An unpublished update of the NEP-II Base Case projection, by U.S. DOE/Policy and Evaluation in January 1980, indicates total primary energy use of 106 quads in year 2000. The major differences from NEP-II are significantly higher world oil prices, lower economic growth, and significant reductions of nuclear energy and imported oil contributions, and a substantial increase in coal use. The updated projection of coal use by DOE increased 20 percent by 7 quads to 43 quads in year 2000 despite the overall 11 quad reduction in energy use.

** Excludes 1.8 quads of biomass used in paper and pulp industry, not accounted in 1977 base year statistics.

Some key assumptions about energy supplies other than coal that are implicit in the reference WOCOL projections in Table 16-5 include:

- Conventional oil production drops from 9.4 mbd in 1977 to 6.5 mbd in 2000.
- Shale oil and enhanced oil recovery add 2 mbd to domestic oil supplies by 2000.
- Conventional gas production drops from 19.5 tcf in 1977 to 14 tcf in 2000.
- Unconventional gas (tight sands, Devonian shales, etc.) and gas imports add 3 tcf/year by 2000.
- Contributions from new renewable energy technologies increase from negligible levels today to 3-5 quads in the year 2000.[14]

14 While no attempt has been made here to identify which renewable technologies would provide this contribution, the size of the task is illustrated by U.S. Department of Commerce estimates that the following combination of measures could, if feasible, provide 5 quads of energy by year 2000: installing solar heating devices on 15 million homes (one-third of all new homes and retrofit of 10% of existing homes); conversion annually of 67 million tons of municipal sewage and trash, 120 million tons of animal waste, and 1.4 billion tons of agricultural waste; production of 500,000 barrels per day oil equivalent of alcohol in 380 facilities using grain from 45 million acres (14% of 1975 U.S. cultivated land); and construction of 100,000 windmills (@ 100 kWe) to provide 10 GWe-installed electric capacity.

- Nuclear power capacity increases by three-to-six fold over 1977 levels by the year 2000.
- About 8-9 mbd of imported oil continues to be available to the United States throughout the century.

Both the WOCOL and DOE projections in Table 16-5 indicate a major role for coal in providing a large share of the increase in U.S. energy requirements over the 1977-2000 period. In the reference WOCOL cases, for example, coal provides two-thirds of the total increase in primary energy supplies. By comparison, the DOE projections for NEP-II show coal providing about 55% of the increase in U.S. energy use over the period; however, the updated DOE projections of January 1980 show coal providing a much greater share—about 95% of the increased energy needs, on a net basis.

WOCOL reviewed the oil import and nuclear power assumptions contained in the reference Low Coal and High Coal projections in each of the country studies. As described in *Coal—Bridge to the Future*, the combined country projections would lead to a requirement for total OECD oil imports in year 2000 (about 29-30 mbd) which is considerably greater than what is likely to be available (21-22 mbd). Moreover, a seven-ten fold expansion in OECD nuclear power capacity was implied in the reference projections. Based on this WOCOL review, country teams evaluated possible responses to a limitation on world oil availability and to delays in their projected expansion of nuclear power. For coal-producing countries such as the United States, increases in coal exports, required to help compensate for the effect of the limitations in coal importing countries, were considered in addition to the expanded domestic requirements for coal.

LIMITATION ON WORLD OIL AVAILABILITY

The United States WOCOL team analyzed the possible impacts of reducing the projected year 2000 oil imports to 5 mbd, compared to 1977 imports of 8.5 mbd and reference import projections in year 2000 of 8.4 mbd in the Low Coal Case and 9.2 mbd in the High Coal Case. The required savings represent about 20% of the total U.S. oil use, which was 18.3 mbd in 1977 and projected to range from 17-19 mbd in the reference WOCOL projections for year 2000.

IMPACT ON DOMESTIC COAL USE

Table 16-6 shows a representative distribution of projected oil consumption by market, which was used to develop oil substitution measures for the WOCOL analysis.

A representative set of energy supply measures have been developed for WOCOL which could, if implemented, achieve the necessary savings.[15]

- Oil use in utility boilers is reduced to 0.3 mbd by year 2000 (in both cases) by substitution of coal, compared to 1.8 mbd oil use in 1977.
- Oil use in industry boilers is reduced to 0.5 mbd by year 2000 (in both cases), compared to 1.0 mbd in 1977, by substitution of coal.

---

[15] These measures are approximately compatible with various proposals under consideration by the U.S. government in January 1980, designed to reduce oil use in electric utility boilers and to increase the pace of synthetic fuel development, among other things.

451

Table 16-6. Projected Oil Consumption by Sector, 1977–2000 (mbd)

Sector	1977	1985 Low Coal Case	1985 High Coal Case	1990 Low Coal Case	1990 High Coal Case	2000 Low Coal Case	2000 High Coal Case
Transportation	9.7	9.6	9.9	9.7	10.1	9.7	10.8
Residential/Commercial	3.3	2.8	2.8	2.8	2.8	2.0	2.3
Industry: Nonboiler uses	2.5	2.6	2.6	2.6	2.8	2.4	3.0
Industry: Boilers	1.0	1.0	1.1	1.1	1.2	1.0	1.4
Electric Utilities*	1.8	2.3	2.3	2.3	2.3	2.0	1.5
Total Oil Consumption	18.3	18.4	18.7	18.5	19.2	17.2	19.0
Total Oil Imports	8.5	8.4	8.6	8.6	9.3	8.4	9.2

* Includes a small amount of oil use in gas turbines for peaking purposes.

- Supplies of unconventional gas are increased from 1 tcf/yr in year 2000 in the reference projections to 2-3 tcf/yr (1-1.5 mbdoe).
- Coal-based synthetic fuels provide the balance required.[16] This increases the year 2000 coal-synfuel projections to 1.3 mbdoe in the Low Coal Case and to 3.1 mbdoe in the High Coal Case. Production of 0.3-0.5 mbdoe of oil and gas from coal by 1990 appears possible if a "crash" program is implemented immediately.

The total effect of the assumed oil-saving measures is to increase projected year 2000 domestic coal requirements by 20-25% above the reference projections. Additional savings from other oil conservation measures, over and above those implied in the reference WOCOL projections which indicate U.S. oil use holding roughly constant at the 1977 level through the year 2000, would reduce somewhat the need for the specific measures outlined above.

In implementing the coal-related measures, special attention should be devoted to those coal technologies which can provide the earliest impact in the most competitive way, for example:

- direct use of coal in cement plants and under utility or industry boilers whenever possible;
- use of coal-oil mixtures as a way to produce incremental oil use reductions at existing oil installations where complete conversions are not possible; and
- use of proven technology to produce low and medium-Btu gas from coal.

IMPACT ON COAL EXPORT REQUIREMENTS

The responses of countries in Western Europe and Japan to a limitation on world oil availability will involve increases in their coal import requirements, as well as other measures to compensate for reduced oil imports. A considerable portion of such increased coal imports would have to be provided by the United States. As the World Coal Study analysis indicates, only the United States and

[16] Shale oil already provided 1 mbd in the reference projections and was not increased further.

452

Australia are capable of exporting significantly more than 100 mtce by the year 2000. Moreover, the United States is the only nation identified by WOCOL which appears to be capable of exporting significantly more than 200 mtce by the year 2000. Demand for U.S. coal exports was estimated to increase from the reference case estimates (125-200 mtce) to a range of 200-350 mtce by year 2000 under the conditions of an oil limitation.

IMPACT ON TOTAL U.S. COAL REQUIREMENTS

Table 16-7 shows that the effect of the oil limitation assumptions would be to increase total U.S. coal (domestic and export) requirements projected in year 2000 by 335 mtce (28%) to 1,535 mtce in the Low Coal Case (A-1) and by 460 mtce (24%) to 2,360 mtce in the High Coal Case (B-1).

Table 16-7. Possible Impact of World Oil Limitation on U.S. Coal Requirements (mtce)

	Low Coal Case (A-1)			High Coal Case (B-1)		
	1985	1990	2000	1985	1990	2000
Incremental Coal Increase						
Electric Sector	25	52	115	25	62	75
Industry Sector	5	15	35	5	23	60
Synfuel Feedstock	0	35	110	0	60	175
Exports	10	35	75	10	30	150
Total Coal Increase Under Oil Limitation	40	137	335	40	175	460
Reference Total Coal Requirements	725	798	1,200	805	1,075	1,900
Total Coal Requirements With Oil Limitation	765	935	1,535	845	1,250	2,360

NUCLEAR DELAYS

The possible impacts on both domestic and export coal requirements of delays in nuclear power expansion have also been considered. The nuclear delay analysis in the United States uses the assumption that no new construction licenses are granted until after 1990. Such a delay could limit the increase in U.S. nuclear power capacity to about 150 GWe in year 2000, a level equivalent to completing only the capacity now under construction.

IMPACT ON DOMESTIC COAL USE

The reference Low Coal Case projection included the nuclear delay assumption, corresponding to the assumed slow increase in electricity demand growth, so estimates of domestic coal use in this case need no further adjustment.

In the High Coal Case, the delay assumption requires reduction of the projected year 2000 nuclear capacity from an assumed 300 GWe to 150 GWe, with a corresponding increase of 300 mtce/yr in the requirement for other sources of fuel for electricity generation (or a decrease in electricity load growth assumptions toward the Low Coal Case levels). Coal would have to provide most, if not all, of the offsetting fuel supplies, as electricity expansion from oil, gas, hydro, and other sources is very limited. For purposes of the WOCOL analysis, it has been assumed that coal provides the entire offsetting 300 mtce/yr in year 2000.

IMPACT ON COAL EXPORT REQUIREMENTS

Delays in the nuclear power expansion programs of other countries would be likely to lead to significant increases in U.S. coal exports, since the countries with the largest projected nuclear expansions (for example, Japan, France, Federal Republic of Germany) have little opportunity for expanding their coal-production potentials beyond current projections.

The WOCOL analysis indicates that, under the conditions of both a limitation on world oil availability and delays in nuclear power expansion, world coal import requirements are likely to approach 900-1,000 mtce by year 2000, even if energy demand grows very slowly. WOCOL concluded that these import requirements could be satisfied only if the exports from the United States rise to 300-400 mtce per year. Accordingly, it has been assumed here that under these conditions U.S. coal exports reach 350 mtce by the year 2000 for both Low Coal and High Coal Cases.

IMPACT ON TOTAL U.S. COAL REQUIREMENTS

Figure 16-9 shows the impacts on coal needs of (1) the assumed limitation on world oil availability and (2) superimposed on that, delays in the expansion of nuclear power. The two charts show separately the impact of these two variations on the reference Low Coal Case and High Coal Case projections.

Compared to the reference Low Coal and High Coal Case (A,B) projections, in which coal use increased from 560 mtce in 1977 to a range of 1,200-1,900

Figure 16-9. WOCOL Projected Range of Total U.S. Coal Requirements (1977–2000)

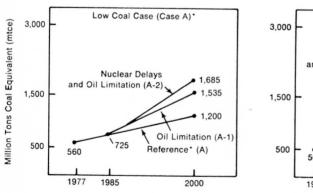
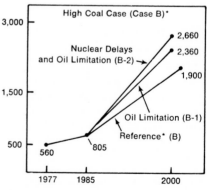

Note: Includes domestic and export requirements in units of mtce. 1 mtce = 1.15 million short tons of bituminous coal at 12,000 Btu/lb and 1.6 million short tons of sub-bituminous coal at 8,500 Btu/lb.

* The Low Coal Case assumes growth in primary energy use of 1.2%/yr for the 1977-2000 period, whereas the High Coal Case assumes 2.2%/yr primary energy growth.

454

mtce in year 2000, the coal needs would increase as shown to 1,535-2,360 mtce in the oil limitation analysis (A-1, B-1), and to 1,685-2,660 mtce under assumptions of combined oil limitations and nuclear delays (A-2, B-2). Thus, a three-to five fold increase in coal requirements over 1977 levels is implied under conditions assumed in the oil and nuclear energy supply limitations, corresponding to a rate of growth of coal requirements of 4.5-7% per year. The acceleration in requirements after 1985 is very rapid, with 1985-2000 growth rates of 5.8-8.3% per year.

The projections of coal use by market sector for the WOCOL case variations are shown in Table 16-8. For comparison, the DOE projections of NEP-II and the 1980 unpublished update are also shown.

Table 16-8. WOCOL Projected Range of Total U.S. Coal Requirements by Market Sector, 1977 and 2000 (mtce)

| Coal Market Sector | Year 1977 | Year 2000 | | | | | | | |
| | | WOCOL Low Coal Case | | | WOCOL High Coal Case | | | DOE | |
		Reference (Case A)	With Oil Limitation (A-1)	With Nuclear Delays & Oil Limitation (A-2)	Reference (Case B)	With Oil Limitation (B-1)	With Nuclear Delays & Oil Limitation (B-2)	NEP-II Base Case	1980* Update
Electric	372	800	915	915	1,170	1,245	1,545	810	975
Metallurgical	77	100	100	100	110	110	110	100	100
Industry/Retail	60	125	160	160	220	280	280	230	225
Synthetic Fuels	0	50	160	160	200	375	375	150	275
Export	50	125	200	350	200	350	350	100	100
Total Coal Requirements	560	1,200	1,535	1,685	1,900	2,360	2,660	1,390	1,675

* Unpublished update of NEP-II projection by U.S. DOE/Policy and Evaluation in January 1980.

COAL SUPPLY

This section describes the coal reserves of the United States and includes estimates of the coal production expansion needed to meet the WOCOL estimates of domestic and export coal demand. Indicative coal mining costs are also given.

COAL RESERVES

The demonstrated coal reserve base of the United States, shown in Table 16-9, totals 438 billion short tons of coal in place, of which 297 billion tons (68%) is mineable by underground methods and 141 billion tons (32%) by surface mining methods. After accounting for coal losses during mining, there are roughly 270 billion short tons[17] of economically recoverable reserves. This is enough to supply coal at the rate of 1979 U.S. coal production for 350 years, and more than adequate to meet any foreseeable production expansion in this century and well into the twenty-first century.

Coal is found in 31 states and currently mined in 26. Six states contain more than 75% of the nation's coal reserves—Montana (28%), Illinois (16%), Wyoming (13%), West Virginia (9%), Pennsylvania (7%), and Kentucky (6%). About one-half of all U.S. reserves are in the West, with one-quarter shares in Appalachia and the Midwest each. Most of the Western reserves are of sub-bituminous rank, with a heat content of 8,000-10,000 Btu per pound, and some

---

[17] Corresponds to about 200 billion metric tons of coal equivalent.

Table 16-9. Demonstrated Coal Reserve Base (Billion Short Tons)

State	Anthracite Underground	Anthracite Surface	Bituminous Underground	Bituminous Surface	Subbituminous Underground	Subbituminous Surface	Lignite Underground	Lignite Surface	Total² Underground	Total² Surface	Total²
Alabama	—	—	1.7	0.3	—	—	—	1.1	1.7	1.4	3.1
Alaska	—	—	0.6	0.1	4.8	0.6	—	(³)	5.4	0.7	6.2
Arizona	0.1	(³)	—	0.3	—	—	—	—	—	0.3	0.3
Arkansas	(³)	—	0.2	0.1	—	—	—	(³)	0.3	0.1	0.4
Colorado	—	—	8.5	0.7	4.0	0.1	—	3.0	12.5	3.8	16.3
Georgia	—	—	(³)	(³)	—	—	—	—	(³)	(³)	(³)
Idaho	—	—	(³)	—	—	—	—	—	(³)	—	(³)
Illinois	—	—	53.1	14.8	—	—	—	—	53.1	14.8	68.0
Indiana	—	—	8.9	1.8	—	—	—	—	8.9	1.8	10.7
Iowa	—	—	1.7	0.5	—	—	—	—	1.7	0.5	2.2
Kansas	—	—	—	1.0	—	—	—	—	—	1.0	1.0
Kentucky, East	—	—	9.1	4.5	—	—	—	—	9.1	4.5	13.5
Kentucky, West	—	—	8.5	4.0	—	—	—	—	8.5	4.0	12.5
Louisiana	—	—	—	—	—	—	—	NA	—	NA	NA
Maryland	—	—	0.9	0.1	—	—	—	—	0.9	0.1	1.0
Michigan	—	—	0.1	(³)	—	—	—	—	0.1	(³)	0.1
Missouri	—	—	1.4	3.6	—	—	—	—	1.4	3.6	5.0
Montana	(³)	—	1.4	0.6	69.6	33.8	—	15.8	71.0	49.6	120.6
New Mexico	—	—	1.3	(³)	0.9	1.9	—	—	2.2	2.4	4.6
North Carolina	—	—	(³)	—	—	—	—	—	(³)	—	(³)
North Dakota	—	—	—	—	—	—	—	10.1	—	10.1	10.1
Ohio	—	—	13.1	6.1	—	—	—	—	13.1	6.1	19.2
Oklahoma	—	—	1.2	0.4	—	—	—	—	1.2	0.4	1.6
Oregon	—	—	—	—	(³)	(³)	—	—	(³)	(³)	(³)
Pennsylvania¹	7.0	0.1	22.3	1.4	—	—	—	—	29.3	1.5	30.8
South Dakota	—	—	—	—	—	—	—	0.4	—	0.4	0.4
Tennessee	—	—	0.6	0.3	—	—	—	—	0.6	0.3	1.0
Texas	—	—	—	—	(³)	—	—	3.2	(³)	3.2	3.2
Utah	—	—	6.3	0.3	—	—	—	—	6.3	0.3	6.6
Virginia	0.1	—	3.3	0.9	—	—	—	—	3.4	0.9	4.3
Washington	—	—	0.3	—	0.8	0.5	—	(³)	1.1	0.5	1.6
West Virginia	—	—	33.5	5.1	—	—	—	—	33.5	5.1	38.6
Wyoming	—	—	4.0	—	27.6	23.7	—	—	31.6	23.7	55.4
Total²	7.2	0.2	182.0	46.9	107.7	60.7	—	33.6	297.0	141.4	438.3

¹ Includes measured and indicated resource categories as defined by the Bureau of Mines and the U.S. Geological Survey and represents 100 percent of the coal in place.
² Sum of the components may not equal total due to independent rounding.
³ Less than 0.05 billion short tons.
NA: Not available.

Source: DOE Annual Report to Congress, Volume III, 1977, Statistics and Trends of Energy Supply, Demand, and Prices.

Western states (e.g., Montana, North Dakota) also contain large lignite deposits. Sixty-five percent of the Western coal is on government-owned land. On the other hand, the bulk of reserves in Appalachia and the Midwest is bituminous coal and privately owned.

The sulfur content of U.S. coal reserves is indicated in Figure 16-10. Western reserves are primarily low-sulfur (less than 1%) whereas the bulk of Midwestern reserves are high sulfur (greater than 3%). The sulfur content of Appalachian coal reserves ranges from low to high.

Table 16-10 summarizes the quality of several representative coals—by sulfur, ash, and Btu content.

Figure 16-10. U.S. Coal Reserves—Sulfur Content

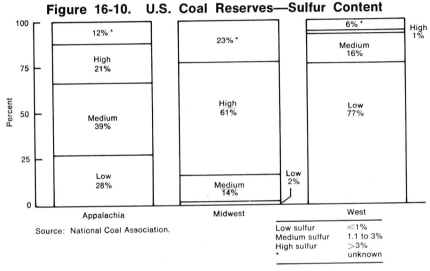

Source: National Coal Association.

Low sulfur	≤1%
Medium sulfur	1.1 to 3%
High sulfur	>3%
*	unknown

Table 16-10. Illustrative Quality Characteristics of Representative Coals

State	Coal Type	Btu/lb.*	% Sulfur*	% Ash*
Pennsylvania	Bituminous	12,067	2.03	15.0
West Virginia (North)	Bituminous	12,516	2.39	12.1
Ohio	Bituminous	11,047	3.42	15.8
Kentucky (East)	Bituminous	11,784	1.23	12.5
Illinois	Bituminous	10,775	2.92	11.4
Alabama	Bituminous	11,740	1.43	14.1
Texas	Lignite	6,601	0.66	12.0
Colorado	Bituminous	10,925	0.49	9.4
Wyoming	Subbituminous	9,037	0.50	8.3
Utah	Bituminous	11,569	0.63	11.9
North Dakota	Lignite	6,556	0.65	9.9
Montana	Subbituminous	8,957	0.64	7.6
Pennsylvania	Anthracite	8,607**	0.69	27.3*

* On "as received" basis.
** Data distorted by reclaimed anthracite which lowers heat value.

Source: Federal Energy Regulatory Commission, 1978, *Annual Summary of Cost and Quality of Electric Utility Plant Fuels, 1977,* Table III.

COAL PRODUCTION

U.S. coal production is shown for 1977 and 1979 in Table 16-11, by region and mining method. Production increased from 688 million short tons in 1977 to 770 million tons in 1979. Appalachia produces over half of the nation's coal, with three states—West Virginia, East Kentucky, and Pennsylvania providing 40% of total U.S. coal output. Although production continues to increase, Appalachia's market share has declined somewhat since the early 1970's due to increased production in the Western states.

A representative projection of the regional mix of sources needed to expand U.S. coal production to meet the WOCOL Low Coal and High Coal Case requirements is shown in Table 16-12. Total coal production is piojected to rise to 1.5 billion short tons in year 2000 under the assumptions of the Low Coal Case (A) and to 2.5 billion tons in the High Coal Case (B).

The projection shows the dominance of underground mining of Appalachian coals and surface mining of Western coals. In addition, a large increase in the share of Western coal is expected by year 2000, rising from 20% today to 50% in the year 2000. The increase in low-Btu Western coal output leads to a decline in the average Btu content of U.S. coal from 23 million Btu/short ton currently to 21 million Btu/ton in year 2000.

Table 16-12. Representative Projection of Regional Coal Expansion, 1977–2000 (Million Short Tons)

Region	1977	1985 Low Coal Case	1985 High Coal Case	1990 Low Coal Case	1990 High Coal Case	2000 Low Coal Case	2000 High Coal Case
Appalachia							
Underground	205	225	240	240	320	375	550
Surface	185	130	150	130	160	130	175
Total	390	355	390	370	480	505	725
Midwest*							
Underground	53	60	80	70	125	120	215
Surface	94	75	90	80	105	95	135
Total	147	135	170	150	230	215	350
Gulf Surface Lignite	16	45	55	55	70	80	100
West							
Underground	13	40	50	50	70	80	100
Surface	122	345	360	400	550	620	1,225
Total	135	385	410	450	620	700	1,325
Total Production	688	920	1,025	1,025	1,400	1,500	2,500

* Midwest includes the Illinois Basin and states of Western Interior, excluding Texas, from Table 16-11.

Source: Primary data from Office of Technology Assessment, *Direct Use of Coal* (1979).

Table 16-11. U.S. Coal Production by States and Method of Mining, 1977 and 1979 (Million Short Tons)

Region and State	Underground 1977	Underground 1979	Surface 1977	Surface 1979	Total 1977	Total 1979
Appalachia						
Alabama	6.8	8.1	14.6	15.7	21.2	23.8
Georgia	—	—	.18	.54	.18	.54
Kentucky, E.	41.0	41.0	51.1	59.6	92.1	100.6
Maryland	.26	.31	3.0	2.4	3.3	2.8
Ohio	13.9	14.0	32.3	31.6	46.2	45.6
Pennsylvania	38.4	38.5	44.9	48.5	83.2	86.9
Tennessee	4.7	4.8	5.6	7.2	10.3	11.9
Virginia	26.2	26.0	11.6	16.2	37.8	42.2
West Virginia	74.0	92.2	21.4	20.5	95.4	112.7
Total[a]	205	225	185	202	390	427
Illinois Basin						
Illinois	29.6	32.5	24.3	26.6	53.9	59.1
Indiana	.52	.61	27.5	26.7	28.0	27.3
Kentucky, W.	23.0	18.0	27.8	26.5	50.8	44.5
Total[a]	53	51	79.5	78.8	132.7	130.9
TOTAL,[a] EAST	258	276	264	282	523	558
Western Interior						
Arkansas	.02	.025	.55	.54	.57	.62
Iowa	—	.22	.52	.45	.52	.67
Kansas	—	—	.63	.68	.63	.68
Missouri	—	—	6.6	5.4	6.6	5.4
Oklahoma	—	—	5.3	5.8	5.3	5.8
Texas	—	—	16.8	25.3	16.8	25.3
Total[a]	.02	.25	30.4	38.1	30.5	38.4
Far West						
Alaska	—	—	.66	.56	.66	.56
Arizona	—	—	11.5	11.5	11.5	11.5
Colorado	4.0	5.4	7.7	12.6	11.9	17.9
Montana	—	—	29.3	32.4	29.3	32.4
New Mexico	—	.80	11.3	11.5	11.3	12.3
North Dakota	—	—	12.2	14.1	12.7	14.1
Utah	9.2	8.7	—	—	9.2	8.7
Washington	—	—	5.1	5.1	5.1	5.1
Wyoming	—	0.7	44.5	70.3	44.5	70.9
Total[a]	13.2	15.6	122.1	157	135.6	173.5
TOTAL,[a] WEST	13.2	15.8	152.6	196.1	166.1	211.9
TOTAL,[a] U.S.	272	292	417	478	688	770

[a] Totals are rounded.
Source: U.S. Department of Energy (January 1980).

Table 16-13. WOCOL Projected Range of U.S. Coal Production Requirements, 1977 and 2000

| | 1977 | Year 2000 | | | | | |
| | | Low Coal Case | | | High Coal Case | | |
		Reference (Case A)	With Oil Limitation (A-1)	With Nuclear Delays & Oil Limitation (A-2)	Reference (Case B)	With Oil Limitation (B-1)	With Nuclear Delays & Oil Limitation (B-2)
Total Coal Requirements (mtce)	560	1,200	1,535	1,685	1,900	2,360	2,660
Total Coal Production* (million short tons)	688	1,500	2,000	2,200	2,500	3,000	3,500
Appalachia & Midwest	537	720	900	975	1,075	1,300	1,500
Gulf & West	151	780	1,100	1,225	1,425	1,700	2,000

* Totals are rounded for year 2000.

460

The preceding section of this report illustrated the possible effects of oil limitations and nuclear delays on increasing U.S. coal requirements by up to 40% over the reference Low Coal and High Coal case projections. Using the same mix of Eastern coal shown in the preceding table, Table 16-13 assesses the coal production requirements for the sensitivity cases. As shown, the range of coal production required in the year 2000 grows from 1,500-2,500 million tons under the reference Low Coal and High Coal conditions, to 2,000-3,000 million tons with the oil limitation assumption, and to 2,200-3,500 million tons under the assumption of nuclear delays and oil limitation.

THE ECONOMICS OF COAL SUPPLY—PAST COAL PRICES

Figure 16-11 shows U.S. coal prices in the period 1947-1979. The average FOB mine prices are for all bituminous coals and lignites mined, including the higher-priced metallurgical coals. Figure 16-12 presents the price movement in current dollars for 1965-1979. The price of coal in constant 1977 dollars declined between 1948 and 1968 because of the strong competitive pressure from oil and natural gas, and because of the improvements in mine productivity which were achieved by use of continuous mining machines in underground mines and the increased share of high-productivity surface mining. Table 16-14 presents the productivity of U.S. coal mining for the 1948-1978 period.

The year 1969 marked a turning point in the coal industry. Government regulations affecting both supply and demand for coal, changing conditions in the world oil market, and instability in the coal labor force converged to reverse the long-term coal price stability. In 1969 and 1970 the demand for coal by utilities, domestic steel companies, and export customers all increased, making for a tight market. At the same time, the Federal Coal Mine Health and Safety Act was implemented, which resulted in declines in underground mine productivity and lower coal production from existing underground mines. As a result, the long-term downward trend in coal prices was reversed. Between 1968 and 1973, real coal prices increased by 43 percent. Surface mine productivity also began to decline, contributing to the upward pressure on prices.

Figure 16-11. Average Price of United States Coal, FOB Mines (1947–1979)

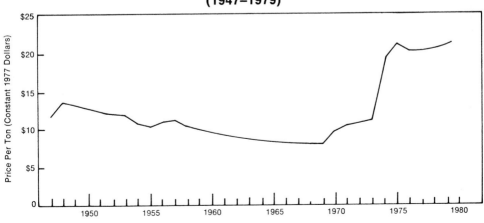

Source: U.S. Department of Energy (January 1980).

461

Figure 16-12. Average Price of United States Coal, FOB Mines— Surface and Underground (1965–1979)

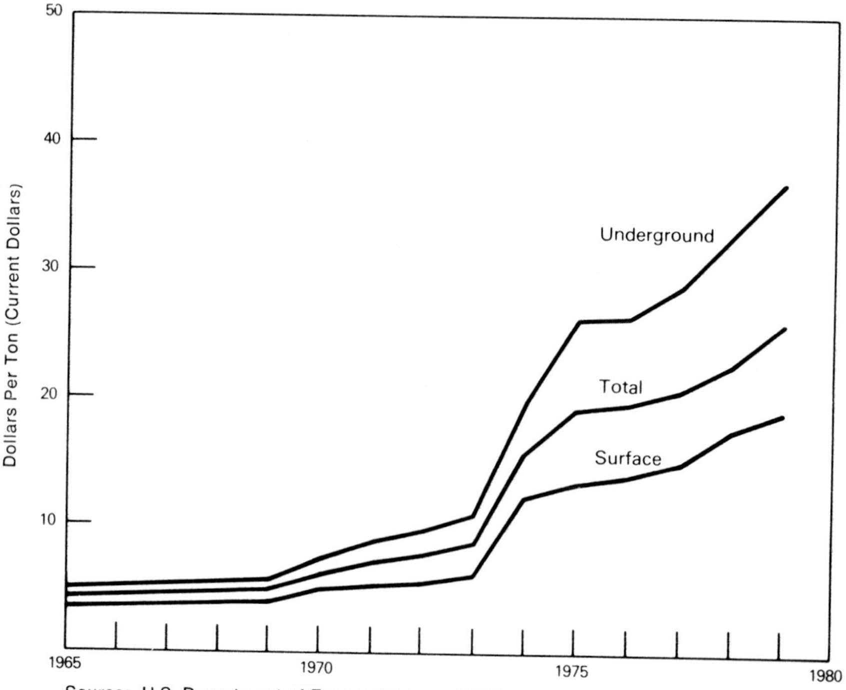

Source: U.S. Department of Energy (January 1980).

The Arab oil embargo of 1973-1974 occurred at a time when the coal indus-try was already having difficulties. The East Coast electric utility market was highly dependent on imported residual oil because such oil had a price and quality advantage over domestic coal. Although most of the imported utility oil was from non-Arab countries, fears of oil supply instability and shortages, combined with the much higher oil prices, caused an increase in the demand for coal. Labor conditions in the coal fields were also unsettled in 1974. Because a long strike by the United Mine Workers (UMW) Association was anticipated in November of that year, consumers tried to build up inventories before the strike to meet expected peak winter demands.

This éxacerbated the already tight market and pushed spot coal prices up sharply because of the low short-run supply elasticity for coal. However, once the panic buying ceased and demand softened, the prices stabilized—albeit at a higher level. Since 1975, the real price of coal (as expressed by the average FOB price in constant 1977 dollars) has remained at approximately the same level. Coal supply has also expanded significantly.

THE ECONOMICS OF COAL SUPPLY—FUTURE COAL PRICES

Future coal prices will be affected by many factors, including market antici-pations, local, state and national taxes on coal mining, escalation in labor rates and machinery prices, etc.

Table 16-15 summarizes a recent DOE projection of coal mining cost in-creases for several representative U.S. coals.

Table 16-14. Productivity in Bituminous Coal and Lignite Mining, 1948–1978 (Average Short Tons per Man-Day)

Year	Underground Mines	Surface Mines	All Mines
1948	5.31	15.28	6.26
1949	5.42	15.33	6.43
1950	5.75	15.66	6.77
1951	6.08	16.02	7.04
1952	6.37	16.81	7.47
1953	7.01	17.73	8.17
1954	7.99	19.80	9.47
1955	8.28	21.17	9.84
1956	8.62	21.37	10.28
1957	8.91	21.87	10.59
1958	9.38	21.84	11.33
1959	10.08	22.94	12.22
1960	10.64	23.31	12.83
1961	11.41	25.29	13.87
1962	11.97	27.22	14.72
1963	12.78	29.30	15.83
1964	13.74	30.05	16.84
1965	14.00	32.76	17.52
1966	14.64	34.23	18.52
1967	15.07	35.87	19.17
1968	15.40	34.64	19.37
1969	15.61	36.00	19.90
1970	13.76	36.26	18.84
1971	12.03	35.88	18.02
1972	11.91	36.33	17.74
1973	11.66	36.67	17.58
1974	11.31	33.16	17.58
1975	9.54	26.69	14.74
1976	9.10	26.40	14.46
1977	8.70	26.90	14.74
1978	8.25	25.00	14.55

Source: U.S. Department of Energy.

Table 16-15. DOE Projection of Future FOB Mine Costs for Representative Coals, 1977–1995 (Constant 1978 Dollars)

Coal Type	1977		1985 Projected		1995 Projected	
	$/ton	$/tce	$/ton	$/tce	$/ton	$/tce
Montana/Wyoming Subbituminous	7	10.50	8.40	12.50	10.50	15.75
Rocky Mountain (Utah) Bituminous	20	23	24	28	31	36
N.E. Great Plains (North Dakota) Lignite	4	8.50	6	12.50	7	15
Illinois Mid-Bituminous	18	23	22	28	27	34
Appalachia (Pennsylvania) Bituminous	25	29	28	32	35	41

Source: Energy Information Administration, U.S. Department of Energy.

The DOE projection shows an increase in the real FOB cost of most coals of about 25-50 percent over the next twenty years. However, the future costs of the Western surface-mineable coals are projected to remain less than the costs for mining coal today in Appalachia and the Midwest, even after adjusting for calorific content differences. Thus, the expected increasing share of lower-cost Western coals in the U.S. production mix will tend to moderate increases in the weighted national average coal cost.

This was also the conclusion of a major study conducted by the Energy Modeling Forum (EMF) at Stanford University in 1978, *Coal in Transition 1980-2000*:

> "Costs of coal extraction increase slowly with cumulative production, particularly in the West . . . the competitive functioning of the coal market and the possibility of substitution among supplying regions limit changes in the delivered cost of fuels."

The EMF study found that if the expansion of coal production is sustained gradually over a long period, a production expansion to 2.5 billion short tons could be achieved by year 2000 with only a moderate increase in real dollars in the national average coal supply cost at the mine. Figure 16-13 summarizes the EMF results for four scenarios. In the EMF "Reference" case, with required coal production of about 2.5 billion tons in year 2000, the average real coal price (1975 constant dollars) remained at about $0.80 per million Btu throughout the 1975-2000 period. Only in the EMF "Crunch" case, which assumed a very large coal production increase to about 4 billion tons in year 2000, coupled with other assumptions "designed to represent conditions that are the most unfavorable to the development of the national coal resources," did the national average coal price increase by more than 25 percent in real terms above the 1975 level by year 2000.

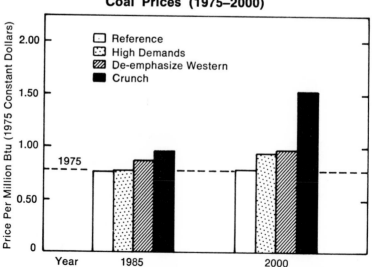

Figure 16-13. EMF Projection of Future National Average Coal Prices (1975–2000)

Source: *Coal in Transition: 1980–2000*, Energy Modeling Forum, Stanford University, September 1978.

COAL TRANSPORTATION

After coal is mined and processed, it is transported to another location for combustion. Trucks and belt conveyors serve "mine-mouth" facilities. Highways, railroads, waterways, and slurry pipelines are the transportation mode for longer distances. Energy from mine-mouth power plants can be transmitted by high-voltage transmission cable. The cost of transportation is a major determinant of the regional mix of coal production. In addition, the revenues earned from transporting coal will be important to the U.S. transportation industry.

THE U.S. COAL TRANSPORTATION SYSTEM

RAILROADS

About 55% of the coal consumed in the United States is transported in railroad cars. Coal is moved by rail almost entirely in open-topped hopper cars or gondola cars, which can be unloaded by turning the car completely over or by unloading from the top. The cars are generally loaded from the top at mine sidings or coal-loading installations central to a number of mines. Coal from the mines is lifted into silos or onto storage piles, travels by gravity or conveyor, and then moves through a chute into the car.

The average hopper car carries about 75 tons of coal. Older cars average 55 tons, and the newer ones move over 100 tons at capacity. The complete cycle of loading, hauling to the unloading point, unloading, and returning for another cargo averages 13 days for each car. Although this is a shorter turn-around time than is experienced for any other type of bulk movement, inactivity is still a major factor in the economics of coal movement by railroad. The size of hopper cars that can be accommodated depends on roadbed conditions and the weight the track can tolerate. Western coal unit trains use 100-ton hopper cars; Eastern shipments often require the older 55-ton hoppers.

Unloading facilities for hopper cars, like loading facilities, are large-scale, permanent installations. They may take the form of trestles running over storage piles, into which coal is dumped from the bottom of moving cars, or they may be rotary dumpers, which tip the entire car over, spilling its contents. Cars with swivel couplings need not be uncoupled to unload by rotating. Some loading and unloading facilities can handle thousands of tons per hour. A typical requirement would be to load three trains per day, consisting of 100 cars of 100 tons net loading each; and provide a loading rate of 4,000 tons/hour.

A particularly efficient type of rail service for major shippers of coal and other bulk commodities is provided by unit trains. This type of train, designed to take advantage of economies of scale, generally carries a single commodity in dedicated service between two points in sufficient volume to achieve cost savings. The cars are designed for automated loading and unloading, and the train is operated by procedures that minimize switching and time-consuming delays in freight yards.

A typical coal unit train consists of six 3,000-horsepower locomotives and 100 hopper cars with carrying capacities of 100 tons each. Roughly four such trains per week are therefore required to deliver 2 million tons of coal per year. Speeds vary considerably depending on track conditions, but 20 to 50 miles per hour is a common range.

465

WATERWAYS

The shipment of coal by barge or other water carrier requires the tugs, or self-propelled vessels, which push the "tow," composed of as many as 36 barges, usually of 1,500-ton capacity, from a loading dock to an unloading dock. A great variety of sizes, shapes, drafts, and power capability characterizes the towboat fleet.

The loading facilities used for barges resemble some rail loading facilities. They generally entail a conveyor belt carrying coal from a stockpile to a movable chute, which can dump the coal into waiting barges along a pier. Unloading facilities are different, however: barges must be unloaded without the aid of gravity, usually by a crane equipped with a clamshell bucket. The unloaded coal is generally moved by belt conveyors to storage yards. One modern unloader consists of two revolving scoops, which can clean out a barge in three passes.

On the Great Lakes, oceans, and coastal tidewaters, single bulk cargo carriers are used. The Great Lakes vessels being built to carry Western coal to a Detroit utility plant are 1,000 feet long and each carry 62,000 tons of coal. They are self-unloading, using long conveyor belts traversing the length of the ships.

The inland waterways themselves have been constructed and maintained by the Federal Government, with the exception of the New York State Barge Canal. Since the first appropriation to the U.S. Army Corps of Engineers for this purpose in 1824, billions of dollars have been spent to make possible the large-scale commercial traffic now using these internal waterways. In general, the improvement of a waterway to make it navigable involves deepening and widening the channel by dredging and constructing dams and locks. Erosion control along sections of the riverbank and operation of the dams and locks are also part of the Federal role. There were 255 navigation locks and dams being operated by the Corps of Engineers as of June 1, 1978. The size of the locks available on the river systems is the primary limiting factor on river traffic.

HIGHWAYS

Trucks carried about 15 percent of coal transported in the U.S. in 1978. As opposed to the average haul of 300 miles by railroad, and 480 miles by barge, the average highway shipment of coal is only 50 to 75 miles.

The public highway trucks carry a total of 15 to 25 tons each. The standard diesel tractor is used to pull one and sometimes two trailers, depending on weight limitations. Coal movement to nearby power plants takes place on private roads using vehicles too large for public highways; some of these vehicles can carry up to 150 tons of coal. The trucks may be loaded from a fixed chute, but are more often loaded by shovels or front-end loaders directly at the side of the coal seam in a surface mine. Most trucks are dumpers. Truck shipments are sometimes used in connection with deep-mine operations, but most often are connected with strip-mine operations.

SLURRY PIPELINES

Transport by this mode involves three major stages:

- grinding the coal and mixing it with liquid (generally water) to form the slurry;
- transmission through the pipeline; and

- dewatering the coal for use as a boiler fuel, for storage or for transloading to another transportation mode.

Coal is assembled from a mine or group of mines at a single point where mixing, cleaning, or other beneficiation may take place, and where the slurry is prepared. Preparation begins with impact crushing, followed by the addition of water and further grinding to a maximum particle size of one-eighth of an inch. More water is then added to form a mixture that is about 50% dry coal by weight, and the resulting slurry is stored in a tank equipped with mechanical agitators to prevent settling. Water is not necessarily the only slurry medium, and oil—as well as methanol derived from the coal itself—has been proposed.

The slurry from the agitated-storage tanks is introduced into a buried steel pipe and propelled by pumps located at intervals of 50 to 150 miles, depending upon terrain, pipe size, and other design considerations. The slurry travels at about 6 ft/sec. Ideally, the flow is maintained at a rate that minimizes power requirements while maintaining the coal in suspension. Once started, the flow must continue uninterrupted or the coal could gradually settle and possibly plug the pipe. The slurry pipeline at Black Mesa, Arizona, has ponds into which the pipeline can be emptied in the event of a break or other interruption.

At the downstream end of the pipeline, the slurry is again introduced into agitated tank storage, from which it is fed into a dewatering facility. Dewatering is accomplished by natural settling, vacuum filtration, or by centrifuge, and the finely ground coal still suspended in the water can be separated by chemical flocculation. Additional thermal drying is generally required before use. The reclaimed water can be used in an electric-generating station's cooling system to condense steam—or it could theoretically be recycled in a return pipeline.

TRANSPORTATION SYSTEM EXPANSION FOR DOMESTIC COAL USE

On a national scale, U.S. coal development is not likely to be constrained by the availability of transportation infrastructure. Transportation facilities and equipment can be planned and constructed within the time frame required to construct large electric power facilities or industrial plants or large coal mines, so that adequate transport planning, investment and improvements can take place prior to the requirement for coal transport infrastructure. However, local capacity constraints could develop prior to 1985, and bottlenecks that do develop could alter the current pattern of coal flow. The transport system in the U.S. is flexible, and both route and mode choices can be adjusted to alleviate possible capacity limitations.

A major expansion of the U.S. coal transportation system will be required to accommodate the projected increases in coal production and use. The rapid growth in Western coal in particular will place new demands on the nation's capacity to transport coal. The lower Btu content of Western coal means that 25-40% more coal tonnage, compared to Eastern coal, must be transported to meet a given energy requirement. Moreover, the Western coals must generally be transported greater distances (up to 1000 miles) to markets.

Calculation of specific capacity expansion requirements depends on a number of assumptions regarding interregional coal supply-demand patterns, fraction of the coal transported by the competing modes, existing capacity of the system, and other variables. Table 16-16 presents one recent estimate of U.S. coal transportation requirements associated with an expansion of U.S. coal production to 2.7 billion short tons by year 2000.[18]

Table 16-16. Coal Transportation Requirements, 1976–2000

Mode	Flow (Million Tons)		Fraction by Mode		Average Haul Length (Miles)	
	1976	2000	1976	2000	1976	2000
Conventional Train	230	390	0.34	0.14	490	520
Unit Train	155	1,350	0.23	0.50	580	990
Coal Barge	190	460	0.29	0.17	650	440
Coal Truck	90	230	0.14	0.09	50	50
Slurry Pipeline	—	250	0	0.10	—	980
Total Coal	665	2,680	1.00	1.00	480	940

The table shows that total coal transportation requirements could increase from 320 billion ton-miles in 1976 to 2,500 billion ton-miles in year 2000 under the assumed conditions. It is important to note that, due to an increasing proportion of Western coals, the average coal haul length was projected to nearly double over the period, so that in this calculation, transport capacity needs grew eightfold while production increased only fourfold.

Capacity increases equivalent to the following combination of new facilities could achieve the necessary transport system expansion:

- 10 new slurry pipelines @ 25 million tons/year and 1,000 miles long;
- 2,200 new coal unit trains @ 10,500 tons (105 cars each carrying 100 tons, 6 locomotives per train);
- 6,000 new conventional trains @ 7,225 tons (85 cars each carrying 85 tons, 3 locomotives per train);
- 380 new coal barges @ 21,000 tons (15 barges each carrying 1,400 tons, 1 towboat); and
- 16,000 new coal trucks @ 25 tons

EXPANSION OF TRANSPORTATION SYSTEM FOR EXPORT COAL

The United States is a potential major exporter of steam coal to the international market. A key element in this future role is the U.S. capability to transport steam coal from the interior mining regions to port areas and provide at these port areas sufficient handling and ship-loading capacity. Coal export requirements could require substantial expansion of existing facilities at the East and Gulf Coast coal ports and in addition the development of new coal port facilities on the East, Gulf, and West coasts. It is important to recognize also that the inland transport requirements for coal export will place burdens on the nation's transport system over and above the needs for domestic coal expansion.

---

[18] Source: "Engineering a Transition to Coal," J. Michael Gallagher and Ralph G.J. Zimmermann, Bechtel National, Inc., *Natural Resources Forum*, July 1979. Prepared for EMF *Coal in Transition* Study.

An evaluation of the current and prospective coal port capacity and potential constraints to port expansion was conducted for WOCOL by Bechtel National, Inc.[19] The capabilities were assessed based on coal export scenarios describing possible mine-to-port coal flow patterns. Three levels of total U.S. annual coal exports by year 2000 were considered: 125 mtce, 200 mtce, and 350 mtce. The key findings of this WOCOL assessment are:

- *Port Capacity.* Significant expansions of port capacity, including new ports, would be required in the Lower Mississippi, West Coast and Alaskan port areas to accommodate all three levels of coal exports. In the East, new port areas would need to be established to accommodate the two higher export levels investigated.
- *Domestic Mine-to-Port Transport Links.* The Eastern railroads serving coal export ports may require some main-line upgrading but of greater priority will be upgrading and expansion of coal-gathering branch lines and train makeup and storage yards. In the West, with no undue concentration of coal export traffic on a single line, export tonnages of 125-200 mtce/yr could require only modest capital additions. The projected tonnage of the highest case would, however, likely require major capital expansions by the western railroads. The inland waterway system serving the Gulf Coast export ports would be generally adequate for all three export levels. In all cases, additional rail cars, locomotives, and barges would be required.
- *Estimated Costs.* Capital requirements are estimated to be $910 million (1979 dollars) in the lowest case; over $2 billion in the 200 mtce case, and on the order of $5 billion in the 350 mtce export case. These estimates pertain to fairly well-definable investment requirements such as rail cars, main line upgrading, barges, and additional port capacity. Additional investment would be necessary for new or upgraded gathering subsystems bringing coal from mines to train or barge assembly terminals.
- *Potential Constraints.* Regulatory and institutional considerations would likely be the most significant constraint to the U.S. developing the capability for expanded coal exports. In particular, these factors would impact expansion of port capacity.

CAPITAL REQUIREMENTS FOR COAL FACILITIES

Managing a transition to coal and other energy sources from present reliance on petroleum will be a major task involving a large array of coal mines, rail lines, coal pipelines, power plants and coal conversion facilities. All these facilities require a commitment of capital and other resources.

COAL CHAINS

One way to visualize the implementing actions needed is through individual coal chains of mine-to-user facilities. An illustrative U.S. export coal chain, involving coal from underground coal mines in the Western United States to electric power plants in Japan, is illustrated in Figure 16-14, along with estimates of the facility and resource requirements.

---

[19] The complete report of the Bechtel export ports and transport infrastructure assessment is included in Appendix 1.

Figure 16-14. Illustrative Implementation Requirements for a Typical U.S. Export Coal Chain

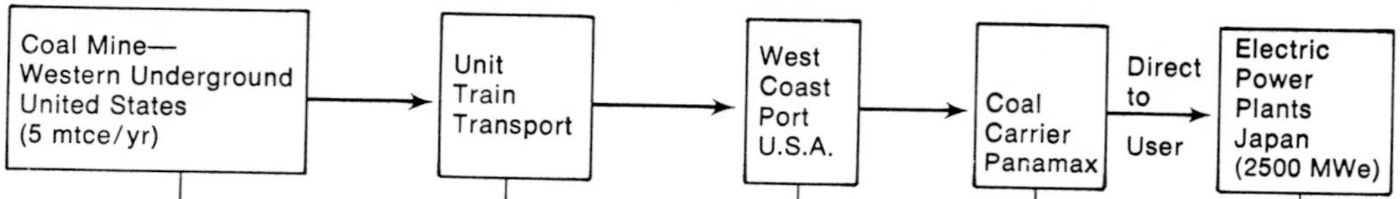

Coal Mine— Western Underground United States (5 mtce/yr) → Unit Train Transport → West Coast Port U.S.A. → Coal Carrier Panamax → Direct to User → Electric Power Plants Japan (2500 MWe)

	Mines	Trains	Port	Ships	Power Plants	Total System
Coal Flows	5 mtce/year 5.75 million short tons/yr	same	same	same	same	5 mtce/yr 5.75 million s.t./yr
Facilities Unit Size	2 million s.t./yr	105 cars @ 100 ton, 60 trips/yr, 1000 mi 650,000 s.t./yr	10 millions tons/yr	52,000 s.t., 10 trips/yr 520,000 s.t./yr	800 MWe	
# Required	2.9 mines	8.8 trains	0.6 ports	11.0 ships	3.1 plants (2500 MWe)	
Lead Times†	3 years*	1 year	2.5 years	1 year	5 years	5 years
Costs Total capital††	$300 million	$75 million	$75 million	$350 million	$2400 million	$3.2 billion
Labor Required Total Construction	900 man years		400 man years		12,000 man years	13,300 man years
Annual Operating	3000 m-y/yr	1400 m-y/yr	100 m-y/yr	700 m-y/yr	750 m-y/yr	5,950 m-y/yr

* Lead times for coal mines assume that resource exploration has previously been completed and refer only to bringing the first phase of capacity into production.
† Lead times for actual project execution after all permits granted.
†† January 1978 dollars.

Implementation of a coal chain to mine, move, and use about 5 mtce/yr coal in power plants involves large sums of capital—about $3 billion. User facilities—the power plants or synthetic fuel facilities—account for most of the capital costs and have the longest construction lead time in the chain. Typically, the capital costs for the power plant or conversion facility are larger than those for the coal supply and transport infrastructure by a ratio of 3:1 or more. The same is true for construction labor requirements. This situation is, however, reversed in the case of annual operating labor needs, where mines and railroads require larger operating work forces than the more capital-intensive user facilities.

Lead times for actual construction of new power plants and synthetic fuel facilities are about five years for actual project construction. Total lead times can be much longer—perhaps twice as long—including all preliminary steps to evaluate sites, prepare environmental analyses, secure sources of financing, and obtain licenses and permits. These preconstruction lead times also tend to be very long in opening new coal mines.

The long lead times for the coal-consuming facilities show the essential role of new orders for coal-fired power plants, industrial boilers, or synthetic fuel facilities as the driving force in activating the whole chain of coal supply and transport activities.

CAPITAL REQUIREMENTS FOR THE TOTAL COAL SYSTEM

The investment costs of expanding U.S. coal production, transport and use may amount to about $500 billion over the next twenty years, according to a recent study prepared for the EMF.[20] That study determined that expansion to 2.7 billion short tons by year 2000 might require the following cumulative investments (constant 1977 dollars) for the 1977-2000 period:

- Coal mining: $55 billion, of which:
  —Underground = $23 billion
  —Surface = $32 billion
- Coal transportation: $62 billion, of which:
  —Rail = $50 billion
  —Pipelines = $9 billion
  —Barges and trucks = $3 billion
- Coal-using (synfuel and electricity) plants: $360 billion (includes $60 billion for scrubbers)

The additional capital requirements for the transport capacity and ports necessary to support U.S. coal exports have been estimated for WOCOL. As shown in Table 16-17, capital requirements necessary to support U.S. exports of 350 mtce by year 2000 could amount to about $5 billion, or only about 1% of the capital needed for facilities associated with domestic coal use. Less than half of this $5 billion figure is required for port capacity expansion, with the remainder for inland transport system additions.

---

[20] Source: "Engineering a Transition to Coal," J. Michael Gallagher and Ralph G.J. Zimmermann, Bechtel National, Inc., *Natural Resources Forum*, July 1979. Prepared for EMF *Coal in Transition* Study.

Table 16-17. Capital Expenditures Required for Year 2000 Coal Exports (Millions of 1979 Dollars)

Region and Facility	Export Level—Year 2000		
	125 mtce	200 mtce	350 mtce
Eastern Ports			
Rolling stock	$190	$ 370	$ 550
Railroad upgrading	10	60	120
Port expansion	Nil	40	110
Mobile			
Barges/Towboats	15	40	45
Port expansion	Nil	5	5
Lower Mississippi			
Barges/Towboats	290	700	1,650
Terminals[1]	80	260	700
West Coast			
Rolling stock	160	375	1,070
Railroad upgrading	50	100	200
New ports	60[2]	160[3]	470[4]
Alaska			
Rolling stock	25	40	65
Railroad upgrading	10	15	20
New port	20	30	50
Total	$910	$2,195	$5,055

[1] Including upriver barge-loading terminals.
[2] Los Angeles/Long Beach and San Francisco Bay Area.
[3] Los Angeles/Long Beach, San Francisco Bay Area and Portland Area.
[4] Los Angeles/Long Beach, San Francisco Bay Area, Portland, and Seattle Area.

Source: Appendix 1 of this report, Bechtel National, Inc.

AVAILABILITY OF CAPITAL FOR COAL AND ENERGY FACILITY INVESTMENTS

The EMF study estimated that the entire energy industry could require a capital investment of about $1.6 trillion for the 1977-2000 period, as detailed in Table 16-18. Under the assumptions of that study, the coal share of total energy investment requirements amounted to about 30 percent.

It was also estimated for the EMF[21] that the total energy investment requirement, though very large as an absolute sum, would amount to only about 20 percent of the private capital pool projected to be available over the same period.

[21] Source: "Secondary Industry Requirements," E.D. Griffith, Appendix I to *Coal in Transition: 1980-2000*, Energy Modeling Forum, Stanford University, 1978.

This assumed that 60 percent of the energy industry's demand for capital would be generated from internal sources, and 40 percent sought in the capital markets. Historically, the energy industries have attracted slightly less than 20 percent of the gross private investment available.

The EMF concluded that the availability of capital would not pose a general constraint to coal expansion, but individual projects would have to attract investments on their own merits:

"Thus, it would appear that capital markets will be able to meet the needs of energy development. The key question, however, is not availability of capital, as such, but the ability of each sector of industry, or even each project, to attract the capital needed. Capital availability to support coal industry expansion will ultimately depend on a return on investment in coal at least as attractive as other sectors of business, and having that return assured by long-term supply contracts."

U.S. ENVIRONMENTAL LAWS, REGULATIONS AND STANDARDS PERTAINING TO COAL PRODUCTION AND UTILIZATION

Over the last decade the United States has developed an elaborate and complex system for establishing, interpreting and enforcing U.S. environmental laws, standards and regulations. During the last few years a number of new laws have been passed and standards revised which affect all aspects of coal supply and use. Collectively, these laws define the manner in which coal can be mined, transported, and burned or converted in the United States.

This section reviews regulations governing the use of coal in the United States, and identifies the costs of complying with various existing or proposed U.S. standards. General issues affecting the use of coal, such as health and safety effects, effects of CO_2 on climate, and the role of technology in mitigating impacts, are discussed in Volume 1, Chapter 4, "Environment, Health, and Safety." A primary source for much of the material discussed here is *The Direct Use of Coal*, a study by the Office of Technology Assessment (OTA) of the Congress of the United States, April, 1979.

OVERVIEW OF U.S. ENVIRONMENTAL LAWS, STANDARDS, AND REGULATIONS

Each step along the coal chain from the mine through consumption and disposal has impacts on the environment. Figure 16-15 illustrates these impacts and Figure 16-16 shows the jurisdiction of major federal control legislation. Table 16-19 is a guide to the current federal regulations pertaining to coal production and utilization in the United States. Many environmental standards and regulations are in the process of revision. New legislation, amendments, or regulatory policy may significantly alter the future application of these standards, and, hence, the cost and effect of these standards on U.S. coal production and consumption.

EVOLUTION OF U.S. AIR POLLUTION STANDARDS

The United States Clean Air Act of 1970 established the mechanism by which specified levels of air contaminants are to be achieved. This act also gave the Environmental Protection Agency (EPA) the responsibility and authority to control air pollution in the United States and its territories.

First, among other responsibilities, EPA was required to identify the air contaminants of concern (Criteria Pollutants). Next, the Administrator of EPA was

Table 16-18. Cumulative (1977–2000) Capital Requirements of the Energy Industry, by Region and Energy Sector, EMF Reference Case ($ Billions, March 1977—Constant Dollars)

ENERGY SECTOR	R1 (Northeast)	R2 (Mid-Atlantic)	R3 (South Atlantic)	R4 (East North Central)	R5 (East South Central)
Oil					
Exploration, Development, and Production	0.2	0.5	1.3	3.0	2.0
Refining and Processing	4.7	7.3	2.0	9.8	2.0
Pipelines	0.2	0.9	0.2	1.3	0.2
Tankers, Barges, Trucks	0.9	3.5	1.1	2.3	0.8
Bulk Stations	0.1	0.2	0.2	0.3	0.1
Other	0.0	0.2	0.0	0.0	0.0
Total Oil	6.0	12.7	4.9	16.7	5.0
Oil Shale	0.0	0.0	0.0	0.0	0.0
Gas					
Exploration, Development, and Production	0.0	0.3	0.6	0.4	0.5
Pipelines	0.0	0.3	1.1	0.2	0.7
LNG Tankers	0.4	0.4	0.4	0.0	0.0
Distribution	0.6	2.3	1.0	3.8	2.0
Other	0.8	1.1	0.7	0.0	0.0
Total Gas	1.8	4.4	3.8	4.4	3.1
Coal					
Underground Mining	0.0	3.8	6.8	2.6	6.4
Surface Mining	0.0	0.9	0.0	3.3	5.8
Rail	1.6	7.3	2.7	21.0	2.8
Pipelines	0.0	0.0	0.0	0.8	0.0
Barges, Trucks	0.0	0.5	0.4	1.1	0.5
Total Coal	1.6	12.5	9.9	28.8	15.6
Coal Synthetics	0.0	0.0	0.0	14.9	8.4
Nuclear Fuel Cycle	0.4	1.3	7.1	0.0	5.2
Solar	3.8	7.5	24.9	2.0	17.4
Electric Utilities					
Coal-Fired	4.4	22.0	17.5	75.6	16.6
Sulfur Removal Facilities	1.8	7.3	7.3	12.4	6.9
Nuclear	17.4	39.2	46.5	52.2	49.5
Hydro and Pumped Storage	0.0	6.4	7.3	0.0	1.7
Oil and Gas	1.0	1.2	2.8	3.4	1.9
Geothermal	0.0	0.0	0.0	0.0	0.0
Total Generation	24.6	76.1	81.5	143.6	76.6
Transmission and Distribution	8.3	33.5	28.6	30.8	19.8
Total Utilities	32.9	109.6	110.1	174.3	96.5
Total Energy Industry	46.6	148.1	160.7	241.3	151.2

R6 (West North Central)	R7 (West South Central)	R8 (Northern Mountain)	R9 (Southern Mountain)	R10 (Northern Pacific)	R11 (Southern Pacific)	R12 (Offshore Atlantic)	R13 (Offshore Gulf)	R14 (Offshore Pacific)	TOTAL REGIONS
2.7	58.8	5.2	6.5	5.4	34.7	2.0	15.1	7.1	144.5
1.4	11.0	1.0	1.4	2.5	12.7	0.0	0.0	0.0	56.0
0.7	0.5	0.1	0.7	0.3	1.3	0.0	0.0	0.0	6.3
0.5	3.1	0.2	0.5	0.9	5.5	0.0	0.0	0.0	19.3
0.1	0.3	0.0	0.1	0.1	0.3	0.0	0.0	0.0	1.6
0.0	2.4	0.0	0.0	0.1	0.3	0.0	0.0	0.0	3.1
5.4	76.1	6.5	9.2	9.3	54.8	2.0	15.1	7.1	230.8
0.0	0.0	0.0	0.0	0.0	0.0	0.0	0.0	0.0	0.0
2.3	49.3	1.4	3.9	3.0	4.5	0.0	25.0	0.6	91.8
1.5	2.2	0.0	1.3	2.7	1.1	0.0	0.0	0.0	11.1
0.0	0.0	0.0	0.0	0.0	3.5	0.0	0.0	0.0	4.8
1.1	5.8	0.3	1.1	0.5	2.4	0.0	0.0	0.0	20.8
0.0	0.0	0.0	0.0	2.0	1.7	0.0	0.0	.0.0	6.3
4.9	57.3	1.7	6.3	8.3	13.1	0.0	25.0	0.6	134.8
0.0	0.0	0.0	2.9	0.0	0.0	0.0	0.0	0.0	22.5
1.2	1.0	16.3	3.9	0.1	0.0	0.0	0.0	0.0	32.5
7.3	3.3	0.4	2.4	0.1	0.6	0.0	0.0	0.0	49.5
2.0	1.0	1.6	2.8	0.0	0.4	0.0	0.0	0.0	8.7
0.1	0.1	0.1	0.1	0.0	0.0	0.0	0.0	0.0	3.0
10.5	5.5	18.4	12.1	0.2	1.0	0.0	0.0	0.0	116.3
7.3	0.0	0.0	0.0	0.0	0.0	0.0	0.0	0.0	30.6
0.4	0.8	1.4	1.9	5.4	0.5	0.0	0.0	0.0	24.3
2.0	38.4	0.0	28.9	0.0	67.1	0.0	0.0	0.0	192.0
54.2	49.5	7.2	1.9	1.9	18.1	0.0	0.0	0.0	269.1
8.6	7.7	0.8	0.7	0.1	5.8	0.0	0.0	0.0	59.6
6.3	28.2	0.0	6.3	21.2	16.8	0.0	0.0	0.0	283.6
1.1	0.4	0.5	1.5	3.2	2.8	0.0	0.0	0.0	24.8
1.8	3.1	0.1	0.4	0.8	3.9	0.0	0.0	0.0	20.5
0.0	0.0	1.1	4.5	0.0	23.2	0.0	0.0	0.0	28.8
72.1	88.9	9.7	15.2	27.2	70.7	0.0	0.0	0.0	686.3
17.6	20.1	3.6	7.1	9.6	13.9	0.0	0.0	0.0	192.9
89.7	109.0	13.3	22.3	36.8	84.7	0.0	0.0	0.0	879.2
120.1	287.1	41.3	80.6	60.0	221.2	2.0	40.2	7.7	1,608.0

Source: "Engineering a Transition to Coal," J. Michael Gallagher and Ralph G.J. Zimmermann, Bechtel National, Inc., *National Resources Forum,* July 1979. Prepared for EMF *Coal in Transition* Study.

Figure 16-15.   Environmental Disturbances from Coal-Related Activities

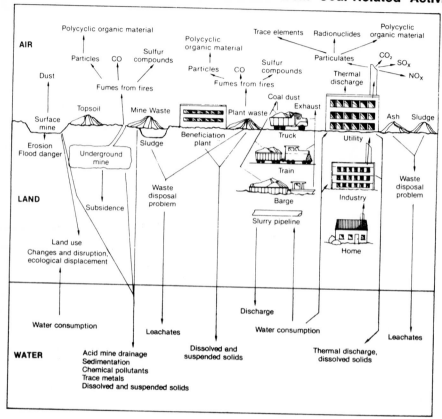

Source: *The Direct Use of Coal,* Prospects and Problems of Production and Combustion; Washington, D.C., Office of Technology Assessment, 1979.

required to promulgate, for these pollutants, national allowable levels in the ambient air which he determined will protect health and welfare. In 1971, EPA promulgated National Ambient Air Quality Standards (NAAQS) (see Table 16-20) for the current six Criteria Pollutants—sulfur dioxide, nitrogen dioxide, particulate matter, carbon monoxide, hydrocarbons, and photochemical oxidants.

These National Ambient Air Quality Standards (expressed in micrograms per cubic meter) establish maximum concentrations permitted in the ambient air. Those related to the combustion of coal in stationary sources are: sulfur dioxide (SO_2), particulate matter (TSP, total suspended particulates) and nitrogen dioxide (NO_2). For each pollutant, two standards were issued. Primary standards were set at levels necessary to protect the public health and were to be met no later than three years from the date of promulgation (subject to limited extensions of up to three years). Secondary standards were designed to protect the public from adverse effects to their welfare, such as crop damage and corrosion of materials and were to be met in a time frame considered reasonable by the Administrator. Both sets of standards were set at levels intended to provide "an adequate margin of safety."

Figure 16-16. Jurisdiction of Federal Control Legislation

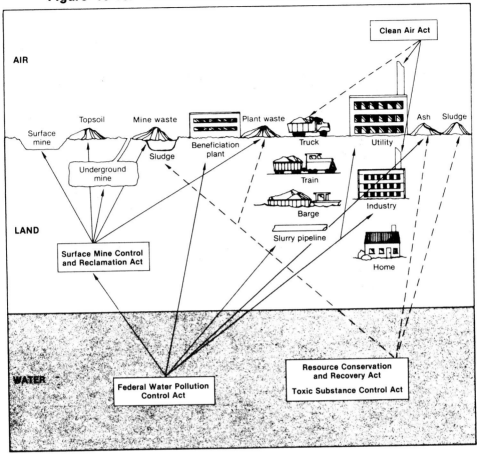

Source: *The Direct Use of Coal,* Prospects and Problems of Production and Combustion; Washington, D.C., Office of Technology Assessment, 1979.

Table 16-19. Guide to Current Federal Regulations Pertaining to Coal Production and Utilization in the United States

1. Surface Mining Regulations—U.S. Department of Interior—regulations cover state and Federal programs

2. Mineral Leasing Act of 1920 as amended by P.L. 940377 (Coal Leasing Amendments Act of 1975)

3. P.L. 94-579, Federal Land Policy and Management Act of 1976. In addition, other specific management systems which control land resources or mineral development are:
   a. The National Forests (Administered by the Forest Service of the Department of Agriculture)
   b. The National Parks (National Park Service, Department of Interior)
   c. Wild and Scenic Rivers (Fish and Wildlife Service, Department of Interior)
   d. Game Ranges and Refuges (Fish and Wildlife Service, Department of Interior)

477

e. Other public lands managed for multiple use by Department of Interior Bureau of Land Management

f. Wilderness Act of 1964 (16 U.S.C. 1131 as amended)

4. P.L. 93-205, December 28, 1978, the Endangered Species Act of 1973 as amended by P.L. 94-359 and 94-325 (35 U.S.C. 1531-1543)

5. P.L. 95-164, November 9, 1977, the Federal Safety and Health Act of 1977 (which amended the Federal Coal Mine Health and Safety Act of 1969, P.L. 91-173)

6. Federal Mine Safety and Health Amendments Act of 1977 requires mine operators to train miners in accordance with a plan approved by Secretary of Labor

7. P.L. 95-239 (H.R. 4544), the Black Lung Benefits Reform Act of 1977, March 1, 1978; and P.L. 95-227 (H.R. 5322), the Black Lung Benefits Revenue Act of 1977, February 10, 1978

8. Clean Air Act, as amended (1977 amendments in P.L. 95-95). The following upcoming governmental actions under the Clean Air Act, as amended, may affect coal users or producers:

   a. Revision of New Source Performance Standards (NSPS), Section III
   b. Prevention of Significant Deterioration (PSD) of air quality, Title I, part C
   c. Unregulated Hazardous Air Pollutants, Section 122
   d. Study of environmental effects of sulfates and fine particulates, Section 122(b)
   e. Revisions of State Implementation Plans (SIPs), Section 110(a)(3)(D)
   f. Review of National Ambient Air Quality Standards, Section 109(d)
   g. National Emission Standards for Hazardous Emissions, Section 112
   h. Regional Consistency of Air Quality Requirements, Section 301
   i. Innovative Technology Waivers under NSPS, Section 111(k)
   j. Short-term (three hours or less) Ambient Standard for NO_x, Section 101(c)
   k. Stack Height Regulations, Section 123
   l. Revisions of EPA's December 1978 "offset" ruling for new facilities in "nonattachment" areas, Title I, Part D
   m. Visibility Protection Program, Section 169A

9. Water Quality Regulations

   a. Clean Water Act of 1977
   b. Best Practical Control Technology (BPCT)
   c. NSPS for effluent discharges from mines and new preparation facilities
   d. Best Management Practices (BMP)
   e. Priority Pollutants/Toxics
   f. Water Quality Standards

10. P.L. 93-523, Safe Drinking Water Act, December 16, 1974 (42 USC 300 et seq.)

11. P.L. 94-580, Resource Conservation and Recovery Act of 1976 (42 USC 6901 et seq.)

12. P.L. 92-574, Noise Control Act of 1972, October 27, 1972 (42 USC 4901–4918; 49 USC 1431)

13. FEA Authorization Act of 1977 (P.L. 95-70), Energy Supply and Environmental Coordination Act (ESECA)

14. P.L. 95-620 Power Plant and Industrial Fuels Use Act (FUA)

Note 1: Abstracted from Appendix B of "International Coal Technology Summary Document," December 1978, prepared by the U.S. Department of Energy with the assistance of The Energy Systems Planning Division.

UNITED STATES

Table 16-20. Summary of U.S. National Ambient Air Quality Standards

Pollutant	Averaging Time	Primary Standards	Secondary Standards	Federal Reference Method (FRM)	Comments
Particulate Matter	Annual (Geometric Mean)	75 μg/m³	60 μg/m³	Hi-Volume Sampler	The secondary annual standard (60μg/m³) is a guide for assessing SIPs to achieve the 24-hour secondary standard.
	24-Hour*	260 μg/m³	150 μg/m³		
Sulfur Oxides	Annual (Arithmetic Mean)	80 μg/m³ (0.03ppm)	—	Pararosaniline	
	24-Hour*	365 μg/m³ (0.14ppm)	—		
	3-Hour*	—	1,300 μg/m³ (0.5ppm)		
CO	8-Hour*	10 mg/m³ (9ppm)	(Same as Primary)	Non-Dispersive Infrared Spectrometry	
	1-Hour*	40 mg/m³ (35ppm)			
NO_2	Annual (Arithmetic Mean)	100 μg/m³ (0.05ppm)	(Same as Primary)	Jacobs-Hochheiser (Rescinded)	The continuous Saltzman, Sodium Arsenite (Christie), TGS, and Chemiluminescence have been proposed as replacements for the J-H method. New FRM to be decided upon by Jan. 1975.
Photochemical Oxidants	1-Hour*	160 μg/m³ (0.08ppm)	(Same as Primary)	Chemiluminescence	The FRM measures O_3 (ozone)
Hydrocarbons (Non-Methane)	3-Hour* (6 to 9 a.m.)	160 μg/m³ (0.24ppm)	(Same as Primary)	Flame Ionization	The HC standard is a guide to devising SIPs to achieve the Oxidant standard. The HC standard does not have to be met if the oxidant standard is met.

* Not to be exceeded more than once per year.

Note: The air quality standards and a description of the reference methods were published on April 30, 1971 in 42 CFR 410, recodified to 40 CFR 50 on November 25, 1972.

January 30, 1974 - JDC.

Source: Table A-2, EPA-450/2-76-002a, September 1977, State Implementation Plan Emission Regulations for Sulfur Oxides: Fuel Combustion, Second Edition.

U.S. Environmental Protection Agency, Office of Air and Waste Management, Research Triangle Park, North Carolina.

STATE IMPLEMENTATION PLANS (SIP)

To implement these standards, the Act required each state to adopt and submit to EPA a plan for attaining, maintaining, and enforcing the National Ambient Air Quality Standards in all regions of the state. Each state, therefore, decided (for each Criteria Pollutant) the allowable emission rates to maintain local ambient air levels below the standards and decided which emission sources to control and to what extent. The State Implementation Plans (SIPs) prescribed emission limiting regulations, timetables for compliance with the limitations, and any other measures, such as siting requirements, land-use and transportation controls, which were necessary to ensure attainment and maintenance of the standards. The plans were reviewed by EPA and approved if they demonstrated that at a minimum the primary standards would be attained within three years (subject to the compliance date extension provisions of the Act) and that secondary standards would be attained within a reasonable period of time.

While the primary responsibility for enforcing SIP regulations rests with the individual states, the Administrator of EPA is also responsible for assuring that all implementation plan requirements are fulfilled. As a result, EPA provides technical and legal assistance to the states in enforcing SIP regulations. If any state fails to enforce its implementation plan regulations, the Federal Government may initiate a number of administrative or legal actions directed toward non-complying sources.

NEW SOURCE PERFORMANCE STANDARDS (NSPS)

In addition to the SIP limitations, emissions from "new" sources are restricted further by Federal Standards of Performance for New Stationary Sources (commonly referred to as New Source Performance Standards—NSPS). A new emission source is one which is designed and constructed after the formal promulgation of new source regulations. Examples include newly constructed facilities, new equipment which is added to existing facilities, and existing equipment which is modified in such a way that emissions are increased. New source standards limit emissions from various types of sources (such as fossil-fuel fired steam generators, municipal incinerators) which the Administrator determines may contribute significantly to endangering public health and welfare. For these sources, the Act requires the Administrator to promulgate emission limitations which will require installation of the best systems of emission reduction which he determines have been adequately demonstrated. Cost factors are considered but do not determine this decision. Federal new source standards are designed to help prevent the occurrence of new air pollution problems to encourage improvements in emission control technology, and to provide a mechanism for controlling pollutants which the EPA suspects are hazardous, but for which insufficient information is available to regulate such pollutants under other provisions of the Act.

EPA is required to reassess periodically the efficacy of the standards for the Criteria Pollutants; and, as new pollutants of concern are identified, EPA must add these to the category of Criteria Pollutants and set standards for them.

SUMMARY OF NAAQS, SIP, NSPS

A summary of the National Ambient Air Quality Standards, an example of the state emission limitations for coal-fired electric power plants in the State of Illinois, and the national new source performance standards for SO_2, TSP, and

NO_2 is contained in Table 16-21. The variation among states in the way emission limitations are expressed is significant and it is not possible to provide a convenient summary of these state standards for emission regulations. However, for those states which express limitations in pounds per million Btu (these include many states) the limitations range from between 0.2 to 6.0 pounds per million Btu for SO_2, and from 0.03 to 0.8 pounds per million Btu for particulates (TSP).

Table 16-21. U.S. Environmental Control Standards and an Example of State Limitations Which Impact on Coal Utilization

Pollutant	National Ambient Standards[1]				State or Area Emission Limitations for Existing Sources[2]* (lbs. per million Btu)		National New Source Performance Standards for Emission Limitations (lbs. per million Btu)
	Primary[3]		Secondary[4]		Major Metropolitan Areas	Rural	
	Annual Mean	Max.—once per year	Annual Mean	Max.—once per year			
SO_2	80 μg/m³	365 μg/m³ 24 hr.	60 μg/m³	260 μg/m³ 24 hr. 1,300 μg/m³ 3 hr.	1.8	6.0	1.2
TSP	74 μg/m³	260 μg/m³ 24 hr.	60 μg/m³	150 μg/m³ 24 hr.	2.0 (old) 1.0 (new)	2.0 (old) 1.0 (new)	1.0
NO_2	100 μg/m³	none	100 μg/m³	none	0.9	none	.9

* For coal-fired power plants in State of Illinois.
[1] Limits on ground level concentrations.
[2] Limits on stack emissions for sources burning solid fuel in the State of Illinois.
[3] Intended to protect public health.
[4] Intended to protect public welfare—i.e., plants, materials, etc.

NEW SOURCE PERFORMANCE STANDARDS (NSPS)

The amendments to the Clean Air Act in 1977 included a requirement for EPA to devise more stringent New Source Performance Standards (NSPS) for fossil-fuel stationary sources. These standards were revised to include both allowable emission limitations (lb/MBtu) and a percent reduction in emissions of SO_2 (Table 16-22). The Congress directed that the NSPS reflect the best technological system of continuous emission reduction, considering cost, energy and environmental impact.

The revisions effectively require use of flue gas desulfurization—FGD—plus possible coal cleaning for high-sulfur coal, increased NO_x control with possibly increased maintenance requirements, and increased use of baghouses, particularly for high-resistivity fly ash.

The new NSPS standards include the following:

- 90% to 70% removal of SO_2, using a 30-day averaging period, depending on the level of controlled emissions, with bypass provisions. Credit can be given for sulful removal prior to combustion.
- 0.03 lb/MBtu, 99% removal, and 20% opacity for particulates.
- 0.6 lb/MBtu NO_x and 65% removal for bituminous coal.

These requirements place increasing restraints on the ability of electric utilities and industrial plants to burn coal directly without flue gas desulfurization

Table 16-22. New Source Performance Standards

Emission	Fuel	Emission Limit	Percent Removal
Sulfur dioxide	Solid or Solid Derived	1.20 lbs/MBtu	90% if controlled emissions are greater than 0.6 lbs/MBtu. 70% if controlled emissions are less than 0.6 lbs/MBtu.
	Liquid or Gaseous	0.80 lbs/MBtu	90%
Nitrogen oxides	Gaseous— Coal-derived All other	0.50 lbs/MBtu 0.20 lbs/MBtu	25%
	Liquid— Coal-derived Shale oil All other	0.50 lbs/MBtu 0.50 lbs/MBtu 0.30 lbs/MBtu	30%
	Solid— Coal-derived Lignite Subbituminous Bituminous Anthracite	0.50 lbs/MBtu 0.60 lbs/MBtu 0.50 lbs/MBtu 0.60 lbs/MBtu 0.60 lbs/MBtu	65%
Particulate	Solid	0.30 lbs/MBtu	99% *
	Liquid	0.30 lbs/MBtu	70% *

* Removal percentage is not controlling—compliance with emission limit satisfies removal requirement.

equipment (and/or, possibly, more costly low-sulfur coal). Best Available Control Technology (BACT) is required for all new plants by the '77 amendments, so flue gas desulfurization equipment will be required for all major new coal-burning sources.

FACILITY SITING

The time required for siting power plants and other major coal-using facilities has increased substantially in recent years because of the numerous new permits and approvals required from the various federal and state agencies. Provisions for siting in "Prevention of Significant Deterioration Areas" and in "Non-Attainment Areas" have added several years to the time required for siting in such areas, and these provisions may eliminate many possible sites. Some electric utilities now schedule an eight- to ten-year project cycle (from perception of need to in-service demand) for coal-fired power plants, as compared to a ten- to twelve-year cycle for a nuclear-fueled power plant.

PREVENTION OF SIGNIFICANT DETERIORATION (PSD) AREAS

A region with air quality cleaner than an ambient air standard is a Prevention of Significant Deterioration (PSD) area.

The Clean Air Act includes comprehensive provisions designed to prevent the significant deterioration (PSD) of air quality in areas where the air is cleaner than the NAAQS require. The PSD increments for Class I areas (usually national parks, monuments, or wilderness areas) allow the lowest increase in ambient concentrations over the baseline, and, thus, the fewest new stationary sources, while the Class II increments allow the greatest increase. In no event may a new source located in a clean air area cause the concentration of any pollutant to exceed either the national primary or secondary ambient air quality standard. At present, the PSD regulations apply only to emissions of particulate matter and SO_2. Regulations for NO_x, hydrocarbons, photochemical oxidants, and carbon monoxide are to be promulgated in the future.

To obtain a permit to locate a new source in an area subject to the PSD regulations, the applicant must demonstrate that the source will meet all applicable emission limitations under the state implementation plan as well as performance standards for new sources and emission standards for hazardous pollutants, and that the source will apply the best available control technology (BACT). BACT is determined on a case-by-case basis, taking into account energy, environmental, and economic impacts and other costs. In addition, the applicant must demonstrate, based on air-quality monitoring data and modeling techniques, that allowable emissions from the source will not cause or contribute to air pollution in violation of the NAAQS or PSD increments. The permit applicant also must provide an analysis of the source's air-quality-related impacts on visibility, soils, vegetation, and anticipated induced industrial, commercial, and residential growth.

The 1977 provisions apply to more categories of sources than before and are expected to increase the costs of facility siting. In addition, there are two situations in which facility siting will probably be constrained. First, PSD permits will not be available for large new sources in areas where the difference between the baseline concentration and the NAAQS already is less than the allowable increment. Second, where there are several sources that are exempt from the PSD requirements because of their size or date of construction, such exempt and un-reviewed sources may preempt the available increments and foreclose siting for larger new facilities.

NONATTAINMENT AREAS

A "Nonattainment Area" is one in which there is found to be a pollutant(s) which exceeds any national ambient air-quality standard for that pollutant. In such an area, states are required to develop a plan to provide for attainment of each NAAQS not later than December 31, 1982, as a precondition for the construction or modification of any major stationary source in any such (nonattainment) area on or after July 1, 1979.

A major new source cannot locate in a nonattainment area unless:

(1) Emissions are controlled to the greatest degree possible using LAER (Lowest Achievable Emission Rate—this is the lowest emission rate required by any state or the lowest rate achieved in practice, whichever is more stringent.)

(2) If more than equivalent offsetting emission reductions (offsets) will be obtained from other existing sources in that area.

Nonattainment programs will impose severe constraints not only on increased coal use but on other industrial growth in these areas. As of 1977, most of the Air Quality Control Regions (AQCRs) had not attained the primary particulate standards, while 15% had not met the SO_2 standards. Wherever a new source would exacerbate an existing NAAQS violation, the permit applicant must apply the lowest achievable emission rate (LAER) and must secure from existing sources in the area emission reductions that more than offset the emissions from the proposed facility. The cost of meeting these two requirements is high, and securing the offsetting emission reductions is difficult. Consequently, new sources are more likely to be located in rural areas where the NAAQS have been achieved. In addition, major modifications to existing sources in nonattainment areas probably would be rejected in favor of new sources in clean-air areas.

OTHER SITING REQUIREMENTS

Additional constraints on siting are imposed by the permit requirements of the Clean Water Act, the Army Corps of Engineers, and agencies having jurisdiction over federal lands, as well as by the general requirements of NEPA, the National Historic Preservation Act (NHPA), the Fish and Wildlife Coordination Act (FWCA), and the Endangered Species Act. The Clean Water Act is structured around the quality of water necessary for a variety of uses, including public water supplies, propagation of fish and wildlife, recreational, agricultural, industrial and other purposes, and navigation. New facilities must obtain a permit under the National Pollution Discharge Elimination System (NPDES). The permit incorporates all applicable effluent limitations and water-quality standards promulgated under the Clean Water Act, and an applicant must demonstrate that these limitations and standards will be met. In addition, if the plans for a combustion facility require any structure to be built in navigable waters (such as a cooling-water intake structure or barge-loading facility), a permit must be obtained from the Army Corps of Engineers. Corps regulations stipulate that no such permit may be issued until the applicant demonstrates that all other necessary Federal, State, and local permits, certifications, or other authorizations have been obtained. Finally, if the coal combustion unit or any of its support facilities (such as transmission lines) are to be located on federal land, a permit must be obtained from the federal agency having jurisdiction over that land, in addition to the usual state and local agency permits.

All coal-combustion facilities which need a federal permit of some kind will trigger the environmental impact statement (EIS) requirements of NEPA. Although the EIS is prepared by the federal agency issuing the permit, it is based on analyses submitted by the applicant, and the length of time required to prepare the federal EIS depends on the quality and completeness of those analyses. In addition, before issuing a permit the lead federal agency must obtain certification from various other federal, state and local agencies that their jurisdictions are satisfied as a certification from the Secretary of the Interior that the facility will not jeopardize the continued existence of an endangered species of plant or animal. Under the FWCA, when a federally permitted project would result in the modification of any water body (for example, reduction of water flow because of additional water consumption by cooling towers), the permitting agency must consult with the Fish and Wildlife Service and with the state agency having supervisory authority over fish and wildlife prior to issuing the permit. Issuance of the permit may be enjoined until consultation and coordination has occurred, and serious consideration must be given to recommendations for mitigation of impacts to fish and wildlife. Finally, regulations promulgated under the NHPA require all permitting agencies to determine whether there are historic, archeological, architectural, or cultural resources affected by the proposed action that are listed in the National Register of Historic Places or are eligible for listing. If any of these resources may be affected, the permitting agency must obtain comments from the Advisory Council on Historic Preservation.

Of all these requirements, the Clean Air Act will have the most far-reaching consequences in terms of the number of sites foreclosed to coal-combustion facilities. However, the cumulative effect of all these provisions, each with extensive interagency and public participation requirements, will be to lengthen significantly the time necessary for site approval. When numerous state and local permits and other requirements are added in, this added lead time can become costly, both in terms of project financial requirements and in terms of delayed expansion of energy sources.

OTHER PROVISIONS OF THE 1977 AMENDMENTS TO THE CLEAN AIR ACT (PUBLIC LAW 95–95)

STACK HEIGHT

In determining emission limitations, no regulatory credit is given for stack heights that exceed "good engineering practice"—defined as 2.5 times building height—or for any other dispersion techniques, such as higher than normal stack gas exit velocity or temperature, or the use of capacity of fuel switching to ensure meeting ambient standards.

INTERSTATE POLLUTION ABATEMENT

States also must identify and prohibit any stationary source from emitting an air pollutant in amounts that prevent attainment or maintenance by any other state of an ambient air quality standard, or that interfere with measures required to prevent significant deterioration of air quality or to protect visibility. A state or government subdivision may petition EPA to require control of sources in another state.

NONCOMPLIANCE PENALTIES

The noncompliance penalty will be assessed against a major stationary source that is not in compliance with limitations or schedules under a state implementation plan, NSPS, hazardous pollutant emission standards, or interim requirements of an EPA enforcement order. The penalty will include any economic value that accrued to an owner because compliance was delayed beyond July 1, 1979, minus any capital and maintenance expenditures made to bring the source into compliance.

VISIBILITY PROTECTION

This section of the 1977 amendments to the CAA establishes as a national goal the prevention of any future, and the remedying of any existing, impairment of visibility (reduction in visual range and atmospheric discoloration) in mandatory Class I federal PSD areas as a result of man-made air pollution. The emission control method that will be used to abate visibility degradation from existing sources is the best available retrofit technology. These provisions are designed to protect visibility in areas primarily important for scenic values, such as national parks, and are expected to affect the siting of coal-fired facilities. EPA's regulations, which were to be promulgated not later than August 1979 (this deadline was not met), are to require SIP revision in order to achieve visibility improvement by retrofitting plants in existence for less than 15 years, as well as by adopting a long-term strategy for progress toward a national visibility goal. Proposed fossil-fuel-fired power plants with a design capacity of more than 750 MW must demonstrate that they will not cause or contribute to the significant impairment of visibility in any of the specified areas. However, until the visibility regulations have been promulgated, it is not possible to determine their impact on the costs of, or site selection for, coal-fired facilities.

NITROGEN OXIDE (NO$_x$) STANDARD

EPA is revising and will soon reissue its NO$_x$ criteria with reference to short-term exposure periods (3 hours). Congress specifically directed that the revised criteria "include a discussion of nitric and nitrous acids, nitrates, nitrosaminos and other carcinogenic and potentially carcinogenic derivatives of oxides of nitrogen." Until the substance of these regulations is clear, it is not possible to assess their impact on new coal-fired facilities.

UNREGULATED POLLUTANTS

By Congressional mandate, EPA must review information on radioactive emissions, cadmium, arsenic and polycyclic organic matter emitted during coal production and use, and will establish regulations if it is determined that they will "cause, or contribute to, air pollution which may reasonably be anticipated to endanger public health."

This provides a mandate to EPA for regulation of possibly hazardous trace substances, and integrates a control scheme over the emissions of substances which may be hazardous or toxic if sufficiently concentrated, which is also present in the

Clean Water Act of 1977, the Toxic Substances Control Act of 1976, and the Resource Conservation and Recovery Act of 1976.

OTHER REGULATIONS PERTAINING TO COAL

THE SURFACE MINING CONTROL AND RECLAMATION ACT OF 1977 (SMCRA)

The Surface Mining Control and Reclamation Act was designed to reduce environmental disturbances associated with surface coal mining operations and to prohibit surface mining in areas that cannot be reclaimed. It requires that states establish permit programs for surface mines and procedures for designating areas unsuitable for mining. The federal government retains regulatory authority until adequate state programs are in place. Under the Act, all surface mining permits require that the mining operations meet all applicable environmental protection standards—for example, those regarding restoration of the land to its original contour, waste disposal, and revegetation. More stringent standards apply to some areas, such as prime farm land, steep slopes, alluvial valleys and timberlands.

The applicable standards which have been proposed are being contested by the coal industry which claims these standards provide little opportunity for flexibility or technical innovations in meeting the principal objectives of the Act, and lead to excessive increases in coal production costs.

The full impact of the Act has yet to be determined. However, depending on how the law is administered and enforced, significant blocks of surface mineable reserves could be eliminated from future development. In particular, the "alluvial valley floor" provision could eliminate significant tonnages of Powder River Basin coals from future development, and in the Midwest the "prime agricultural lands" provision could restrict future surface mining from many areas. The net effect of these removals would be to encourage underground mining, especially in areas east of the Mississippi River.

THE MINE HEALTH AND SAFETY ACT (MHSA)

A major regulatory initiative that affected underground mining was the 1969 Coal Mine Health and Safety Act, which was revised in 1977. This Act was designed to improve the safety conditions in coal mines and to reduce the number of mining injuries and fatalities. Its provisions require coal operators to devote more personnel and equipment to ventilation, rockdusting, methane and dust monitoring, roof control, maintenance, and retrofitting machinery with safety features, among other things. Implementation of the Act has resulted in major decreases in the number of coal mine fatalities and injuries since 1969. However, implementation of the Act's measures has also contributed to the decline in underground mine productivity, which has increased the costs of mining and reduced the nominal capacity of existing mines, thus requiring that new capacity be developed to offset the reduced capacity of existing mines.

THE RESOURCE CONSERVATION AND RECOVERY ACT (RCRA) OF 1976

Combustion by-products (including bottom ash, fly ash and SO_2 scrubber sludge) contain materials which appear to make them subject to the stringent rules relating to the treatment, storage and disposal of hazardous solid wastes. In proposing new regulations, EPA created a class of special wastes, which include the high-volume power plant wastes, and now plans to propose standards for controlling them by June of 1982 and promulgate them by June of 1983.

FEDERAL COAL LEASING

The Federal government owns 65% of Western coal reserves and indirectly controls another 20%. Given the major role projected for Western coal in the expansion of coal use, the federal leasing policy emerges as a major factor in future coal development. Yet no comprehensive federal coal leasing policy now exists, and there has been a leasing moratorium since 1970 with the exception of small-scale emergency leasing at existing mines.

In 1976 Congress passed the Federal Coal Leasing Amendments Act to revise the 1920 Mineral Leasing Act. Among other things, the 1976 amendments make leases more complicated to obtain, and require that the leases be developed within ten years or they are automatically terminated (i.e., "due diligence"). In 1977 the Bureau of Land Management (BLM) issued regulations to implement the Act. The Department of the Interior has been reviewing overall coal leasing policy, and there are now plans to resume federal leasing in 1981, coupled with vigorous enforcement of the "due diligence" requirements.

INDICATIVE ENVIRONMENTAL COSTS FOR NEXT GENERATION OF U.S. POWER PLANTS

Coal-fired power plants built in the United States over the next 10–20 years will be quite different from plants built 10 years ago, reflecting, among other things, the additional environmental controls required to meet more stringent environmental standards.

Pulverized coal boilers will continue to be used. The plants will be more coal-specific because of furnace design criteria and environmental control equipment criteria. About 25% of the total capital investment will be for equipment needed to meet these more stringent environmental standards.

The major changes in new coal-fired electric power plants, as opposed to those designed for the 1970's, are likely to be:

- Plant Cooling Systems—In many locations wet tower or dry tower cooling systems will be used in place of once-through cooling systems.
- Particulate Control Systems—Electrostatic precipitators and/or baghouses will be used to reduce the total amount and size of the particulates released.
- SO_2 Scrubbers—Scrubbers will be used to reduce the level of SO_2 emissions. These will change from the "throwaway" systems which produce large amounts of wet sludge (about 1 ton of sludge for every 4 tons of high-sulfur coal) to regenerative systems where the absorbent material can be reused and the waste is solid. Reliable operation of the scrubber will continue to be an important consideration.
- NO_x Control—Combustion control techniques will be used to reduce NO_x emissions.
- Waste Water Treatment—Waste water from power plants will be treated before it is discharged.
- Ash and/or Sludge Disposal—New disposal techniques for ash and SO_2 scrubber sludge will be used—possibly treating one or both of these as hazardous waste.

488

Table 16-23, prepared for WOCOL by the Electric Power Research Institute (EPRI), provides a summary of the costs, on a per ton of coal basis, for the various environmental standards and control techniques discussed, for a specific coal type and for the power plant and economic conditions described. Each of these costs can vary rather considerably with changes in any of the parameters.

Table 16-24 provides indicative cost estimates, on a per ton of coal basis, prepared by a typical utility—Commonwealth Edison Co., compared to the EPRI estimates.

It can be seen that the total control equipment costs can reach $20/ton or more (on an annualized basis), which approximates the costs of coal now delivered to electric utilities. Coal costs would then be about $40-50/ton which is roughly comparable to $10/barrel oil equivalent.

SUMMARY OF ENVIRONMENT, HEALTH AND SAFETY

Over the past ten or fifteen years, environmental, health and safety laws and regulations have been established in the United States at the federal, state, and local levels. The complex of laws, regulations, and regulatory institutions have also provided for significantly increased public participation in decision-making. Existing standards now govern nearly all aspects of energy supply activities, including the manner in which coal can be mined, moved, and burned or processed.

One effect of the regulatory process, as it has been implemented, has been a substantial increase in the time it takes to plan, site, design, engineer and build a coal-fired power plant. In 1970, for example, a large coal-fired power plant could be sited, engineered and built in as few as three or four years. Today, the engineering and construction of such a plant still takes only 4-5 years, but the site planning, environmental assessment analyses, and additional environmental permit requirements stretches out the total project cycle to between eight and ten years, and sometimes longer.

The increased project lead time has been accompanied by a large increase in total project cost. In 1970, a large coal-fired power plant could be built for a total cost of $150 to $200 per kilowatt of installed capacity. Today, a similar plant is expected to cost between $800 and $1000 per kilowatt. Similar increases have occurred for other types of power plants as well. Of course, a considerable part of the cost increase is the effect of escalation in construction labor, materials and equipment which has occurred over the decade, but about half or more of the increase is due to the additional environmental control equipment required and the financial costs associated with the longer project lead times.

Unfortunately, the evolution of environmental, health and safety standards has not been closely integrated with national energy policy. In some cases at least, energy and environmental policies have actually been in conflict. For example, the conversion of coal-fired utility boilers to oil and the building of new oil-fired plants to meet environmental restrictions has exacerbated the country's dependence on oil imports.

The rapid expansion of coal production and use, which is required to reduce U.S. dependence on oil imports and to compensate for delays in nuclear power expansion, will be possible only if the environmental standards for mining, moving and using coal are clear and stable, and integrated with an energy policy which encourages the expansion of coal. The decision process for siting new coal facilities must be expedited, while still providing opportunities for review by interested parties.

489

Table 16-23. Coal Utilization Costs[a]

Summary of Costs on $/Ton of Coal Basis

Particulate Control	*ESP (Cold Side)*		*Baghouse*	
Emission standard, lb/10^6Btu	0.1	0.03	0.1	0.03
Levelized cost (1978-2007)	2.8	3.8	3.0	3.0
1978 cost	1.5	2.0	1.6	1.6

SO_2 Control	*Limestone*[b]	*Regenerative*
Emission standard, % removal	85	95
Levelized cost (1978-2007)	26	32
1978 cost	14	17

Solid Waste Disposal	*Ash Conventional*	*Ash Hazardous*	*Ash Plus Sludge Conventional*
Levelized cost (1978-2007)	1.20	10 to 18	4.8
1978 cost	.65	5 to 10	2.5

NO_x Control	*Combustion Control*	*Post-Combustion Control*
Emission standard, lb/10^6Btu	0.6	0.2
Levelized cost (1978-2007)	0.4 to 1.0	12 to 16
1978 cost	0.2 to 0.5	6 to 9

Waste Water Treatment	*Conventional*	*Zero Discharge*
Levelized cost (1978-2007)	0.6 to 4.0	4 to 6
1978 cost	0.3 to 2.0	2 to 3

Plant Cooling Systems	*Wet Tower Conventional*	*Dry Tower Conventional*	*Dry Tower Ammonia*
Levelized cost (1978-2007)	1.75	20	10
1978 cost	0.9	11	5

BASES

Coal

- Illinois bituminous
- 10,000 Btu/lb HHV, as received
- 4%W sulfur (average)
- 16%W ash

Power Plant

- 70% capacity factor
- 10,000 Btu/kWh heat rate

Economic

- 18% levelized annual fixed charges
- 6% annual inflation rate (all costs)
- 10% annual weighted cost of capital
- 30 year levelizing period (1978-2007)
- 1978 cost = 30 year levelized cost/levelization factor
- Levelization factor = 1.886

[a] Costs developed principally from "Potential Impact of EPRI Programs on Environmental Control Costs for Coal-Fired Power Plants" by K.E. Yeager, C.R. McGowin, and S.B. Baruch.

[b] Does not include sludge disposal cost (see solid waste section).

Source: Electric Power Research Institute.

Table 16-24. Indicative Cost Estimates for Specific Environmental Measures for Electric Utility Coal Utilization in U.S.—New Sources ($/ton of coal, 1978 dollars)

	Total Cost Typical Utility Est.[1]		EPRI[2] Est.[3]
A) Control of Thermal Discharges—			
Cooling Towers			
1) Wet—Conventional	0.8		0.9
2) Dry—Conventional	7.0		11.0
3) Dry—Ammonia	N.A.		5.0
B) Particulate Control			
1) ESP—0.1 #/MBtu	1.5		1.5
2) ESP—0.03 #/MBtu	2.0		2.0
3) Baghouse—0.1 #/MBtu	1.6		1.6
4) Baghouse—0.03 #/MBtu	1.8		1.6
C) SO$_x$ Control[4]	Low S	High S	
1) Limestone FGD—85% removal	7.0	18.0	14.0
2) Regenerative FGD—95% removal	N.A.	N.A.	17.0
3) Dry FGD—85% removal	9.0	30.0	N.A.
4) Dry FGD—95% removal	N.A.	N.A.	N.A.
D) NO$_x$ Control[4]			
1) Combustion control (where possible)	0.2-0.3		0.2-0.5
2) Postcombustion control— NO$_x$ selective			6.0-9.0
3) Postcombustion control— SO$_x$/NO$_x$ scrubber	7.5-18.0		
E) Combustion By-Products Disposal			
1) Ash—Conventional	0.3		0.7
2) Ash—As hazardous material[5]	N.A.		5.0-10.0
3) Ash plus FGD sludge—Conventional	N.A.		2.5
4) Ash plus FGD sludge—Hazardous[5]	N.A.		N.A.
F) Wastewater Treatment			
1) Conventoinal—BPT	0.4-0.8		0.3-2.0
2) Zone discharge—BAT	N.A.		2.0-3.0
G) Noise Control—External Plant Only			
1) Cooling towers	N.A.		N.A.
2) FD fans	N.A.		0.2-0.5
3) Transformers & OCBs	N.A.		N.A.
4) Coal handling—train switching— car dumping—barge/ship unloading	N.A.		N.A.

Notes:

N.A. Not available at this time.

[1] Estimates developed by Commonwealth Edison Co., Chicago, Ill.

[2] Electric Power Research Institute—For bases of estimates see Table 16-23.

[3] Estimates vary from "typical" because of different range of parameters considered.

[4] Does not include sludge disposal cost—see (E).

[5] Depends upon pending regulatory requirements.

APPENDIX 1

TRANSPORTATION AND PORT REQUIREMENTS TO SUPPORT U.S. COAL EXPORTS BY YEAR 2000*

INTRODUCTION

BACKGROUND

Early in the World Coal Study deliberations, it became apparent that the United States could potentially become a major exporter of steam coal by 2000. With significantly increased worldwide demand for steam coal, the United States, along with other nations having substantial coal reserves, might respond to market forces and supply steam coal to the international market. An essential element in its role as a major steam coal exporter is this country's capability to transport steam coal from the interior mining regions to port areas and provide at these port areas sufficient handling and ship loading capacity. As a result, an assessment was undertaken of U.S. transportation and port capabilities to accommodate coal exports in 2000.

OBJECTIVES

This assessment sought to:

- Identify present U.S. transportation and port facilities and capabilities;
- Determine additional capacity required;
- Estimate costs of the additional capacity; and
- Describe policy constraints related to meeting the transport/port requirements

BASIS OF THE ASSESSMENT

Because this assessment is focused on broad implications of increased U.S. steam coal exports and attendant policy issues, several premises were developed to serve as the assessment bases. These premises, summarized below, generally characterize world coal demand and a possible U.S. coal industry response. They also serve to correlate the results with other findings of the World Coal Study.

Quantities of U.S. Coal Exports in 2000

Two levels of annual U.S. coal exports in 2000 were initially considered:

- *A Low Coal Case* of 125 million metric tons coal equivalent (mtce), comprised of 60 mtce of metallurgical coal and 65 mtce of steam coal.
- *A High Coal Case* of 200 mtce, comprised of 70 mtce of metallurgical coal and 130 mtce of steam coal.

These two levels were utilized in consideration of demands for U.S. coal projected by the WOCOL importing countries in the Low and High Coal utilization cases, respectively.

- *A Sensitivity Case* of 350 mtce was examined to reflect potential export coal requirements should world steam coal demand expand beyond that now anticipated.

---

* A summary of this analysis which was performed by Bechtel National, Inc. for WOCOL, is included in the section entitled Coal Transportation.

Development of Coal Export Scenarios

To evaluate capabilities of the U.S. transportation and ports network, it was necessary to develop coal export scenarios describing mine-to-port coal flows within the U.S. These scenarios allocated export coal production to coal mining regions, to transportation corridors, and to port areas. These scenarios were conceived using judgmental considerations including allocation of potential export production among U.S. mining regions, existing transportation networks, and port areas. Demand destinations as projected by the WOCOL importing countries were also a key consideration. No attempt was made to optimize the coal export scenarios for factors such as high-quality coal (high heating value, low sulfur) or least cost (FOB port) because these requirements have not been sufficiently developed by the importing nations to serve as a basic consideration in determining likely coal sources. Steam and metallurgical coal were treated independently in establishing likely coal sources. As such, the scenarios used in this transportation and port assessment are three of a large number of cases which might logically be developed to project the movement patterns of U.S. coal exports from mining region to port. Although the scenarios used in this analysis reflect the best judgment of the U.S. country team as to reasonable coal export movements for purposes of assessing U.S. infrastructure capabilities, they are not intended to be an optimized forecast of coal production or traffic increases by region in response to world steam coal demand. Actual coal flows will develop through a highly complex market response to demand over the next one to two decades.

Growth of Domestic Transportation Traffic

Growth of domestic traffic, both coal and other commodities, was outside the scope of this assessment. With increased U.S. dependence on coal, requirements for its transportation from the major producing areas can be expected to increase significantly by 2000. Other traffic will grow at least at "historical" rates.

Shipments of domestic steam coal will move to many and widely scattered power plants using, only in part, the same traffic routes as coal moving to the export market. Because of this diffusion and limited impact on export routes, it is not possible in a useful way to assess the cumulative impact on transport facilities.

APPROACH

This assessment is based primarily on published sources. To supplement the open literature, particularly for determining port capacities, discussions were held with the operators of most of these facilities.

Capital costs for transportation system and port expansions were estimated using a factor approach. Standard unit rates were developed for transportation equipment, e.g., rolling stock, barges and for port ship loading equipment. The unit rates were applied uniformly, regardless of location.

U.S. COAL EXPORTS AND PORT FACILITIES: 1977

EXPORT VOLUMES

The year 1977 was selected as most typical of current export volumes. Because of a prolonged coal miners' strike and a depressed overseas market, coal exports were abnormally low in 1978.

In 1977, the U.S. was the world's leading coal exporter with shipments of 49.3 million metric tons (50 mtce) to more than 30 countries. Export coal originated almost exclusively from the Appalachian coal region in the eastern U.S. Most of this was exported via eastern seaboard ports, a lesser amount via Lake Erie ports to Canada, and a relatively minor amount through the Gulf. Steam coal, virtually all of which was shipped to Canada, represented less than a quarter of total coal exports. Since the balance of this report deals with ports and transportation in which physical tons rather than calorific equivalents are important, all further references to "ton" mean metric tons unless specifically identified as tce.

PORTS

The distribution of 1977 exports by port and by destination is shown in Table A1-1. Figure A1-1 shows areas and the inland transport links discussed in this report.

The ports at the lower end of Chesapeake Bay, collectively called Hampton Roads, consist of Newport News and Norfolk, Virginia. The main channel depth is maintained at 45 feet. Hampton Roads is the largest coal export port complex in the U.S., its 22 million ton volume in 1977 constituting 45% of all U.S. coal exports. These ports receive their coal principally from West Virginia and eastern Kentucky by rail. Each port is owned and operated by the railroad serving it; the Chesapeake and Ohio Railroad (C&O) in the case of Newport News, and the Norfolk and Western Railroad (N&W) in the case of Norfolk. The major characteristics of this and other ports described below are listed in Table A1-11 of this Appendix.

Table A1-1. U.S. Coal Exports in 1977, by Destination and Port of Export (Million Metric Tons)

Port of Export[1]	Destination				
	Europe	Japan	LDC's	Canada	Total
Hampton Roads	10.0	8.6	3.4	—	22.0
Baltimore	2.2	3.1	1.1	—	6.4
Philadelphia	0.6	—	—	—	0.6
Great Lakes[2]	—	—	—	15.4	15.4
Mobile	1.1	1.6	0.6	—	3.3
New Orleans	—	1.1	0.2	—	1.3
Total	13.9	14.4	5.3	15.4	49.0[3]

[1] Ports handling more than 500,000 tons.
[2] Includes Toledo, Sandusky, Lorain, Ashtabula, and Conneaut.
[3] Accounts for 99 percent of export tonnage.

The port of Baltimore, located at the upper end of Chesapeake Bay, handled 6.4 million tons of export coal in 1977, or 13% of the U.S. total. The main channel depth is maintained at 40 to 42 feet. The port is served by three railroads: ConRail, Baltimore and Ohio (B&O) and Western Maryland. The latter two, together with the C&O, are part of the Chessie System. Most of the coal exported through Baltimore originates in West Virginia and Pennsylvania and is handled by the B&O through its Curtis Bay facility.

494

Ameriport is the collective name for the ports on the Delaware River extending from Wilmington, Delaware to Trenton, New Jersey, and includes port facilities located in Philadelphia. This port complex is served primarily by ConRail and is not a major coal handling port. In 1977, about a half-million tons were exported. Peak tonnages have been less than two million tons per year.

Lake Erie coal ports serve the Canadian market. In 1977, 31 percent of all coal exports passed through these ports, all located in Ohio, extending from Toledo on the west to Conneaut on the east. This coal originates in Kentucky, Ohio, Pennsylvania, and West Virginia, and is shipped by rail to the ports. Inasmuch as coal exports to Canada are projected to decline by the year 2000, no further consideration has been given to these ports.*

TRANSPORTATION FACILITIES

Recent traffic densities of rail lines serving these ports and handling export coal are shown in Table A1-2.** Table A1-3*** lists traffic densities of western rail lines terminating at four Pacific Coast port areas. These transportation systems could be utilized in a future expanded coal export program.

The inland waterway system, particularly the Mississippi River and its tributaries, is an important transportation artery to the Gulf Coast ports. Coal is the largest single commodity shipped on the inland waterways; of the nearly 470 million tons total shipments in 1976, more than 20 percent was coal. Shipments on segments of the waterway system are detailed in Table A1-4.

Table A1-4. Primary Features of Mississippi River System

Area	Miles	1976 Tonnage (Million Tons)		Locks	
		Total	Coal	Number	Minimum Size (feet)
Middle & Lower Mississippi	1,140	287.8	19.9	None	—
Ohio River	500*	148.4	78.3	8	1200 × 110
Tennessee River	460*	26.3	9.3	10	600 × 110
Arkansas River	448	6.5	0.2	17	600 × 110

* Maximum upriver distance from which exported coal is likely to be loaded.

Most of the major inland waterways (60%) are presently maintained at a 9-foot project depth, accommodating an 8½-foot barge draft; however, 12-foot depths are available on the lower Mississippi approximately 70 to 80% of the year, and along much of the Ohio River system. The more northerly inland waterways are subject to seasonal limitations in that they are closed by ice for approximately four months of the year.

* It is physically possible to export coal to other countries from these ports by shipping through Lake Ontario and via the St. Lawrence River to tidewater. However, canals and locks would restrict shiploads to about 30,000 tons, making this route noncompetitive.
** See page 498.
*** See page 499.

Figure A1-1. U.S. Mining Regions, Major Inland Transportation Routes, and Ports of Export

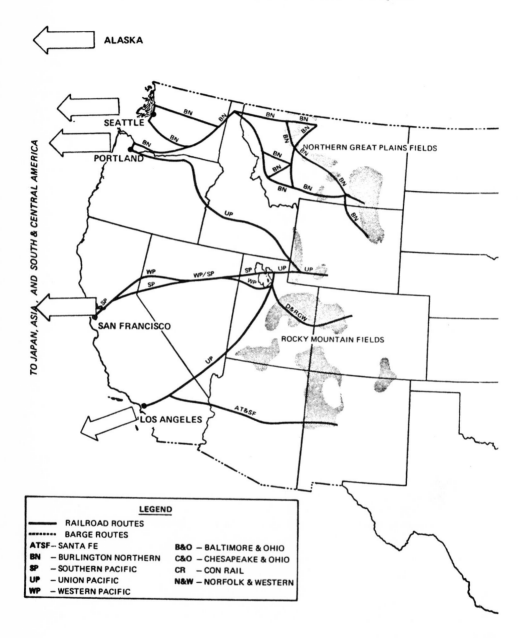

Figure A1-1.   U.S. Mining Regions, Major Inland Transportation Routes, and Ports of Export (cont.)

Table A1-2. Existing Railroads Serving Export Coal Ports in the East and Gulf

Port	Carrier	Mining District North and Central Appalachia	Route	Effective Trackage	1974 Actual Traffic Density Average Gross[2] ton-miles/mile × 10⁶	Traffic Control[3]
Norfolk	N&W	Virginia, W. Virginia, Kentucky	Roanoke	3	30-40 & over	Chiefly CTC
Newport News	C&O	Virginia, W. Virginia, Kentucky	Lynchburg/Richmond	1	25	Chiefly CTC
	C&O	Virginia, W. Virginia, Kentucky	Covington/Staunton/Richmond	1	—	—
Baltimore (B&O-WM)[1]	Chessie	Penn., W. Virginia, Ohio	Grafton/Cumberland Elkins/Cumberland	2 1	40 & over —	Chiefly CTC
Philadelphia	ConRail	Pennsylvania	Pittsburgh/Harrisburg	Multiple	40 & over	CTC

[1] Western Maryland Railroad.
[2] Gross meaning weight of cars and contents in short tons.
[3] CTC = Centralized Traffic Control.

Table A1-3. Potential Western Railroads for Export Coal Traffic

Port	Carrier	Mining District	Route	Effective Trackage	1974 Actual Average Gross Traffic Density ton-miles/mile $\times 10^6$	Traffic Control[1]
Seattle	BN	Montana & NE Wyoming	Gillette/Billings/Shelby/Spokane	1	20	ABS & CTC
			Billings/Missoula/Spokane	1	10	CTC & ABS
Portland	BN	Montana & NE Wyoming	Gillette/Billings/Spokane/Vancouver	1	20	CTC & ABS
			Billings/Missoula/Spokane/Vancouver	1	—	CTC & ABS
	UP	SW Wyoming	Cheyenne/Pocatello/Hinkle	1	—	AB
San Francisco Bay Area	SP + WP	Utah, SW Wyoming, W. Colorado	SW Wyoming (UP)/Ogden or SLC/Ogden or SLC/Colorado, Utah (D&RGW)/SLC	2	35	CTC & ABS
Los Angeles	UP	Utah, SW Wyoming, W. Colorado	SW Wyoming/Ogden/SLC/Barstow/Colorado, Utah (D&RGW)/SLC	2	30	CTC
	ATSF	New Mexico	Albuquerque/Barstow	2	over 40	CTC
Anchorage[2]	Alaska Railroad	Nenana & Matanuska Fields Beluga Fields	Nenana/Anchorage; Matanuska/Anchorage Located adjacent Cook Inlet	1	3	Man

[1] CTC = Centralized Traffic Control.
ABS = Automatic Block Signals.
Man = Manual Block.
[2] Possibly Whittier as alternate or companion port.

Many of the major waterways are "canalized" by systems of locks and dams which permit year-round operation with respect to water level availability, and improved transportation economics by virtue of barge movement in a "slack water" system. The locks of these dams provide some of the more significant restrictions and limitations on the flow of traffic through the inland waterways. The two most typical lock sizes established by the Corps of Engineers are 110 feet by 600 feet and, more recently, 110 feet by 1,200 feet.

Two Gulf of Mexico ports handled about 9% of the export coal trade in 1977. One of these, Mobile, reached its peak coal activity in that year, handling 3.3 million tons. This metallurgical coal originated in northern Alabama (the southernmost portion of the Appalachian coal region). The port is served by four railroads, but over 80% of the coal arrives by barge. The Mobile Bay channel is 40 feet deep.

The bulk terminal at New Orleans has never been a factor in the coal export trade. Maximum water depth is 36 feet and facilities are limited.

Approximately 40 miles downriver from New Orleans are two privately owned barge-ship-barge bulk transfer terminals, one of which opened in 1979. The other (Electro-Coal) terminal exported 1.3 million tons in 1977. Forty feet of water is available at these terminals. Neither are presently rail-served. Ports in this area, including New Orleans, will hereafter in this report be referred to as "Lower Mississippi" ports.

The Pacific Coast, including Alaska, has no port facilities dedicated to coal handling. In recent years, there have been relatively small export coal shipments from the Port of Long Beach's bulk handling facility. Water depth at Long Beach is 40 feet.

COAL EXPORT SCENARIOS

Two reference cases of coal exports in the year 2000 were developed. The Low Coal Case was premised on U.S. coal exports of 125 mtce (65 mtce steam coal; 60 mtce metallurgical coal); the High Coal Case, 200 mtce (130 mtce steam coal; 70 mtce metallurgical coal). These data are shown in Table A1-5, together with the assumed 350 mtce Sensitivity Case distribution.

These tonnages were then "distributed" to U.S. mining regions, and in turn to port areas. This allocation by mining region is shown in Table A1-6 for both reference cases and the sensitivity case. Considerable judgment was necessary in assigning the necessary coal production to the major coal regions and also, although to a lesser extent, in choosing the ports and domestic transport links to be used. The actual division of tonnage among the three major production regions, i.e., Appalachia, Illinois Basin (Midwest) and Rocky Mountain/Great Plains, will depend upon a host of factors including domestic coal demands, environmental regulations, and commercial decisions by U.S. firms and the importing countries. It is highly likely, however, (as Table A1-5 indicates) that as exports are increased, increasingly significant amounts must be shipped from the Illinois Basin and Western U.S. origins.

The coal export scenarios on which this assessment is based could result in the export of considerable quantities of coals characterized by high sulfur content-high heating values and low sulfur content-low heating values. Ideally, coal users typically seek low-sulfur–high-heating value coals, given acceptable comparative economics. Should customers for U.S. coal exports find high-sulfur coal to be un-

Table A1-5. Projected U.S. Coal Exports in Year 2000 by Destination Area

Area	Low Coal Case (125 mtce)			High Coal Case (200 mtce)			Sensitivity Case (350 mtce) Steam Plus Met
	Steam	Met	Total	Steam	Met	Total	
Europe	22	20	42	72	30	102	205
Japan	29	25	54	47	25	72	110
Less Developed Countries	6	6	12	6	10	16	25
Canada	8	9	17	5	5	10	10
Total	65	60	125	130	70	200	350

Table A1-6. U.S. Exports in the Year 2000 by Mining Region (mtce)

Region	Low Coal Case	High Coal Case	Sensitivity Case
Appalachia	95	132	180
Illinois Basin	12	31	80
Arkansas/Oklahoma	2	4	5
Western U.S.	14	30	80
Alaska	2	3	5
Total	125	200	350

acceptable, coal produced in the Illinois Basin for export would be reduced from the quantities used in this assessment. Conversely, if coal demand was skewed toward high-heating value coal with high sulfur content being immaterial, lesser quantities would originate in the Northern Great Plains and greater quantities would originate in the Illinois Basin and Appalachia. However the U.S. ability to provide low sulfur-high heating value for export may be limited. As a result, a significant portion of U.S. coal available for export may be of a quality less than ideally preferred by demand sources. These coals available for export could include those with high sulfur and low heating value.

PORT AND MINE-PORT TRANSPORT LINK REQUIREMENTS FOR YEAR 2000

PORTS

Table A1-7 is a listing of projected exports by port for the Low Coal, High Coal, and Sensitivity Cases, together with 1977 tonnages for comparative purposes. Shown in addition is the estimated annual capacity of each port, based on existing facilities. This estimate was derived primarily by using ship berthing and bulk loading capacities obtained from published sources. This was modified as necessary based on discussions with port operators reflecting other potential constraints such as storage and handling facilities, tidal conditions, and maintenance requirements.

It is apparent from the table where the potentially most serious constraints exist; namely, Hampton Roads (in the High Coal Case and Sensitivity Case scenarios) and the Lower Mississippi, West Coast and Alaska in all cases. In evaluating projections against estimated port capacity, it must be borne in mind that, in some cases, domestic coal is also handled through these facilities. This is primarily true of the Great Lakes ports where the foreign (Canada)/U.S. is about equally divided. However, domestic shipments are also significant at Baltimore (1½ to 2 million tons per year) and Hampton Roads (about 4 million tons per year).

Philadelphia and Baltimore each have several terminals over which the relatively modest tonnage increases could be spread if necessary. B&O's Curtis Bay terminal in Baltimore is the largest, with a present capacity of nearly 14 million

Table A1-7. U.S. Coal Exports by Port—Actual and Projected (Million Metric Tons)

Port	Actual 1977	Low Coal Case	High Coal Case	Sensitivity Case	Current Capacity
		Actual Year 2000			
Great Lakes	15.4	16	10	10	*
Philadelphia (Ameriport)	0.6	4	5	9	4
Baltimore	6.4	13	16	19	16
Hampton Roads	22.0	46	75	101	55
Mobile	3.3	5	8	9	6
Lower Mississippi	1.3	23	54	126	10
West Coast	<1	13	29	81	3
Alaska	Nil	3	5	8	Nil
Miscellaneous	0.3	—	—	—	—
Total	49.3	123	202	353	

* Not evaluated.

tons per year. Added capacity could be achieved by deepening the 40- to 42-foot channel, but this has been opposed by environmental groups for many years. The coal arriving at these northern ports is from "metallurgical country," so the much greater projected growth of steam coal will not benefit these ports.

Hampton Roads, on the other hand, is better situated to handle increases in both metallurgical and steam coal. Its capacity consists of about 25 million tons at C&O's Newport News facility and 30 million tons at N&W's Lambert's Point facility in Norfolk. On a sustained basis, tonnages in excess of those would be limited by car storage and dumping capability. Depending on vessel size requirements, new piers and probably channel deepening would also be required. Thus, the two ports at Hampton Roads could handle the low scenario tonnage with existing facilities; but substantial improvements (including conversion to or addition of ground storage) would be required to meet the high scenario tonnage. At the higher tonnages projected, it is also highly questionable whether direct car-to-ship loading will continue to be feasible. Direct car-to-ship operations are now a serious and uneconomical obstacle because the coal is primarily metallurgical. This high-valued product is often consigned in small batches from mine to ship, necessitating this type of operation. Steam coal exports would be a large-volume, lower-valued commodity, likely requiring a different mode of operation. Ground storage of coal may be necessary at locations some distance removed from the port. Capital costs associated with these operational changes would be substantial. Alternatively, other East Coast port areas, now currently considered oil ports, may develop coal-handling capabilities.

Because the export portion of tonnage moving through the Great Lakes ports is expected to decline by 2000, no further consideration has been given to these ports, nor to the rail lines serving them.

The source of coal exported through Mobile is currently limited to northern Alabama, the southern extremity of the Appalachian fields. If the Tennessee-Tombigbee Waterway is completed in the late 1980's, as planned, connecting the Tennessee and the Tombigbee Rivers, Mobile's market area may expand somewhat to include Tennessee, and possibly even southeastern Kentucky. The economics of this market broadening will continue to be constrained by barge tow limits, however. Thus, it appears that modest expansions could accommodate the most optimistic projections of coal exports through Mobile.

In contrast, the Lower Mississippi and West Coast ports, never before significant factors in U.S. coal exports, must prepare to meet the growth of Illinois Basin and western coal export demands. Illinois Basin coal exports would most logically move via barge down the Mississippi for transshipment. In addition, there is likely to be substantial tonnage from other sources, primarily Appalachian coal, but also western coal shipped by rail to barge terminals on the Upper Mississippi and Arkansas coals. Appalachian coal will originate from areas in Eastern Kentucky, Ohio and West Virginia located near the Ohio River. Virtually all of this coal is likely to be barged, although a mine-to-river haul by rail or trucks would usually be required.

There has been considerable discussion in recent years of new coal terminals in the Houston/Galveston area. These would not be the most logical export locations for coal being barged down the Mississippi. Western coal might be shipped via rail to Houston/Galveston terminals for export, but rapidly escalating rail rates are reducing this potential. Accordingly, no further consideration has been given to this port area.

On the West Coast, Utah coal has been exported sporadically and in small amounts (1 million tons/year) through the Port of Long Beach. To meet the year 2000 requirements of any scenario, a minimum of two new coal terminals would be required. Logistically, the San Francisco Bay Area and the Los Angeles/Long Beach area would be the preferred locations. A Portland, Oregon location, perhaps near Astoria, may be an alternate, or even a third terminal. The Seattle, Washington, area might ultimately be needed if tonnage were to originate in northern Wyoming or Montana. This would not be likely under the low tonnage scenario.

Present coal production in Alaska is well under a million tons, none of which is exported. Among the several Alaska coal fields, the low-sulfur Beluga and Nenana fields are the prime export sources. In the case of Beluga, a grass-roots coal terminal and supporting infrastructure would have to be constructed on Cook Inlet. Nenana coal could be transported southward by rail, most likely to Whittier, where coal terminal facilities would have to be constructed.

Domestic (Mine-Port) Transport Links

The inland transport corridors which would be substantially impacted by any of these export scenarios, and hence need to be investigated relative to their capabilities, are the following:

(1) The C&O's rail system between West Virginia and Newport News;

(2) The N&W's rail system between West Virginia and Norfolk;

(3) The Mississippi River waterway from approximately St. Louis southward; and

(4) The rail lines extending from the Rocky Mountain and Northern Plains areas to the U.S. West Coast

To an even greater extent than is true of ports, railroad capacity must be assessed in relationship to the total volume of traffic handled, not only export coal, but domestic coal and merchandise traffic also. For perspective, 1977 railroad traffic in the U.S. is compared in Table A1-8 with the estimated rail portion of U.S. export coal tonnages examined in this assessment.

Table A1-8. 1977 Railroad Traffic Compared to Projected U.S. Export Coal Traffic (Million Metric Tons)

Year		Coal—Export	Coal—Total	All Traffic
1977		45	377	1,330
2000	Low Coal Case	104	—	—
	High Coal Case	157	—	—
	Sensitivity Case	272	—	—

The coal export scenarios result in annual average increases in export coal traffic of 3.7% (Low Coal Case), 5.6% (High Coal Case) and 8% (Sensitivity Case). The average annual increase of all coal rail traffic resulting from increases in coal exports would be substantially less. Other traffic, including domestic coal, will no doubt grow also, although at a lower rate of increase, perhaps in the 2- to 3-percent range. The data are intended to illustrate that export coal will be a significant and increasing share of the total rail market. This aggregated data, however, masks the fact that most of the export coal growth will be concentrated on the C&O and N&W in the east, and on four or five rail systems in the west.

In attempting to estimate what railroad-related capital improvements are necessary to meet year 2000 demands, two serious obstacles are encountered. One is defining and determining "capacity." The other is how to allocate incremental plant expansions to specific traffic categories such as export coal. For example, capacity is a function of traffic "mix" plus a host of other factors; e.g., single versus multiple tracks, number and spacing of sidings, sophistication of the signalling system, track and roadbed quality, and grades and curvature dictated by terrain. Because of these many factors, the capacity of a rail system or segment cannot be determined precisely. The approximate capacity of various track/signal configurations has been estimated as follows:

Signalling System	Track Capacity: Single Track	Trains per Day* Double Track
Manual Block System	10-15	35-45
Automatic Block Signals (ABS)	25-35	55-65
Centralized Traffic Control (CTC)	30-40	75-90

* Trains per day means the number of trains passing any one point along the main line in any one day.

Both the C&O and N&W lines to the ports are primarily double-track, CTC-equipped. Existing traffic densities are probably well below-mainline capabilities. Traffic increases may require some mainline upgrading, perhaps even the addition of a third track. However, of greater priority will be upgrading and expansion of the coal gathering branch lines and train makeup and storage yards. Both carriers have extensive rail networks in the coal fields which serve to collect cars from many mines before consolidation into large (150-225 car) trains for shipment to tidewater.

The mine regions in the West extend from southern Wyoming through Utah and western Colorado to northern New Mexico. Wyoming coal would originate on the Union Pacific (UP) and could move to Los Angeles/Long Beach, San Francisco or Portland. Utah and western Colorado coal would originate on the Denver and Rio Grande Western Railroad (D&RG) and most logically be shipped to Los Angeles/Long Beach via the UP or the San Francisco Bay Area via the Southern Pacific (SP) or Western Pacific (WP). New Mexico coal would originate on the Santa Fe Railway (AT&SF) and be handled by that carrier to Los Angeles/Long Beach.

All these routes are generally double-track, CTC-equipped. Assuming no undue concentration on a single route, the projected tonnages of the two reference scenarios should require only modest capital additions. The near tripling of the High Coal Case scenario tonnage to that shown in the Sensitivity Case, however, cannot be easily dismissed. Under this Sensitivity Case scenario, lower Btu coal from northeastern Wyoming may enter the export picture, and be transported by the Burlington Northern (BN) to a north coast port such as Seattle. Nevertheless, this tonnage level would likely require major capital expansions by the western railroads.

The inland waterway system would be an important transportation corridor for increased coal export. This system includes the middle and lower portions of the Mississippi River extending for a distance of 1,140 miles from St. Louis to the Gulf, as well as portions of the Ohio, Tennessee and Arkansas Rivers.

The large tonnage increase projected to be exported through terminals on the lower Mississippi will come primarily from the Illinois Basin. This tonnage will be loaded on barges on either the Mississippi or on the Ohio near its junction with the Mississippi. The latter is "open" water (i.e., without locks), so capacity is almost unlimited. Barges will move south in tows comprised of as many as 30 barges or more (about 1,350 tons each).

Lock restrictions on the Ohio limit tow sizes to 15 barges. However, there are relatively few locks on the lower Ohio and they are all sized at 1,200 feet. The lower Ohio is generally believed to have a great deal of excess capacity at present.

Both the Tennessee and Arkansas Rivers are much more restrictive in terms of channel size and number and size of locks. The relatively small increases foreseen for export coal traffic or these waterways should not place any unusual demands on these facilities, however.

COST OF TRANSPORTATION AND PORT FACILITIES REQUIRED BY YEAR 2000

Order-of-magnitude capital costs have been estimated for the two reference scenarios and the Sensitivity Case. These costs represent the incremental facilities and equipment necessary to increase the export tonnages above the 50 mtce shipped in 1977. No replacement costs to sustain the 50 million ton volume are included.

Certain well-defined elements can be estimated with reasonable accuracy. These include:

(1) Freight cars and locomotives required to handle that portion of the incremental tonnage projected for rail haul;

(2) Barges and towboats required to handle that portion of the incremental tonnage projected for movement on inland waterways; and

(3) The cost of new coal ports and terminals on the Pacific Coast (including Alaska), on the Lower Mississippi, and at upstream locations for barge loading.

Capital costs of rolling stock, barges and towboats are well established in the commercial market. Capital costs for new, grass-roots ports are dependent on site specific and commercial design considerations. However, for purposes of this generic assessment, the capital costs of new ports, including piers, shiploaders, storage, and handling equipment is based on $6 (1979 dollars) per metric ton of new capacity. This figure represents recent estimates for new, grass-roots ports. No allowance is included for regional variations in construction costs. The cost of port expansions assumes the existing piers are adequate, but that some equipment on the piers or in the storage yard needs upgrading. As such, port expansion costs are taken at $2 (1979 dollars) per metric ton of expanded capacity. It must be noted that costs associated with upgrading and expanding existing ports, especially those in the Hampton Roads area, are judgmental in the absence of a well-defined plan and established design. As such, these estimates should be viewed as only an indication of what the actual costs might be.

Railroad upgrading may consist of, for example, lengthening sidings, installation of higher speed turnouts, upgrading of bridges, eliminating excessive curves or grades and improving signalling systems. Cost estimates reflect an allowance ranging from $4,000 to $50,000 per route mile for such work depending on the increase in traffic density. As in the cost estimate for port expansions, without a design for rail system upgrading, only a judgmental cost estimate is possible.

Capital cost estimates are shown in Table A1-9. These estimates are 1979 costs, unescalated, and without contingency. For reference, the number of specific rail and barge equipment which served as the estimate basis are given in Table A1-10.

Capital requirements for the investment categories shown are $910 million in the Low Coal Case. Rolling stock, e.g., rail cars and locomotives constitute the largest requirement, at $375 million, closely followed by barges and towboats at $305 million. New ports on the West Coast and Alaska would be less than 10 percent of overall investment. In the High Coal Case, with total requirements of over $2 billion, capital requirements for barges and towboats become the primary investment area. The Sensitivity Case requirement is on the order of $5 billion.

Table A1-9. Capital Expenditures Required for Year 2000 Coal Exports (Millions of 1979 Dollars)

Category	Low Coal Case	High Coal Case	Sensitivity Case
Eastern Ports			
Rolling Stock	$190	$ 370	$ 550
Railroad Upgrading	10	60	120
Port Expansion		40	110
Mobile			
Barges/Towboats	15	40	45
Port Expansion		5	5
Lower Mississippi			
Barges/Towboats	290	700	1,650
Terminals[1]	80	260	700
West Coast			
Rolling Stock	160	375	1,070
Railroad Upgrading	50	100	200
New Ports	60[2]	160[3]	470[4]
Alaska			
Rolling Stock	25	40	65
Railroad Upgrading	10	15	20
New Port	20	30	50
Total	$910	$2,195	$5,055

[1] Including upriver barge-loading terminals.
[2] Los Angeles/Long Beach and San Francisco Bay Area.
[3] Los Angeles/Long Beach, San Francisco Bay Area and Portland Area.
[4] Los Angeles/Long Beach, San Francisco Bay Area, Portland, and Seattle Area.

Table A1-10. Total Rail and Barge Equipment Estimated for U.S. Coal Export Scenarios (Number of Equipment Items)

Equipment	Low Coal Case	High Coal Case	Sensitivity Case
Rail Cars	13,650	27,500	47,300
Locomotives	730	1,480	2,600
Barges	1,045	2,525	5,845
Tow Boats	30	74	156

The costs of new or upgraded gathering subsystems required to bring coal by truck, conveyor or railroad to train or barge assembly terminals are not included in the table. The identification of these systems accurate enough for cost estimating purposes would require detailed analysis outside the scope of this assessment. Further, such costs would be intimately tied to specific allocation of exported coal to particular mines. The economic impact of these gathering subsystems should not be minimized, however. For example, the Federal Highway Administration estimated in late 1978 that $7.3 billion was needed to build and repair roads used for hauling coal, nearly 90 percent of that in Appalachia. Because the estimated capital requirements reflect only those items which may be costed with any degree of assurance and because other less-defined investments will assuredly be required, the total capital requirement likely would be greater than the cost estimate reported.

CONSIDERATIONS POTENTIALLY CONSTRAINING DEVELOPMENT OF U.S. TRANSPORTATION AND PORT CAPABILITIES TO SUPPORT THE EXPORT MARKET

For the U.S. to serve as a substantial supplier of coal to the international market in 2000, an integrated system of facilities must be in place. In addition to production capacity, port and transportation facilities serving that production capacity are necessary. Installation of incremental capacity must be coordinated in both location and schedule with the intentions and needs of the coal purchasers. To achieve the necessary capability, a number of commercial and institutional entities must work in concert. Objection, lack of positive decision-making, or delay on the part of these entities may lead to inability to accommodate export demand. As a result, commercial aspects, construction and fabrication abilities and institutional factors must be considered as potential constraints.

COMMERCIAL CONSIDERATIONS

Commercial considerations include both a positive decision to proceed with projects to expand capacity and the ability to secure the necessary financing. In the U.S., railroads, barge operations, and many ports/coal terminals are owned and operated by commercial firms. Some ports are owned and operated by quasi-public agencies associated with city or state governments. Decisions by commercial firms are based on market demand and return on investment assessments. Accordingly, discussions and commitments as appropriate are necessary between coal purchasers and commercial firms providing transportation and port services. This must be accomplished with sufficient lead time to accommodate design and construction schedules.

The ability of commercial or quasi-public entities to finance capital improvements is highly variable. To a large degree it depends on the economic health of the organization as well as their competing demands for capital. U.S. railroads, for example, range from those in or near bankruptcy to firms well able and currently in the process of investing in new plant and equipment. For privately owned coal ports, a good example is the lower Mississippi area where a number of private investors have indicated a willingness to participate in ownership and operation of new capacity. Modernization plans by quasi-public entities such as those operating some ports may be impacted by political considerations.

No significant, clear-cut barriers can be assuredly identified which may serve as commercial constraints to providing transportation and port facilities for coal exports. However, it remains problematical whether the commercial decision-making and commitment process will be initiated in an appropriate time frame and evolve with sufficient speed to accommodate a rapid increase in coal exports.

EQUIPMENT FABRICATION

The U.S. has an approximate annual production capacity of 80 to 90,000 railcars, 1,500 locomotives, 1,000 inland barges and 100 towboats. Given this production capacity, the equipment requirements estimated to support the Low Coal, High Coal and Sensitivity Cases of coal exports may be readily accommodated unless these requirements are compressed into a short time frame. This equipment fabrication capability should not be considered as a constraint.

REGULATORY AND INSTITUTIONAL CONSTRAINTS

In the U.S. a network of regulations exists which control development of new projects and expansion of existing facilities. These regulations govern environmental quality, land use and related social concerns. The regulatory network is administered by entities at all levels of government, ranging from federal agencies to city departments. Prior to construction of a specific project, a series of reviews and approvals is required by a number of agencies. This process demands significant time in the project development schedule; it may also result in a failure to proceed because one regulatory agency delays or denies the required approval. As a result, regulatory and institutional factors represent a serious potential constraint to the U.S. installing new facilities to serve the coal export market within the necessary time frame.

For upgrading of rail lines, this issue is of lesser significance, particularly when modernization of existing corridors is involved. If, however, new corridors must be established with significant change in existing land use and the attendant alterations in environmental conditions, regulatory and institutional constraints may develop.

One issue associated with rail transportation of coal which is gaining increasing attention is unit train traffic at grade through communities. As the number of unit trains passing through populated areas increases, so does opposition from the inhabitants. For coal exports, this opposition must be considered both near the mining districts and near large-volume port facilities which may have concentrated nearby population. This factor may be of key significance near West Coast port areas which have no history of coal rail transport.

New port facilities, particularly at grass-roots sites, may be substantially impacted by the regulatory and institutional network, with some regional variation. All states have some form of coastal management commission controlling land use. In general, expansion of existing port areas is favored by regulatory agencies and the public in comparison to industrialization of "natural" areas. In the populated and heavily used Eastern coastal areas, conversion of the remaining "natural" areas to industrial use is carefully controlled by federal and state government and is opposed by environmental groups. Expansion and modernization of existing port areas is the more attractive opportunity on the East Coast. On the Gulf Coast, potential port sites are more numerous and because coastal shipping is an important economic factor, port facilities are relatively more accepted by the public. The concern for industrialization of marsh areas or "wetlands" is nevertheless present. Use of coastal frontage is also tightly controlled by the Pacific Coast states. The Pacific coastline is prized for its aesthetic and recreational qualities. Again, expansion of existing port areas to incorporate coal loading is more attractive than "grass-roots" sites.

Channel dredging has been challenged for many years and is now tightly controlled by regulation. As a result, development of new shipping lanes and enlargement of existing ones to accommodate larger and more economical vessels may be constrained by regulation and public opposition.

Regulatory and institutional factors governing establishment of port facilities and shipping lanes is viewed as the most significant potential constraint to the U.S. supplying coal to the international market.

Table A1-11.   Description of Existing U.S. Coal Ports

Port	Berth or Pier Length (ft.)	Water Depth (ft.)	Maximum Loading Rate (t/hr)	Maximum Vessel Size (000 dwt)*
Hampton Roads				
Newport News				
C&O Coal Pier #14	1,078	45	8,200	80
C&O Pier #15	1,000	38	1,500	45
Norfolk				
N&W Pier #6	1,800	45	7,200	80
N&W Pier #5	1,000	36	2,250	40
Baltimore				
Curtis Bay Coal Pier (B&O RR, ConRail, Western Maryland)	900	40	5,500	55
Ameriport				
Greenwich Coal Pier 124S (ConRail)	1,100	40	1,000	55
Port Richmond				
Camden Marine Terminals	1,550	30-35	500	40
Mobile				
McDuffie Bulk Coal Facility	850	40	3,600	55
New Orleans Area				
Public Bulk Terminal Wharf	2,235	36	2,800	40
Electro Coal Transfer Dock	2,000	40	3,700	55
International Marine Terminal	1,480	40	6,300	55

* Approximate. May vary, depending upon tidal and other navigational conditions, ship lengths and configuration and acceptable standards of risk.

APPENDIX 2

AGE PROFILE OF ELECTRIC POWER PLANTS*

Plant Type	% of Existing Capacity Installed During Time Period				
	1970–77	1960–69	1950–59	1940–49	Before 1940
Fossil Steam	44.7	35.6	13.1	4.8	1.9
Coal	54.4	38.5	2.8	3.5	0.8
Oil	31.2	31.3	25.4	8.1	3.9
Gas	40.0	34.4	20.7	3.1	1.8
Gas Turbines/ Internal Combustion/ Combined Cycle	76.7	19.4	1.4	1.2	1.4
Hydroelectric	25.0	33.9	20.2	7.0	13.9
Nuclear	92.1	7.9	–0–	–0–	–0–
Other	44.2	55.8	–0–	–0–	–0–
Total	50.1	31.0	11.4	4.2	3.2

* As of December 31, 1977.

APPENDIX 3

SUPPORTING COAL AND ENERGY DATA FOR WOCOL PROJECTIONS
Summary Worksheet

I. Coal Use, Production, and Trade	1977	1985 A	1985 B	1990 A	1990 B	2000 A	2000 B	1977-2000 Avg. annual growth—%/yr. A	B
Coal use in major markets (mtce)									
Metallurgical	77	85	85	90	90	100	110	1.1	1.6
Electric	372	500	560	533	748	800	1170	3.4	5.0
Industry	60	70	80	85	112	125	220	3.2	5.8
Synthetic Fuels	0	0	0	5	5	50	200	–	–
Residential/Commercial*	–	–	–	–	–	–	–	–	–
Total coal use	509	655	725	713	955	1075	1700	3.3	5.4
Distribution of coal use by market sector (%)									
Metallurgical	15	13	12	13	10	9	6	—	—
Electric	73	76	77	75	78	74	69	—	—
Industry	11	10	11	12	12	12	13	—	—
Synthetic Fuels	0	0	0	1	1	5	12	—	—
Residential/Commercial	1	1	1	1	1	1	1	—	—
Total coal use	100%	100%	100%	100%	100%	100%	100%	—	—
Coal consumption/imports (mtce) Consumption									
Metallurgical	77	85	85	90	90	100	110	1.1	1.6
Steam	432	570	640	623	865	975	1590	3.6	5.8
Total coal consumption	509	655	725	713	955	1075	1700	3.3	5.4
Imports									
Metallurgical	2	5	5	5	5	6	10	–	–
Steam	–	2	2	2	5	5	7		
Total coal imports	2	7	7	7	10	11	17		
Coal production/exports (mtce) Production									
Metallurgical	114	130	130	140	145	154	170	1.2	1.6
Steam	443	588	668	651	920	1035	1713	3.8	6.1
Total coal production	557	718	798	791	1065	1189	1883	3.3	5.4
Exports									
Metallurgical	39	50	50	55	60	60	70	1.4	2.0
Steam	11	20	30	30	60	65	130	8.0	11.3
Total coal export	50	70	80	85	120	125	200	3.6	5.8

* Included with industry.

Summary Worksheet

II. Coal's Role in Total Energy System	1977	1985 A	1985 B	1990 A	1990 B	2000 A	2000 B	1977-2000 Avg. annual growth–%/yr. A	1977-2000 Avg. annual growth–%/yr. B
Total Primary Energy Use (mtce)									
Oil, Domestic	704	772	772	758	758	650	650	--	--
Oil, Imported	650	642	661	657	711	646	708	--	--
Gas, Domestic	655	655	655	625	625	540	540	--	--
Gas, Imported	36	72	72	72	72	72	72	--	--
Nuclear	96	200	220	280	320	300	600	--	--
Hydro, Solar, Other	86	144	144	180	170	327	240	--	--
Coal, Domestic	507	648	718	706	945	1064	1683	--	--
Coal, Imported	2	7	7	7	10	11	17	--	--
Total energy use	2736	3140	3250	3285	3610	3610	4512	1.2	2.2
Coal penetration (%)	19	21	22	22	26	30	38	—	—
Total primary energy (mtce) input to electricity									
Oil and Gas	255	250	250	240	240	175	135	--	--
Hydro, Solar, Other	86	110	110	117	117	150	150	--	--
Nuclear	96	200	220	280	320	300	600	--	--
Coal	372	500	560	533	748	800	1170	--	--
Total energy input	809	1060	1140	1170	1425	1425	2055	2.5	4.1
Coal penetration (%)	46	47	49	46	52	55	57	—	—
Total electric capacity (GWe)									
Oil and Gas	200	214	214	214	214	185	175	--	--
Hydro, Solar, Other	70	82	82	86	86	100	100	--	--
Nuclear	45	100	110	140	160	150	300	--	--
Coal	202	284	305	300	380	465	625	--	--
Total capacity	517	680	711	740	840	900	1200	2.5	3.7
Coal Penetration (%)	39	42	43	41	45	51	51	—	—
Peak load	395	520	570	600	700	760	1020	2.9	4.2
Peak reserve margin (%)	31	31	25	23	20	18	18	—	—
Total oil imports (mbd)	8.5	8.4	8.6	8.6	9.3	8.4	9.2	--	--
Total oil consumption (mbd)									
Transportation	9.7	9.6	9.9	9.7	10.1	9.7	10.8	--	--
Residential/Commercial	3.3	2.8	2.8	2.8	2.8	2.1	2.3	--	--
Industry—Boilers	1.0	1.1	1.1	1.1	1.2	1.0	1.4	--	--
Industry—Other	2.5	2.6	2.6	2.6	2.8	2.4	3.0	--	--
Electric utilities	1.8	2.3	2.3	2.3	2.3	2.0	1.5	--	--
Total oil consumption	18.3	18.4	18.7	18.5	19.2	17.2	19.0	--	--
World oil price assumed for national coal analysis (1979 U.S. dollars/barrel)	$20*	20	25	22.50	30	25	35	--	--
Economic growth assumed for national coal analysis (GNP, billion 1978 dollars)	$1900	2450	2450	2870	2870	3600	3600	2.8	2.8

* Uses current price of $20/barrel (June 1979 U.S. dollars) as baseline world oil price and as floor price throughout the period.

PART II

NON-WOCOL
COUNTRIES AND REGIONS

Estimates of coal production and use together with estimates of coal imports and exports for non-WOCOL countries and regions have been incorporated into the analysis in *COAL—Bridge to the Future*—the final summary report of the World Coal Study. These estimates were based on special studies prepared by several WOCOL members and on other information which was available from other sources during the course of the Study. This section summarizes that data and its sources in accordance with the WOCOL geographical aggregation described below:

WOCOL Geographical Regions

OECD Region

* Canada
* United States
* Denmark
* Finland
* France
* Federal Republic of Germany
* Italy
* Netherlands
* Sweden
* United Kingdom
* Japan
* Australia
  Other OECD

Developing Regions

* India
* Indonesia
  East and Other Asia
  Latin America
  Republic of South Africa
  Other Africa

Centrally Planned Economy Countries

* Poland
* People's Republic of China
  Soviet Union
  Other Centrally Planned

* Represented with members in WOCOL.

Source: Figure 2-1, page 87, COAL—Bridge to the Future.

that may be used to realize their economic development plans. In this situation it is assumed that strenuous efforts will be made to develop indigenous coal reserves, where the potential is particularly large in Greece and Turkey. In both countries brown coal production is capable of making a significant contribution to meeting energy demand. However, even under the most optimistic assumptions for domestic production, a considerable coal import requirement is projected, ranging from 56 mtce to 74 mtce in year 2000, roughly equally divided between steam and metallurgical coals. This represents a four-to-sixfold expansion in total coal imports from 1977.

Table 17-1. Energy and Economic Statistics for Non-WOCOL Europe Countries, 1977

Country	Population (Millions)	GDP ($ Billions)	GDP Per Capita ($1,000)	Energy Consumption (mtce)	Energy Use Per Capita (tce)	Energy Use Per GDP (tce/$1,000)
Higher GDP/ Capita Group						
Austria	7.52	47.95	6.4	36.97	4.9	0.77
Belgium	9.83	79.21	8.1	70.89	7.2	0.89
Luxembourg	0.36	2.78	7.7	5.76	16.0	2.07
Norway	4.04	35.59	8.8	42.00	10.4	1.18
Switzerland	6.33	60.59	9.6	33.36	5.3	0.55
Lower GDP/ Capita Group						
Greece	9.28	26.21	2.8	22.59	2.4	0.86
Ireland	3.19	9.38	2.9	11.14	3.5	1.19
Portugal	9.80	16.30	1.7	15.96	1.6	0.98
Spain	36.67	115.59	3.2	106.65	2.9	0.92
Turkey	42.13	47.44	1.1	50.23	1.2	1.06

Table 17-2. Coal Production and Imports for Non-WOCOL Europe Countries, 1977 (mtce)

Country	Hard Coal Production	Brown Coal Production	Coal Imports
Austria	—	—	2.547
Belgium	7.430	3.100	6.475
Greece	—	23.810	0.483
Ireland	0.050	4.600	0.868
Luxembourg	—	—	0.537
Norway	0.460	0.460	0.420
Portugal	0.195	0.195	0.415
Spain	11.200	5.500	4.331
Switzerland	—	—	0.143
Turkey	4.600	8.500	—

NON-WOCOL
COUNTRIES AND REGIONS

Estimates of coal production and use together with estimates of coal imports and exports for non-WOCOL countries and regions have been incorporated into the analysis in *COAL—Bridge to the Future*—the final summary report of the World Coal Study. These estimates were based on special studies prepared by several WOCOL members and on other information which was available from other sources during the course of the Study. This section summarizes that data and its sources in accordance with the WOCOL geographical aggregation described below:

WOCOL Geographical Regions

OECD Region	*Developing Regions*
* Canada	* India
* United States	* Indonesia
* Denmark	East and Other Asia
* Finland	Latin America
* France	Republic of South Africa
* Federal Republic of Germany	Other Africa
* Italy	
* Netherlands	*Centrally Planned Economy Countries*
* Sweden	
* United Kingdom	* Poland
* Japan	* People's Republic of China
* Australia	Soviet Union
Other OECD	Other Centrally Planned

* Represented with members in WOCOL.

Source: Figure 2-1, page 87, COAL—Bridge to the Future.

The material is organized into seven chapters:

Chapter 17—*Non-WOCOL OECD*, was drafted by Brian K. Elms, based on technical studies prepared by Shell Coal International Limited. J. Michael Gallagher assisted with final editing.

Chapter 18—*Republic of South Africa*, was written by J. Michael Gallagher, based on data provided by H.T. Burger of the Department of Environmental Planning and Energy of the Republic of South Africa.

Chapter 19—*Overview of Developing Regions*, was written by Robert P. Greene and J. Michael Gallagher based on material prepared by Gerald Foley, Detlef Wiegand, and Marc Ippolito.

Chapter 20—*East and Southeast Asia*, was written by the WOCOL Japan National Committee. J. Michael Gallagher assisted with final editing.

Chapter 21—*Latin America*, was written by Detlef Wiegand based on technical studies prepared for the World Energy Conference, and J. Michael Gallagher assisted with final editing.

Chapter 22—*Africa*, was written by Detlef Wiegand, based on technical studies prepared for the World Energy Conference. J. Michael Gallagher assisted with final editing.

Chapter 23—*Centrally Planned Economy Countries*, was written by J. Michael Gallagher based on data published by the World Energy Conference.

CHAPTER 17

NON-WOCOL OECD

Detailed descriptions of the coal projections and the full texts of the national reports for each of the 12 OECD countries participating in the World Coal Study are included in previous chapters of this volume. These 12 WOCOL countries account for more than 90 percent of the total OECD GNP, energy use, coal use and production.

A special study has been prepared by WOCOL members to provide projections of coal production, use, import and export for the OECD countries in Western Europe which did not participate in WOCOL.* This special study includes ten countries: Austria, Belgium, Greece, Ireland, Luxembourg, Norway, Portugal, Spain, Switzerland and Turkey.

These countries form a dichotomous grouping in terms of economic development. A population of 28 million lived in 1977 in five small countries with GDP per capita greater than $6,000: Austria, Belgium, Luxembourg, Norway, and Switzerland. A larger population of 101 million lived in the five lower-income countries. The total GDP and total energy consumption in 1977 was roughly evenly split between the two groups.

Table 17-1 summarizes some of the relevant economic and energy data concerning the ten countries for the year.

None of the countries has a coal mining industry of large significance, and consequently little coal consumption has developed outside the iron and steel industry. Existing imports are also small and largely of metallurgical coal in most countries. Table 17-2 breaks down existing coal production and imports for 1977.

In energy terms one other feature of these countries deserves special mention, that is, the high proportion of electricity generated by hydroelectric stations which, in 1977, accounted for 57 mtce, or 42 percent of the total primary energy input to electricity power generation. Hydroelectric capacity makes exceptional contributions in Norway, Switzerland, Austria and Portugal. While some expansion is possible, hydroelectricity cannot be expected to make a major contribution to meeting future increases in electricity demand, even in those countries.

An assessment of the coal requirements to the year 2000 for the ten non-WOCOL European countries has been made and is summarized in Table 17-3. The projected increases are dominated by the needs of the lower GDP/capita group of countries, for which coal represents a readily available source of energy

---

* Estimates for all the OECD countries except Iceland and New Zealand are provided either in the WOCOL country studies or in this chapter. The IEA Steam Coal Study estimated that coal use and production in Iceland would be zero throughout this century, and that New Zealand's coal use would increase from 2.4 mtce in 1977 to 7.7 mtce in 2000, with all the coal produced domestically.

that may be used to realize their economic development plans. In this situation it is assumed that strenuous efforts will be made to develop indigenous coal reserves, where the potential is particularly large in Greece and Turkey. In both countries brown coal production is capable of making a significant contribution to meeting energy demand. However, even under the most optimistic assumptions for domestic production, a considerable coal import requirement is projected, ranging from 56 mtce to 74 mtce in year 2000, roughly equally divided between steam and metallurgical coals. This represents a four-to-sixfold expansion in total coal imports from 1977.

Table 17-1. Energy and Economic Statistics for Non-WOCOL Europe Countries, 1977

Country	Population (Millions)	GDP ($ Billions)	GDP Per Capita ($1,000)	Energy Consumption (mtce)	Energy Use Per Capita (tce)	Energy Use Per GDP (tce/ $1,000)
Higher GDP/ Capita Group						
Austria	7.52	47.95	6.4	36.97	4.9	0.77
Belgium	9.83	79.21	8.1	70.89	7.2	0.89
Luxembourg	0.36	2.78	7.7	5.76	16.0	2.07
Norway	4.04	35.59	8.8	42.00	10.4	1.18
Switzerland	6.33	60.59	9.6	33.36	5.3	0.55
Lower GDP/ Capita Group						
Greece	9.28	26.21	2.8	22.59	2.4	0.86
Ireland	3.19	9.38	2.9	11.14	3.5	1.19
Portugal	9.80	16.30	1.7	15.96	1.6	0.98
Spain	36.67	115.59	3.2	106.65	2.9	0.92
Turkey	42.13	47.44	1.1	50.23	1.2	1.06

Table 17-2. Coal Production and Imports for Non-WOCOL Europe Countries, 1977 (mtce)

Country	Hard Coal Production	Brown Coal Production	Coal Imports
Austria	—	—	2.547
Belgium	7.430	3.100	6.475
Greece	—	23.810	0.483
Ireland	0.050	4.600	0.868
Luxembourg	—	—	0.537
Norway	0.460	0.460	0.420
Portugal	0.195	0.195	0.415
Spain	11.200	5.500	4.331
Switzerland	—	—	0.143
Turkey	4.600	8.500	—

Table 17-3. Summary Coal and Energy Projections for Non-WOCOL Europe Countries

I. Coal Use, Production, and Trade	1977	1985		1990		2000		1977-2000 Avg. annual growth—%/yr.	
		A	B	A	B	A	B	A	B
Coal use in major markets (mtce)									
Metallurgical	19	25	27	29	34	39	54	3.4	4.8
Electric	26	40	42	51	57	89	106	5.5	6.3
Industry	5	6	7	6	9	7	15	2.0	5.0
Synthetic Fuels	1	1	2	2	3	2	4	0.9	5.0
Residential/Commercial	4	4	5	4	5	3	5	-1.0	1.0
Total coal use*	55	76	83	92	108	140	184	4.2	5.4
Distribution of coal use by market sector (%)									
Metallurgical	33	33	33	32	31	28	29	—	—
Electric	48	53	51	55	53	64	58	—	—
Industry	9	8	8	7	8	5	8	—	—
Synthetic Fuels	2	1	2	2	3	1	2	—	—
Residential/Commercial	8	5	6	4	5	2	3	—	—
Total coal use	100%	100%	100%	100%	100%	100%	100%	—	—
Coal consumption/imports (mtce) **Consumption**									
Metallurgical	19	25	27	29	34	39	54	3.4	4.8
Steam incl. BC	36	51	56	63	74	101	130	4.6	5.7
Total coal consumption*	55	76	83	92	108	140	184	4.2	5.5
Imports									
Metallurgical	6	10	9	13	14	24	32	6.2	7.3
Steam*	11	17	18	22	26	37	51	5.4	6.9
Total coal imports*	17	27	27	35	40	61	83	5.7	7.1
Coal production/exports (mtce) **Production**									
Metallurgical	13	15	18	16	20	15	22	0.6	2.3
Steam	25	34	38	41	48	64	79	4.2	5.1
Total coal production	38	49	56	57	68	79	101	3.2	4.3
Exports									
Metallurgical	Neg								
Steam	Neg								
Total coal export	Neg								

* These figures include estimates for Finland, which joined WOCOL after these non-WOCOL projections were prepared. With Finland estimates removed, non-WOCOL European steam coal imports would grow from 7 mtce in 1977 to 32-42 mtce in 2000, and total coal use increases from 51 mtce in 1977 to 135-175 mtce by 2000.

Table 17-3. Summary Coal and Energy Projections for Non-WOCOL Europe Countries (cont.)

II. Coal's Role in Total Energy System	1977	1985		1990		2000		1977-2000 Avg. annual growth-%/yr.	
		A	B	A	B	A	B	A	B
Total Primary Energy Use (mtce)									
Oil, Domestic	31	48	48	52	52	42	42	1.3	1.3
Oil, Imported	195	237	247	266	318	363	440	2.7	3.6
Gas, Domestic	4	8	9	14	15	14	14	5.6	5.6
Gas, Imported	20	32	33	38	41	54	62	4.4	5.0
Nuclear	9	25	25	36	37	57	62	8.4	8.8
Hydro, Solar, Other	61	73	74	83	83	104	106	2.3	2.4
Coal, Domestic	55	76	83	92	108	140	184	4.2	5.5
Coal, Imported	17	27	27	35	40	61	83	5.7	7.1
Total energy use	378	474	543	535	633	652	781	2.5	3.25
Coal penetration (%)	19	22	20	24	23	31	34	—	—
Total primary energy (mtce) input to electricity									
Oil and Gas	39	28	35	21	31	12	8	-5.3	-7.1
Hydro, Solar, Other	61	75	94	87	123	99	225	2.1	5.8
Nuclear	9	27	27	37	40	61	67	8.7	9.1
Coal	26	40	42	51	57	89	106	5.5	6.3
Total energy input	135	170	198	196	251	261	406	2.9	4.9
Coal penetration (%)	19	24	21	26	23	34	26	—	—
Total electric capacity (GWe)									
Oil and Gas	28	26	20	14	18	8	6	-1.9	-6.9
Hydro, Solar, Other	54	67	68	81	84	90	109	2.2	3.1
Nuclear	4	19	22	33	36	75	105	13.6	15.3
Coal	17	19	28	34	38	59	70	5.6	6.5
Total capacity	103	131	138	161	176	232	290	3.5	4.5
Coal Penetration (%)	16.1	14.8	20.2	21.1	21.5	25.2	24.2	—	—
Peak load									
Peak reserve margin (%)									
Total oil imports (mbd)	2.6	3.1	3.2	3.5	4.2	4.8	5.8	2.7	3.6
Total oil consumption (mbd)									
Transportation	1.1	1.5	1.5	1.7	1.9	2.2	2.6	3.1	3.8
Residential/Commercial	0.6	0.8	0.8	0.8	0.8	0.9	0.9	1.8	1.8
Industry—Boilers	0.6	0.7	0.8	0.8	1.0	1.1	1.5	2.7	4.1
Industry—Other	0.1	0.1	0.1	0.1	0.1	0.1	0.1		
Electric utilities	0.3	0.4	0.5	0.5	0.5	0.5	0.5	2.2	2.2
Total oil consumption	3.1	3.9	4.2	4.3	5.0	5.5	6.6	2.5	3.3
World oil price assumed for national coal analysis (1979 U.S. dollars/barrel)	$14.5	18	22	18	25	18	30	1	3.25
Economic growth assumed for national coal analysis (GNP, billion 1978 dollars)	550	683	724	783	860	1026	1213	2.75	3.5

CHAPTER 18

REPUBLIC OF SOUTH AFRICA

The Republic of South Africa (RSA) produced 73 mtce in 1977, of which 12 mtce was exported. This made RSA one of the ten largest coal producers and exporters in the world. Moreover, the Republic of South Africa is expected to remain one of the world's largest exporters of coal throughout this century.

Current information for RSA coal use, production, and export potential by the year 2000 was provided to WOCOL by Mr. H.T. Burger, Assistant Director of that government's Department of Environmental Planning and Energy.

Projections of coal use by market sector are provided in Table 18-1. Coal use is projected to increase from 61 mtce in 1977 to a range of 148-173 mtce in year 2000. The electric sector, which accounted for 57% of the total coal use in 1977, continues as the primary coal market throughout the next two decades. Significant growth in the industrial, metallurgical, and synthetic fuel use of coal is also projected.

Within the Republic of South Africa coal is expected to continue providing about 75 percent of all primary energy consumption. It is particularly interesting to note that coal provides 98% of the fuel for electricity in 1977, and 80% in 2000 (see Table 18-1 on the next page).

Coal exports from the Republic of South Africa amounted to 12.7 mtce in 1977 and 15.4 mtce in 1978. Most of the exports consisted of steam coal. Coal export potential is expected to increase to 44 mtce in 1985 and 55 mtce by year 2000. However, preliminary information provided by Mr. Burger indicates that an export potential of 70-80 mtce could be feasible by the year 2000, given that (1) there is a large increase in international coal demand, (2) constraints such as capital and infrastructural requirements can be met, and (3) there is a continued positive appraisal of RSA coal reserves. A level of 100 mtce appears to represent the extreme upper limit to South African export potential in the year 2000.

Table 18-1. Coal Use in Final Demand Sectors

WOCOL
Country: Republic of South Africa
Units: mtce

Coal Market Sector	1977	1985 Low Coal	1985 High Coal	1990 Low Coal	1990 High Coal	1995 Low Coal	1995 High Coal	2000 Low Coal	2000 High Coal
Electric	35	41	44	52	57	70	78	84	98
Industry	7	9	10	10	11	12	15	13	18
Metallurgical	6	7	8	9	11	13	16	17	21
Synthetic Fuels	2	22	22	22	22	22	22	22	22
Residential/Commercial	11	11	12	11	13	12	13	12	14
Total Coal Use	61	90	96	104	114	129	144	148	173
Total Primary Energy Use	78	117	121	137	147	155	185	189	236
Coal Penetration (%)									
Total Energy	78%	77%	79%	76%	78%	83%	78%	78%	73%
Electricity	98%	88%	88%	89%	89%	N/A	N/A	80%	80%
Industry									

CHAPTER 19

OVERVIEW OF DEVELOPING REGIONS

The largest coal producer and consumer in the developing world is India, which was a member of WOCOL and provided the country study in Part I, Chapter 8 of this report. Indonesia was also a WOCOL member and provided the country report in Part I, Chapter 9.

Estimates for developing countries and regions used by WOCOL were based on special studies prepared for the World Coal Study by Study members.

The WOCOL analyses of developing country regions of East and Southeast Asia, Latin America, and Africa (which are reported in Chapters 20-22 following), together with the country team estimates for India and Indonesia, indicate a large increase in coal use in the developing countries, from 150 mtce in 1977 to a range of 600-900 mtce by the end of the century. India alone projects an increase from 72 mtce in 1977 to 280 mtce by the year 2000. Indonesia indicates a growth from less than 1 mtce in 1977 to about 20 mtce in the year 2000.

One of the principal coal uses will be for electricity generation in newly industrializing countries without large hydroelectric resources (e.g., South Korea, Taiwan, Philippines, and some countries of Latin America). Steam coal requirements in the developing countries of East and Southeast Asia could be as high as 190 mtce, compared to less than 20 mtce in 1977.

The World Bank report, *Coal Development Potential and Prospects in the Developing Countries* (October 1979), became available during the course of our study and was an important reference on coal production and export prospects within the developing countries. The attached Table 19-1 from that report is provided for reference, illustrating by country production prospects to 1990.

Because oil was inexpensive, convenient to transport and use, and readily available until the early 1970's, exploration for coal in the developing countries has been much less widespread and less intensive than exploration for oil and natural gas. Much of the present resources of coal are located in the northern temperate zone. Although the southern hemisphere is less favorable for coal deposits from a geological viewpoint (i.e., less extensive large sedimentary basins), there are large coal resources in Australia and the Republic of South Africa, and there is some optimism that expanded exploration in the southern hemisphere and in the less developed regions of the northern hemisphere will result in the discovery of significant new coal reserves. For example, recent exploration in the southern part of Africa, particularly Botswana and Tanzania, as well as in Indonesia, is yielding favorable results. The world's coal resources and reserves could be significantly larger and more widely distributed geographically than was previously thought.

The World Bank publication notes that coal production in the developing

Table 19-1. Coal Production Prospects of Developing Countries

	Recoverable Reserves[1] Million tce	Production Million tce			
		1977	1980	1985	1990
Africa					
Botswana	3,500	0.2	0.2	0.3	5.0
Morocco	(96)	0.6	0.9	1.0	1.1
Mozambique	80	0.4	1.0	2.0	3.0
Nigeria	90	0.3	0.3	1.0	3.0
Rhodesia	755	2.5	4.0	4.6	5.2
Swaziland	1,820	0.1	0.5	1.5	5.0
Zaire	(73)	0.1	0.1	0.1	0.1
Zambia	5	0.8	1.3	1.9	2.5
Tanzania	(360)	2/	2/	2.0	3.0
Burundi	n.a.	2/	2/	2/	2/
Algeria	(20)	2/	2/	2/	2/
Angola	(500)	–	–	–	2.0
Cameroon	(500)	–	–	–	–
Benin	n.a.	–	–	–	–
Egypt	(80)	–	–	–	–
Ethiopia	n.a.	–	–	–	–
Madagascar	(92)	–	–	1.0	2.0
Malawi	(14)	–	–	–	–
Niger	n.a.	–	–	–	–
Sierra Leone	n.a.	–	–	–	–
Somali	n.a.	–	–	–	–
Tunisia	n.a.	–	–	–	–
Total Africa	7,220	5.0	8.3	15.4	31.9
Asia					
Afghanistan	(85)	0.2	0.2	0.2	1.0
India	33,700	99.7	125.0	145.0	190.0
Indonesia	1,430	0.2	0.2	3.5	12.0
Iran	193	0.9	1.0	1.5	1.5
Pakistan	(1,375)	1.0	1.5	2.0	3.0
Philippines	(87)	0.3	0.3	1.6	4.0
Korea	386	17.3	19.0	22.0	25.0
Taiwan	(680)	2.9	4.0	5.0	6.0
Turkey	793	7.4	9.8	13.0	16.2
Viet Nam	(3,000)	6.0	10.0	15.0	20.0
Thailand	(78)	0.2	0.5	2.0	6.0
Burma	(280)	2/	2/	2/	2/
Bangladesh	519	–	–	–	2.0
Brunei	(1)	–	–	–	–
Malaysia	(75)	–	–	–	2.0
Laos	n.a.	–	–	–	–
Total Asia	38,583	136.1	171.5	211.2	288.7
Latin America					
Argentina	290	0.5	2.3	3.5	7.5
Brazil	8,098	3.5	6.4	10.0	20.0
Chile	162	1.2	2.0	2.5	7.5
Colombia	443	3.7	5.0	10.0	20.0
Mexico	875	6.0	6.7	8.0	9.3
Peru	105	2/	0.2	0.3	0.4
Venezuela	978	0.1	1.2	5.0	8.8
Bolivia	n.a.	–	–	–	–
Haiti	(7)	–	–	–	0.3
Ecuador	(22)	–	–	–	–
Guatemala	n.a.	–	–	–	–
Honduras	(0.2)	–	–	–	–
Panama	n.a.	–	–	–	–
Total Latin America	10,951	15.0	23.8	39.3	73.8

[1] Figures in parentheses represent "geological resources," since no "reserve" data available.

[2] Output below 0.1 million tce in 1977.

Source: *Coal Development Potential and Prospects in the Developing Countries,* World Bank, October 1979.

countries accounted for only about 5 percent of the total 1977 world coal production. About 50 developing countries have known coal resources, and about 30 of these are currently producing coal. A large expansion in coal production and use was projected in this report for the developing countries. In addition to meeting an increasing share of their domestic energy needs, some of these countries, notably Colombia but also Indonesia and Botswana, for example, may have significant potential for exporting coal in the future.

Rapid coal development in the developing countries will require both increased production and increased domestic use of coal. Many of the developing countries have neither the financial resources nor the technical and managerial know-how to launch major coal development programs on their own. Thus international, regional, and bilateral agencies, as well as private mining companies, are likely to be required to play a major role in supporting the developing countries in an analysis of their coal potential, in an assessment of the role that coal could play in their total energy supply balances, and in providing, where appropriate, financial and technical support for the implementation of coal projects.

WOCOL estimates of coal production, use, exports and imports for the developing regions have been incorporated into the overall analysis reported in *COAL— Bridge to the Future*. The principal data supporting that analysis are described in the three chapters that follow:

- Chapter 20—East and Southeast Asia, based on a special study of this region prepared by the Japan National Committee for the World Coal Study.
- Chapter 21—Latin America and Chapter 22—Africa, based on updates of World Energy Conference studies provided to WOCOL by Detlef Wiegand, Bergbau-Forschung Gmbh, Federal Republic of Germany.

In addition, the attached tables, 19-2 and 19-3, compare the estimates for these three regions with independent projections provided to WOCOL by Marc Ippolito, Charbonnages de France based on an internal CdF study.

Table 19-2. Comparison of Estimates of Coal Supply and Demand in Latin America and Africa (mtce)

	Bergbau-Forschung GmbH Report 1979				Charbonnages de France 1979			
Latin America:	Cons.	Prod.	Exp.	Imp.	Cons.	Prod.	Exp.	Imp.
Argentina	20.0	8.8	--	11.2	20	5	-	15
Brazil	45.3	18.9	-	26.4	55	25	-	30
Chile	5.7	5.8	0.4	0.3	5	5	-	-
Colombia	19.5	31.9	12.4	-	15	25	10	-
Mexico	66.6	59.0	11.6	18.2	50	40	-	10
Peru	6.5	6.5	-	-	5	5	-	-
Venezuela	19.2	16.0	-	3.2	15	10	-	5
Other Countries	0.5	-	-	0.5	-	-	-	-
Total Met-Coal	91.2	42.8	7.0	55.5	65	30	10	45
Total Steam-Coal	92.1	104.1	17.4	5.4	100	85	-	15
Total Coal	183.3	146.9	24.4	60.9	165	115	10	60
Africa:								
Algeria	-	-	-	-	5	-	-	5
Botswana	0.7	0.7	-	-	-	10	10	-
Egypt	-	-	-	-	10	-	-	10
Morocco	2.1	2.2	0.3	0.2	5	5	-	-
Mozambique	2.3	6.5	4.2	-	5	10	5	-
Nigeria	1.3	1.5	0.3	-	5	-	-	5
Rhodesia	8.0	12.0	4.0	-	10	10	-	-
Swaziland	2.3	6.1	3.8	-	-	5	5	-
Tunisia	-	-	-	-	5	-	-	5
Zaire	2.6	1.4	- -	1.2	-	-	-	-
Zambia	3.1	3.1	0.1	0.2	5	5	-	-
Other Countries	1.8	1.4	0.3	0.7	10	5	-	5
Total Met-Coal	6.9	9.1	3.9	1.8	30	15	10	25
Total Steam-Coal	17.3	25.8	9.1	0.5	30	35	10	5
Total Coal	24.2	34.9	13.0	2.3	60	50	20	30

Table 19-3. Comparison of Estimates of Demand for Steam Coal in East and Southeast Asia (mtce)

	Japan National Committee Report 1979		Charbonnages de France 1979
East and Southeast Asia:	(High)	(Low)	
Bangladesh	-	-	5
South Korea	92	74	40
Hong Kong	6	6	5
Malaysia	3	3	5
Philippines	16	16	10
Singapore	5	5	5
Taiwan	66	55	15
Thailand	1	1	10

CHAPTER 20

EAST AND SOUTHEAST ASIA

Within the developing countries of Asia, India is by far the largest producer and user of coal. A detailed description of coal prospects in India, which participated in WOCOL, is reported in Part I, Chapter 8. Prospects for Indonesia, which also participated in WOCOL and is a potential future exporter of coal, are reported in Part I, Chapter 9.

A special study of coal prospects in countries of East and Southeast Asia which did not participate in WOCOL was prepared by the Japan National Committee for the World Coal Study. The countries studied include the Republic of Korea, Taiwan, Hong Kong, Malaysia, the Philippines, Singapore, and Thailand.

The projections prepared by the Japanese team indicate a large increase in steam coal use in these 7 developing countries of East and Southeast Asia, from less than 20 mtce currently to 160-190 mtce by the year 2000. In addition to the requirements for steam coal, a large expansion in metallurgical coal use is also projected from less than 5 mtce in 1977 to 40-50 mtce by year 2000. Because of the limited coal production potential, essentially all of the coal would need to be imported.

The two largest coal users within this region are expected to be the Republic of Korea and Taiwan, where ambitious programs to expand the use of coal, especially in electric power plants, are already under way. The projections contained in this study indicate that these two countries are likely to be among the largest coal importers in the world over the next two decades.

REPUBLIC OF KOREA

GNP for Korea is assumed to grow at 9.8% per year from 1975 to 1985, 9% for 1985-1990 and 8.0% for 1990-2000. Electric power demand/GNP elasticity is implied at 1.15 for 1975-1985, 1.10 for 1985-1990 and 1.05 for 1990-2000.

As to the total electric power production up to 1990, estimates of the KDI (Korean Development Institute) are used as reference. Power sources are recomposed due to reduction of nuclear capacity according to the latest study as follows.

	Nuclear Capacity (GWe)	
	Low Coal Case	High Coal Case
1985	3.7	3.7
1990	9.0	9.0
2000	20.0	30.0

No additional oil-fired capacity is assumed after 1990. The KDI's estimate is used for projection of coal use in other sectors. It amounts to 45 mtce for 2000 in which residential use is to increase at 5.6% per year for 1975-2000.

TAIWAN

GNP for Taiwan is assumed to grow at 7.7% for 1980-1985, 6.8% for 1985-1990, and 6.5% for 1990-2000. Electric power demand/GNP elasticity is implied at 1.44 for 1980-1985, 1.63 for 1985-1990, and 1.54 for 1990-2000.

As for nuclear capacity, the government's plan is taken up to 1990. Upper limit of nuclear capacity is assumed at 30% of the total power capacity for 2000. No additional oil-fired capacity is assumed after 1990.

The coal use in other sectors is tentatively set down as 5% of the total energy consumption.

SOUTHEAST ASIA

A macro-approach is taken in the projections for Hong Kong, Indonesia, Malaysia, Philippines, Singapore and Thailand due to limited information available.

Per capita energy consumption and per capita electric power consumption are respectively estimated based on elasticity per capita GDP, which is given by the regression equation. There are two types of equations; one is a world universal model based on 614 basic data for 99 countries, where 15 regions are identified, between 1965 and 1975, and another is an Asian regional model based on 59 basic data for 11 countries between 1965 and 1975.

The basic data are based on the UN Statistical Yearbook. In this projection, the latter Asian regional model as shown below is employed.

1. $\text{Log}_e E_1 = -1.77055 + 1.32489 \, \text{Log}_e X - 0.473518E - 02T$
$(0.10078) \quad\quad (0.29573 \, E - 02)$
$R = 0.87934$
$S = 0.663505$

2. $\text{Log}_e E_2 = -4.49440 + 1.72530 \, \text{Log}_e X - 0.417931E - 02T$
$(0.97026E - 01) \; (0.28472 \, E - 2)$
$R = 0.93005$
$S = 0.638814$

E_1 represents per capita primary energy consumption and E_2 per capita electric power consumption, and the other symbols used in these equations are as follows:

X: Per capita GDP

T: Time

The rate of economic growth is assumed as follows according to a study on Long-Term Projections of Economic Growth in ESCAP Member Countries.

Rate of Economic Growth
(%/yr)

	1975-1980	1980-1985	1985-1990	1990-2000
Hong Kong	9.1	6.2	6.3	6.3
Indonesia	5.7	5.6	6.1	6.1
Malaysia	9.5	7.9	7.6	7.6
Philippines	8.5	8.3	8.5	8.5
Singapore	5.4	6.8	6.8	6.8
Thailand	6.8	5.9	5.9	5.9

The possible share of coal-fired power generation is surmised at by country based on relevant power development program. Its percentage of share to the total electricity production is respectively assumed as follows:

Assumed Percentage of Coal-Fired Power Generation
(%)

	1990	2000
Hong Kong	60	60
Indonesia	80	80
Malaysia	30	30
Philippines	20	40
Singapore	70	80
Thailand	15	20

Information on steam coal use in sectors other than electricity is not sufficiently available, and estimates have been therefore provided only for the Philippines.

SUMMARY OF STEAM COAL PROJECTIONS

Table 20-1 summarizes the Japanese team projections for steam coal use and imports in the seven countries of East and Southeast Asia. The following tables provide detailed statistics by country, including information on existing coal-fired electric power plants now in various stages of development in the individual countries.

Table 20-1. Summary of Steam Coal Use and Imports for East and Southeast Asia, 1975-2000 (mtce)

Country	1975	1985	1990	2000 High	2000 Low
Korea					
Demand	10	23	35	92	74
Indigenous Supply	12	9	5	5	5
Import	–	14	30	88	69
Taiwan					
Demand	3	8	13	66	55
Indigenous Supply	3	1	1	1	1
Import	–	7	12	65	54
Hong Kong					
Demand	–	1	2	6	6
Indigenous Supply	–	–	–	–	–
Import	–	1	2	6	6
Philippines					
Demand	–	2	4	16	16
Indigenous Supply	–	2	4	4	4
Import	–	–	–	12	12
Thailand					
Demand	–	–	–	1	1
Indigenous Supply	–	–	–	1	1
Import	–	–	–	–	–
Malaysia					
Demand	–	–	1	3	3
Indigenous Supply	–	–	–	–	–
Import	–	–	–	3	3
Singapore					
Demand	–	–	2	5	5
Indigenous Supply	–	–	–	–	–
Import	–	–	2	5	5
Total					
Demand	13	34	57	190	160
Indigenous Supply	15	12	10	11	11
Import	–	22	47	179	149

Table 20-2. Potential Demand for Steam Coal, 1975-2000 (mtce)

Country	Sector	1975	1985	1990	2000 High Case	2000 Low Case
Korea, Rep. of	Electricity	0.55	6.55	14.20	47.17	28.45
	Other	9.69	16.31	20.80	45.25	45.25
	Sub total	10.24	22.86	35.0	92.42	73.70
Taiwan	Electricity	0.48	5.15	9.31	55.70	49.73
	Other	2.34	2.42	3.44	10.76	5.08
	Sub total	2.82	7.57	12.75	66.46	54.81
Hong Kong	Electricity	--	0.81	2.50	5.77	--
	Other	--	--	--	--	--
	Sub total	--	0.81	2.50	5.77	--
Philippines	Electricity	--	0.72	1.72	10.78	
	Other	0.10	1.72	2.53	5.47	
	Sub total	0.10	2.44	4.25	16.25	
Thailand	Electricity	0.05	0.22	0.48	1.35	
	Other	--	--	--	--	
	Sub total	0.05	0.22	0.48	1.35	
Malaysia	Electricity	--	--	1.20	3.30	
	Other	--	--	--	--	
	Sub total	--	--	1.20	3.30	
Singapore	Electricity	--	--	1.60	4.70	
	Other	--	--	--	--	
	Sub total	--	--	1.60	4.70	
Total	Electricity	1.08	13.4	31.0	128.7	
	Other	12.13	20.5	26.8	61.5	
	Total	13.21	33.9	57.8	190.2	

531

Table 20-3. Coal Use in Final Demand Sectors for Republic of Korea, 1975-2000 (mtce)

Sector	1975	1985	1990	2000 High Case	2000 Low Case
Electricity	0.55	6.55	14.20	47.17	28.45
Industry	3.94	14.31	21.78	44.27	44.27
Iron & Steel	2.08	11.0	15.40	29.30	29.30
Other Industry	1.86	3.31	6.38	14.97	14.97
Residential	7.83	13.00	14.42	30.28	30.28
Total	12.32	33.86	50.40	121.72	103.00

Table 20-4. Electricity Production for Republic of Korea, 1975-2000

		1975	1985	1990	2000 High case	2000 Low case
Power Plant Capacity (MWe)	Total	4,720	15,460	24,790	55,530	55,530
	Hydro	620	1,700	1,910	1,910	1,910
	Nuclear	--	3,730	9,000	20,000	30,000
	Coal-fired	210	3,000	6,500	26,240	16,240
	Oil-fired	3,650	7,030	7,380	7,380	7,380
Annual Energy Output (GWh)	Total	19,887	74,499	119,437	267,566	267,566
	Hydro	1,332	3,724	4,180	4,180	4,180
	Nuclear	--	19,605	47,304	105,120	157,680
	Coal-fired	1,551	18,396	39,858	132,406	79,846
	Oil-fired	17,003	32,774	28,095	25,860	25,860
Fuel Consumption (1000 tce)	Total	7,084	26,542	42,551	95,326	95,326
	Hydro	475	1,327	1,489	1,489	1,489
	Nuclear	--	6,985	16,853	37,451	56,176
	Coal-fired	553	6,554	14,200	47,172	28,446
	Oil-fired	6,057	11,676	10,009	9,213	9,213

Table 20-5. Electricity Statistics for Taiwan

	1977	1985	1990	2000 Coal Low Case	Coal High Case
Economic Growth Rate (%)	(72 – 77) 6.8	(80 – 85) 7.66	(85 – 90) 6.75	(90 – 2000) 6.5	6.5
Electric Power Capacity (MWe)	7,020	16,390	27,630	71,670	71,670
Total Electric Power Production (GWh)	29,724	74,049	128,360	332,933	332,933
Coal fired (GWh)	1,490	15,943	28,820	153,975	172,445
Growth Rate of Electric Power Production (%)	(72 – 77) 11.2	(80 – 85) 11.0	(85 – 90) 11.0	(90 – 2000) 10.0	10.0
Elasticity of Electricity to GDP	1.65	1.44	1.63	1.54	1.54
Coal-fired Plant					
Electricity Production (1000 tce)	480	5,150	9,310	49,730	55,700
Capacity (MWe)	—	260	470	32,255	35,769
Nuclear Power Capacity (GWe)	640	5,210	8,810	25,020	21,500

Table 20-6. Electricity Production in Taiwan, Low Coal Case

	1977	1985	1990	2000
Installed Capacity (MWe)	7,020	16,388	27,632	71,670
Hydro	1,365	2,246	3,371	3,400
Oil-fired	5,019	6,332	10,751	11,000
Coal-fired		2,600	4,700	32,255
Nuclear	636	5,210	8,810	25,015
Total Electric Power Production (GWh)	29,724	74,049	128,360	332,933
Hydro	3,999	5,902	8,859	8,935
Oil-fired	24,144	24,820	44,376	38,544
Coal-fired	1,490	15,943	28,820	153,975
Nuclear	91	27,384	46,305	131,479
Total Fuel Consumption				
Oil $(10^3 Kl)$	5,818.7	5,981.6	10,694.6	9,289.1
Coal $(10^3 ton)$	481.3	5,149.6	9,308.9	49,733.9

Table 20-7. Electricity Production in Taiwan, High Coal Case

	1977	1985	1990	2000
Installed Capacity (MWe)	7,020	16,388	27,632	71,670
Hydro	1,365	2,246	3,371	3,400
Oil-fired	5,019	6,332	10,751	11,000
Coal-fired		2,600	4,700	35,769
Nuclear	636	5,210	8,810	21,501
Total Electric Power Production (GWh)	29,724	74,049	128,360	332,933
Hydro	3,999	5,902	8,859	8,935
Oil-fired	24,144	24,820	44,376	38,544
Coal-fired	1,490	15,943	28,820	172,445
Nuclear	91	27,384	46,305	113,009
Total Fuel Consumption				
Oil $(10^3 Kl)$	5,818.7	5,981.6	10,694.6	9,289.1
Coal $(10^3 ton)$	481.3	5,149.6	9,308.9	55,699.7

Table 20-8. Estimated Energy Consumption (1980-2000) for Hong Kong

	1975	1980	1985	1990	2000
	1970-75	1975-80	1980-85	1985-90	1990-2000
GDP Total (in Million U.S. Dollars)	4,500	6,944	9,397	12,730	23,363
Population Total (in Millions)	4.3	4.6	4.9	5.2	5.7
GDP Growth Rate (%/year)	6.0	9.06	6.24	6.26	6.26
Population Growth Rate (%/year)	1.39	1.36	1.36	1.22	0.89
GDP per Capita Growth Rate (%/year)	4.5	7.32	4.42	4.49	4.49
Primary Energy Consumption per Capita (in Kilogram of Coal Equivalent)	1,277	2,028	2,696	3,599	6,415
Electric Power Consumption per Capita (in KWH)	1,705	3,089	4,460	6,477	13,657
Total Primary Energy Consumption (in Thousand Ton of Coal Equivalent)	5,501	9,349	13,295	18,858	36,724
Total Electric Power Consumption (in Million kwh)	7,343	14,238	21,995	33,935	78,181
Total Electric Power Consumption (in Thousand Ton of Coal Equivalent)	903	1,751	2,705	4,174	9,616
Coal Use (in Thousand Ton of Coal Equivalent)	--	--	811	2,504	5,770

Table 20-9. Estimated Energy Consumption (1980-2000) for the Philippines

	1975	1970-75	1980	1975-80	1985	1980-85	1990	1985-90	2000	1990-2000
GDP Total (in Million U.S. Dollars)	9,098		13,706		20,376		30,622		69,172	
Population Total (in Millions)	42.5		49.8		57.9		66.6		84.9	
GDP Growth Rate (%/year)		6.1		8.54		8.25		8.49		8.49
Population Growth Rate (%/year)		3.34		3.22		3.06		2.84		2.46
GDP per Capita Growth Rate (%/year)		2.60		5.11		4.99		5.45		5.45
Primary Energy Consumption per Capita (in Kilogram of Coal Equivalent)	326		452		623		882		1,772	
Electric Power Consumption per Capita (in KWH)	291		444		670		1,050		2,579	
Total Primary Energy Consumption (in Thousand Ton of Coal Equivalent)	13,850		22,518		36,058		58,777		150,506	
Total Electric Power Consumption (in Million kwh)	12,359		22,092		38,814		69,959		219,111	
Total Electric Power Consumption (in Thousand Ton of Coal Equivalent)	1,520		2,717		4,774		8,606		26,951	
Coal Use (in Thousand Ton of Coal Equivalent)	--		--		716		1,721		10,780	

Table 20-10. Estimated Energy Consumption (1980-2000) for Thailand

| | 1975 | 1980 | 1985 | 1990 | 2000 |
	1970-75	1975-80	1980-85	1985-90	1990-2000
GDP Total (in Million U.S. Dollars)	8,928	12,377	16,460	21,914	38,839
Population Total (in Millions)	41.9	49.1	57.2	66.0	84.4
GDP Growth Rate (%/year)	6.5	6.75	5.87	5.89	5.89
Population Growth Rate (%/year)	3.27	3.23	3.11	2.89	2.49
GDP per Capita Growth Rate (%/year)	3.1	3.35	2.66	2.85	2.85
Primary Energy Consumption per Capita (in Kilogram of Coal Equivalent)	284	353	420	505	732
Electric Power Consumption per Capita (in KWH)	189	250	313	398	643
Total Primary Energy Consumption (in Thousand Ton of Coal Equivalent)	11,900	17,333	24,021	33,339	61,765
Total Electric Power Consumption (in Million kwh)	7,910	12,280	17,911	26,254	54,253
Total Electric Power Consumption (in Thousand Ton of Coal Equivalent)	973	1,510	2,203	3,229	6,673
Coal Use (in Thousand Ton of Coal Equivalent)	50	150	220	480	1,350

Table 20-11. Estimated Energy Consumption (1980-2000) for Malaysia

	1975	1980	1985	1990	2000
	1970-75	1975-80	1980-85	1985-90	1990-2000
GDP Total (in Million U.S. Dollars)	5,696	8,973	13,125	18,914	39,273
Population Total (in Millions)	12.3	14.2	16.3	18.5	22.3
GDP Growth Rate (%/year)	6.7	9.52	7.90	7.58	7.58
Population Growth Rate (%/year)	2.89	2.93	2.77	2.55	1.89
GDP per Capita Growth Rate (%/year)	3.7	6.36	4.96	4.87	4.87
Primary Energy Consumption per Capita (in Kilogram of Coal Equivalent)	584	875	1,203	1,645	3,073
Electric Power Consumption per Capita (in KWH)	468	788	1,188	1,779	3,985
Total Primary Energy Consumption (in Thousand Ton of Coal Equivalent)	7,176	12,425	19,581	30,359	68,419
Total Electric Power Consumption (in Million kwh)	5,757	11,193	19,343	32,837	88,715
Total Electric Power Consumption (in Thousand Ton of Coal Equivalent)	708	1,377	2,379	4,039	10,912
Coal Use (in Thousand Ton of Coal Equivalent)	--	--	--	1,212	3,274

Table 20-12. Estimated Energy Consumption (1980-2000) for Singapore

	1975	1980	1985	1990	2000
	1970-75	1975-80	1980-85	1985-90	1990-2000
GDP Total (in Million U.S. Dollars)	2,952	3,844	5,346	7,418	14,282
Population Total (in Millions)	2.3	2.4	2.6	2.8	3.1
GDP Growth Rate (%/year)	9.5	5.43	6.82	6.77	6.77
Population Growth Rate (%/year)	1.61	1.61	1.57	1.42	1.00
GDP per Capita Growth Rage (%/year)	7.70	3.75	5.16	5.27	5.27
Primary Energy Consumption per Capita (in Kilogram of Coal Equivalent)	2,270	2,892	4,026	5,642	11,080
Electric Power Consumption per Capita (in KWH)	1,973	2,699	4,133	6,386	15,244
Total Primary Energy Consumption (in Thousand Ton of Coal Equivalent)	5,117	7,064	10,628	15,982	34,672
Total Electric Power Consumption (in Million kwh)	4,448	6,591	10,912	18,091	47,702
Total Electric Power Consumption (in Thousand Ton of Coal Equivalent)	547	811	1,342	2,225	5,867
Coal Use (in Thousand Ton of Coal Equivalent)	--	--	--	1,558	4,694

540

Table 20-13. Proposed Coal-Fired Projects (1980-2000) in Republic of Korea

(1,000 tons)

Coal-fired Power Plant			1980	1981	1982	1983	1984-1992	2000
SAMCHUM-PO	(decided)							
	No.1	500MW			500	1,000	1,000	1,000
	No.2	500MW				1,000	1,000	1,000
KOJUNG	(decided)							
	No.1	500MW				500	1,000	1,000
	No.2	500MW					1,000	1,000
Total	2,000MW				500	2,500	4,000	4,000

Remarks: (1) 500 MW × 5 units are under planning for startup after 1984.
(2) If above projects become firm, at least 5 million tons per year will be added to the listed requirement, making the total 9 million tons in 1990 and onward.

Table 20-14. Proposed Coal-Fired Projects (1980-2000) in Taiwan

(1,000 tons)

		1980	1981	1982-1984	1985	1986	1987-1992	2000
HSINTA, SOUTHERN TERMINAL								
(decided)								
No. 1	500MW		1,200	1,200	1,200	1,200	1,200	1,200
No. 2	500MW			1,200	1,200	1,200	1,200	1,200
(under planning)								
No. 3	750MW						1,800	1,800
TAICHUNG CENTRAL TERMINAL								
(under planning)								
No. 1	600MW				1,440	1,440	1,440	1,440
No. 2	600MW					1,440	1,440	1,440
No. 3	750MW						1,800	1,800
Total			1,200	2,400	3,840	5,280	8,880	8,880

Remarks: (1) Existing oil-fired and coal/oil-fired power stations are under serious consideration for conversion to coal.
(2) Combined with port expansion plan, 500 MW × 4 units coal-fired power plants are planned for mid-1980's onward at Su-Ao.
(3) Additional 3 to 4 units will be added to the planned Hsinta and Central terminal, respectively, subject to electricity demand growth in latter half of 1980's and in 1990's.
(4) Including additional requirement, coal import for power generation in 1990 may well exceed 20 million tons.

541

Table 20-15. Proposed Coal-Fired Projects (1980-2000) in Hong Kong

(1,000 tons)

	1980	1981	1982	1983	1984	1985	1986-87	1988-89	1990-91	1992/2000
PO LO TSUI, LAMMA ISLAND										
(decided)										
No. 1 250MW			450	450	450	450	450	450	450	450
No. 2 250MW					450	450	450	450	450	450
(under planning)										
No. 3 250MW							450	450	450	450
No. 4 250MW								450	450	450
No. 5 350MW									630	630
No. 6 350MW										630
TOP SHEK KOH, HONG KONG										
(decided)										
No. 1 350MW			840	840	840	840	840	840	840	840
No. 2 350MW					840	840	840	840	840	840
(under planning)										
No. 3 350MW						840	840	840	840	840
No. 4 350MW							840	840	840	840
TOTAL			1,290	1,290	2,580	3,420	4,710	5,160	5,790	6,420

Table 20-16. Electric Power Development Plan (1978-1987) in the Philippines

Power Plant	Installed Capacity (MW)	1978 (GWh)	1979 (GWh)	1980 (GWh)	1981 (GWh)	1982 (GWh)	1983 (GWh)	1984 (GWh)	1985 (GWh)	1986 (GWh)	1987 (GWh)
LUZON											
Dual-Fired Ther. 1	225						1,250	1,250	1,250	1,250	1,250
Dual-Fired Ther. 2	300								1,663	1,663	1,663
Sub-Total		0				0	1,250	1,250	2,913	2,913	2,913
VISAYAS											
Naga T. I	55.0			56	337	337	337	337	337	337	337
Naga T. II	55.0						337	337	337	337	337
Negros T. I	55.0							337	337	337	337
Leyte T. I	55.0									169	337
Negros T. II	55.0										169
Sub-Total		0	0	56	337	337	674	1,011	1,011	1,180	1,517
MINDANAO											
Dual-Fired	150							832	832	832	832
Dual-Fired	150									832	832
Sub-Total		0	0	0	0	0	0	832	832	1,664	1,664
TOTAL		0	0	56	337	337	1,924	3,093	4,756	5,757	6,094
PHILIPPINES											
Hydro		3,044	3,261	3,830	3,865	4,202	6,109	7,055	9,201	10,895	14,200
Diesel		413	1,634	2,361	2,715	3,029	3,200	3,200	3,200	3,200	3,200
Power Barges		--	--	262	392	392	392	392	392	392	392
Thermal (oil)		11,416	13,141	13,716	13,716	13,716	13,716	13,278	13,278	13,278	13,278
A)Thermal (coal)		--	--	56	337	337	1,924	3,093	4,756	5,757	6,094
Geothermal		20	590	2,283	3,445	3,674	3,674	3,674	3,674	4,394	5,114
B)Total		14,893	18,626	22,508	24,470	25,350	29,015	30,692	34,501	37,916	42,278
A /B (%)		0	0	0.2	1.4	1.3	6.6	10.1	13.8	15.2	14.4
Coal Requirement for Electricity (1,000 tce)		0	0	21	127	127	724	1,164	1,790	2,167	2,293

Note: (1) Based on Calendar year.
(2) Data Source: Luzon Integrated Grid—Generation Expansion Program, Dec. 31, 1977 prepared by NPC Visayas Power Grids—Generation Expansion Program, Dec. 31, 1977 prepared by NPC Mindanao Power Grid—Generation Expansion Program.
(3) NPC: National Philippine Corporation.

Table 20-17. Electric Power Development Plan in Thailand

Power Plant	1977 (Existing) Installed Capacity (MW)	System Capability (GWh)	1978 (MW)	(GWh)	1979 (MW)	(GWh)	1980 (MW)	(GWh)	1981 (MW)	(GWh)	1982 (MW)	(GWh)	1983 (MW)	(GWh)	1984 (MW)	(GWh)	1985 (MW)	(GWh)	1986 (MW)	(GWh)
EXISTING																				
Krabi (Lignite Fired)	20.0	96																		
(Lignite Fired)	20.0	96																		
(Lignite Fired)	20.0	96																		
NEW PROJECTS																				
New Mae Moh 1			75.0	361																
New Mae Moh 2			75.0	361																
New Mae Moh 3									75.0	361										
Coal-fired Total	60.0	289	150.0	723					75.0	361										
(A) Coal-fired Accumulated Total	60.0	289	210	1,012	210.	1,012	210	1,012	285	1,373	285	1,373	285	1,373	285	1,373	285	1,373	285	1,373
Coal Requirement for Electricity (1,000 tce)	(186)		(650)		(650)		(650)		(882)		(882)		(882)		(882)		(882)		(882)	
(B) Total	2,832	11,175	3,282	12,114	3,522	13,291	3,765	14,573	4,252	15,983	4,290	17,371	5,090	18,873	5,515	20,515	5,515	22,323	6,165	24,333
(A)/(B) (%)	2.1	2.6	6.4	8.4	6.0	7.6	5.6	6.9	6.7	8.6	6.6	7.9	5.6	7.3	5.2	6.7	5.2	6.2	4.6	5.6

Note: (1) Data Source: *Electric Power in Thailand 1977*.
(2) Utilization factor is estimated at 55%.

544

Table 20-18. Electric Power Development Plan (1977-1986 F.Y.) in Malaysia

Project

	1976 F.Y. (MW)	1977 (MW)	1978 (MW)	1979 (MW)	1980 (MW)	1981 (MW)	1982 (MW)	1983 (MW)	1984 (MW)	1985 (MW)	1986 (MW)
Hydro	(Existing)	0	380	0	0	0	72	120	200	200	0
Thermal		120	0	120	240	240	0	0	0	250	250
Steam (Oil-fired)		120	0	120	240	240	0	0	0	250	250
Diesel		0	0	0	0	0	0	0	0	0	0
Total		120	380	120	240	240	72	120	200	450	250

Installed Capacity at the End of Fiscal Year

	1976 F.Y. (MW)	1977 (MW)	1978 (MW)	1979 (MW)	1980 (MW)	1981 (MW)	1982 (MW)	1983 (MW)	1984 (MW)	1985 (MW)	1986 (MW)
Hydro	265.4	265.4	645.4	645.4	645.4	645.4	717.4	837.4	1,037.4	1,237.4	1,237.4
Thermal	922.5	1,042.5	1,042.5	1,162.5	1,402.5	1,642.5	1,642.5	1,642.5	1,642.5	1,892.5	2,142.5
Steam (Oil-fired)	850.0	970.0	970.0	1,090.0	1,330.0	1,570.0	1,570.0	1,570.0	1,570.0	1,820.0	2,070.0
Diesel	72.5	72.5	72.5	72.5	72.5	72.5	72.5	72.5	72.5	72.5	72.5
Total	1,187.9	1,307.9	1,687.9	1,807.9	2,047.9	2,287.9	2,359.9	2,479.9	2,679.9	3,129.9	3,379.9

Shares (%)

	1976 F.Y.	1977	1978	1979	1980	1981	1982	1983	1984	1985	1986
Hydro	22.3	20.3	38.2	35.7	31.5	28.2	30.4	33.8	38.7	39.5	36.6
Thermal	77.7	79.7	61.8	64.3	68.5	71.8	69.6	66.2	61.3	60.5	63.4
Steam (Oil-fired)	71.6	74.2	57.5	60.3	64.9	68.6	66.5	63.3	58.6	58.2	61.2
Diesel	6.1	5.5	4.3	4.0	3.5	3.2	3.1	2.9	2.7	2.3	2.2
Total	100.0	100.0	100.0	100.0	100.0	100.0	100.0	100.0	100.0	100.0	100.0

Note: (1) 1976 F.Y. begins at 1st September 1975 and ends at 31st August 1976.
(2) Data Source: 27th Annual Report 1st September 1975-31st August 1976, National Electricity Board of the States of Malaya.

Table 20-19. Proposed Coal-Fired Projects (1980-2000) in Singapore

Coal-Fired Power Plant	1980 – 1986	1987	1988	1989	1990	1991	1992	2000
PULAN SERAYA Phase 1 (MW)	–	700	–	–	–	–	–	–
PULAN SERAYA Phase 2 (MW)	–	–	–	–	700	–	–	–
PULAN SERAYA Phase 3 (MW)	–	–	–	–	–	–	–	700
Total (MW)	–	700	–	–	700	–	–	700
Coal-fired Accumulated Total (MW)	–	700	700	700	1,400	1,400	1,400	2,100
Coal Requirement for Electricity (1,000 tce)	–	1,600	1,600	1,600	3,200	3,200	3,200	4,800

CHAPTER 21

LATIN AMERICA

A special regional study of coal prospects in countries of Latin America was prepared for WOCOL by one of its members, Detlef Wiegand, Bergbau-Forschung GmbH, Federal Republic of Germany. This study, which is based on an update of the 1977 World Energy Conference coal data for this region, estimated future levels of coal production, use, export, and import for both steam coal and metallurgical coal to the year 2000.

The estimates indicate a rapid 11-fold growth of coal use in Latin America from 16 mtce in 1975 to 183 mtce in 2000. There is also a large expansion of coal production. Coal imports are projected to increase from 5.7 mtce in 1975 to 61 mtce in 2000, largely in Argentina, Brazil, and Mexico. Most of the projected imports are of metallurgical coal, although it is possible that the increasing importance of coal could lead to steam coal imports greater than estimated. Estimated exports of 25 mtce in 2000 are principally from Colombia and Mexico.

The following material provides the detailed resource, reserves, production and use data for Latin America. Data for the principal countries—Argentina, Brazil, Chile, Colombia, Mexico, Peru, Venezuela—are provided as well as the aggregated statistics for the region.

Table 21-1. Major Coal Resources and Coal Reserves of Latin America (mtce)

Country	Resources		Reserves	
	h. c. [1]	b. c. [1]	h. c.	b. c.
Main countries				
Argentina	--	384	--	290
Brazil	4,040	6,042	2,510	5,588
Chile	300	2,857	36	126
Colombia	7,633	685	950	46
Mexico	5,448	--	875	--
Peru	852	50	105	--
Venezuela	1,630		978	--
other Latin American countries	35	4	--	--
Total	19,938	10,022	5,454	6,050

[1] h.c. = hard coal   b.c. = brown coal
The coalification limit between hard coal and brown coal was fixed at 23.76 MJ/kg (equivalent to 5,700 kcal/kg) related to air-dried, ash-free substance.

547

Table 21-2. Coal Resources of the Other Latin American Countries

Country	coal type	estimated coal deposits (million tonnes)	comments
Bolivia	all grades	unknown	scattered deposits not of economic importance
Costa Rica	lignite	unknown	no economically reserves
Ecuador	peat, lignite and subbi- tuminous	13	deposits are badly, faulted and fractured
Guatemala	lignite	unknown	
Honduras	lignite	1	very low grade lignite
Panama	lignite	unknown	
Paraguay	bituminous	unknown	uneconomical
Puerto Rico	lignite	small amounts	low quality
Uruguay	bituminous	25	low rank, high ash, high sulfur, uneconomical

Table 21-3. Coal, Production, Use, Import, and Export Projections for Latin America

	met-coal (mtce)[*]					
	1975	1980	1985	1990	1995	2000
Production	5.8	13.2	21.8	29.4	36.0	42.8
Consumption	10.1	19.3	37.5	52.6	73.5	91.2
Import	4.5	9.2	18.8	27.5	42.3	55.5
Export	0.1	3.1	4.1	4.3	4.8	7.0

* met coal = metallurgical coal including blending coal for coke production.

steam coal (mtce)					
	1975	1980	1985	1990	1995	2000
Production	6.9	21.8	47.6	68.3	82.0	104.1
Consumption	6.2	19.0	35.7	50.1	69.9	92.1
Import	1.2	2.0	3.3	0.7	2.2	5.4
Export	0.8	4.6	15.2	19.2	18.3	17.4

total coal (mtce)					
	1975	1980	1985	1990	1995	2000
Production	12.7	35.0	69.4	97.7	118.0	146.9
Consumption	16.3	38.3	73.2	102.7	143.4	183.3
Import	5.7	11.2	22.1	28.2	44.5	60.9
Export	0.9	7.7	19.3	23.5	23.1	24.4

COUNTRY: ARGENTINA

Most of the coal reserves are situated and mined around the Rio Turbio by the state-owned monopoly Yacimientos Carboniferos Fiscales (YCF). The coal tends to be of inferior quality but after treatment or blending it is suitable for steam raising. Mixed with high-grade coking coal, Argentinian coal is made available for steelmaking. The Port of Rio Gallegos is used for shipping coal to other parts of the country. Today, the main consumer is the Hydro and Electric Energy Agency. The main coal imports today come from the USA, Poland, Australia and Columbia. In 1977, about 1.1 million tons of coal were imported. The planned need for coal for additional thermal generating plants will in the foreseeable future be met by production from Argentinian reserves. Self-sufficiency does not include coking coals and imports will be required to match the growth of the Argentinian steel industry.

549

Country: Argentina

met-coal (mtce)						
	1975	1980	1985	1990	1995	2000
Production	0.4	0.6	1.3	1.3	1.5	1.8
Consumption	1.5	2.0	4.5	6.5	8	10
Import	1.2	1.4	3.2	5.2	6.5	8.2
Export	-	-	-	-	-	-

steam coal (mtce)						
	1975	1980	1985	1990	1995	2000
Production	0.2	2.6	3.5	3.7	5	7
Consumption	0.7	2.4	3.5	4.0	6.5	10
Import	0.5	-	-	-	1.5	3
Export	-	-	-	-	-	-

total coal (mtce)						
	1975	1980	1985	1990	1995	2000
Production	0.6	3.2	4.8	5.0	6.5	8.8
Consumption	2.2	4.4	8.0	10.5	14.5	20
Import	1.7	1.4	3.2	5.2	8	11.2
Export	-	-	-	-	-	-

COUNTRY: BRAZIL

All of Brazil's known reserves occur in the south of Santa Caterina, Rio Grande do Sul and Parana. Coal tends to be dirty and run-of-mine output is greatly reduced when processed to give a coal of marketable quality. The Brazilian coal mines are primarily privately owned. The metallurgical coal from domestic sources is of a blended coking coal type. Most of the steam coal produced is consumed in power plants.

In the future the Brazilian iron and steel industry plans to increase steel production from 7.6 million tons of steel in 1974 to 26 million tons (1980) to 40.2 million tons in 1985. This means a substantial increase of import of coking coal. The expansion plans for the national steel production requires that 30% of the national coke production be made from indigenous coal. As a consequence, an enormous quantity of steam coal would be produced along with the coals used in metallurgy.

Brazil and Poland have negotiated a trade agreement whereby Polish coking coal will be shipped to Brazil in exchange for Brazilian iron ore. The contract covers a period of 10 years until 1990 and involves a total tonnage of 70 million metric tons. By 1985, Brazilian imports from Poland are projected to rise to 10 million metric tons.

There are existing plans for coal gasification. One deep mine of the Companhio Rio Grandense de Mineracao (CRM), which will be onstream in 1982, is already a consequence of the potential for coal gasification. The gas is to be transformed into ammonia, town gas and reducer gas for making sponge-iron in a mini steel plant. Siderurgica Brazileira (SIDERBRAS) and the Polish KOPEX Organization will form a 0.5 billion US-$ joint venture to develop coal deposits situated in Colombia. The coal produced will be exported to Brazil.

The German Krupp-Koppers GmbH has been awarded a contract to build a coal gasification plant in San Jeronimo in the state of Rio Grande do Sul. The raw gas is to be converted into ammonia for the fertilizer industry. The state-owned Petrobras has ordered this plant.

met-coal (mtce)						
	1975	1980	1985	1990	1995	2000
Production	0.8	1.6	3.6	3.8	4.0	4.2
Consumption	3.2	6.6	15.0	20.0	26.1	30.6
Import	2.4	5.0	11.4	16.2	22.1	26.4
Export	-	-	-	-	-	-

Country: Brazil

steam coal (mtce)						
	1975	1980	1985	1990	1995	2000
Production	1.6	2.0	5.2	9.0	11.5	14.7
Consumption	1.3	2.9	6.9	9.0	11.5	14.7
Import	-	0.9	1.7	-	-	-
Export	-	-	-	-	-	-

total coal (mtce)						
	1975	1980	1985	1990	1995	2000
Production	2.4	3.6	8.8	12.8	15.5	18.9
Consumption	4.5	9.5	21.9	29.0	37.6	45.3
Import	2.4	5.9	13.1	16.2	22.1	26.4
Export	-	-	-	-	-	-

COUNTRY: CHILE

The coal mining industry is carried out by private companies. The most important is the Lota-Sweiger Coal Company with a production rate of about 80% in Chile. The depressed conditions in the Chilean coal industry decreases the profits of the private companies. To maintain the jobs of the miners, the government of Chile has nationalized most of the industry. The nationalization was effected by Corporation de Fomento de la Production (CORFO). In 1971 the Lota-Sweiger Coal Company was nationalized. A new organization, Empresa National del Carbon S.A. (ENACAR), was founded to operate the state-owned coal mines. ENACAR plans to export coal to Brazil, Argentina and Spain.

Chile does not have sufficient energy resources; it has to import 70% of its oil needs. The increasing costs of imported crude oil forces the country to develop and explore its own energy resources. Therefore, a steam plant operated by Corporacion National del Cobre (CODECCO) is being converted from oil to coal; also, the Empresa Nacional de Mineria (ENAMI) plans to use some 100,000 tons of coal per year in the copper smelters as a substitute for oil. The Paipote copper facility (ENAMI) has switched in 1976 from oil to coal. Domestic coals are only of moderate coking quality and must be blended with imported coking coal.

Country: Chile

met-coal (mtce)						
	1975	1980	1985	1990	1995	2000
Production	0.3	0.5	0.6	0.7	0.7	0.8
Consumption	0.5	0.7	0.8	0.9	1.0	1.1
Import	0.2	0.2	0.2	0.2	0.3	0.3
Export	-	-	-	-	-	-

steam coal (mtce)						
	1975	1980	1985	1990	1995	2000
Production	1.1	1.3	2.5	3.5	4.5	5.0
Consumption	0.3	1.2	2.0	3.2	3.8	4.6
Import	-	-	-	-	-	-
Export	0.8	0.1	0.5	0.3	0.7	0.4

total coal (mtce)						
	1975	1980	1985	1990	1995	2000
Production	1.4	1.8	3.1	4.2	5.2	5.8
Consumption	0.8	2.0	2.8	4.1	4.8	5.7
Import	0.2	0.2	0.2	0.2	0.3	0.3
Export	0.8	0.1	0.5	0.3	0.7	0.4

COUNTRY: COLOMBIA

Colombia, the country with the biggest coal resources in Latin America, is making intensive efforts to extend coal mining, which has been so far done only on a small-scale basis and in many mines. Global estimations on the total geological resources range from 40 to 80 billion tons, but detailed knowledge of existing coal resources is very limited.

The Colombian coalfields are situated mainly in the Eastern Cordillera; some coal deposits are located in the Western and Central Cordillera region. The coal ranges from gas coal to anthracite. The objective is to increase the present coal production for ensuring the energy supply in the country and for exports up to 30 million tons in the distant future. In addition to the development of a more extensive coal mining industry, it is necessary to improve the infrastructure of the country and to make transportation, and also the harbors, more efficient or to develop them. The most promising underdeveloped reserves are those of coking quality in El Cerrejon and La Jaguar, which could well be developed for export. Today the export of steam and met coal is only about 200,000 t/year to Brazil, Venezuela, Peru, Ecuador and The Netherlands, but for the future the export potential seems to be considerable. Countries like Brazil, Poland, Romania, Spain, the USA and the Federal Republic of Germany are engaged in the Colombian coal industry.

met-coal (mtce)						
	1975	1980	1985	1990	1995	2000
Production	0.8	4.9	5.4	7.0	10.0	14
Consumption	0.7	1.9	2.3	4.0	6.0	7
Import	-	-	-	-	-	-
Export	0.1	3.0	4.1	3.0	4.0	7.0

steam coal (mtce)						
	1975	1980	1985	1990	1995	2000
Production	2.2	3.6	9.1	11.0	14.0	17.9
Consumption	2.3	3.4	4.6	6.5	8.9	12.5
Import	-	-	-	-	-	-
Export		0.2	4.5	4.5	5.1	5.4

Country: Colombia

total coal				(mtce)		
	1975	1980	1985	1990	1995	2000
Production	3.0	8.5	15.5	18.0	24.0	31.9
Consumption	3.0	5.3	6.9	10.5	14.9	19.5
Import	-	-	-	-	-	-
Export	0.1	3.2	8.6	7.5	9.1	12.4

COUNTRY: MEXICO

The principal coal reserves of Mexico lie in the three areas of Barrancas, Oaxaca and Coahuila. Only the coal of Coahuila is of coking quality. The Mexican steel industry's total demand for coal cannot be met by indigenous production, therefore, coking coal has to be imported. All of the coking coal will be imported from Canada, Australia and the United States. A significant portion of Mexico's steel industry requirements have to be imported directly as coke. The new discoveries of the important oil and gas fields make the forecasts of production and the consumption of steam coal very optimistic.

met-coal				(mtce)		
	1975	1980	1985	1990	1995	2000
Production	3.5	4.3	6.1	10.6	13.0	15.0
Consumption	4.2	6.9	9.8	16.0	26.3	34.2
Import	0.7	2.6	3.7	5.8	13.3	19.2
Export	-	-	-	-	-	-

Country: Mexico

steam coal	(mtce)				
	1975	1980	1985	1990	1995	2000
Production	1.6	8.1	21.6	31.7	38.0	44.0
Consumption	1.3	3.8	11.6	17.7	26.0	32.4
Import	0.6	-	-	-	-	-
Export	-	4.3	10.0	14.0	12.0	11.6

total coal	(mtce)				
	1975	1980	1985	1990	1995	2000
Production	5.1	12.4	27.7	41.7	51.0	55.0
Consumption	5.5	10.7	21.4	3.7	52.3	66.6
Import	1.3	2.6	3.7	5.8	13.3	19.2
Export	-	4.3	10.0	14.0	12.0	11.6

COUNTRY: PERU

Coal deposits have been detected in a number of places along the Andean ranges, mainly in the Oyon area. The coals are both anthracite and bituminous. Today Peru does not mine coal in significant quantities, but for the future, an increase of production is planned. At Alto Chicama the Polish consulting company, KOPEX, has explored some coal deposits. The annual production will be brought to 1.5 million tons by 1985. A power plant with four units of 120 MW each is planned. The coke demand is estimated at about 1.3 million tons by 1982. Peru will meet its future demand for both coking and noncoking coals by its own production—for that reason no imports will be required.

Country: Peru

met-coal (mtce)	1975	1980	1985	1990	1995	2000
Production	-	0.3	1.4	1.6	1.8	2.0
Consumption	-	0.2	1.6	1.6	1.8	2.0
Import	-	-	-	-	-	-
Export	-	0.1	-	-	-	-

steam coal (mtce)	1975	1980	1985	1990	1995	2000
Production	0.1	1.2	2.0	2.4	3.5	4.5
Consumption	0.1	1.2	1.8	2.0	3.0	4.5
Import	-	-	-	-	-	-
Export	-	-	0.2	0.4	0.5	-

total coal (mtce)	1975	1980	1985	1990	1995	2000
Production	0.1	1.5	3.4	4.0	5.3	6.5
Consumption	0.1	1.4	3.4	3.6	4.8	6.5
Import	-	-	0.2	-	-	-
Export	-	0.1	0.2	0.4	0.5	-

COUNTRY: VENEZUELA

The main Venezuelan coalfields are in the Eastern Cordillera and in the region of Naricual. The coal industry is government-owned. Despite the large deposits of oil and gas, consideration has been given to increase coal production. Two large mines at Zulia with an annual output of 4 million tons are planned. They will supply coal to a projected new integrated steel complex and a coal-fired power plant with a final capacity of 3,500 MW by 1996. Six 250-MW units will be built at first, followed by six 400-MW units. The Montan Consulting GmbH of the FRG is engaged in the Naricual coal field to increase coal production and to build both a preparation plant and a coking plant. Today the national steel industry imports coke from the FRG, Japan and Colombia, but in the future Venezuela will be independent from coal imports, and there is even the possibility of exporting small amounts of both steam coal and met coal.

met-coal (mtce)	1975	1980	1985	1990	1995	2000
Production	-	1.0	3.4	4.8	5.0	5.0
Consumption	-	1.0	3.5	3.5	4.2	6.2
Import	-	-	0 1	-	-	1.2
Export	-	-	-	1.3	0.8	-

steam coal (mtce)	1975	1980	1985	1990	1995	2000
Production	0.1	3.0	3.7	7.0	9.5	11.0
Consumption	0.1	4.0	5.2	7.5	10.0	13.0
Import		1.0	1.5	0.5	0.5	2.0
Export	-	-	-	-	-	-

Country: Venezuela

total coal (mtce)						
	1975	1980	1985	1990	1995	2000
Production	0.1	4.0	7.1	11.8	14.5	16.0
Consumption	0.1	5.0	8.7	11.0	14.2	19.2
Import	-	1.0	·1.6	0.5	0.5	3.2
Export	-	-	-	1.3	0.8	-

COUNTRY: OTHER COUNTRIES OF SOUTH AMERICA

met-coal (mtce)						
	1975	1980	1985	1990	1995	2000
Production	--	--	--	--	--	--
Consumption	--	--	0.02	0.05	0.10	0.15
Import	--	--	0.02	0.05	0.10	0.15
Export	--	--	--	--	--	--

steam coal (mtce)						
	1975	1980	1985	1990	1995	2000
Production	--	--	--	--	--	--
Consumption	0.07	0.11	0.14	0.15	0.20	0.35
Import	0.07	0.11	0.14	0.15	0.20	0.35
Export	--	--	--	--	--	--

Country: Other Countries of South America

total coal			(mtce)			
	1975	1980	1985	1990	1995	2000
Production	--	--	--	--	--	--
Consumption	0.070	0.11	0.16	0.20	0.30	0.50
Import	--	--	--	--	--	--
Export	--	--	--	--	--	--

REFERENCES:

1. Future World Markets for Non-coking Coal.
   Report, Battelle-Institut e.V., Frankfurt a. Main, 1976.
2. An Appraisal of World Coal Resources and Their Future Availability.
   Peters, Schilling, Pickhardt, Wiegand, Hildebrandt, 1978.
3. Die Bergwirtschaft der Erde.
   Friedensburg, Dorstewitz, Enke-Verlag Stuttgart, 1976.
4. Kohle in Entwicklungsländern.
   Bundesanstalt für Geowissenschaften und Rohstoffe.
   Hannover, Juli 1977.
5. Journals:

   World Coal, International Coal Trade, Coal Age, Engineering and Mining Journal, WID Energiewirtschaft, European Coal Information Agency, Glückauf, Colliery Guardian, Financial Times, Frankfurter Allgemeine Zeitung, Handelsblatt.

CHAPTER 22

AFRICA*

A special regional study of coal prospects in developing countries of Africa* was prepared for WOCOL by one of its members, Detlef Wiegand, Bergbau-Forschung GmbH, Federal Republic of Germany. This study, which is based on an update of the 1977 World Energy Conference coal data for this region, estimated future levels of coal production, use, export, and import for both steam coal and metallurgical coal to the year 2000.

The estimates indicate little coal expansion in Africa, with coal use growing only to 24 mtce in 2000 from 6 mtce in 1975. Coal production expands somewhat more—to 35 mtce in 2000, with small amounts of export projected from Mozambique, Rhodesia, and Swaziland. Botswana also has the reserve potential to support exports of coal if infrastructure developments are carried out.

The following material provides the detailed resource, reserves, production and use data for Africa. Data for the principal countries of Botswana, Morocco, Mozambique, Nigeria, Rhodesia, Swaziland, Zaire, and Zambia are provided as well as the aggregated statistics for the region.

Table 22-1. Major Coal Resources and Coal Reserves of Africa (mtce)

Country	Resources h.c.[1]	Resources b.c.[1]	Reserves h.c.	Reserves b.c.
Botswana, Rep. of	100,000		3,500	
Morocco	200		80	
Mozambique	400	--	--	--
Nigeria	--	180	--	90
Rhodesia	7,130	--	755	--
South Africa, Rep. of	57,566	--	26,903	--
Swaziland	5,000	--	200	--
Zaire	808		570	
Zambia	228	--	40	--
Others	1,560	60	400	--
Total	172,892	240	31,878	90

[1] h.c. = hard coal   b.c. = brown coal
The coalification limit between hard coal and brown coal was fixed at 23.76 MJ/kg (equivalent to 5,700 kcal/kg) related to air-dried, ash-free substance.

* Projections for the Republic of South Africa, which is a major coal exporter, are provided in Chapter 18.

561

Table 22-2. Coal Resources of the Other Countries of Africa

Country	coal type	estimated coal deposits (million tonnes)	comments
Algeria	bituminous	60	economically recoverable
Ethopia	lignite	20	low quality coal
Kenya	lignite	unknown	thin seams in great depth
Lesotho	bituminous	--	small production for power generation
Madagascar	bituminous and lignite no coking coal	--	small production for power generation
Malawi	bituminous	7	no existing mining industry
Tansania	bituminous and lignite	800	for power generation and blending

Table 22-3. Coal Production, Use, Import, and Export Projections for Africa*

met-coal		(mtce)**			
	1975	1980	1985	1990	1995	2000
Production	1.33	2.46	4.16	5.20	6.68	9.05
Consumption	1.59	2.90	3.63	4.55	5.65	6.90
Import	0.37	0.76	0.93	1.30	1.57	1.75
Export	0.12	0.24	1.46	1.95	2.50	3.90

steam coal		(mtce)			
	1975	1980	1985	1990	1995	2000
Production	4.29	9.61	15.07	18.45	21.10	25.82
Consumption	4.47	7.02	8.60	11.40	13.60	17.27
Import	0.38	0.10	0.15	0.35	0.45	0.50
Export	0.20	2.35	5.65	6.30	6.45	7.05

total coal		(mtce)			
	1975	1980	1985	1990	1995	2000
Production	5.62	12.07	19.23	23.65	27.78	34.87
Consumption	6.06	9.92	12.23	15.95	19.25	24.17
Import	0.75	0.86	1.08	1.65	2.02	2.25
Export	0.32	2.59	7.11	8.25	8.95	10.95

* Excludes Republic of South Africa, see Chapter 18.
** met coal = metallurgical coal including blending coal for coke production.

563

COUNTRY: REPUBLIC OF BOTSWANA

Most of the coal reserves are in the east part of the country. Coal qualities are poor and there are no existing coking coal deposits. One mine is in production. The present coal output is low, but increases in production have recently taken place at the Morupule Colliery near Palapye. Consumers of coal production are the Botswana Power Corporation and the BCL Ltd. (owner of a nickel-copper mine). The annual production is projected to reach up to 1 million metric tons in the future.

met-coal (mtce)	1975	1980	1985	1990	1995	2000
Production	-	-	-	-	-	-
Consumption	-	-	-	-	-	-
Import	-	-	-	-	-	-
Export	-	-	-	-	-	-

steam coal (mtce)	1975	1980	1985	1990	1995	2000
Production	0.07	0.40	0.43	0.50	0.60	0.72
Consumption	0.07	0.40	0.40	0.50	0.60	0.72
Import	-	-	-	-	-	-
Export	-	-	-	-	-	-

total coal (mtce)	1975	1980	1985	1990	1995	2000
Production	0.07	0.40	0.43	0.50	0.60	0.72
Consumption	0.07	0.40	0.43	0.50	0.60	0.72
Import	-	-	-	-	-	-
Export	-	-	-	-	-	-

COUNTRY: MOROCCO

The coal, mainly anthracite, is mined by the state-owned Société des Charbonnages Nord-Africains (CNA) at Djerada in the east. There are plans to double the production to 1 million tons by 1980. Nearly 80% of the annual production is burnt in the power station at Djerada. In the future, limited quantities of anthracite could be made available for export.

met-coal (mtce)						
	1975	1980	1985	1990	1995	2000
Production	0.161	0.40	0.500	0.500	0.600	0.700
Consumption	0.161	0.40	0.550	0.600	0.650	0.900
Import	-	-	0.05	0.10	0.150	0.200
Export	-	-	-	-	-	-

steam coal (mtce)						
	1975	1980	1985	1990	1995	2000
Production	0.464	0.650	0.700	0.950	1.200	1.500
Consumption	0.434	0.600	0.600	0.800	1.000	1.200
Import	-	-	-	-	-	-
Export	0.030	0.050	0.100	0.150	0.200	0.300

total coal (mtce)						
	1975	1980	1985	1990	1995	2000
Production	0.625	1.050	1.200	1.450	1.800	2.200
Consumption	0.595	1.000	1.150	1.400	1.650	2.100
Import	-	-	0.050	0.100	0.150	0.200
Export	0.030	0.050	0.100	0.150	0.200	0.300

COUNTRY: MOZAMBIQUE

Since early 1978 the only existing mining company, Companhia Carbonifera de Mozambique (CCM), has been state owned. The annual output is running at around 700,000 tons and consideration is being given to its expansion. A great part of the annual production consists of coking coal. Given infrastructure, it might be possible to increase the production up to about 7 million tons in the longer term. Mozambique could have a coal export potential of about 5 million tons before the end of the century. Today Romania, Japan, Malawi and the GDR are importing coal from Mozambique.

met-coal	(mtce)					
	1975	1980	1985	1990	1995	2000
Production	0.300	0.46	0.76	0.90	1.10	2.50
Consumption	0.200	0.20	0.20	0.30	0.30	0.30
Import	-	-	-	-	-	-
Export	0.100	0.14	0.56	0.60	0.80	2.20

steam coal	(mtce)					
	1975	1980	1985	1990	1995	2000
Production	0.20	0.94	1.64	2.30	3.00	4.00
Consumption	0.52	0.600	0.700	1.20	1.50	2.00
Import	0.32	-	-	-	-	-
Export						

total coal	(mtce)					
	1975	1980	1985	1990	1995	2000
Production	0.50	1.40	2.40	3.20	4.10	6.50
Consumption	0.72	0.80	0.90	1.50	1.80	2.30
Import	0.32	-	-	-	-	-
Export	0.10	0.48	1.50	1.70	2.30	4.20

COUNTRY: NIGERIA

Coal production, adversely affected by the civil war, is now gradually coming back to normal having reached some 300,000 tons per year. The coal is produced by the state-owned Nigerian Coal Corporation. The peak production was reached in 1958 when nearly 1 million tons was mined. Exports to Ghana mainly for railway use are again taking place. The British Company, Powell Duffryn Technical Services, is preparing a feasibility study of the future development of the Nigerian coal mining industry.

met-coal (mtce)						
	1975	1980	1985	1990	1995	2000
Production	-	-	-	-	-	-
Consumption	-	-	-	-	-	-
Import	-	-	-	-	-	-
Export	-	-	-	-	-	-

steam coal (mtce)						
	1975	1980	1985	1990	1995	2000
Production	0,300	0,950	1,100	1,200	1,300	1,500
Consumption	0,250	0,850	0,950	1,00	1,050	1,250
Import	-	-	-	-	-	-
Export	0,050	0,100	0,150	0,200	0,250	0,250

total coal (mtce)						
	1975	1980	1985	1990	1995	2000
Production	0,300	0,950	1,10	1,20	1,30	1,50
Consumption	0,250	0,850	0,950	1,00	1,050	1,250
Import						
Export	0,050	0,100	0,15	0,20	0,25	0,25

COUNTRY: RHODESIA

Coal is mined by Wankie Colliery Company Ltd., Salisbury, a subsidiary of Anglo-American Corporation. The coal production in 1978 was about 2.2 million tons, half opencast workings. The export potential is theoretically good, depending on political considerations. Production at present is largely geared to satisfy home consumption, but coal is exported also to Zaire and Zambia. The Industrial Development Corporation (IDC) of Rhodesia has been exploring for coal with the ultimate goal of building an oil-from-coal plant to supply the country with its entire fuel needs. Exploration was concentrated southeast of Wankie. There is enough coal in the area to provide nearly all the country's fuel needs for the next 25 years.

met-coal (mtce)						
	1975	1980	1985	1990	1995	2000
Production	0.30	0.70	0.80	1.00	1.50	2.00
Consumption	0.30	0.70	0.80	1.00	1.50	2.00
Import	--	--	--	--	--	--
Export	--	--	--	--	--	--

steam coal (mtce)						
	1975	1980	1985	1990	1995	2000
Production	2.20	4.30	7.20	7.50	8.50	10.00
Consumption	2.18	2.90	3.80	4.30	5.10	6.00
Import	0.01	--	--	--	--	--
Export	0.03	1.40	3.40	3.20	3.40	4.00

total coal (mtce)						
	1975	1980	1985	1990	1995	2000
Production	3.50	5.00	8.00	8.50	10.00	12.00
Consumption	2.48	3.80	4.70	5.30	6.60	8.00
Import	0.01	--	--	--	--	--
Export	0.03	1.40	3.40	4.30	3.40	4.00

COUNTRY: SWAZILAND

The Swaziland Collieries Ltd., a subsidiary of Anglo-American Corporation, has produced about 134,000 tons in 1978. This coal was mainly for railway, industrial and domestic markets. Only a small quantity is exported. Future prospects are considered to be good; production of about 6 million tons, nearly 4 million tons for export, is possible. Coking coal is exported to Kenya, Japan and Mozambique.

met-coal (mtce)	1975	1980	1985	1990	1995	2000
Production	0.07	0.20	1.00	1.50	2.00	2.10
Consumption	0.05	0.10	0.10	0.15	0.30	0.40
Import	--	--	--	--	--	--
Export	0.02	0.10	0.90	1.35	1.70	1.70

steam coal (mtce)	1975	1980	1985	1990	1995	2000
Production	0.05	1.20	2.50	3.50	3.50	4.00
Consumption	0.05	0.50	0.70	1.00	1.30	1.90
Import	--	--	--	--	--	--
Export	--	0.70	1.80	2.50	2.20	2.10

total coal (mtce)	1975	1980	1985	1990	1995	2000
Production	0.12	1.40	3.50	5.00	5.50	6.10
Consumption	0.10	0.60	0.80	1.15	1.60	2.30
Import	--	--	--	--	--	--
Export	0.02	0.80	2.70	3.85	3.90	3.80

COUNTRY: ZAIRE

The coal is produced by Charbonnages de la Luena S.A., Brüssel, a subsidiary of Union Minière. The consumers of the coal are the power stations and the copper industry. A part of the coal is blended with Rhodesian coking coal for producing a coke suitable for copper smelting.

met-coal (mtce)	1975	1980	1985	1990	1995	2000
Production	--	--	--	--	--	--
Consumption	0.35	0.40	0.50	0.70	0.90	1.00
Import	0.35	0.40	0.50	0.70	0.90	1.00
Export	--	--	--	--	--	--

steam coal (mtce)	1975	1980	1985	1990	1995	2000
Production	0.09	0.120	0.30	0.80	1.00	1.400
Consumption	0.09	0.120	0.30	1.00	1.20	1.60
Import	--	--	--	0.20	0.20	0.20
Export	--	--	--	--	--	--

total coal (mtce)	1975	1980	1985	1990	1995	2000
Production	0.09	0.12	0.30	0.80	1.00	1.40
Consumption	0.09	0.12	0.80	1.70	2.10	2.60
Import	0.35	0.40	0.50	0.90	1.10	1.20
Export	--	--	--	--	--	--

COUNTRY: ZAMBIA

The coal is produced by Maamba Collieries Ltd., Lusaka, in the south of the country. With capital aid from the African Development Bank and the FRG, the mines at the Maamba region will be modernized. Only part of the coal is usable in the copper industry, therefore met coal from Rhodesia has to be imported. The main uses of Maamba coal are in copper smelting, cement and fertilizer production, and for steam raising (Zambia Railways and the Zambia Electricity Board).

met-coal (mtce)	1975	1980	1985	1990	1995	2000
Production	0.49	0.63	0.75	0.90	1.08	1.35
Consumption	0.51	0.70	0.80	1.00	1.20	1.50
Import	0.02	0.03	0.05	0.10	0.12	0.15
Export	-	-	-	--	-	-

steam coal (mtce)	1975	1980	1985	1990	1995	2000
Production	0.32	0.40	0.50	0.90	1.10	1.70
Consumption	0.28	0.35	0.40	0.80	1.00	1.60
Import	-	-	-	-	-	-
Export	0.04	0.05	0.10	0.10	0.10	0.10

total coal (mtce)	1975	1980	1985	1990	1995	2000
Production	0.81	1.03	1.25	1.80	2.18	3.05
Consumption	0.79	1.05	1.20	1.80	2.20	3.10
Import	0.02	0.03	0.05	0.10	0.12	0.15
Export	0.04	0.05	0.10	0.10	0.10	0.10

COUNTRY: OTHER COUNTRIES OF AFRICA

Only Algeria and Tansania have announced plans for future utilization of coal. Algeria, for example, has made contracts with the German Ruhrkohle AG to import in the future 330,000 tons of coking coal per year. The coal resources of Tansania may be substantial, but the coal is of poor quality like in most "other countries of Africa." Coal tends to be dirty with high ash and water content. Most of the coal deposits contain bituminous coal and lignite.

met-coal (mtce)

	1975	1980	1985	1990	1995	2000
Production	0.01	0.07	0.35	0.40	0.40	0.40
Consumption	0.02	0.40	0.68	0.80	0.80	0.80
Import	0.01	0.33	0.33	0.40	0.40	0.40
Export	--	--	--	--	--	--

steam coal (mtce)

	1975	1980	1985	1990	1995	2000
Production	0.60	0.65	0.70	0.80	0.90	1.00
Consumption	0.60	0.70	0.75	0.80	0.85	1.00
Import	0.05	0.10	0.15	0.15	0.25	0.30
Export	0.05	0.05	0.10	0.15	0.30	0.30

total coal (mtce)

	1975	1980	1985	1990	1995	2000
Production	0.61	0.72	1.05	1.20	1.30	1.40
Consumption	0.62	1.10	1.43	1.60	1.65	1.80
Import	0.06	0.43	0.48	0.55	0.65	0.70
Export	0.05	0.05	0.10	0.15	0.30	0.30

REFERENCES:

1. Future World Markets for Non-coking Coal.
   Report, Battelle-Institut e.V., Frankfurt a. Main, 1976.

2. An Appraisal of World Coal Resources and Their Future Availability.
   Peters, Schilling, Pickhardt, Wiegand, Hildebrandt, 1978.

3. Die Bergwirtschaft der Erde.
   Friedensburg, Dorstewitz, Enke-Verlag Stuttgart, 1976.

4. Kohle in Entwicklungsländern.
   Bundesanstalt für Geowissenschaften und Rohstoffe.
   Hannover, Juli 1977.

5. Journals:
   World Coal, International Coal Trade, Coal Age, Engineering and Mining Journal, WID Energiewirtschaft, European Coal Information Agency, Glückauf, Colliery Guardian, Financial Times, Frankfurter Allgemeine Zeitung, Handelsblatt.

CHAPTER 23

CENTRALLY PLANNED ECONOMY COUNTRIES

The Centrally Planned Economies (CPE's) of Eastern Europe and Asia are large producers and users of coal, accounting for more than 50% of world coal use in 1977. The largest coal producers and users among the CPE's were the Soviet Union (510 mtce), the People's Republic of China (373 mtce), and Poland (167 mtce), with the other CPE countries accounting for about 250 mtce.

Detailed descriptions of the coal projections and the full texts of the national reports for the People's Republic of China and Poland, which participated in the World Coal Study, are included in Chapters 3 and 13 of this volume.

Projections of coal production and export for the Soviet Union and other CPE countries were based on the 1978 World Energy Conference* work, which indicates an expansion of Soviet Union production to 1,100 mtce by year 2000, with production from the other CPE countries growing to about 375 mtce. These WEC projections represent about a doubling of production from the Soviet Union/ Eastern Europe region over the 1977-2000 period.

In the case of coal export projections, some limited expansion of exports from the Soviet Union can be expected. However, much of the Soviet reserves are low-calorific brown coals located in Siberia. Costly transport infrastructure requirements make it less likely that these reserves would be available for major exports as solid coal over the next twenty years. For the WOCOL analysis of world coal trade, the WEC estimates have been utilized, showing an increase of Soviet Union exports from 25 mtce in 1977 to 50 mtce in 2000. The WOCOL estimates for Poland and PRC export potentials in year 2000 are 50 mtce and 30 mtce, respectively, which agree with the WEC projections (see Chapters 3, 13 for more detail).

The Soviet Union also imports some steam coal, amounting to 9.1 mtce in 1977. Total CPE coal imports in 1977 amounted to 35 mtce,** roughly equally divided between steam coal and metallurgical coal. In addition to the Soviet Union, other CPE coal importers were: Bulgaria, 6.2 mtce; Czechoslovakia, 5.6 mtce; German Democratic Republic, 5.9 mtce; Hungary, 1.9 mtce; Poland, 1.0 mtce; Romania, 2.3 mtce; and Yugoslavia, 2.4 mtce. The WOCOL coal trade analysis assumes that CPE coal imports increase slightly from 35 mtce in 1977 to 50 mtce in year 2000, although any such projections must be considered very uncertain, as little information is available.

---

* Source: *World Energy: Looking Ahead to 2020*, World Energy Conference, 1978.
** Source: *World Coal*, November 1979, compiled by G. Markon.

575

Standard Fuel/Energy Equivalences

	mtce/yr	bdoe	10³ bdoe	mtoe/yr	million cfd natural gas	10⁹ m³/yr natural gas	million kWh/yr*	TJ/yr
1 million tce/yr	1	13,121.3	13.12	.646004	76.1048	.7447	8,141	29,307.6
1 bdoe	76.211×10^{-6}	1	10^{-3}	49.2326×10^{-6}	5.8×10^{-3}	56.75×10^{-6}	.620432	2.23356
1 thousand bdoe	76.211×10^{-3}	1×10^3	1	49.2326×10^{-3}	5.8	.05675	620.432	2.233.56
1 million toe/yr	1.54798	20,311.8	20.3118	1	117.808	1.1528	12,602.1	45,367.6
1 million cfd natural gas	13.140×10^{-3}	172.414	.172414	8.48837×10^{-3}	1	.009785	106.971	385.096
1 × 10⁹ m³/yr natural gas	1.3428	17,620	17.620	.8675	102.2	1	10,932	39,356
1 million kWh/yr	$.122835 \times 10^{-3}$	1.61178	1.61178×10^{-3}	79.3521×10^{-6}	9.34833×10^{-3}	$.9148 \times 10^{-4}$	1	3.6
1 TJ/yr	34.1208×10^{-6}	.4477	$.4477 \times 10^{-3}$	22.0422×10^{-6}	2.59676×10^{-6}	0.2541×10^{-4}	.277778	1

* Caloriffic value equivalence of electricity generated in electric power stations by given quantities of fuel would be reduced according to power station thermal efficiency. A multiplier of 35% is a representative figure.

Source: *Coal Pocket Book*, Shell Coal International (1977).

Unit Nomenclature and Standard Abbreviations

Throughout this report the following nomenclature and abbreviations have been used.

bbl	barrel	mbd	million barrels per day
bdoe	barrel(s) per day oil equivalent	mbdoe	million barrels per day oil equivalent
Btu	British thermal unit	mg	microgram
Btu/lb	Brtish thermal unit per pound	MJ	Mega joule = 10^6J
cf	cubic feet	MHD	magnetohydrodynamics
cfd	cubic feet per day	mtce	million tons (metric) coal equivalent
CIF	cost including insurance and freight	mtoe	million tons (metric) oil equivalent
CO	carbon monoxide	MWe	megawatt(s) of electric generating capacity = 1000 kWe
CO_2	carbon dioxide		
CPE's	Centrally Planned Economies		
COM	coal-oil mixture	NGL	natural gas liquids
DWT	deadweight ton	NO_2	nitrogen dioxide
EC	European Community (formerly EEC)	NO_x	nitrogen oxides
		OBO	ore/bulk/oil combination carrier
FBC	fluidized bed combustion		
FGD	flue gas desulfurization	OECD	Organization for Economic Cooperation and Development
FOB	freight on board		
GDP	Gross Domestic Product		
GNP	Gross National Product	OPEC	Organization of Petroleum Exporting Countries
GRT	gross-registered tons		
GWe	gigawatt(s) of electric generating capacity = 1000 MWe	ppm	parts per million
		PPR	Polish People's Republic
HCV	high calorific value	PRC	People's Republic of China
IEA	International Energy Agency	quad	quadrillion (10^{15}) Btu
IMF	International Monetary Fund	R & D	research and development
kcal/kg	kilocalories per kilogram	SNG	Substitute Natural Gas
kg	kilogram(s)	SO_2	sulfur dioxide
km	kilometer(s)	SO_x	sulfur oxides
km²	square kilometer(s)	SRC	solvent refined coal
kWe	kilowatt(s) of electric generating capacity	t	tons (metric)
		tce	tons (metric) coal equivalent
kWh	kilowatt hour	tcf	trillion cubic feet
lb	pound	toe	tons oil equivalent
LCV	low calorific value	TJ	terajoule = 10^{12} joules
LDC's	Less Developed Countries	TSP	total suspended particulates
LNG	Liquefied Natural Gas	tWh	tera watt hours
m²	square meter(s)	WEC	World Energy Conference
m³	cubic meter(s)	yr	year